All my Best
For you
Paul Breau

Your
Enlightened Soul

by: Paul Breau

D1291986

Inner Abbey Order (IAO)
Copyright ©2001

Email: yes@brunnet.net
WebSite: www.yourenlightenedsoul.com

Front cover painting by Erin O'Shea

Published by:
Partners Publishing Ltd.
Fredericton, New Brunswick Canada
Phone: 506-450-9768 • Fax: 506-450-2546
Email: partners@nb.aibn.com • Website: www.partnerspublishing.com

ISBN 0-9686656-2-4

Part One ~ Chapters

Part Two ~ Poetic Verse

Part Three ~ Short Stories

Acknowledgements

The author wishes to express deep gratitude to all those who have paved the road and opened hearts towards modern day spirituality. Theosophists of old and new, Rosicrucians, Thelemites, Magicians and Mystics alike have all assisted humanity in expanding global consciousness with the Light of spirituality. Numerous authors have made available unto the public, subject matter that is deeply inspiring thus furthering the passion to seek the orbit of which we are all ultimately bound.

A special regard to all sources of information over time that have provided me with the inspiration to compile the material and stories that have come to fashion this volume.

Expressed ebullience to the diligent artists who have painstakingly portrayed my sketchy ideas to the stories and chapters. Their skillful creativity should not go unnoticed.

Particularly for the long efforts of Erin O'Shea, I am most grateful. She has uniquely woven a talent into pictorial form to heighten the readers' imagination.

Carl Parker has also supplied a skilled hand of artistic efforts throughout this volume and has my appreciation for his enduring hours of creativity causing splendid results.

The contributing artist's input and zestful enthusiasm has been instrumental in the pictorial representation of the information herein.

Dru Bryan extended diligent hands to keyboard and assisted me in editing the short stories. For that I am most beholden for his push in opening my eyes wide and bright.

Any comments from the readers may be sent to any particular artist, the publisher or the author at either of the following email addresses:

yescomment2002@yahoo.com or yescomment@hotmail.com

Lastly to all dear friends and family who have assisted and supported the years of research and experience without which this book would not have been possible, I express my heart herein.

ILLUSTRATIONS

PART THREE

Introduction

This volume consistently emphasizes the importance of balance in life and making adjustments that assist in personal well being, growth and the fulfillment of experienced enlightenment. Soul seeking journeys brighten our path to further create ambitions and make us yearn for deeper insight and greater understanding while broadening our perspective. The diversity and practical principles herein should help to evolve the spiritual perspective that we inherently strive to attain. Assimilating the exercises and information should enable clarity to be achieved during such a miraculous search. The following essays are fundamental and are elaborated in numerous other texts by many other authors. It is the author's optimism that the seeker will affirm the genuine importance of these subjects for an honest progression in a soul-searching crusade.

Fathoming and interpreting the majestic symbols of the tarot cards is a lifetime meditative practice. Associating them with other appropriate data upon the Tree of Life releases a mental-emotional stimulus enabling our mind to enter them as doorways into the collective unconscious through subjective realms of phenomena. The process allows us to ultimately reach objective consciousness. The poetic verses in Part Two are added to amuse as well as provoke some mystical thought for these tarot doorways and the pathways they are attributed to. Similarly, the short stories of Part Three include some attributions to the specific tarot trump they are related to and may edify journeys for the mind to wander and then contemplate. Most of the stories have some previous true experiences associated with them, the poetic verses are a result of expression and the foremost essays should assist our endeavors to pick up a part of life that should be soundly adhered to for responsible and progressive advancement in the esoteric arts.

Projecting enthusiasm into our journeys with a liturgy of positive principles at our side becomes not only entertaining but fulfills the need of being acquainted with the countenance of our psyche, the vast subconscious world that we may tap into and retrieve as desired. Rejuvenating and channeling our energies gathers further metaphysical and psychological abilities that uplift us into a self-creative atmosphere. Focusing our sight and desires are important to achieve transformation experiences with nature on loftier levels.

The plethora of the tarot, astral consciousness, meditation, the aura, kundalini, chakras, personal healing techniques, cataloging qabalistic symbols and astrological attributions are intensive topics but they assist us in surmounting the hurdles along the royal road of self-discovery. Becoming acquainted with our soul, spirit, higher self and the hierarchy of inner world presence expands our horizon and steers us as travelers while consciously manipulating self-control. When we begin to formulate our personal interests and build positive creative visualization techniques as step by step procedures to qualifying our efforts, then our world can change in a short time and open to a vast, virtually unlimited potential.

The whole subject of the occult sciences has been blatantly abused just as religion has, and are seldom paid proper respect in the general world of today. There are definite problems that increase each moment throughout the world and it belongs to each one of us as individual stars of humanity to do our part, become the example and fulfill our own destiny in an orbit that is affiliated with our innate nature. Misuse of power has always been a dilemma in society. In the case of latent powers being used for purposes that the media ascribe to ritual murders, sociopath serial killings and all such grief, it will be said that such misuse of power has nothing to do with occult sciences in proper. People who commit crimes under the guise of occult, magic or pagan facades commit them for the attention and from personal problems they do not care to correct. It is realized sooner or later that such karma further envelops the criminal into long lasting retribution and so it is never too late to turn a cheek on such destructive activity.

There may never be a virtual Utopia but as we strive to educate, channel, create and balance our life we find the momentum that keeps us in our particular orbit to become equally stronger. Realizing that every person is truly a star and that we can do anything within our particular scope, is the beginning of releasing greater potential and experiencing the essence of liberty. Remolding parts of our present life to realize the Path that we are undertaking for a fulfilled life is a process of awakening to set in motion a line of success and perceiving the light before us to become brighter.

In earlier years we all had dream castles in the sky and to some extent some of them are still there. Materialization begins when the subconscious is stimulated into action to make things occur. Being in tune with our congenital energies allows us to cause changes to occur in conformity with our needs and requirements in life. We create most of what happens to us and are capable of making significant changes as we become in tune with working on the inner planes. The expedient changes and uncertainties occurring in life are a dramatic result of this new age as the movement of Aquarius draws restructuring in the mentality of mankind.

Our dreams and desires can become fulfilled in a tangible and coherent manner through the awareness of the Inner Light. We may revise them along the way but always hold them with the reverence they so deserve. Anything that has been put or programmed into our mind can carry on for a long time given the proper energy boost behind it. Creativity is the joy of properly employed power and reflects a focused mind with an efficient organization of principles that have been adhered to. Knowledge gained from creative expressions may be utilized to the most sublime possibilities with simple yet effective secrets that have been planted like seeds to grow in the vast subconscious. Each moment of life is precious and with awareness of the spiritual path, it is realized to a much greater extent.

Some key points have been repeated throughout this fundamental volume for the explicit purpose of illustrating their significance. This book may be read from front to back or begun anywhere so that the reader may gradually finish it at leisure. There is no required order of reading the material herein. It is sincerely desired that the multitude of principles within will be used beneficially and that if explanations seem complex at the outset, the reader will endeavor to make light of it with understanding sooner or later.

01 May 2001
New Brunswick

ALTERING CONSCIOUSNESS

"Some people are terribly afraid of anything outside the few narrow identities they always function in: by staying in one or the other of those identity states constantly, they never feel the fear of the unknown."

States of Consciousness - Charles T. Tart

Attention is often dispersed with the obstacles that confront us in daily life such that our focus towards a state of well being looses pace with our personal schedules. There is much more events and objects that take a grab of our attention in this faster pace society then ever before. Exiting the routine of a hum-drum atmosphere to enjoy creative, stimulating, and inspiring states of mind can become a routine, just as everything else that we have become accustomed to. Great results and fulfillment in life can become as habitual as we desire by setting up practices each day to direct and focus attention towards personal well being and developing conscious awareness. Minutes spent in such a pursuit will prove to be very beneficial within days of practice. This becomes a practice of mental manipulation combined with focusing attention in physical activity to promote our recuperation and strengthening our will power to begin doing what we set as goals in our life.

Focusing attention is a simple and effective practice to help us realize that we have greater abilities within that may be harnessed to provide more benefits for our life. As an example of focusing such inner potency, choose any subject or object that you wish and meditate on it with utmost devotion and attention, not allowing your mind to waver into other subjects. You may decide to focus on a part of your body, some other physical object or something that induces a sense of peace and harmony. You may have some subject of faith that you wish to project worship or selflessness towards, or simply opening awareness of your body and feeling each and every part in a conscious effort to send positive healing energy towards that area. You may wish to sit comfortably in a chair and radiate some emotion of love outwards, to the world. In the later instance, imagine and feel energy surrounding your entire body. Picture it circumnavigating your entire area and continue so doing until it goes throughout your neighborhood, town, country, continent, until you feel it strong enough to circle the planet and outreach into the Universe. There are countless methods in mentally performing positive actions and at the same time using the mind as a great and useful tool under your control. You are not the seemingly ceaseless thoughts in your mind but something much more divine. The mind is a specific tool for you to employ and not become a slave of. The passive and active side of the mind work hand in hand to direct and accept states of consciousness for an ever-expanding experience. Meditating effectively is the beginning of touching an unlimited potential and realizing how to materialize the innermost desires.

There is a chance that anyone can overdo a good thing and become a servant to the subject opposed to a master thereof. A firm foundation entails comparative and advanced studies in the subjects that you are interestedly involved in pursuing. This becomes a gradual process of development and begins the ladder of scaling to heights of ambition with experiences above the normal states of consciousness. A scientific grasp in the reality of psychology and parapsychology will enable any student of meditative practices to avoid getting lost in mental and emotional entanglements or being snared in the domains of the ego faculty that generally makes our decisions in daily life.

There has always been the danger that people get involved with groups or organizations for the wrong reasons, even if apparently sincere during initial stages. There is nothing wrong in interacting with people of like interests and ideals, however, struggles of power, control and egotistical bolstering may come into effect, thereby thwarting the original intentions. Whether you learn through reading and personal initiation or instruction from others, always read between the lines for the underlying significance to see where you are headed. Never take esoteric (heart initiated ideologies) and exoteric (mentally initiated dogma) for granted and learn to develop intuition as well as all your senses to learn what is right for your well being and your course through life. Some writers and leaders of organizations may have all the best intentions and strongly believe in what they have to say, but it does not mean that it is a cosmic law. Their teachings may not have validity beyond their self-pride, and therefore can misguide and cause more injury by being intrinsically misleading rather than beneficial.

There are several systematic and scientific approaches to classifying the various states of consciousness that are capable of being attained through experimental techniques. We shall begin in simplistic terms from my memory of reading some of the works of G.I. Gurdjieff. He was one of many world spiritual teachers of the past, and instructed at his Harmonious Development of Man near Paris in the 1920's. He wrote voluminously upon the nature of man and that we may be looked upon as being in either of three stages of awareness. Those stages are that of the asleep, waking up, and the fully awakened stage. Most people are in the "asleep" stage of their life development. Evolution in this stage does not really occur. When they work with great effort to be in the waking up stage with conscience as well as consciousness, their course of evolution is capable of making significant progress.

How do you know that you are not dreaming of reading these lines at this present moment? The component of realization in our self-awareness allows us to say to ourselves that we are presently awake and that it is such and such a time and we are presently in such a place reading this. Our association with the waking state tells us that we are conscious and are not in a dream state. The degree of self-awareness varies from moment to moment. As a person is driving down the road for example, their attention may wonder and their subconscious takes partial control of driving through previous conditioning. Being aware of self-awareness is an active conscious effort opposed to simply paying attention to any particular activity or object. This active state of conscious control is an awareness of being aware that can be attained through time and with patience of practicing assertive mental control techniques. The Buddhist practice of vipassana is when a person is aware of what is happening without thinking about what is happening. In such a mind state we are barring our reactions to what is occurring to the extent of any feelings, sensations or thoughts. With the understanding of how to manipulate our mind and use it as an instrument, opposed to being used by it through social and emotional reactions, we may ascend to becoming the conscious pilot of directing outcomes for our material plane of existence.

This involves considerable honest effort, critical self-analysis, and an intricate appreciation for attaining to levels that we know must exist yet require training to achieve. Thoughts that mingle in the mind and absorb energy and attention may be considered to be weak and idle thoughts, or those that distract the focusing of our will power. As a person thinks so shall they become, has been stated in so many ways throughout the past. This is painstakingly simple yet undeniably complex due to a myriad of mindsets that have shaped the average person into a heavy sleep and unconcerned state. Every thought and idea does not have power enough to change ones life, however as the mind is trained to focus and be under control of not allowing distractions to sway it constantly, it then surpasses a dormant stage. Dormant stages may be the result of being fixated on distractions and thoughts of other people and objects. Such distractions should not exist during the practice of self-mastery for mind control.

The recondite experience of altering awareness becomes a self-fulfilling occurrence. It is the altering of mental manipulation to refined realizations, leaving go of old conceptions and allowing for new perceptions to dawn in a natural progression of efficiency. In other words, as we progress, it becomes naturally easier to further progress because we do not allow ourselves to be deluded by making the same mistakes over, as generally set by the self-aggrandizing ego. Such a sense of freedom surpasses self-pity, jealousy, anger, irritation, indignation, envy and a host of other befallen attributes on the lower emotional levels. We basically learn to jump out of our usual impositions and become engulfed in greater potentials. We ascend normal blockages and become realized.

One of the most fundamental abilities that any human possesses is that of choice. This differentiates us from being captive to a harness led by restricting emotions, not unlike the behavior of animals. The problem of self-limitations arises over and over again. We are not always performing the best choices each moment and therefore we are never caught up with the requirements to allow us to be completely free, and this is usually by choice or lack of perception in seeing one. Actions that can change our daily existence will have a dramatic affect on what will happen in our future. The conscious effort of making better choices is one of the greatest tools at our disposal. It will eliminate the ripples on the pond, the worries and thoughts that distract the gulf of the mind and allow us to see what is ahead. It will tell us what particular efforts will bring us towards a particular goal, and eventually provide an all-round clear-seeing capability.

The doctrine of suffering and the way towards the cessation of suffering as put forth by Gotama Buddha changed many minds from the liberation of ritual sacrifices of the Brahmins. In fact, this created a new energy sensation throughout the eastern world and was made possible through the example the Buddha set forth and the conviction he was able to portray in the minds of men. His first two Noble Truths as he called them were "Everything is Sorrow" and, "The cause of Sorrow is Desire". As with all great religious teachers and throughout all ages, truths are illustrated as inherently simple, fundamental principles and convinced the disciple to achieve spirituality.

Sir Richard Burton once wrote- "He noblest lives and noblest dies who makes and keeps his self-made laws." Everyone has a particular system of creeds and methods to which they adhere in performing actions and achieving desired results. Without building further facades to mask our identity, we can achieve altered states of consciousness through gaining a mutual relationship with our soul. Distorted perceptions are caused for several reasons. Thoughts and emotions exist on different planes and each contain substance and have had years and years to develop defense mechanisms in preventing us from seeing clearly through them. Our 'awakening' results when we are no longer bombarded by random thoughts and able to choose freely from our inner storehouse to increase our abilities and develop our faculties. We may make explicit little rules to follow and train our mind to become gradually aware of embracing the inevitable changes in our life. Here is such an example, and to each their own, as you may wish to fabricate your own rules to suit your requirements and interests.

1. **Everything we do may be questionable.** When we ask questions we receive knowledge and can compare what we thought to be true to what may bring us closer to truth. From someone else's perspective, our actions may be a waste of time or foolish, so in questioning our actions we may decide to choose beneficial conduct and reactions in each event to produce better results. It provides more choices.

2. **Change is one thing we can count on.** The mind is programmed from a series of past events and prevents us from living the creation of new events. One way to prevent history from repeating itself is to live in the now and accept each difficult or complex situation at face value and not prolong the conditioning that we perceive as a personal agony.

3. **We cannot see what we do unless from another perspective.** Insight involves, not only the ability to observe our actions but to be in such a state as to alter and change them at will. Commanding our thoughts means that we are above them, on another level and are using them from a higher or deeper perspective.

4. **There is a purpose in all things.** Opportunities come when we are past judging everything around us and live in the harmony of seeing purpose in all things. Without labeling everything as either good or bad, seek the qualities that eventually change all things as a positive affirmation of endless potential.

5. **Mistakes are inevitable, but perception avoids them.** Imperfection, relative as it is, can transform into greater perfection. When we make mistakes and allow them to continue, we are not taking our self very serious. On the other hand, when we are afraid of making a mistake, we become a closed door to new possibilities, expanding horizons and entertaining journeys.

6. **Each experience is vital and has purpose.** We do not have to chase experience because experience lives within us. Focus will alter perception and expand realization. Adventure is an unlimited avenue of resources waiting for us to share in the igniting of our passions.

7. Our response becomes more important than the incident. Anything that becomes bothersome or imposes limitations with blockages is not as crucial as what is done about it. Focused force behind intelligent response is an attentive approach that usually prevents mistakes from recurring.

8. Observation is essential to accept change. To create positive changes, we should accept to get out of old routines and habits. We should be aware and recognize what stilts growth, what decays dynamism and what prevents positive outcomes to constantly occur in our life.

9. People will end up doing what they want to do. It may be a struggle to succeed, to overcome and to abolish negative patterns but generally people do try to do their perceived best. Being critical of others is easy and sometimes appears even enjoyable, but all to often it leads to less focus on self-improvement. Only through experience will others actually embrace change for the better and there is no better proof than to live by example.

10. Everyone is part of a complete systematic-matrix. Motivation is an achievement in itself. Depression, anxiety and concern are circumstances that everyone faces in life. Be reassured that you are not alone, that there are countless others suffering in one way or another and that the road you face is easier than the one tread by several other people. Indecision or confusion is a result of not being in touch with our infinite abilities and is part of setting parameters from previous conditioning. There is some great attachment between every single thing in life and can be almost likened to a systematic-matrix.

The person who works and struggles for perfection develops abilities that surpass their previous life-style. If internal dissatisfaction is realized, then progress begins by strengthening the desire to struggle towards improvement. External dissatisfaction usually results in conflict with ourselves and then others. To obliterate external dissatisfaction, efficient means should be employed according to what has to be accomplished. If for example, our daily life seems so busy with work, cooking, cleaning, organizing, and continuous responsibilities, then by working smarter may be the answer towards preventative backlog. Scheduling our activities allows us to accomplish the maximum during the time allotted and when we have time to relax we can truly relax and recuperate. Laziness is as much a habit as addictive gambling and just as futile when it comes to accomplishing our goals in life. Leisure and entertainment is one thing but when it gets us in a rut and we constantly seek more of it then addiction and attachment to those mental and emotional globs begin to run our lifestyle. Essentially, we require quiet, yet productive alone time to refocus and to set our sights straight to work on any particular goals.

Sooner or later however there comes some inkling, an awakening that stirs us and deep within we have a sense that there is more to life. More to strive for and become aware of. More to accomplish and realize towards our particular destiny. We may involve other people with it, especially the one we care about most but the true test is if we can communicate those deepest secrets with our friends and not loose focus of what our attainment truly requires.

Shared feelings and thoughts stretch further than between two people that partake in them. Mass feelings of the same variety exist across towns, through continents and parts of the world at the same time. Such group minds or mental and emotional masses, as we shall refer to them here, share the certain domains upon the inner planes. They have been responsible for the starting of wars and such grand scale movements that have occurred in life throughout the history of mankind. When we near another person, their mind and emotions have an effect on how we think, feel and react to any given incident, even though we claim to have our own mind. These is a certain amount of force that attracts us to the field of single or massive thought forms and emotions surrounding an idea or suggestion from another person. Everyone encounters problems in life, some of which are attracted to us by what we do, think and feel. The gravitational pull of particular thoughts and feelings may be diminished by an earnest effort on our behalf of not attracting or allowing them by focusing our attention elsewhere.

Handling daily stress and situations in a more refined, collective atmosphere with a puissant smile is actually easier said than done. There are tricks, and there are means to do it and all it takes is freeing our mind to realize that. Being a level above the problem and not being trapped into its' atmosphere allows us to make decisions to overcome it. In order to do this we have to actually practice not being interested in particular thoughts and emotions. A simple trick to observe is when someone tells us it is a beautiful day, we may wish to respond something of an opposite nature just to keep ourselves in check. "Beautiful? Do you know how many people are actually dying at this moment?" would be an extreme response example but nonetheless it allows us to not be captured in the atmosphere of the thought and emotion from the other person. Every avenue of research will prove that the first principle of magic, called differentiation, is required to realize an objective state of mind. Distinguishing between any two subjects or objects in order to realize a truth, develop a more accurate analysis and comprehend the relationship between any other thing is a mental process of separation and association. Replying to the antithesis during conversation allows us to not simply accept another person's point of view but to see a relation between two opposites and correlate a new and perhaps more accurate perspective. Using this simple tactic may prove to be much fun in experiencing the responses some would yield as well as opening the ability of using more of our mind instead of relying on the other person and the magnetic attraction of their thoughts. This allows us to decide exactly what we wish to say and do, according to our goals, without distraction. This simple exercise is cited as an example of training and focusing the mind not to accept every single thing everyone else says. It assists us in being free from "magnetic attraction" either emotionally or otherwise.

Breathing in deeply during times of stress can disconnect us from surrounding turmoil and allow us to refocus on what we previously decided was a goal to achieve. In the meditative state, for example, we can abstain from ordinary discrete sensory perceptions and then use the mentality for a focused and concentrated effort towards an elevated state of consciousness. Upon completion of such a practice, people usually remark on the feeling of being refreshed, a complete sense of well being, the sensation of aliveness and in being more coherent with the ability to function and react more proficiently.

Self-fulfillment is an arduous task in self-discovery, development, commitment and internal exploration. There are no quick and painless methods to reach such an extensive goal. Unity is the ultimate result of travelling the road in seeking self-truth. Thoughts themselves can be lies to the awakened Self. Any course or book purporting to give someone Understanding and Fulfillment usually seeks gratification of a nature not akin to spirituality. Such traits as Understanding and Fulfillment come after years of painstaking work and not from an overnight venue. Honest insight and personal cleansing are required in achieving a credible rise in consciousness that may be functionally maintained. Understanding is something we strive to give others but it is a quality only attainable when the person has prepared to become realized. Spirituality is an ever-present quality when we become opened to its realization.

In 1976 I began with the study of A. A. Brill's book, Psychoanalytic Psychiatry. It was somewhat like cleaning out the mental compartments of a young and eager teenager before remodeling the complete dwelling for an efficient place to live. The initial stage of sorting through the previous fourteen years of life and understanding that each experience was a natural part of my present mentality was a wearisome task. It allowed me to accept what occurred, knowing that no matter how bad any incident was, I am still myself and can work with that to seek and fulfill what it is I will one day find. This is where we all must begin. Sorting through the fallacies that have been placed and stored over years of conditioning and programming.

We have all experienced a feeling of rising above an unfortunate situation that tempts us to feel down and depressed. Mental programming may insinuate that if such and such a condition is allowed to deter us, it will prove of little worth or hamper personal well being or personal life choices. It is therefore not going to affect our mental process and annoy or disturb us from the direction we desire to go towards. The rising above sensation may come into play with a sense of inherent freedom that personal choice is a successful combatant. Thus it is that no matter what incidents disturbed our life previously, we are most capable of simplifying, directing and elevating the consciousness into states that will improve, strengthen and change our nature. There are no superior and inferior human beings. We are all equally capable of fulfilling our destiny and attaining any desired success along the way, provided we use affective means to do so.

The importance of 'comprehending to the best of our ability' should not be underestimated. It strengthens the mental muscles into not accepting half answers and prevents an overall lethargic mentality. The real enemy in most instances is that of confusion, whether we wish to acknowledge it or not. Everything, good and bad, seems to have a start, middle and ending to it. Each episode in our life begins a certain way, then it eventually involves work and finally culminates to a climax and completion. There is a formula called I.A.O. (Isis, Apophis, and Osiris), which demonstrates this phenomena as an explanation. During the Isis stage, everything is wonderful, new and exciting. The middle stage of Apophis is generally the loathsome part, which brings detestation, weariness and apathetic acceptance that we must endure as the hardest part of the ordeal. In the final stage of Osiris a new and superior condition arises that brings us to a realization or success after the peak was reached. This is considered to be a formula of Tiphereth (The Sun) which the person who understands it is conscious of their self as a person liable for suffering but anxious to transcend that stage to become one with their Higher Self. It will be touched upon in the Qabalah chapter.

The decision to clarify, cleanse and develop the mind with tricks of analysis, differentiation, and seeking Understanding is the beginning of readying ourselves to uplift and exalt consciousness, perception or awareness. The objective of this is not to make our life more complex but rather to see through everything and make it ultimately simplistic. To lift the veils of secrecy and answer our most profound questions about life is to put the purest of aspirations into our cup in order that the true child within will shine radiantly, as a Silver Star residing within us. Coming to grips with our reality ultimately allows us to know ourselves and to begin destiny in leaps and bounds.

The altering state can be readily seen in nocturnal dream states. As we awaken we realize a life that we leave behind and quickly forget but are perplexed at analyzing for the sake of rational comprehension (See dream chapter). Other methods of altering consciousness may work partially with the use of certain drugs however I deter the reader from such unnatural resources. Drugs all to easily become addictive and proves in most cases to weaken the mental muscles and willpower opposed to developing it accordingly. All work with the mind, body and soul should be done under perfect and normal control without the use of artificial means.

There are methods of hypnotic depth, which can be a useful self-help implement in rising above the normal conscious level. Again, in my earlier years I was amazed at the simple ability to bring friends and associates into different dimensional awareness by using the hypnotic state. I began self-hypnosis during school years to enable me to pass with greater ease, all of my examinations. It soon developed into a useful aid in assisting others in their personal desires and for good intent. Many instances proved that while the person was in the state there were no inhibitions that hampered them from giving requested information. One gentleman lost his wedding ring but within ten minutes under hypnosis was able to tell me where it was misplaced a few weeks previous. Another person who wished to be the best player on their hockey team approached me and within a months work he arose as the team's star. Another young man who moved to my hometown from Calcutta had taken on the habit of smoking. After a few in depth discussions I put him in the Trance State and began the work on ridding him of the smoking habit. It took additional sessions but was easier to induce him as a count of five was post hypnotically stored into his memory as a count under which he would be hypnotically induced. Even a separation of several days would come to prove that when he visited for a cup of tea and sat at my kitchen table I would walk across the room nonchalantly counting to five and turn to see his head resting towards his chest. Hypnosis is a wonderful tool for many reasons and can be used alone or with a friend provided there is a certain trust and honor that exists.

One incident of noteworthy recall is that of a relative who wished to know about his previous life. After several discussions we finally decided to embark into his subconscious. The episode was almost an hour and was audio taped for later verification. My relative had revealed names of people, incidents, descriptions of houses, friends and territory where he resided in a remote part of England, in his past life. The eventual conclusion of his previous death being that he fell off the side of a sea vessel while it was docked and was squished between it and the docking station. A few weeks later he got back to me with confirmation of some information I requested him to search for. I then played the tape to him and left it to him for continual investigation. The subconscious is a definite storehouse and wealth of information and potential. Tapping into it in a systematic and safe way can be like having a micro universe at our fingertips, just like doing an Internet Search for information retrieval.

The three main dimensions of hypnotic depth are that of role-playing/involvement; trance, and archaic involvement. Role-playing involvement is when all the motivational striving and the cognitive structures are below conscious compliance and become directed in a non-conscious way. The experience and behavior is no longer under conscious control and does not have the subjects' conscious intent. Trance depth hypnosis is when the subjects' orientation has become nonfunctional with their sense of awareness. Trance is not confined to some ecstatic mystic experience but rather includes the point prior to awakening, which we generally associate as the state of dreaming. Upon awakening we feel like we are in the middle of two worlds. On the one side we feel that the Dream State was the minds' total blanket of reality and on the other side we experience a rapid collection of data and awareness bringing us back to the normal state of affairs. Just moment's previous, while dreaming, normal reality was isolated and non-existent. The Dream State becomes faded as awakening occurs, bringing us vividly into awakened reality and recognition. This is also a trance state not unlike the hypnotic one, which is directed by the performer to achieve the desired outcome. Archaic involvement is a special kind of hypnotic transference relationship where the persons' objects are formed in the mind of the hypnotist. All instances involve functioning in a state of consciousness that is different than the routine state of daily awareness.

Although alpha rhythm is not normally depicted in open eye tests during electroencephalograph (EEG) examinations, Zen monks are known to mediate with their eyes open while displaying being in a great awareness state. Alpha waves indicate that the brain is in a relaxed yet very alert state. Such patterns in meditative states are indicative of a certain perfected ability and control over bodily functions. Zen Buddhists are known to meditate with their eyes open and focused at a certain point in front of them. Perfected yogis, however, have shown no response to stimulation during such examinations. The difference may be within their different philosophical followings. The monks believe in being in the Here-Now and living in each moment to the fullest extent whereas certain yogis believe that the physical plane is one of illusion and that they must transcend it.

Exercises in meditation with path workings, as will be touched upon in the chapter on Qabalah, can be used to transcend normal consciousness experiences and come into touch with any predetermined OBJECTIVE or SUBJECTIVE State of consciousness. This is of particular interest as a predisposed plan on what we will aspire towards and will achieve with inner plane transcendence. Within the depths of the subconscious there is a connection between each Individual soul and the World soul and with that we are capable of feeling the rise and fall of cosmic tides that perpetuate worldly events and occurrences. Consciousness is capable of being directed and focused in the most astute and abstruse manners.

Solitude generally refers to being alone, however with inter-dimensional cosmic existence we are never completely alone and are connected to a hierarchy that encompasses the 'greater scheme of things'. Thus it is that so much of what some refer to as miracles may be logically analyzed and attributed to laws of the inner planes and may be ascertained to cause particular results. The ability of psychics being able to tune or channel their awareness using a portion of their connectivity on the inner planes to see, hear, or communicate with certain energies and vibrations is synonymous with such inner plane laws. Every person is capable of developing such amazing talents through devotion and practice but in retrospect we find and realize what it is in life we require in order to be ultimately fulfilled. Some vain wishes prove to become more of a hindrance in later stages. The work is done in the preparation and the results of success to whatever degree are merely manifestations of the cause that was worked as part of evolving on the Path.

Every person is inherently different with how they feel and accept intellectual stimuli. Values differ from one person to the next, and the manner that each person deals with life issues is never the same. Maintaining some objectivity towards development with a fervent desire to experience altered consciousness is consequential for achievement. Adequately and accurately judging the level and state of consciousness helps to compare one experience to another. It has been said that in reaching the depths of sorrow there is no where to go but up. Understanding can be just as much sorrowful since it involves all and everything into acceptance. When we feel the pain of another person we tend to desire to uplift them out of that pain. There are many ways to uplift another person provided that we are not attached or distracted with the emotions and guilt conditions that may trap consciousness into the particular dominant sentiment.

Communication is a multi-faceted jewel, which brings us in touch with other people in ways that can have few limitations and great potential. Recognizing our internal masculine or assertive energy and feminine passive energy is notably significant in understanding communication upon any level. On the four planes of being there is a switch in the character role predominating every person. On the physical plane man is masculine but in the astral, in a sublime sense, he is feminine. The same holds true for a woman, on the astral she is the opposite of her physical vehicle, she is astrally masculine. On the mental plane she is again feminine and the male is again masculine. On the spiritual plane she is masculine and the male is feminine. The terms masculine and feminine on each plane do not do justice however. Using the principles of Yin and Yang in their place will be closer to realizing the effect of the male and female natures upon the planes. Psychologically this explains very much about behavior, communication, and the physical results of mingling with a person of opposite sex. Take for example that man's feelings are generally passive whereas his body is assertive. The opposite is generally true of females. The age old theories of man being the mentally superior is simply due to the masculinity of man on the mental plane and the female being receptive on the mental plane. Of course in today's life style we are striving for equality as in essence we ARE, but only opposite in sexual nature, on each plane. This is a subject that can be meditated upon to realize the interplay effect of masculine and feminine qualities as in the yin (feminine) and yang (masculine) of our character and manner of expressive communication.

The physical make-up of all material has certain mass and atomic structure. The etheric and astral counterparts of our body also have somewhat of a lesser mass attached to them. Attention is primarily focused on the physical plane and is therefore bounded by the nominal dimensions of time and space however, becoming aware of our finer grades of existence will heighten the potential for rewarding altered states. This includes the acknowledgment of our intuitive psychic sense, for which there are numerous simple exercises to practice. For example, obtain a deck of playing cards and have a close friend hold one card at a time while concentrating on the color of the card. In turn, close your eyes and make the effort to guess what color your friend is looking at. Usually the first thought, as intuition would have it, is the correct one. There will be times where contradicting thoughts will come into play and wrong answers evident, but practice improves results. This simple practice of psychic capability is not only fun to work with but will prove to be important throughout life. As there are 52 cards, correctly and intuitively guessing over 30 is a pretty good result. After several successful attempts, try to guess the suit (Hearts, Clubs, Diamonds, Spades) to continue your developmental phase. At one point you will be able to guess, or know, the exact card the person is holding and out of 52 cards, you will come to realize that it is no longer just a guessing game. This is mentioned for several reasons. Through such practices we connect our mental processing, build confidence and increase our psychic intuition. Also it signifies that there is a sense beyond the physical senses and on another plane, we can obtain factual information as though thought has energy and can travel. If you have ever stared at someone from behind and felt you were able to make the person turn around and see who was staring, you will find it peculiarly interesting that it seems you can send thoughts and vibrations with your conscious mind. Another simple exercise for practical purposes is putting a toothpick in a glass of water and concentrating on moving it in any direction you choose. Do not be discouraged if it does not work immediately but over time you will find that you have abilities to do such things by having worked on them long and diligently. I have been witness to watching a friend cause it to rain at the moment he said it would and to rain harder as he mentioned it will. I stood there in amazement as he uttered the words "lighter" and "harder" in-between watching the directed changing weather condition. Critical as I was about the incident, evidence proved that he had a link with either knowing the weather or somehow causing it.

There appears to be a sense of a neurological immortality as we traverse through the dimension of time. In transporting consciousness, people have used items such as crystals, water, mirrors, and even polished metal as oracles in the mystic experience of reflecting inwards. They become something of an inter-dimensional modem, capturing a life force that can be utilized to evolve the consciousness beyond the normal physical realm.

Limitations imposed through social upbringing have shaped the general population into thinking and acting very similarly and to define what normalcy means. It has been beneficial on the one hand but detrimental on the other. As we seek to be entertained, the downfall is that we become less and less entertaining ourselves. Imagination and creativity is the price to pay for becoming followers of certain mortal barriers that has occurred around the persona and prevented society from tapping into the unlimited source of power that is within. We become limited to our personalities and find stress and problems that perhaps wouldn't exist if we worked more fervently with expanding and growing. Being solely guided by the ever-changing lower ego becomes self-deceptive and stagnant. All of the components within the mind, such as Intellect, Memory, Will, Reason and Imagination provide a wealth of ability waiting to be unleashed and used to fulfill our greatest dreams in life. Nothing is achieved without time and effort, yet each little success in life prompts us in a forward direction and becomes part of our memory such that experience may be recalled and advanced. Altering consciousness to explore the internal dimensions becomes an accessible venture as we strengthen our will to do so. Consciousness can be uplifted or altered and directed similarly as we can direct our dream desires during the sleeping state and ascend our daily thoughts and daydreams during the semi-awakened state. ★

UNDERSTANDING DREAMS

"If you can dream - and not make dreams your master;
If you can think - and not make thoughts your aim,
If you can meet with triumph and disaster
And treat those two imposters just the same..."
Rudyard Kipling (1865-1936)

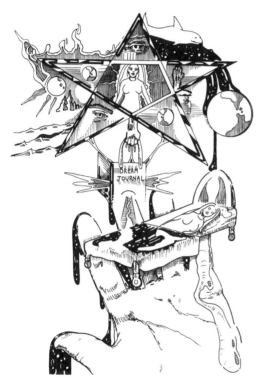

Dreams have a significant role in our life when information is obtained from them to advance our insight. Learning to accurately recall and then interpret dreams is a personal process that can help to change the dreams we have. When awakening in the morning, consciousness usually informs us of a myriad of responsibilities and we tend to quickly forget about the dream state that just preoccupied a portion of our previous hours of rest. During the course of a day, the average person sleeps approximately eight hours. Consequently, in any given week, the average time spent asleep is forty to fifty hours and over the course of a seventy-year lifetime, we spend over twenty years asleep. Of those twenty years asleep, approximately five of them are occupied in dreams.

The dream state is a very unstable period of the sleep stage. It usually results in a person becoming awake from dreaming after intervals of every ninety minutes. The eyes do not generally open during these ninety-minute interval processes of the sleep stage, which causes the mind to shift from the first ninety-minute interval into the next. The second interval occurs at one hundred and eighty minutes after we are asleep then another one at the two hundred and seventy minute period of sleep, and so forth until the final phase of awakening. Dreams usually occur at the end of these ninety minute intervals and prior to fully awakening we tend to be stirred into awakening about five times before the dream actually terminates and we become fully awake. People that claim not to dream are usually inclined to awaken after a stage other than dream sleep whereas those who awake during the course of dream sleep tend to recall some dreams that have occurred. It takes only minutes to stir-up our mind when we awake and then the ability of recalling our dreams diminishes. We begin to mentally fidget and become physically active as our mind is diverted too far away from the dream experience to avidly recall them.

The mind is an orderly, dynamic mechanism that does not cause thoughts such as in dreams, to happen haphazardly. What occurs, according to some analysts, is determined by events that precede the dream. Thought patterns can be a predictable series of events just as the dynamics of physical actions. Carl Jung, and the contemporary psychiatrist M. Scott Peck, held the opinion that the mind is a predictable and consistent set of machinery at work. Self-esteem and well being are attainable components through a positive analytical approach whereas repression is said to divide the conscious components into unconscious behavior mechanisms, lowering our sense of validity. We are aware of the repression of avoided feelings and when they come through in dreams, it shows the intimate contact they hold when we analyze them. Learning how to identify feelings that are not integrated between our conscious and unconscious enables us to accept what we think and feel and resolve it for our well being. It reconstructs our sense of identity and unifies our processing so we are not dealing with the duality that causes our consciousness to further separate from our unconsciousness.

Developing our conscious ability of choice within our dreams will curve our inhibitions and allow us to take a stand for what we wish to achieve. During dreaming, we can feel the environment in much the same way as we do while awake. We have all sensory organs at work and we evaluate what is occurring at every corner. There has to be some clue to let us know that we are dreaming, that it is an unawake stage in our life and that we can manipulate it. The clues are everywhere, during dreams we are not following laws of the physical plane. Events occur and follow one another that would not normally occur in life. The incidents are a mixture of what is being processed in our unconscious mental activity. From a conscious standpoint, most events appear to be a riddle and absurdly out of order. When we are dreaming we sometimes realize that we are because the events are slightly out of sync with the real world.

An important factor in learning to work with our dreams is in properly recalling them and making them a part of our life. To functionally accomplish this, we have to train ourselves to wake up very slowly and try to partially continue living in the dream state so that they may be accurately recorded. Having a Dream Diary or Dream Journal will help to recall dreams upon awakening once the habit of writing them down in the morning has been adopted. When recording the dream(s) that are recalled, here are a few key notes to consider:

1. Write down complete details as if you were experiencing them again.
2. Attempt to summarize key factors in the dream, and note all types of scenery and stimulus felt.
3. Describe the overall feeling received from the dream.
4. Where did the dream take place?
5. What was most vivid in the dream and how did you react to it?
6. How would you best associate the occurrence of the dream with what is happening in your personal life?

By repeating several times before falling asleep, 'I will remember my dreams! I will wake up slowly and remember my dreams!' we are confirming to ourselves the required effort to make it happen. We can record them in an organized fashion so that they are easy to read and interpret later in the day when we wish to reflect upon them again.

Life will show some significant changes when we record, categorize, analyze and begin to grasp the fundamental concerns in our dreams. Dreams are generally an unrecognized cornerstone in how we perceive and feel during a third of our lifetime and provide another venue in viewing the activity of our soul. Carlos Castenada in his book, The Art of Dreaming refers to a practice of going to sleep in our lucid dream and awakening within another lucid dream, allowing for the ability of maintaining it stronger and longer with more vivid experiences than the original one. Mental control provides us with an endless road of manipulation to fathom in the playground of our dreams and imagination.

Colors in dreams may signify sensations as they are strongly related to our personal aura and development occurring through the seven chakras. Most people do not refer to colors in dreams as they generally only recall images in the dreamscape without color coming into play. If a color is recalled it strikes the image as being vibrant and more potent in our dream messages. A study done by Carl Jung and Fritz Perls notes the importance of colors and their relationship in the matter of dreams. There had been a color test developed by Dr. Luscher and in using Gestalt therapy, where individuals role-played the feelings associated and generated with different colors. The results correlated with the experiences discussed by people waking up from dreams and recalling similar colors with similar emotions attached to them in their dreams. An example of this would be dreaming of something that is deep red. The Luscher table signifies red with "vitality" and the "the desire to live life to its fullest". Analysis of this concludes that the person is living life to the fullest or else is restricted from so doing and deeply desires to. Similarly the color green/yellow signifies "demand for appreciation and recognition", in which case the dreamer may have a problem in dealing with the need for such recognition in their life. The object dreamt of does not have to be the color it actually would be in real life. People may shield some emotions by imagining the color in accordance with how they feel. An example would be in dreaming about large trucks that are all gray. The person, in this case, may be an assertive or pushy kind of individual if we link the large trucks to such a characteristic. The Luscher table signifies gray to mean non-involvement and shielding an activity so the person in this particular dream could be demonstrating that they wish to ignore their over-assertive and pushy nature with other people.

Dreams can be warnings, an enactment of feelings from memories, desires trying to be fulfilled or a variety of other situations that our mind is unraveling and sorting through. Some dream images are startling and produce frightening experiences. Awakening from a nightmare and being alarmed from vivid dreams that stir fright and violence may become a dire concern. Popular dream literature suggests that we should confront an enemy when such appears in our nightmares. Learning to maintain a positive attitude and not allowing fear to interfere with the repression of feelings may enable us to develop the instinct of challenging what we are confronted with. In life we are invariably responsible for our own happiness and as a result, the outcome of what affects us. Over exaggeration and harping on such emotions that dreams may amplify can induce fear to a greater extent and for that reason, we should attempt to simplify, purify, express and refine what is in our mind and to confront our concerns face forward.

Violence in our dreams may signify problems that we are attempting to resolve. Violent dreams may illustrate, in a symbolic manner, particular traits associated to being distraught with certain other people or with ourselves. If the issues at hand are traumatic, they may require professional assistance in dealing with them and such authorities should be consulted. When death is experienced in a dream, it does not necessarily represent physical death. We are still quite alive and well on the physical plane, but through our mind we have yearned to experience a dramatic change and metamorphosis. Such dreams of dying let us know that we are going through an evolution and generally suggest a positive outcome whereas killing in a dream may be a metaphoric assertion of venting anger from being concerned about incidents in life. When death of someone we know is in a dream it may be triggered from the fear we have of possible separation, loss or transition in a relationship we hold with someone.

Realizing that we can manipulate our dreams is encouraging and develops greater competence. Confronting our fears and enemies will prove that we can change an outcome to better suit our desires. Before going to sleep at night, we may repeat that we will have pleasant dreams, feel harmony and such positive reinforcements that will undoubtedly affect how we behave in the dreams. Upon awakening we should try to remain in the same resting position and do not move while attempting to relive the circumstance in the dream and how we would wish the outcome to be. It takes practice and efforts to achieve results, but before long we will be changing parts of our dreaming cycles in the manner we so direct. If we feel particular terrors during light sleep and find ourselves waking up abruptly to a sitting position and perhaps shouting, this is sometimes referred to as night terror and is a different matter to deal with. In such a case, experimentation to avoid such disturbances is the only remedy, as no two people suffer from the exact same distress. The only suggestion, offered from this elementary essay, is to create a positive daily routine and then observe the results thereafter.

The ability to fly in dreams is a common occurrence. This generally illustrates the power to overcome obstacles and flee from an enemy or predicament. When buildings or power lines seem to intrude along the way, this generally represents that the person has obstacles in life that prevent control and freedom. Water in a dream typically signifies an emotional current that affects mood. Being in water suggests being comfortable with the emotions and the ability to breathe under water shows the capacity to approach unconscious feelings with greater awareness. Unclear water illustrates uncertainty with emotions and turbulent water may indicate a clamor of emotional activity. Fire in a dream may signify a transition or stage of growth taking place, otherwise it may indicate a flaring passion and rise in creativity. Generally, dream symbols may be self-interpreted, just as we would interpret emotions that are occurring at any particular instant.

Dreams may be a useful tool in creative problem solving and have been used by scientists, artists, musicians, athletes, writers and a host of other people in exploring answers to perplexities. Opening the dream-gate introduces us to an Odyssey of invaluable self-awareness and permits us to administer therapy and healing in our constantly changing life.

Dreams connect residual information or data from our daily activities to our imagination and memory during sleeping hours. Dreams attempt to associate different, unfamiliar events, places and people together within the boundaries of our psyche. These perimeters are set by the imagination, and are broader than when we are awake. For instance, when we think of a car, we usually associate it with a car that is familiar to us at first, then randomly make choices of other cars to think about. In the dream state, there is a wandering tendency to choose anything that resembles car in memory, without making a conscious choice, and is delivered as a visual image through the multi-network programming that occurs in our brain. In a case of great emotion attached to either trauma or happiness induced excitement, dreams reflect the dominant emotion that are attached to the incident. Therefore, if we feel vulnerable and concerned about anything, dreams will broadly attach that assertive emotion with several combined images and become a roundabout way of illustrating our emotional attachment in an experience. This is one basic explanation of disturbances or thrilling excitement within dreams. One specific incident in life may trigger several unrelated incidents in a dream, all of which contain the same dramatic emotions weather they be related to guilt, helplessness, concern or splendor and enthusiastic excitement.

Our dreams may seem to occur in layers within our subconscious when we attempt to consciously translate their disorderly or disfigured images. The real meanings of our visions sometimes allude us during the waking state because they seem so far and so distant from our normal life routines. The study of dreams and what causes them has been well documented and categorized as a scientific venue and is a wealth for us in unraveling, personally filtrating and understanding the fabric that creates them. The storehouse that fabricates our dreams may be giving us a warning or simply enacting a part of the diffusion that we yearn to mold together in our life.

Residual information may occupy gaps in our memory such as is the cause of having hypermnestic dreams. During these episodes we experience partial information from past experiences and they become connected to further processing. In such a dream we may recall the name of a person during an incident that occurred earlier in life but consciously did not realize we knew their name. We may also have the occurrence of the completion of some event that we were previously involved in but did not realize the outcome at the time it actually occurred or other pertinent information about it. Our psyche has the remarkable ability of picking up information that makes us wonder where it came from and how it was fashioned.

Our fears of trekking into unknown turf are generally from messages or associations that are stored in our subconscious mind. The vastness of our unconscious is none other than a formative expression of nature in her wild, free and untamed sense of expression. The lineage of our unconscious is not the ogre monster that some schools of thought make it out to be. It is constantly being stored with data and those who delve into the subconscious and harvest it by further planting positive affirmations for future retrieval benefit the rewards. Our misinterpretation and allegations of subconscious phenomena creates a certain amount of havoc on its own accord. As Carl Jung points out in his book on Dreams, "Freud invented the idea of sublimation to save us from the imaginary claws of the unconscious. But what is real, what actually exists, cannot be alchemically sublimated, and if anything is apparently sublimated it never was what a false interpretation took it to be."

What dire problems and traumas that exist in the mind of some individuals become a study for great minds and psychologists to unravel and sort. The complexity seems to be as difficult as we give it substance and life force to survive. Dreams that are intensely exasperating and discouraging may have their link from imaginary fears and negative rooted attitudes. Most dangers are a result of storing and being enslaved to negativity, misdirection and a disinterest in spiritual uplifting and revival from working purification processes. Fear becomes one of those factors of subjugation when we allow interference of aspiring to something greater and thereby further repressing our internal messages.

It is incumbent upon us to venture into the depths of subconscious life if we are to master our chemical compositions and develop the art of understanding with insight. In so doing we must draw upon our own subconscious and interpret our particular patterns, sensations, and reactions to naturally overcome our restrictions and falsities. Although dreams may be looked upon as a state of dis-ease attempting to fulfill unfinished business within the mental domain and disturbing what otherwise could be a profound sleep, they are nonetheless a necessary process of particular fulfillment, recuperation and regeneration.

The hidden and scrambled messages from our dream associations may be the simplest of answers that we are just overlooking. Deciphering and translating our subconscious language may reveal a particular infliction, repression, or desire to express and become self-realized. Our internal conflicts may be hidden and shrouded by a personality but they only become more of a conflict when we do not unlock the portals for subconscious liberation and become attuned to the nature of our soul expression.

A few considerations may be adopted while discussing dreams amongst friends to ensure the transition and analyses of them are pondered with comfort and ease.

1.   Symbols in dreams may represent something different than our first analysis. Taking it at face value may elude us from the truth and misinterpret the subtle meaning.

2.   Dreams are a personal experience and should be shared with those who show concern enough to assist us in our interpretations of them.

3.   Dreams are a part of our psyche and should be considered with an amount of serious interest.

4.   When we discuss our dreams we should talk about them as though they are occurring as we speak and put expression into them as though we are reenacting them. This will assist in recollecting them and makes it more interesting for the listener to fathom.

5.   Personal opinions and interpretations should be saved until after the dream has been totally relayed or written down. This allows us to bring all the actual dream information to the forefront first and then advice and opinions may be formed from the full story.

6.   An actual interpretation of the dream is better than associating it with normal life circumstances and predicaments. It could be that the dream is telling us much more than we want to see into it.

7.   Encouragement with support and motivation are valuable drive devices in seeking interpretations and resolutions from our dream material.

8.   Respect should be paid to anyone discussing his or her dreams. Dreams are a personal matter and ridicule or cornering a person that reveals their inner sanctum of dream life is inappropriate and of no value. Listening is as important as giving advice.

9.   If you believe that you can interpret someone's dream, try to let them figure it out on their own by giving them some ideas to get them into a self-analytical mode so they may form their own interpretation. Assisting them to build their own interpretation is better than providing one that may be inappropriate.

10.   Interpreting a dream may be like piecing a puzzle together. Once the major framework is configured and recognized, then other pieces and relationships may put it together to form a moderately accurate interpretation.

11.   If there are startling concerns that arise from a dream or interpretation, try to look at small ways to work it out and solving any dilemmas to move forward. If a dream seems to be a complete mystery, do not be overwhelmed by it but rather appreciate the fact that the unknown can also be treasured.

12.   The process of interpretation should be a positive step, an enjoyable realization and a discovery that makes us feel a little bit better about closing an enigma.

Dreams help us to regenerate our mind, experience our thoughts with present and past issues and to focus our attention to an area of our life that we are drawn towards. They help us to compensate for imbalances in our conscious attitude, as Carl Jung indicated and they elicit an active and passive integration with our deeper self. They draw from our creative source and impartially sort out our desires and concerns. Many of our predicaments and concerns can be sorted out by dreams. It was through dreams that many of the short stories were fashioned in this book and their pattern to coincide with tarot card themes. Information abounds when we are asleep and the only plight seems to be in putting it together to best serve our interests. The mind seems to have no problem in digging deeply and finding answers and solutions that match our concerns, when we train it to do so. Many of our best ideas and solutions may come to us in dreams and inspirations from them.

Dreams are an altered state of consciousness where we may tap into virtual unthinkable territory and capture the essence of creative potential. They allow us a means of listening to our source and entering the unbounded gulf to face unprecedented challenges and to conquer the field of our limitations. We connect with a certain non-definable energy during dream states and enter it as an experience. It becomes structured through our mental and emotional settings and recognized by our conscious coherence. For brief instances, we may step beyond quantum reality and chaos theory and delve into the sublime order of a rarified creative domain to touch the forces of our visions. The potential to generate new possibilities and charter a lift outside of normal range becomes an extraordinary upgrade of insight within our imaginative reach. Our dreams may take us away from the raw and cruel or they may solve our dilemmas as we decide through efforts. Most certainly they will reveal to us that life is a tangible, changeable, magical substance that we can whirl with at any speed and vibration to coincide with our endeavors of uncovering our most potent abilities. ★

OUR INNER BODIES

"Divine thought cannot be defined, or its meaning explained, except by the numberless manifestations of Cosmic Substance in which the former is sensed spiritually by those who can do so."

The Secret Doctrine- H.P. Blavatsky

The realization of the cosmic substance that comprise our inner bodies and how they are affected by physical circumstances will enable us to strengthen and refine the essence of which they are composed. Nomenclature regarding our inner bodies has been well documented and distributed, especially in theosophical literature. Interest in such subjects is not widespread throughout western culture due in part to the complexity in the study and synthesis that is involved, thus resulting as a dormant topic to most people. The evolutionary chain illustrates that we are all on different levels of comprehension and willingness to learn with a self-analytical, scrutinizing and relative open mind. Having a concern for realizing our inner bodies will assist in reaching a spiritual consciousness.

Classifying the human framework is a matter of belief and opinion, however for this treatise we shall look at the inner bodies as layers within the physical body, similar to the peelings of an onion, one within the other. Surrounding the physical body is a light layer referred to as the etheric body or double which contains what are known as the chakras or seven wheels of vitality. The chakras have numerous functions in supporting life and spiritual awakening. The chakras primarily absorb life-energy called prana and distribute it throughout the body to sustain life. The etheric body is composed of four higher elements called the etheric, the super-etheric, the sub-atomic and the atomic. The etheric body is intimately connected with our physical body and is referred to by the Hindus as the Kama body and absorbs energy from the atmosphere that is delivered from the sun.

The next inner body is a finer level and counterpart to the physical body, called the astral body. The astral body works on a plane separate but within and attached to the physical plane and has seven grades of increasingly finer matter associated to its composition. So-called ghosts and astral entities have the ability of transferring through material objects due to their finer astral composition being able to penetrate through the space within material form. The astral body and plane have been called the emotional plane where our various degree of emotional activity is drawn from and hence the development of our emotional or astral body.

Intellect and thought activity exists in a finer layer than the emotions. They originate in our mental body and have greater effect upon our emotional or astral body than they do on our physical. The mental body and plane is a vivid world within our physical life whereupon we can draw from an unlimited source. Our fourth, inner, body is called the causal body It's name is derived from Karana Sharira, Karana meaning cause. It is distinct from the other bodies in that the etheric, astral and mental bodies gradually disintegrate after death of the physical body. The causal body, however, is somewhat immortal in that it is the vehicle, which stores past life achievement and allows reincarnation to occur. It is a vehicle of the Higher Ego or true form of the individual and upon achieving supernormal evolution, the individual is relinquished of it and resides on the spiritual levels. All of our inner bodies have particular functioning to our life and cycle of growth and reside within one another as a nucleus or core, emanating from our spirit.

As the physical body absorbs energy and sustenance from food and discharges the unused parts through the five excretory organs of the liver, intestines, kidneys, lungs, skin (via sweat, gaseous transmissions etc), so too does the etheric body discharge unused vitality through the pores of the skin. Energy radiating from the etheric is its strongest from the finger tips and toe area. The physical body exudes through these areas as though they were doorways into and out of the etheric body. That is why it is of importance to have these areas clean, otherwise it would be like pouring your drinking water through a used oil filter. Therefore, after washing or showering these bodily pores and releasing contamination from the physical body a sense of rejuvenation is felt. Cleansing reopens the pores for pure vitality absorption.

Astral matter in the astral body is in constant motion, similar to the affect that the molecules of boiling water illustrates. Energy is constantly flowing through the chakras as a result and responds to the vibrations and sensations we feel on the physical plane. Developing awareness and functioning of the chakras allows us to harmoniously balance this ever-flowing energy throughout our bodies.

Our etheric changes and develops just as our physical body does with the intake of food and prana energy consumption. The prana particles create constant change by assisting our growth. The etheric body replaces bodily particles when the Vitality Globule, seen as glowing, shimmering particles in the atmosphere on a sunny day generates prana and causes alterations in our bodies.

The Vitality Globule is a charged atom resulting from a six-fold attraction to six other atoms creating a hyper-meta-proto element that combines on the sub-atomic sub plane. Assimilation of this high energy provides perfection in physical health. Once this charged Vitality Globule is absorbed by the body its' force changes. The spleen chakra is vitally important in taking this energy of charged atoms to different parts of the body by breaking it up into seven components of prana (distinguished by different colors associated with each prana). The dispersion goes to areas of the throat, abdomen and navel center, nervous system, heart center, and base of the spine. Some books with this east Indian doctrine refer to five main streams, and they are not wrong as a few colors join into one stream and bring the original seven prana energies into five main component streams which exit the spleen horizontally to the above mentioned destinations.

When such intrinsic heightening energies are not absorbed, we tend to feel drowsy and unaccomplished by lack of energy intake. This may result in acting as a sponge around people who have an abundance of energy, not unlike the concept of a psychic vampire. This is a basic feature in society, such that we are constantly exchanging feelings and energy levels, sometimes to a demerit of depletion and requiring a break for rejuvenation. It is often the case in spiritual seances where mediums expend this vitalized prana to the forces that are conjured for accomplishing their task.

We constantly emit particles from our aura, in all directions, into the atmosphere. The healthier and stronger we are, the greater is the vitality that may be felt by others. There are positive uses for such energy emitting, prominently in healing techniques. A clairvoyant can see a faint gray mist sprouting from the aura of an average person, which is the etheric counterpart of sodium chloride, or salt particles emitting from that person's body. Pine and eucalyptus trees extract similar constituents from the globules, as does the etheric body and have a soothing effect for people with nervous depletion.

Prana repels germs and hibernating diseases when the lines from the aura are firm and straight otherwise when the lines are drawn down and a person's aura is not vibrant, harboring wounds and irregular fatigue may result. A conscious effort of projecting energy develops this out rush of prana as a preventative measure from inseminating such debris that comes into contact with our aura and inner bodies. This will promote health and develop the etheric sheath like a wall capable of blocking negative influences as well as providing a steady flow of energy within and exerted outwards.

Ectoplasm (from the Greek word ektos, meaning outside, and plasma, meaning mould) is a substance utilized by mediums and is etheric in nature. It is generated mostly from the medium and sometimes from the etheric body of other people, and resembles somewhat like clammy bars of less than an inch to as much as eight inches in diameter. It is used to move physical objects during seances as the ectoplasm protrudes from the mediums' lower body, usually in the feet area, and attaches to an object (table, chair, etc.) thereby lifting it. The ectoplasm is also sometimes directed to the floor and protrudes upwards with more force and lifts the object it is focused at. The former method is strenuous on the medium since it increases the persons weight almost 95% of that of the object being lifted or moved whereas the later method decreases the persons weight as one end of the bar or rod rests upon the floor.

White light practically destroys the formation of the rod created and while the medium is moving an object, any change of lighting could rupture the ectoplasm rod causing undue pain or shock to the medium. Loose clothing is worn during such experiments since tightly woven apparel impedes the effort of a medium in trance as well as affects the strength of the bar. Numerous studies and tests on this subject have been carried out and for such pioneering data the reader is referred to the book - *Phenomena of Materialisation* by Baron von Schrench Notzing (1913).

The astral plane is not so much a separate place as it is an internal condition of human nature. It is the penetrating existence within the physical world and as such occupies the minutest of space, within a physical object. Research has attempted to see the correlation between electrons and astral atoms as such, being perhaps one and the same thing. The chemical atom of hydrogen, for instance, has somewhere between 700 and 1000 electrons and occult research has claimed that there are 882 astral atoms in hydrogen.

Atoms are either Male (positive) or female (negative) in nature. Force comes from the inner astral world through the male atom into the physical world. In the female atom, force exits the physical world and goes into the astral world. This happens to raise an interesting concept about hormones of testosterone and estrogen, their constituent atoms and their interplay upon the physical and emotional planes. The densest parts of the physical anatomy constitute similar dense astral counterparts, which interchange with corresponding atoms through the seven sub-divisions of the astral plane. The first six levels are composed of elemental essence and the loftiest seventh is monadic essence. In the undeveloped person, lusty appetites of mixed and tangled emotions thrive in their astral body and extend as a layer, about a foot beyond their physical body. An intellectual and refined person may have an outline about a foot and a half beyond their physical with a more definite outline to it. A spiritually endowed person will have a much greater, lustrous, clearly defined astral body emanating the finest of particles in the astral sub-levels.

All material objects, living and so-called non-living have an astral counterpart. If a part of a person was amputated, the limb may be removed but its astral limb remains in tact with the rest of the intact astral body as the built form on the astral level has acquired it over a course of development. It will cease from active operation over time since the physical portion has not sustained the astral counterpart. Likewise is true of plants and other living things but not so for material objects such as a vehicle or house. When a part of those are changed or gone, their astral counterpart is not sustained and also thus divides, separates or moves with it.

The color of an astral body is determined by the emotions that it carries. It reflects the kind of person that inhabits it. Black astral aura indicates extreme hatred and avarice, and lurid red illustrates a sensual character, gray shows depression in character, orange exudes ambitious pride and yellow depicts an intellectual character. The colors vary with contrast, hue and the slight mixture of additional colors, paints each person as individual and unique. In a very developed person we would find a fine outline from head to toe of lilac, yellow, rose, blue and green which would all indicate the aspiration, devotedness and cleanliness of their astral body and other bodies.

Emotions are influential to all living things. A study of botany will illustrate that plants are affected by emotions of like and dislike, anger and serenity, just as in the case with animals. They are capable of sensing and reacting to stimuli with either affection of devotion or reprehensible concern. This is similar to the reactions that humans portray during emotional involvement. One of the functions of our astral body is to transfer emotions into our physical body as sensations. Another function of the astral is to transfer physical stimulus through the astral to the mental body or mentality. This filtering process accounts for the different levels and sub-levels of our existence from one body to the next within our constitution.

The chakras in the etheric body also have their corresponding astral counterparts. A fine web of single layered physical atoms is compressed and surrounds the physical body in such a manner as to divide communication from one plane to the next, which is why forces of atomic matter are separated between the physical and astral planes. This web is a sheath and protects us from certain harm to the nervous system. Things such as alcohol, drugs, and tobacco are volatile substances and can burn away at the web until it is finally destroyed and the person's senses become deadened. The results are usually associated with animalism, brutality, and gross materialism such that refined feelings no longer exist and the person is incapable of any highly self-controlled experience or activity. There are other unfortunate results of the broken web such as affecting the sub planes of the astral so that only matter from the lower sub planes filters through as negative and grossly unpleasant sensations and behavior. This is why purity is of such importance in the physical and emotional bodies so that a barrier web is kept between the physical body and lower sub planes of massive and unpleasant lingering influences.

Purity in food consumption also helps to purify the astral vehicle. That is the reasoning for vegetarianism with people involved in purity meditation. They refuse to eat flesh foods in order to avoid exciting animal desires in their lower astral nature. Rhythmic foods such as can be found in grains and fruit are the best for balancing strength with sensitivity. The stress and irritability found in large, busy cities play havoc upon our astral body with rampant penetrating and disturbing noises. Generally, that which promotes longevity and health to the physical body has a corresponding positive affect opposed to deterioration for our inner bodies.

Depression can be caused by such feelings as fatigue, hunger, extreme heat or cold as well as other sensations that come from messages our body sends us. Depression has numerous causes and in most cases may be avoided by recognizing the symptoms. Clouding our aura with negative thoughts can influentially dominate our ambitions and hinder our positive and creative outflow of energy. Thought-forms can have positive or negative affects, and are masses that we create with mental and emotional matter. Author Dion Fortune has elaborately written about protecting and shielding the inner bodies in her book *Psychic Self-Defense*. Thought-forms are a useful tool if they are used to protect a loved one by acting like a shield. They become an agent of defense by erecting a barrier against negative influences and forces. These type of thought-forms are guardians and are often subconsciously developed by mothers in caring for the safety of their children.

Writers create mental images while developing personas for the characters in their story. They effectively strengthen the characters with mental projections of particular traits and thereby find it easier to fabricate the story. This is considered as a type of thought-form and influences the mind of the readers by bringing the person to life in the story. The same holds true for other artistic expressions, paintings, and creations of all types. This is how capable psychics can get in touch with a person, even if that person is deceased. The psychic follows the thought form of a particular object until they find its original source. It also uncovers additional information about the artist or person if the psychic can tap into that texture of the art or object on the inner planes.

People who are developed mentally through meditation are capable of projecting thought forms of particular shapes and cloaking their body with such images. Figures and designs such as the star pentagram and hexagram may be projected as thought forms to provide protection and direction. Purity in thoughts can be used to activate a talisman created to serve a special purpose. Lucky charms, talismans, bracelets, necklaces can all be charged with thought-force and projected energy to combat impurity, to attract particulars or for any desired ambition. Talismans, for example, are used for several purposes such as love or for attracting certain spirits to guide and to care over us while travelling or working.

When our physical body is deceased, the elemental essence of the inner bodies separates from it and will not return to it. The astral body for instance exists in the fourth dimension and returns to that realm, only to reappear in the physical world as a ghost when it has reason to do so. The tesseract is an extension of a six-sided cube and is a physical model that represents the fourth dimension. A line represents the first dimension and a four-sided surface is a physical model of the second dimension. A cube is a model of the third dimension and has 8 points, 12 lines, 6 surfaces and is one solid. The tesseract has 16 points, 32 lines, 24 surfaces and is 8 solids. The concept of the fourth dimension is almost unfathomable in the beginning, but it exists as the astral plane and is not unfamiliar to those with experience. If that should not be complex enough, the mental plane is five-dimensional, and the buddhic plane is six-dimensional. There may be seven or more dimensions beyond the scope of comprehension but to limit our thinking to a three-dimensional world is foolhardy because we are more than physical inanimate objects. P.D.Ouspensky covers the multi-dimensional realms in his exceptional work of *Tertium Organum* (a very interesting book to get and read).

In working with our inner bodies we come to realize other dimensions, utilizing unique abilities for spiritual advancement and learn to solve existing problems here at home. It enables us to fully appreciate the marvels and complexity of human nature and to SEE all sides at once of everything in our midst. It becomes a transcendence of continuous consciousness in realizing our place in the macrocosmos, the great universe of which we are the microcosmic image.

To ordinary sight it appears that the planets in our solar system are quite separated by distance and in which fact they are, in three-dimensional space. In the fourth dimension however they are joined and are a systematic part of one complete whole. The Hindus have associated the solar system to the image of a lotus flower, which is interesting because all petals are connected and rise from a stem. If we place our spread-opened fingertips on a piece of paper and draw a circle around each fingertip on the paper, let each circle represent a planet. In this analogy, the circles are connected through the film material of the paper, which represents space, and the fingers extend from the drawn circle into the hand, then arm and body. The fingers are like extensions of the planets and represent the fourth dimension, connecting all planets as one into the next dimension. This analogy may be used in explaining the correlation of comparative religion. Every religion seeks Truth and Divinity while worshiping a particular Supreme Deity. In the hand and paper analogy, religions may represent the circles just as the planets did. The particular path of each religion may be associated to a finger that extends into the hand of the Supreme Deity. Fathoming this, we can come to realize that the whole Universe is connected through dimensions beyond our physical visibility. All conceptions, beliefs and information are like specks that reside as some fraction of the whole. This may provide some cognizance to capture the truth regarding destiny, planned super-structure of the Universe and the existence of Beings in the Higher Life cycle to cause the major influences upon creation as we know it through spiritual awareness on higher dimensions. There will always be an open gap awaiting to be filled by advanced Beings to assist humanity in the proper course of evolution and for that reason we all strive in returning to our root, our spirit and ultimate essence to play our significant part.

The mental body is composed of thoughts that are formed and concrete. The causal body works with abstract thought that is not formed but rather formless as the essence of principles. The three higher levels of the mental plane comprise the first elemental kingdom and descend into the four lower levels of that plane making the second elemental kingdom. On this lower set of levels is created mental elemental essence. The following third elemental kingdom is on the astral plane and constitutes astral elemental essence. Each kingdom also houses the seven distinct rays of essence, which are particular to that level. All of these planes materialize their essence into the denser forms of matter on the physical level. It is our job as spiritually minded individuals to revert back upwards/inwards, to get away from becoming an inanimate object of materialization and become realized as one with the creator rather than the created.

The composition of the mental body consists of particles of the four lower divisions of mental matter. It is similar to the astral body in that it is built from its' lower divisions of matter just as the physical is built of solids, liquids, gases and etheric particles. The mental body is shaped like an ovoid and as can be presumed, higher (good, positive) thoughts elevate to the top of it whereas lower (evil, negative) thoughts, which include selfishness, sink to the depth of that ovoid. Colors as noted previously, can be seen by clairvoyant vision to detect the type of personality and character in any mental body. There is a single essence, or molecular unit, from the mental body that remains with each of us throughout our incarnations. The rest of the mental body is diluted from one life to the next and does not resemble any similarity to the previous life. The molecular unit, however, is constant and provides for our continuous evolution.

Memory and imagination are concrete forms of the mental faculty on the mental plane and work with and against the inertia of matter on that plane. That is why an expenditure of energy is used to recall mental images and recollections of things stored on the mental plane. Adepts have the distinct ability of channeling images to the physical brain for virtuous manifestation of each mental activity.

The mental body is in itself, an organ of sense. It does not suffer from the inept problem of communication as the physical and astral bodies do, having various senses to deal with. Thoughts are transferred without formulating them into words and meanings as they are made of color and to an extent, sound. It is somewhat like watching a musical selection of colors with vibrations to them. They are exactly what they are by the eventual sensation of the collective tones they comprise. Persistent development allows us to exercise our mental body independently of the other bodies. With this developed faculty the mental body will deliver concrete thoughts to the physical by using the astral and etheric bodies manifesting down the cerebro-spinal system. It also passes the level of consciousness to the causal body and delivers the true state of being to the higher ego. It should be noted, in passing that animals functionally utilize the four lower levels of the mental plane to employ their reasoning faculty, whereas humans have a much further reaching capability.

The colors of the mental body always change, grow and illuminate with development of that faculty. Lack of rational thought and retardation of open-mindedness deteriorates mental growth, proving not only a mundane existence but also a dormant and idle mental capacity. This can become an extreme case of what may be described as warts ossified within the mental body and can not be easily removed unless a substantial change has taken effect to open the person into spiritual REALITY.

The mental faculty can become a mixture of impurities stemming from vanity, arrogance and other assertive quarks. The higher mental plane does, however, transmit its influence into the consciousness and can be viewed as a non-argumentative but clear-seeing ability containing intuitive qualities poured from one atomic plane to another until it becomes a recognized growing state of awareness. The causal body transmits knowledge, beyond the normal senses, of the past, present and future, through the higher mental body to the brain cells and may create a prophet or psychic seer with interesting revelations out of the person when it is actualized.

The mental plane is a film of refined matter that exists for thoughts to travel through and reside. It is quite obviously filled with every thought that is occurring around the world. Sending good thoughts/ vibrations helps the world consciousness to grow and improve to overcome those weaker negative ones that are trying to fill it with averse negativity composed of myriad greed, undue suffering and so forth. Combined thoughts of like minds have much greater power than singular thought projections from single minds, provided all associates are in harmony to project those thoughts. For this reason, elevating consciousness and energy with other people can create a dynamic effect as a group mind on all the planes.

A thought has driving power according to the force it is projected with through the soul. Its elemental essence is shaped according to its nature and is cloaked on the mental plane by a color, which represents its quality. A thought-form involves a complete idea that is transferred to anyone prepared to receive, but can only be received by one person at a time. A thought-wave, however, can reach several people at once. It doesn't include a complete idea but rather the general nature and character of an idea. It is with this incredible ability that a developed person can make thoughts work for them while they are not in the location that the activity is taking place. Thought-forms can be guided and used as agents of the will, to accomplish tasks of a higher nature. Such thought-forms have been fashioned in Christianity as the Angel of the Presence, which is a thought-form and extension of Christ. Similarly, Masonic Lodges may use a portrait of the H.O.A.T.F. to feel the presence and blessing bestowed upon their temple.

The ability to be telepathic (feeling from a distance) means that we can transfer and receive or communicate thoughts without the use of physical means. This is accomplished by transferring the thought from one etheric brain to another. The vibrations of the thought in the mental body are transferred to the astral, then the etheric and off to the other persons' etheric brain to the physical brain for reception and decipher. Another method is between two astral bodies where one person picks up the thoughts/emotions of the other and the transfer does not have to go through the etheric for comprehension. A third method, used for advanced communication by Masters in teaching their students complex information on other planes, is thought transference between two mental bodies. It may one day become a form of communication for mankind as evolution takes it toll and the use of the telephone will be prehistoric equipment. The person transferring has to be self-conscious and in full control on the mental plane in order to properly transfer the thought into another persons' mental body. Consciousness has to be centered in one body at a time, weather it is the physical, etheric, astral, mental or causal. If we have the ability to SEE with our inner bodies, we can look at other people and see what form and colors their inner bodies possess. The incredible splendour of functioning with the mental world is of tremendous value and becomes an asset beyond description if the effort is made to develop the functions therein. There are constant and most remarkable occurrences to see through the inner planes that have an affect upon our life. If we accept to understand and study them, we will learn incredible information that affects the components of our physical body.

The akashic records may be seen in glimpses on the astral plane, but they are a matter fashioned from the mental plane (thus the term akasha). These karmic records or memory banks of all nature can be worked with in the mental plane far better than upon the astral plane. The astral gives a basic reflection, in part, of those records and can be somewhat distorted, like looking at a three dimensional image on a pond, seeing it in only two dimensions. If there were ripples the whole image would be a useless distortion, not to mention that the image is also reversed, being only an image, of the records. The astral plane is not a ripple free, still surface place anyway. A psychic who has only astral sight will not, therefore, get the most accurate picture of past events. On the mental plane, reading the records is very accurate and the difference between one person reading them and another is only in their physical translation of the event. It is similar to a group of people observing an event on the physical plane, where each one may give a different account of what occurred. On the mental plane, it is all seen for exactly what it is, no deception, and without limitation of the actual account. Using the faculties of the causal body will make reading the records even easier.

If we endeavor to revisit a past incarnation by reading the history upon the inner plane, it can be regarded in a usual manner like watching a movie and being a spectator, realizing that it was once our previous life. We may also become somewhat attached to the emotions and thoughts related to that time, which were the original ones of that person we are observing, being our self in a past life. Recovering anything from the akashic records is like reading the universal consciousness within the dimensions of stored history. Training is all that is required to do this, so that mental vision is in control with reading the actual records of past life instead of being duped by reading into thought-forms or other vibrations.

Evil as an active misuse of energy is generated from the four lower levels of the astral plane and is therefore non-existent on higher levels. An ego of a person may have certain imperfection, but it is not evil. An evil-minded character is an ego trapped in the delusions of the lower grades of astral or emotional substance and does not exist in any manner upon the higher mental and causal planes. A direct line of communication exists between the higher ego and consciousness of a person such that information is translated into the lower sub-planes for comprehension. This becomes an uninhibited self-awareness ability of expressing useable knowledge from higher to lower. The linking of the lower and higher self is the fusion of the subconscious with the conscious in realization and activates a super-conscious state.

There are of course many reasons for problems that occur and manifest as estranged mental illness. With obsession as an extreme case, the ego is ousted by an entity only because the ego had such a weak hold upon the inner bodies within the person to begin with. The mental plane is the great meeting location where the Higher Self and Lower self congregate and permeate the divine spark, the ray, to project into the lower worlds and furnish life in the evolutionary process. It is a massive meeting place with three upper levels of formless existence and four lower levels of formed existence. Evil natured tendencies upon the lower levels of the subconscious are filtered and radically replaced by the outpouring growth of positive influences. All of our great achievements are expressed as an illumination and composition of colors in our causal body. Our mental and causal bodies expand with a radiance of colored lights and extend further from our physical body to exemplify our greatest and strongest qualities.

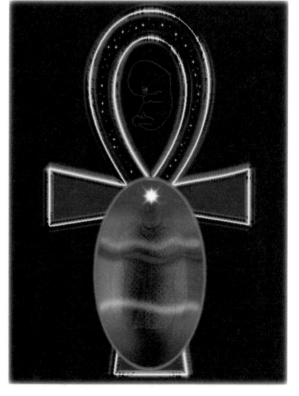

Through the practice of meditation the consciousness can pass into and out of the laya center, which is the layer of neural points between our mental and causal bodies. The mental body is stilled when this shift of consciousness occurs and results in a temporary loss of consciousness as it passes into the next level of higher, causal awareness. With this experience, the consciousness is detached from objects of the lower planes as awareness of the higher plane takes over. At this instant, the ego may shape and mould the mental body with spectacular vibrations from the images of the higher, inner plane of which in normal circumstances we would have no capability of doing. States of Genius may be obtained in this way as well as true intuition and in no way compares to the false attainment of escapism when we wish to believe that we've achieved some super meditative state. When our astral vibrations are stilled the higher mental body will echo forth to give information to the lower personality for us to functionally utilize.

The causal body is sometimes referred to as the Augoeides, a glorified representation of the True Self. Once material-minded consciousness has been conquered as to not interfere with communication from the Higher Self, truth on all pertinent matters becomes an intuitive sixth sense. Purity through refinement in all matters of life is essential for true genius to manifest down the planes as a constant flow of spiritual expression. The work involved to get there is self initiation and becoming an Adept is required in order to function on the higher planes and transmit such influence to the lower. We may have access to the lower matter of the causal plane, and upon travelling the path of wisdom open to the second sub plane, but the Adept uses the whole causal body and causal plane while still maintaining consciousness on the physical plane.

Transferring consciousness to another planet in our solar system can not be done on the astral or mental planes. It can be accomplished with the causal body but more easily by using the buddhic plane (a complex subject requiring lengthy analysis). The atomic matter comprising the causal body is bunched together just as the forces of attraction compress the atoms around a planet. Atoms are free and uncompressed through interstellar space, which causes potential disturbances from comets and meteors when orbiting.

Microscopic exploration is possible through the causal body with use of the point within the brow chakra center, which is likened to a single atom microscope. It can be used on any plane and projected to any distant points for examination with any chosen magnification by opening its spirallae.

A method of foreseeing the future has been associated with the sight through the causal body by an incredible ability of envisioning effects of causes that have been produced. Things that influence life on the lower planes are not readily seen for their outcomes but with causal vision the effect of forces are plainly visible. Therefore proper training in the use of our causal body will reveal what occurs in life before it manifests simply by having causal vision of seeing such forces in action we will also know their results.

Communication with spiritual Masters is inevitable upon the Higher Planes. Their assistance in developing our causal body has great effect. Their radiating influence helps in the growth and furtherance of humanity's evolution. It is with use of the present knowledge that all good can be performed to eliminate crises and man made problems. We should be at the realization that there is work to do and accomplishments will prove what significant success we can be fulfilled with. Theoretical knowledge is as good as our efforts in making use of it. Paving the road to the light-hearted transcendence of spirituality is a purification of daily existence. Opening our inner senses into the vast array of potential from heightened consciousness will connect us to the limitless, to create major positive changes through using the functions of our inner bodies with expended efforts over time. This portion of information may be of assistance to those who desire enough to make those efforts. ★

ASTRAL ACHIEVEMENTS

"If we examine with psychic faculty the body of a newly-born child, we shall find it permeated not only by astral matter of every degree of density, but also by the several grades of etheric matter."

The Astral Plane- C.W. Leadbeater

To travel out of our physical body by conscious effort and return as desired with information that is useful and helpful in daily life would be a wonderful feat and adventure. It is something that every person can do and it is also FREE to learn and achieve. Entering the inner planes of the astral, and even travelling on the physical plane in our astral body to witness events, people, and study subjects, even in other languages, is something truly remarkable and something we are capable of doing. Performing a projection of our consciousness is done to a minor extent every time we are asleep. The bulk of our conscious awareness remains in our physical body therefore we do not direct, control and participate fully in a conscious projection while we are doing it during sleeping hours, unless we develop and train ourselves to do so.

Information may appear disfigured when we awaken and attempt to translate the events that occurred after an astral projection. The information we obtained was from another plane, and to translate it into concepts that our physical plane consciousness accepts becomes a task of training our mind and senses. Recollections can become increasingly distorted as our day goes forward, just like an attempt in accurately recalling and describing a dream. Projecting our astral body is a misleading and often misunderstood concept. Essentially, we are transferring our consciousness to our astral body and then travelling with it, hence projecting it to a destination. We can literally transfer our consciousness to three other planes and travel in either of those planes. They are the etheric plane, the lower astral and higher astral and the lower and higher mental planes. There are also higher planes, namely the causal and spiritual, however their constitution is of such a fine material that we cannot consider it as a plane of travelling within. Each plane is positive to the one below it and negative to the one above it. It is therefore advisable for us to gain knowledge of the one above we are working on in order to function with greater ease and control in the one we travel upon.

Having a quiet place to practice our work is very important. While practicing astral projection, we do not want anyone to touch our physical body while our consciousness is directed out of it. Such sudden startling would cause us to flee back into our physical body with alarm and could result in shock, pain or injury. The sensation of quickly returning to our physical body from an astral experience is similar to the sensation of quickly descending in an elevator. In the case of moving in an elevator, our etheric body shifts due to the rapid motion and tries to keep together with our physical body. There have been incidents where people were found dead near a bomb blast but had no wounds upon their body. Such great vibrations cause a severity in the link, which the etheric has upon the physical, and without the etheric body the physical would not remain alive. Loud noises such as a nearby barking dog or heavy traffic noise causes shifts in our etheric body also. The amount of nourishment and food we consume is related to the strength of attachment from the physical body to our etheric. The greater nourishment we have, the tighter and closer our etheric is attached. Malnutrition causes a very loose connection and separation may occur, making such an individual susceptible to severe problems.

There is more diversity upon the astral (derived from the Latin word astra, meaning 'star') plane than any other plane. There are more levels to it, but we will focus on the lower and higher astral levels here. The lower is closely attached to the etheric level and the higher astral is linked close to the mental plane. The mental plane is composed more of forces and not forms and as such constitutes colors and vibrations as its medium, as outline in Our Inner Bodies. Our sense of directions, which we are familiar with on the physical plane, has no relation on the astral plane. There is no sense of directions as we know them to be up, down, left, right, sideways movement, and there are no large or small comparisons upon the astral. There are distinctions, which will tell us what level we are on such as the particular character of the scenery that we feel and observe. These simple characteristics make the lower and higher sub-levels of the astral plane distinguishable for us.

This information may have some of the less familiarized readers wondering if they can achieve anything of practical value from all of this. If you really want to astrally project, to move your consciousness out of your physical body in a completely controlled manner, and out of your room, down the street, to fly anywhere as it were, you can certainly DO IT. The important points to regard are caution, preparedness and maintain a sincere, humble directive. None of these subjects are new and they are certainly well documented and written about in many books worldwide. As previously mentioned, I strongly suggest that drugs should not to be used for spiritual development. The most important factor in any training is the WILL that is developed in the course and preparation of all operations and the misuse of drugs may cause hallucinogenic delirium or traumatic uninvited experiences. The gradual mind controlling techniques that we gain from developing our will over the course of effort and time will have been the greatest achievement in the long run, and not merely the results that we've obtained.

Astral matter is completely tangible upon its multi-leveled plane. We can even create a body or restyle our astral body to our hearts desire. So much so that it can do certain work for us on the physical while we are asleep or meditating, in an indirect way, using physical plane laws in accordance with our astral functioning. In essence we are performing magic while directing our will towards an accomplishment. It is advisable that we do not go out mentioning our "great" new knowledge to other people since it may diminish the energy we are building for a successful outcome. Not only that but also other people may not be so interested and may distract or discourage us from personal development. They may even criticize the fact that we are attempting honest efforts in learning something new and for whatever reason they may not accept it. We should use our confidence and energy for our personal success and not develop an inflated ego during spiritual progress.

Writing our daily work and achievements in a personal journal is a great idea for many reasons. This could be the beginning of a magical diary as such by recording experiences, development, ideas, and mapping out the inner plane descriptions for our familiarity. It is also advisable that we do not quickly get hopes of visiting departed relatives or friends on the astral plane. Usually after a person dies they are still somewhat asleep and confused of what happened and their functioning is not what they or we would expect after death. They may be trapped in a place on the astral plane until they awaken and move on to where they should be, as if they were sidetracked for a while. Further research in these studies is accessible through most literature on astral plane phenomena and projection. By becoming trained and more aware of working in the astral state, we can avoid much confusion when death does occur at the end of our life. A training exercise to bring familiarity and the achievement of transferring consciousness to and from our astral body will now be covered.

To begin with, plan exactly where you wish to travel to using your astral body. It should be within the confines of your house and not through walls or closed doors during the initial training stage. An adjoining room or room down a hallway is a good place to practice projecting to from the confines of your bed. It is best to ensure that you are not going to be bothered during any practice and to ENSURE that no one will touch you while you are consciously projecting. Burning candles are not a good idea for the main reason that they are a cause of fire and can become a grave concern. Anything that can be of concern to you, such as the telephone or other disturbances should be carefully taken care of beforehand. If you wish to project to a room down the hall from your bedroom, prepare to map the amount of paces away it is. Whatever is your destination it is imperative to become absolutely familiar with it. Draw on paper the plan, how many steps it takes to get there, any details that will ESTABLISH in your mind making it to the destination. You should also note points along the way and can put certain objects there that can be DRIVEN intensely into your memory as a routine. Such objects as an orange, bouquet of flowers or perfume are good to use because they have a strong fragrance and you can easily remember them and so they are good guide points along your route. These objects will prove to be invaluable markers along the way that will make you feel completely adept in knowing each step and its relation to the next as a journey to your destination a short distance away.

Begin by lying down, face up and relaxing in a comfortable position. Imagine an image identical to your physical body directly above it, about a few inches away. Concentrate repeatedly on an identical image of your physical body directly above you. Once you have practiced that for some time, then in a relaxed state transfer your consciousness to that image of yourself. Do not be tense or concerned if it does not happen after several attempts. It is just like learning to get on a bicycle and riding it for the first time. Once you learn to jump out or transfer your consciousness the fear of being able to return it to your body will be gone. After numerous attempts there will be a gut feeling inside telling you that you can DO IT…usually after the first little success. Project your mind to that formed image of your self, hovering atop of you. Try to look back at your body lying on the bed. Feeling Very Relaxed, let your mind, your consciousness slip out of your body and be in that image. Just say- "That is IT, I am OUT of Here, leaving my body, seeing it from above and ABOVE… NOW! I am not lying down on the bed I am uplifting my mind and can SEE my body laying down on that bed." It may take days, weeks or months to actually accomplish this feat, but once you do, wow! Constant practice will enable you to project your consciousness out of your body barrier and gradually learn to see, with astral vision, your surroundings. It is a remarkable and wonderful experience, like the best toy you ever had in your life, and one that will be forever useful. Some people have remarked that it took a significant experience to allow them to project for the very first time. Such an experience of being somewhere in their physical body and such an incident happened that it scared them out of their wits. Then they would return home, nerved and uptight they would enter their bedroom, lay down, and whamo, it finally happened. They felt their consciousness shift out of their body and knew they were capable of doing it. Everyone is different and each person will require certain attempts and experiences to make it happen. If you must suddenly run off to take care of something during an exercise, such as a telephone call, attempt to re-enter your physical body in a slow comfortable manner before physically moving. Feel that you are fitting something back into a box and ensure it is snug fitting and well connected then go take care of what you must

Now that you can switch your consciousness out of your body and into your astral image, go along the route you painstakingly studied and reach the destination point. Along the way concentrate earnestly on seeing, touching and smelling the certain object that you placed there. Transfer your consciousness to your astral body and travel to each point in turn. Successive attempts will bring certain results and you will have those objects as significant markers built in your mind to go and experience with your senses. After some success you will be able to effortlessly do it as the confidence will be there that you can just send your consciousness anywhere you so desire, seeing things that are really happening on the physical and astral planes any time you choose.

It is most generally lower plan attributes that cause problems, conflict and dismay in life. Emotions that are grossly linked to the lower astral/emotional levels cause problems in other levels of our Being (physical and mental). Learning to control our emotions in a mature way and to be above them, to direct them positively, will bring prosperity on all levels especially the material level. We should have the profound realization that all things are materialized effects that commenced from Inner Planes. Remember that as males and females are of opposite polarity on each plane, so is it with each plane in relation to the next. Each plane is positive to the one below it and negative to the one above. From inspiration all creations are conceptualized and formed by thought then put into production with desire upon the astral levels and finally materialized into existence as an outcome. There is more to creation than just that but having this general awareness can keep us alert, awake and with a mature feeling of being above the emotional level to positively actualize any outcome. Maintaining an appreciation and respect for higher life, forces and energy allows us to proceed with our feet firmly planted and to take proper care of our actions. Working with knowledge of the plane above the one we are functioning on is beneficial to positive conduct and not being sidetracked with emotions that sway our efforts.

Astral projection is a relatively new concept to most people but not so much as in past decades. New Age ideas and practices are constantly sprouting with social interaction and media coverage. Characters in movies are flaring with powers that are greater physically and otherwise than we have seen in the past. With the achievement of certain profound abilities also comes a responsibility. Although we are free to express ourselves more now than ever before we should do so in such a manner as is mature to gain spiritually from it. The New Age, ruled under Uranus, has more to offer in this remarkable world than we can possibly use. We have only to open our mind and heart to use all the possibilities advantageously.

There are endless abilities through spiritual progression and astral projection is part of that advancement. Cases of people moving physical objects and transporting the objects to other places while using their astral body to do so is found in documented research. The astral plane is much more adventurous to work with under the direction of our will power. We are capable of performing feats that physical limitations prevent us from doing and learning valuable knowledge that helps our evolution. Being confined to a material consciousness is abundantly clear that it increases crime and dysfunctional behavior. It is my opinion that earnest study of spirituality will curve many of the crises, which are on an increase. Jesus, for example was a true initiate, and I am positively certain that he would shake his head at the state of society today. He has numerous followers in today's world but so few believe in the earnest hard work of practicing such spiritual subjects as are outlined in this book. If this book documented evil intent, it would be obvious, but spirituality does not provoke evil action, it transcends it. There are as many evil practitioners in the various religions as there are in the field of misusing occult sciences. Fanatical behavior is, in my opinion, a result of having no connection to true spiritual teachings. The place referred to as hell and purgatory in religious doctrine is similar to what the Greeks refer to as Hades or the underworld. It is the intermixed lower sub-planes of the astral plane connections to the physical world. The denser, much LESS refined area that is channeled with dread, sloth and ill vibrations is an area of the astral plane where people reside their feelings who cause intentional suffering to others. So-called Hell is not just after-life experience but one that is present in everyday life.

Having digressed, we shall resume the available potentials through awareness on higher levels of the astral plane. Our awareness is not as limited on the astral levels as it is on the physical plane. If, for example, we are looking at an object in the physical world, we perceive that the furthest side away from us is smaller than the nearer side and we are confined to its outer shape and appearance. On the astral, while looking at the same object, all sides are seen for exactly what they are, the same size and at the same time or simultaneously. The object is seen beyond our normal senses of perception. Some writers consider awareness in this respect as perceiving the fourth dimension. That is why translating what we perceive is somewhat difficult in the beginning. When we see numbers on the astral plane and return to physical consciousness we may say that we saw the number 39, but in reality on the astral it was 93. Training our vision and recollection will allow us to properly express what we have experienced.

People and entities on the astral planes are capable of changing shape and it can be deceiving which is why it is important to become familiar with life on the different sub-planes. Training involves bringing our consciousness from the lower to the higher sub-planes of the astral and mental worlds and returning to the physical world without break during the brief intervals or thresholds between each plane. With stability of developing prowess with our concentrated efforts, problems can be generally avoided. Having a concern about being haunted, psychic-attacks, intrusions by thought-forms, and other such possible dangers is normal if we hadn't practiced astral projection before, but such problems are exceedingly rare. Fear of becoming possessed by some creature from 'out there' or 'in there' is, for the most part, only in the minds of those who invite such terrifying experience into their life. In this instance, such people that are susceptible to allowing such a thing to occur should avoid the practice of projecting. The ability to concentrate and maintain a mentally directed effort is of great benefit in gaining advantage from an astral experience. General astral plane awareness and development of the faculties can be accomplished in a relative short period of time, dependent upon the efforts, studies willingness and readiness.

The sub-levels within the astral plane (Theosophists refer to them as 7 in number) are all interconnected. Mapping our awareness of them by recording experiences after performing path workings of the Tree of Life or travelling to distant places will gradually lead us to further exploration and acquiring useable knowledge. To further comprehend this inter- connection between levels, we may use an analogy of the principles of the elements in our physical environment. Water, earth and air are inter-mixed together yet they each have specific properties and exist on their respective level of matter. Earth matter is the lowest and densest level of material. Water sits on the earth but also mixes with the earth, as does the air. There is air mixed with water, as oxygen is in water (H_2O), which is how most sea creatures survive under water and ice. Air also exists in matter, dependent upon the density of the matter. Water evaporates and rises to the sky until it becomes too dense to remain in the air and returns to us as rain. Evaporation, condensation and humidity are all examples of one element connecting into another. Matter also rises into the air, in the form of dust, volcanic eruption or pressure containing substance that exerts upwards, but eventually returns to the earth from whence it came. Such principles of our physical environment will serve to illustrate how the various sub-planes in the astral world can interchange specific properties amongst its levels.

Our immediate astral world extends beyond the earth's atmosphere. It reaches to the moon during perigee but not during apogee. In an astral experience, we can hover high above the earth, observing the curvature and conditions that are occurring at any particular instant. We may even do scientific observation of the carbon cycle that plant life undertakes to produce oxygen or observe weather patterns. Possibilities are endless and the experiences are rewarding. Having awareness with astral-sight, we may perceive flashes of color around our body and that of other people. This signifies the existence of the astral body, similarly as the aura around our etheric double signifies our character. On a yet deeper level we may perceive a finer grade of colors that vibrate at a slower rate displaying our trend of thoughts and higher qualities, which signify our mental body. In an even finer depth we may view the causal body as a remarkable glowing light, which is the vehicle for the Higher Self to manifest emanations of our spirit through and create our reincarnations.

We find through experiencing life on the astral plane, that we possess powers and a remarkable balanced nature. Benefits outweigh non-involvement in the quest for insight and enlightenment as we come to realize a sublime beauty with all that life has to offer. Fixation on the material world may limit such insight, however it is each person's responsibility to open the veils and see reality upon loftier heights. Being bound to the responsibilities of our work, family life, friends and duties is only one facet of our capable achievements and to become fulfilled, a bit of diversity can be an advantage. Gaining experience from astral travelling should illustrate that we can improve our social life by obtaining greater understanding and expressing congenial qualities.

With training, the ability to LOOK closer at physical matter and study it from our astral body perspective becomes invigorating. We are capable of examining physical matter right down to its very constituents of atoms and particles, even closer than what a physical microscope can do. There is no such thing as "dead matter", since every object has an astral counterpart. Plants, wood, metal, rock and all physical matter have either vegetable or mineral astral substance on the lower astral levels which enables us to study them. This in part explains how the astral body can go through closed doors, walls and other material objects. Within all material substance there is space between the molecular structures and that space contains the astral counterpart of the object. That space also provides an astral body to go through it just like water going through a filter. That is why, for instance, ghosts can go through walls. The space between each interconnecting molecule of a substance contains the "inner" life of it with its mineral or vegetable counterpart on the astral level. There is more complexity to this subject but this is an introduction to allow us to begin working and studying life from within it. It is intriguing to consider the Big Bang theory of evolutionary expansion of the Universe. The theory holds the original state of the Universe to have been total mass that blew up and became a continuously expanding event. Similar to blowing up a balloon where the stars and galaxies continue to stretch further away, causing an opening of space and complex properties of inner dimensions to form. Bringing knowledge from the fourth dimension of astral consciousness into this one may help in solving part of our complex puzzles.

Dwellers upon the astral plane are many and varied. Many that reside there are not aware of the physical plane similarly as most of us are not aware of the astral levels and life existing therein. The lowest level of the astral is somewhat drogue and grotesque, which may appear blackened and dark, with its objectionable inhabitants. The next three levels contain entities and beings that appear dense, self-absorbed and dwell in their own created surroundings. The higher three levels, however, have beauty in the surroundings that one would easily associate with the physical world but to a more wondrous extent.

Well experienced, evolved people travel on the higher astral levels using their mental bodies. The mental body is of the same appearance as the physical but is not seen by other inhabitants of the astral plane. If the adept using their mental body wishes for an astral being (another human on the astral plane, non-human entities or artificial entities) to see them, then they merely use astral substance to cloak their mental figure/image for visible appearance on the astral plane. On the higher levels of the astral plane we meet such sincere people from all walks of life around the planet. They may be monks from monasteries, advanced humans experiencing and seeking information or other such souls but the interesting thing is that we can share and exchange information with them on those levels.

There is a mirrored photographic record of everything that ever occurred in life's history, on the astral plane. It has elsewhere been mentioned as the Akashic Records. This vast storehouse of information does not require space as we know it otherwise the inner planes would seem like a vastly crowded place. Psychics are able to tap into information from reading these Records through having contact with the impressions from people and objects. Through the practice of divination, such as tarot, Yi Ching, or crystal gazing we can come into contact with those historic records and retrieve information. Knowledge is gained from previous stored existence and is interpreted from reading the Records in accordance with present circumstances and reveals how the eventual turning wheel will yield an outcome.

Our "neuric" energy heightens before sleep when having such a concern and our consciousness is more than apt to separate from the physical body. During sleep, we are in a relaxed state and our astral body loosens and usually hovers over our physical body. That is why when somebody touches us after drifting off to sleep we tend to shake abruptly as reentry quickly occurs. Sometimes we project to somebody we are closely attached to or in touch with and if we see that person the following day we may have particular feelings about something we shared with them during the course of meeting in the night. While conducting experiences of travelling around my parents' home during my high school years it was not long before I left the house and felt the sensation of travelling over telephone poles containing highly charged electrical wires. The sensation, as I recall, that came from the electricity was an extension of energy beyond their particular vicinity.

If we are mentally and emotionally undisciplined our astral body is a rather shapeless and undefined form but as we progress, it closely resembles our physical body in detail. The astral body is made of a substance that can actually be weighed. Several years ago Dr. Zaalberg of the Netherlands done extensive research on this matter in his laboratories and produced a large five volume documentation on his findings. One of his conclusions was that the astral body was able to expand and contract and that it weighed 69.5 grams (2 1/4oz). His information was in accordance with research done by Dr. Duncan McDougall, which concluded that upon death the physical body looses between 2 and 2 1/4 oz of weight. There are literally hundreds of thousands of documented cases that are so remarkable and thought provoking that we have only to find out what is possible and what is not. Muldoon and Herewood Carrington in their book, *The Phenomenon of Astral Projection*, list numerous documented examples of astral projection reports:

"A Soldier, Exhausted and Hungry, Projects
Astral Somnambulism
Projected During Childhood Illness
Fright Produces externalization
Projection by An Accident
'I Know that it was not a Dream'
Conscious in the Fourth Dimension
Saw Patients Exteriorized During Anesthesia
Shifting Consciousness
A Voice Commanded him To Return
Met his Guides in Person, While Projected
Saw Self being Operated Upon
Projection Associated with Healing
Eight Percipients Saw Halo Over Death-bed
Dream Phantom After Burial Alive
Visits Friends 3 Miles Away
She Healed Him in Her Sleep"

These are just a few titles of documented cases in that particularly very good book on the subject. If we decide to practice and develop our astral abilities we need not have any fear of becoming lost in the astral world. There is a thin cord, called the silver cord, which attaches our astral body to our physical body. Life force for the physical body is sustained through this cord by regulating our breathing during an out of body experience. Our subconscious is always in automatic communication with our body and alarms it with the appropriate message just as when we are asleep. Our astral vehicle always finds its way back into our body.

The sixth sense is sometimes referred to as that of astral perception, the ability to see entities, dwellers and things clearly in the astral world while physically conscious. The seventh sense is said to be when we receive Knowledge from sources that are purely spiritual. Hearing sounds that are not physically present is similar to clairvoyance, or telepathy but is called clairaudience or 'clear hearing'. This may happen when we are physically conscious and people sometimes refer to hearing the sound of a bell. Theosophists refer to this peculiar sound as the Astral Bell, which is common when people refer to experiences of clairaudience. Such sounds are very rare and are usually sent and heard for a definite purpose.

We gain greater insight and truth when we are honest with ourselves about our experiences. It is for that reason that we should work for what we achieve and be analytical about astral projections and the knowledge we may gain from it. We find that there are certain times that are particularly easier to project than at other times. There are many factors involved, and like an artist we may simply not be in the right frame of mind. The phase of the moon and transits of the minor planets may cause an effect on our projecting capability also. Keeping a journal and studying the moon phases in accordance with our exercises is a good idea in learning the best times and circumstances for a projection. Weather patterns such as excessively strong storms and very hot weather happens to affect the ether and etheric plane and it is advised that during initial practices we do not attempt projections during such conditions.

With much experience, environmental conditions will be of no concern since our senses will have been developed and strengthened. The sense of sight and touch are the easiest of the senses to transfer to our astral body. Eventually we will functionally use all five senses on the astral sub-planes. By transferring the senses, it is meant to become aware of them and practice using them. After projecting consciousness a few times we can go to an object such as a table and feel it with our etheric/astral hand. It will not feel the same as when we touch it physically, as the sensation is not the same hardness as we commonly know it to be. Tasting and smelling are more imaginative senses than anything else, since in the astral plane we do not require to use our nose and tongue to retrieve smell and taste data. Practice floating around the object that you chose to test and investigate during a projection and begin observing, feeling, smelling and tasting it to obtain information and enjoy the experience.

During initial stages of attempting astral projection it is possible that we mistake entering the level called the etheric plane with actual sub-planes of the astral world. Once our consciousness enters the etheric plane for a time there is a tendency for us to go into the next plane and levels thereof, just like diving into a pool of water for the first time. With practice we go deeper and explore further. During initial entrance of the etheric level we may hear noises that sound like banging, thrashing, thumping, rattling or even voices. This generally alarms and startles us in the beginning. We tend to think they are actually occurring somewhere in our house but in reality they are not. With successive practice we learn to quiet the noises, if the occasion of hearing them upon entering the etheric plane actually ever occurs.

We have all had the occasion of dreaming where we were walking, or falling or running and had a feeling of helplessness with our legs or arms feeling extremely heavy to move. This very rigid sensation of feeling stuck and glued to a position is characteristic of transferring our consciousness from the etheric plane to the astral plane while we are dreaming at night. We often mistake the etheric and astral planes while we are asleep because they appear so similar. So whenever we experience this stuck feeling, we should not worry or concern ourselves about it, since it is only a transition from one plane to the next. In fact, if we tell ourselves that we are IN the astral plane when this occurs we can use a simple effort of will power to float up and basically begin flying or taking off into the air. Just by saying to ourselves we can FLY will enable us to take off from feeling stuck or confined during such circumstances.

Another common occurrence is the sensation of falling. We do not have to worry about hitting the ground or a hard surface because when we fall during the course of an astral projection we are going through a transition and cannot be hurt by it. The sensation of going through closed doors or walls is almost like going through a wall of molasses or heavy waterfalls. In the beginning it may be difficult to impossible but practice reassures us it is not that hard to do. It feels as though it is drawing us out and upon entering the other side is pulling us back together. It is a completely harmless experience. These instructions should assist in making the initial plunge to the other side, and advance us to further research from the many books covering the subject. Our focus should be on graduating our training to eventually enter the higher astral where the normal astral matter disappears and "lights" of color becomes the surrounding scenery. Each physical action that we do involves not just the physical plane but all planes. Every action that is performed is occurring on all levels of all planes simultaneously as we perform them.

One method of developing our astral body is by studying all components of our physical body over and over. With repeated concentration of observing each finger and each toe until they are committed to memory by staring at them, moving them and feeling them over and over we begin to SEE their individual astral counterparts. After much practice we will see an image of our entire body and know it is our astral body that through concentration we have formed and developed. Because astral matter is so tangible, we can reshape our astral body by mental directed effort, even in the shape of an animal and use it for guarding an object or place anywhere we desire to. Our astral body carries our consciousness and can be used to go anywhere and retrieve information. It can be used to influence our success in life, to help other people in need and to heal the sick. The sky is the limit and to say that something is not possible is to add to the numerous personal doubts we already are trying to clear up.

Astral achievements are a personal opinion of success and determination. The positive outcome is up to the individual using such abilities and taking the time for effort put into it. Refinement involves peeling off the layers that encompass our soul and spirit, yet we require such a strong outer layer of protection that with advancement in such esoteric practice as we come to experience within the world of the astral plane it becomes a natural course of progression. True aspirants seek to eventually become adepts of the art and as such become masters of life and light. Understanding the laws of nature and using them for the benefit of mankind is one of the noblest acts of achievement. ★

YOGA and CHAKRA MEDITATION

"Nothing that actually occurs is of the smallest importance."

Oscar Wilde (1854-1900)

Yoga is a process of attaining unity with our divine self through numerous practices of concentration, contemplation and meditation. The word 'yoga' is derived from the same Sanskrit root as the Greek word Zeugma and the Latin word Jugum. It essentially means Union. The unity to which it refers to is being at one with our True Self and thereby living our True Identity ultimately meaning in harmony with our higher nature. Yoga heightens our awareness to an omnipresent, omnipotent, and omniscient state of being. It is not a branch of any religious doctrine but can assist in the identification of us as a reflection of some greater Universal Force/ Energy/Being.

Those who practice yoga do so for specific reasons. Some people seek a sense of well being whereas others may use yoga for athletic development and still others for obtaining spiritual enlightenment from the practice. Enlightenment is a nifty term and a very relative one as well. Becoming enlightened seems to imply that we have gained a super awareness by practicing methods to become so. If we take away our present feelings and thoughts we may say that there seems to be a void, that nothing else exists, but it is not true. The illusion regarding the term enlightenment is that we seem to chase it, seek it and try to obtain it. With the practice of principles outlined in this chapter, we should come to realize that enlightenment simply exists and all we have to do is halt the unnecessary activity running our conscious mind and we will see that enlightenment is there as though it always existed. Working the following practices will assist us in gaining certain powers, developing our philosophies, and perceiving truths from spiritual and religious literature to a greater extent. For whatever purpose yoga is practiced, there is one thing that it seems to bring to everyone, and that is rejuvenation.

Our normal conscious mind has the ability to accept or reject ideas and suggestions and is developed from education, training, and positive environmental stimulus. It can deteriorate without these positive inputs. Our experiences are stored as memory in our subconscious. Our mind is ever seeking the easiest way to recall information and causes us to perform actions with the least effort unless we train it otherwise. The way our mindset generally works is that we seek rewards and have a bondage to material life until we become spiritually awakened and realized such that we cherish that which we have and are not fretted with concerns about that which we do not have.

It becomes an advantage in preliminary work to use self-suggestions in order to keep our mind focused and wanting to do the practices involved in yoga. Self-suggestion is an invaluable tool for controlling our subconscious because it reinforces and reminds us with tremendous confidence to accomplish what we desire. We must expect with complete devotion that what should happen, will happen. Such positive suggestions will reinforce our desire to succeed. Prior to any yoga practice, prepare to remove any thoughts that are not the sole object of the practice. The power of suggestion has been used throughout our life. It is the teacher's tool for us to learn how to walk, talk, communicate, achieve, develop, create and live successfully or accordingly with society. It can be used to rid our random thoughts by having focused ones.

There are many types of suggestions always at work around us. Physical suggestions are when we use our body to communicate information. Verbal suggestions are when we put emphasis in our speech and repeat them to achieve a desired result from the repetition. Mental suggestions are repeated thoughts to our mind to strengthen and reinforce their ability. Environmental suggestions are the effects that temperature, climate and physical surroundings play upon us. That is why some people like to mediate around lakes, rivers, forests and mountain scenery, which suggest nature and peace. All of these suggestions creates an impression upon us and thereby cause us to react in some way or another. By using the power of suggestion we are performing autosuggestion and can change many facets of our life in a positive way. We will come back to the subject of suggestion on our course through yoga.

Meditation is the act of thinking deeply and continuously upon a subject. We can meditate on virtually anything and upon doing so we should sit in a relaxed position and begin to train our mind to focus on the subject we choose. We will begin here with an exercise called nasal gaze and frontal gaze. The nasal gaze requires that we focus our attention on the tip of our nose with eyes half closed. This effort reacts with the central nervous system, called kundalini sakti and our autonomic nervous system, called the Ida and Pingala or left and right breathing passages. This exercise may cause headaches in the beginning so be careful not to do it for more than a minute to a few minutes at a time, but it will later strengthen the cranial and spinal nerve centers. After several months practice of this we may control and prevent certain mental and physical diseases. To practice the frontal gaze we have to focus our attention between the eyebrows, again with eyes half closed. Meditation on this area helps us with controlling random or wandering thoughts and is the area known as the third eye.

After practicing the above meditation for a comfortable number of sessions over the course of a week we may begin another meditation that is also useful for performing mental projections. This meditation is again, very simple and effective. For this practice we require a low wattage, approximately 10-watt, blue light bulb in a lamp. While sitting in a relaxed position, begin starring at the blue light emitting from the lit bulb in the lamp. Gradually relax each part of the body in turn while gazing at the light. After a short time our entire body should feel very at ease and relaxed, almost to the point of feeling it anesthetized throughout our limbs if we are concentrating properly. After several practices of this, we will feel the power we have over our subconscious mind to the point that it will obey the conscious commands or suggestions we give it.

A very pleasant meditation experience to do outside is as follows. While sitting out on a sunny day, gaze at the atmosphere and observe the small vibrating light spectacles through the air. If at first they are difficult to locate, simply stare into the blue sky until you see flickers of very small light seemingly dancing around in the atmosphere. They are there, they are everywhere and with effort to look at them you will see multitudes of these lustrous little lights. These are vitality globules, each consisting of seven physical atoms. The Hindus refer to these vitality globules as "prana" which can be roughly translated as "vitality energy".

Prana constantly flows through our body in five definitive streams by entering our spleen chakra and dispersing as separate colors to different parts of our body, revitalizing us with renewed energy. While steadily gazing, seek to see different forms or types of tiny light coming into you from all around you. Stare at the horizon and see the reflection of light from all parts of the earth into the atmosphere. Attach yourself to that light and after several attempts you should feel an eternal light within yourself. Become sensitized to your ever-brighter aura and feel the life in all the elements within it.

Later, when back inside your room and relaxing you can also observe movements of natural waves in the air. This takes considerable more effort but with practice you will be able to see the magnetic fields and currents and the light which is attached to that. You should study this phenomenon in all types of light conditions, that is to say in a bright room to a semi-lighted room to a dark room. Make notes after each exercise and describe what you saw, felt and thought from the experiment. Everyone generates and emits a magnetic field around their body. With some people you may see and feel a pleasant array of vibrations from their magnetism and from others it may seem unclear, disturbed or unpleasant. Our instantaneous personal magnetism that we exude is felt by people around us and can be strengthened by efforts through yoga. When we control our mind and waves of thought-emotion our body radiates this magnetic energy and is felt by others as a serene and peaceful atmosphere that reflects our calm nature. Disease and poor health result from a lack of the proper vitality flowing to the organs of our body to replenish them.

Science endeavors to analyze life in a coherent and logical manner in order to obtain objective principles and facts regarding phenomena. Yoga gives us self-control of body and mind and through that obtains both subjective and objective analysis of thought and action. It is a safe, simple, and easy to learn practice which has been used in conjunction with meditation to achieve greater awareness. There are eight limbs of yoga that we must acknowledge in order to achieve the results they claim. Several translations of these limbs of yoga have been given but here they are in a nutshell from one perspective.

1. Yama- Control of our mind and mental waves with acceptance of having a Higher or True Will.
2. Niyama- Observing the principles to obtain the AIM
3. Asana- Practicing yoga in a particular posture that best suits us for yoga.
4. Pranayama- Attention given to regulating our breathing to control our mind.
5. Pratyahara- Completely relaxing every organ and withdrawing our consciousness.
6. Dharana- Fixating our consciousness on specific parts of our body, or any ONE thing, concentration.
7. Dhyana- Constantly suggesting, Meditation.
8. Samadhi- Creating WILL Power and Supreme Power of Consciousness.

Initial practice of yoga should involve taking ten minutes a day to strengthen our ability of concentration. Prior to our concentration exercise we should do a **pre-concentration** cleansing by breathing rhythmically while sitting in our chosen posture. Breath in for seven seconds, hold for one second, exhale for seven seconds, hold for one second, and repeat this five times in a quiet atmosphere. Control of mind and control of body is required for achievement in the practice of yoga. A simple yet effective method of relaxing at any particular time will be mentioned for convenience. By placing our hand upon our stomach we can feel a relaxed energy flow from the hand into the stomach. Feel the circulation of warm comforting energy streaming around the organs within the stomach. We may stimulate these sensations by visualizing and imagining very pleasant, natural, beautiful scenery. This is a helpful little technique to relax our mind from any previous concerns or thoughts.

To practice yoga we must decide upon a posture that is comfortable yet will not put us to sleep. The practice should never be done following a meal because digesting food causes us to become fatigue, bloated and uncomfortable. Sitting in an upright position, back straight and folding our legs together is a common posture if we use a pillow or blanket underneath to avoid our feet and legs from falling asleep. Kneeling on a pillow with our lower legs underneath our buttocks is another posture. Sitting on a chair with our back an inch away from the back of the chair is called the Egyptian God posture and is also a very good yoga position. In any posture, our back should be straight since it is the natural tendency of the head to keep everything below it aligned.

During concentration we should practice pranayama, a specific breathing pattern. We have already done the pre-concentration breathing exercise, now we will learn a breathing technique for concentration. Begin by breathing in to the count of four, holding for another count of four, then releasing the breath slowly to another four and holding for the final four. Repeat this breathing technique until it feels very comfortable to do. We should never attempt to concentrate for a long period of time at first because we can become burnt out without realizing it. Five to ten minutes, upon awakening in the morning and at night is sufficient to begin with.

Our goal is to control our mind from wandering and our body from fidgeting. We are working with the power of suggestion and concentration with effort focused and fixated on the subject or object we have chosen. Any object may be chosen to focus our mind upon and keep it from wandering. If a specific object is chosen to concentrate upon we should stick to that object until success is realized. For simplicity we may use the symbols of the four elements as concentration objects. These symbols are a red triangle for fire, a yellow square for earth, a blue circle for air and a silver moon crescent for water. These symbols are easy to draw and color for our practice. An alternative set of symbols may be made and used such as the planetary symbols painted on colored cards. Whatever object we use for concentration practice, it should be simple and prevent our consciousness from wandering to other thoughts.

After concentrating upon symbols we may focus attention on different parts of our body. Through the practice of relaxation and paying attention to our body we can fixate our efforts on certain bodily parts and cause changes. This concentration exercise involves the gradual initiating of suggestion to the part of our body we concentrate upon. Decide beforehand what area of the body is going to concentrated upon. It is important to give a PAUSE between concentration efforts to feel the sensation that we have commanded to take effect. Begin by focusing attention on the central nervous system and continuously initiate SUGGESTION (Dhyana) to the selected part of the body. After successful practices with individual areas of the body we can do a full practice of each bodily part in turn. For example we may begin with the feet, then legs, abdomen, chest, neck, arms, hands, and finally our head. After several days or weeks of practice we are capable of relaxing our entire body at will. Not only have we achieved different results and learnt more about our body but also achieved inspiration and insight during the state of harmonizing and being at peace.

After several practices with success in concentration and sending suggestions to our body we can perform local pratyahara. This is done with concentration on particular or local parts of our body and withdrawing energy to take charge of our consciousness. We will be withdrawing energy and consciousness from the particular portion of our body we concentrate upon. It is a very serious matter and we should be ready for it before attempting it. The local part of the body we are performing pratyahara on becomes magnetized to an extent. After successive practices we should be ready for general pratyahara which is the whole body instead of one portion. With mastery we will have union of consciousness with the central organ, that of the mind, through that part of the nervous system. We feel the pulsation and electromagnetic motions occurring in our body and connect with the vibrations of supreme consciousness. When advanced in this practice we will feel our entire body become magnetized, pulsating with vibrations causing greater circulation of blood through the area concentrated upon with the effect that any pain previously felt there has diminished. A sensation that the Universe is pulsating and vibrating the same as we are may enter our mind. Being in tune with our nature brings us in tune with cosmic nature. By doing this we will be able to remove the hypnotic suggestions that have been pressed into our subconscious mind which have limited us from conscious manipulation of our body and achieving a super conscious state. We will be able to transfer power to and from all these parts of our body and mind.

There are four stages of relaxation in the practice of pratyahara. Dharana is the stage when our entire body is relaxed as if in a sleep state but our mind is conscious and thinking upon one object or area of the body and extending that thought. Dhyana is an intermediate state when our body is even more relaxed and our mind is under complete control by feeling the most positive conscious sensation with Light from the ability to be "at one" with the object. This is a state of true meditation. Samadhi is the third stage and is when our body is sound asleep and in such a deep state that even heart surgery could be carried out without feeling pain. Our body is under complete mind control and our mind is merged within the Supreme Consciousness. Another level of Samadhi is when we identify ourselves with the Supreme Consciousness and realize absolute enlightenment from that identification. This level is called Samprajnat Samadhi. Nirvana is the fourth stage of pratyahara and is a completion of all and is the deepest state where we realize and see the whole universe within ourselves. Conjointly we see ourselves within the whole universe simultaneously. The one true light is realized with our subconscious merging with our consciousness and we are at ONE with our Self by being at ONE with the Universe.

Yoganidra is the original form of yoga. Using this term, yoga means concentration, and nidra refers to sleep. Our body is in a state that is under complete control of our mind and no part of our body can be raised or moved, similar to paralysis except that we are in control of every function. It is like being under anesthesia with the concentrated ability to remove all mental and physical diseases that we may detect and be bothered by. It works similarly to self-hypnosis and autosuggestion. We tell our self over and over that we are going to relax that we are relaxing, and finally we are fully relaxed. We work with different aspects of our functioning consciousness when we do such a practice.

There is the ego consciousness which is like the "growing child" consciousness within us and the judicial or intellectual consciousness as the super ego, which is the developed part of us giving the final decisions on everything which we do. Our ego is our principle of reality while our judicial consciousness is the principle of Ultimate Reality. They are not always at peace but in somewhat of a conflict with one another. It is an aim of yoga to develop awareness of our higher nature by harmoniously uniting these divisions of our consciousness together, allowing the greater to take over the lower while maintaining grounding.

Our conscious mind works from impulses that occur within our cerebrum. It acts according to the development within the brain and slows down during sleep and dreaming, which is when the subconscious mind takes over. The subconscious controls heart movement, respiration, circulation, digestion, and organ development. Our consciousness enters a super-conscious state when we are in deep concentration and achieves the state of Samadhi. During such profound meditation our psychic energy is transformed to a "free" state of consciousness, referred to as the superconscious mind. This psychic energy travels through the path of kundalini, up the central nervous system, called the sushumna and invigorates our Seven Chakras resulting in our awakening in consciousness with particular enlightenment.

The subconscious mind contains psychic energy that travels through Ida and Pingala (the autonomic nervous system) which uses the kundalini path to send and transform that energy to the subtle bodies of the astral, mental and causal. Our subconscious mind is never at rest; it is at work continuously and responds to suggestions dependent upon how strong the suggestions are. It does anything and everything and seeks no reward, whereas the conscious mind wishes remuneration when it is ordered to do us service. Having said this it is good to treat ourselves for having done a good job with our discipline and studies. Having a happy outlook will bring peace and confidence towards our quest for the supreme state. Believing in ourselves is as important as in the abilities we wish to obtain through yoga. The practice of yoga helps us to unveil the wrappings of our mind, to enter the core of our Being and be united with its influx of Universal Energy. One of many results may be the opening of our third eye, allowing us to be intuitive, psychic and visionary to remarkable knowledge.

Yoga is a serious practice throughout India where there are seven different schools of yoga: 1. Raja Yoga, 2. Karma Yoga, 3. Jnana Yoga, 4. Hatha Yoga, 5. Laya Yoga, 6. Bhakti Yoga, 7. Mantra Yoga. Each of these schools practice developing the seven psychic centers, called Chakras and each instructs their own method of working with chakras. Raja yoga arouses chakra activity through the power of will and suggestion. Laya yoga activates them by arousing the serpent fire (kundalini energy) which is situated at the base of the spine and flows upwards stimulating the centers one by one starting with the root chakra. Once the root chakra or etheric wheel is stimulated into greater activity, the other six chakras begin gradual awakening into further development.

The seven chakras or force-centers are within our etheric-double body, lining our physical body. Their activity causes a flow of energy between our etheric, astral and mental inner bodies. If the chakras are undeveloped, a clairvoyant views them as small vortices about two inches in diameter with a dull glow appearance to them. When they are vivified they are a blazing center of activity and become larger in size.

These chakras are centers of energy and are at work in every person. If they are not developed they are sluggish and then only supply the necessary force for us to functionally operate. When aroused and developed, they become a living light of psychic force with great energy passing through them giving us an enormous amount of potential. Each chakra has a certain number of spokes or petals, which divides them into sections. These spokes are likened to grappling hooks that bind the etheric and astral bodies together. The lower chakras are sometimes referred to as the physiological ones, the middles ones as the personal ones and the higher ones as the spiritual ones.

The chakras are numbered one to seven, beginning at the base of our spine to the tip of our head. The first two chakras receive the fiery earth energy and the energy (prana) from the sun. They are the basic physical energy chakras. The next three chakras work more directly upon our personality. The third Chakra works with the lower astral forces, the fourth with the forces of the higher astral and the fifth with the lower mental plane. The sixth chakra is connected with the pituitary gland and the seventh with the pineal gland. The highest two chakras come into activity when an amount of spiritual development has been accomplished. Some writers have associated certain moral qualities with different chakras as qualities endowed from pronounced vibrations from psychic energy the person emits. Each chakra has a division of quadrants, which have been associated to petals of a flower. To become acquainted with the chakras and their activity, short meditations upon each of them can be done. Their English and Sanskrit names for these chakras and basic descriptions of them are as follows:

Root Chakra-Muladhara - The root chakra is located at the base of the spine. It has four quadrants or petals and resembles the sign of a cross. It is the basis for our existence and survival in this physical world, and if it is blocked, we will feel rootless in our spiritual and physical life. We have to feel equally at home in both places with support and grounding to Earth. When we are born, the nursing period with our mother is very important and should not be shortened because during this period both the mother and child stimulate, develop, and cleanse their root chakras. By uniting their root chakra energies they form a bond such that the child accepts leaving the inner world to enter and become attached to material earth life. If the mother-child bond is not formed and strengthened, the child may become restless and hyperactive as it grows into society. To meditate upon the root chakra, begin by withdrawing the energy from the reproductive organs and directing it towards the lower part of the central nervous system (sushumna). Relax the entire area and feel control over it. This meditation will provide greater control over the sexual organs and feelings associated with it.

Spleen Chakra-Svadhishthana - The spleen chakra also called Dan Ti'en or Hara chakra is located over the spleen, approximately an inch below the navel and an inch inward close to the diaphragm. The spleen chakra receives prana or vitality from the sun and sends it as a red-orange fiery energy to the root chakra. The spleen has six divisions, or petals, and emanates a color reflecting the vital force. It functions the raw energy of our sexuality, emotions, and desires. The element of Water is associated to this chakra and when we become conscious of it we are capable of recollecting our astral journeys and pleasant memories of astral flights. When this chakra is clean and vitalizing it causes us to think positively and will block impurities such as malicious or obnoxious emotions from entering us. A meditation upon the spleen chakra includes the lower limbs, legs and feet and is controlled by the neuro-hormonal mechanism. During meditation we may say "I am relaxing my legs and feel them relaxing fully. They feel heavier and heavier." With practice of this we can make the limbs feel very warm or very cold. The ability of sending blood faster or slower to those areas will be the result and removal of aches and pains in that region of our body may be felt. We must feel the magnetic circulation, pulsation and vibration going through those areas.

Navel Chakra-Manipura - The navel is situated over our solar plexus in the central cavity of the lung area and has ten petals or undulations. Some authors relate the area to the central nervous system above the lumbar region. It is associated to various emotions from the astral world without realizing why because it simply feels the forces and influences that were experienced, both friendly and hostile. The navel chakra is the basis for personal power and metabolic energy. Purity in this area allows us to be at peace with other people, without internal and external conflict and keeps us on the path of learning instead of confronting and fighting. The element for this chakra is fire, allowing us to finish what we've begun and to solve situations correctly as taught in group therapy between two or more people. Meditation upon the navel chakra provides us with a magnetic healing power to repel or remove disease in that area by the current flowing through our internal organs and cleansing them. It also assists in releasing our muscle tensions from pent-up emotions.

Heart Chakra-Anahata - The heart chakra is located a few inches above the solar plexus, over the heart, and has twelve petals to its constitution. When it is aroused we gain clear intuition regarding the happiness or sorrow of other people and we may become compassionate by those feelings being reproduced within us. This chakra is the basis of association and relation with compassion and love ruling the emotions. It is an essential seed in our pursuit to feel the divine radiance and the ability to express pure love to all and everyone. The element for this chakra is air and it is the center of our nervous system allowing us to feel impressions. During meditation we should relax the whole chest area and feel internal electricity moving within our heart to all the external parts of our body. The current flow should be felt through the whole body from the life energy existing within the blood stream as it circulates through our system. We may regulate our breathing during this exercise to achieve different effects. Breathing in for a count of ten seconds as we draw the breath to the lower abdomen we then proceed to hold it for another ten seconds. Then exhale very slowly for a count of twenty seconds. This is an advanced breathing technique but by breathing out slower we retain more of the energy from our inhalation. A key to this chakra is devotion.

Throat Chakra-Vishuddha - The throat chakra is located midway between the skull and the lower neck, approximately an inch inward of the throat. It is in a linear vertical alignment with the spinal chord. This chakra has sixteen divisions or petals and with activation enables us to hear voices, sounds, perhaps music and other noises echoing from the etheric plane. Development of it provides us with the ability of being "clairaudient" on the higher, inner planes. This chakra controls our throat and arms and is activated in talented singers, musicians and orators. Vitality comes to them in the form of light blue streams of prana that goes up to their throat center to give elasticity and strength to that area and provides the great influence they have when heard. The throat chakra is direct and focused for creativity and communication. The element associated to this chakra is sound and vibrations. During such a meditation we should relax our entire neck region and arms while feeling the magnetic pulsation and current arise from our meditation. With practice we will have the ability to completely anesthetize our arms and send heat or cold sensations to them and influence our vocal cords for clear and penetrating speech.

Brow Chakra-Ajna - The brow chakra is between the eyebrows in the central cavity of the brain located at the pituitary gland. It has two large divisions with several smaller ones within resulting in ninety-six undulations or petals in total. There are many more petals in these higher chakras because they deal with a much greater force and represent shades of variant receptors from the primary life force. This chakra is a psychic center allowing us to have visions of people, places and events that occur or have occurred by tapping into the astral and inner planes. The brow chakra governs our imagination and is the basis of our higher intuitive faculty. It allows us to perceive the higher zones of the inner planes and is the center for our consciousness. The element associated to this chakra is Light and arousing it makes us clairvoyant, a receptor for revelations and provides the ability of transcendence. It also has the magnificent capability of studying incredibly tiny objects through a tube that projects from it into the etheric plane. This protruding tube resembles a very thin microscopic snake with an eye at the end. It is depicted in Egyptian art where pharaohs have a snake extending from above their headdress and they related this ability to the brow chakra being awakened and ready for studying or research. The eye of this tube is like a polished ball and draws energy into our brain and provides protection to us. Meditation upon this chakra will open our Third Eye as we focus the invigorating force of magnetic energy, giving us mastery over our entire body and absolute affiliation with our supreme consciousness.

Crown Chakra-Sahasrara - The crown chakra is over the top of our head, located at the pivotal axis point of the skull where the three platting parts of the skull intersect. It is near the frontal lobe, left and right hemispheres of the brain area and associated with the pineal gland. The crown chakra has 960 (972 when the center petals are included) divisions of petals in total. The center of this chakra has an additional gleaming white with gold brilliance that houses an additional twelve divisions or petals. Spiritual progression enlarges this chakra and provides us with a constant consciousness state, without break. That is to say that we can astral travel during night with the same consciousness we use throughout the day. The crown chakra controls all the other chakras and identifies us with Supreme Consciousness in the Meditation State of Nirvana. This achievement of eternal peace, bliss and knowledge comes after a deep and all-embracing wisdom has occurred through the transference of wisdom in silence. Refined thoughts result from this blissfulness and the element associated to this chakra is the essence of Thought. Cleansing this chakra brings us understanding and knowledge of everything without any obscurity regarding life. The influence of this chakra wraps us in a very brilliant aura that causes beautiful and glorious effects upon others. It is the chakra most penetrable for light and is very important to keep it clean.

All seven chakras are insert depressions within our etheric body and allows the divine force to flow through and into us until we become self-realized at which point the chakras becomes prominent and protrudes out like vibrant crowns. Each chakra consists of light in a concentration of vibrations, and when two people meet the vibrations mingle into a pattern through communication. When we speak to another person, our energies from the throat chakras inter-communicate and move, and our eye contact with the other person establishes motion with our crown chakras together. Energy flows between the other person and us during communication, causing light from the two chakras to activate our heart and the solar plexus chakras into further communication activity. From a psychic point of view two people in communication appear somewhat like glimmering rainbows with changing colors that circulate around their chakras and auras.

Thoughts and emotions live and originate from the inner planes and are refined and intensified through the psychic centers of the chakras upon the etheric plane. Fear, for example, if intensified will discharge energy through the chakra at our umbilical area causing us to react in ways particular to the activity of that and other chakras. Undesirable emotions or currents of energy thrive through our navel chakra and can be refined by the qualities of affection and devotion, which are emotions in our heart chakra. Each chakra affects another by the development we have attained.

The great inner energy referred to as the force of kundalini acts like liquid fire coiled about the base of our spine. It lies dormant for most of our life and should remain so unless we have undergone great moral development and evolve in the practices of yoga. Its movement, when uncontrolled, can tear tissues within the body. Arousing it prematurely may cause it to rise a certain level then return in a rushed anxious downward manner, opposed to a proper gradual upward awakening. Such premature awakening may cause incredible discomfort and pain from severe physical injuries. It may result in emotional turmoil causing madness, insanity and possibly death. The danger of its upward motion along the interior of the spine is that it invigorates the chakra centers and acts like an amplifier for all of our moral and immoral qualities. The greater danger is when it returns downwards and inwards to the base of the spine from which it sprung.

The forces of kundalini activates our chakra centers by going through and vivifying them, making them gateways into the astral world. That is why we require to be physically, emotionally and mentally prepared before arousing and unleashing such a strong force as kundalini within us. Special development by a trained teacher will instruct us with breathing exercises, postures, mantras, physical and moral training over a long period as a preliminary to unleashing kundalini to amplify our energies.

There have been special cases reported about premature and sudden kundalini arousal. An accident, which occurred several years ago in Canada, for example, claimed to have caused the kundalini force to stir and significantly change the life of one lady. She reportedly fell down a flight of stairs and the base of her spine hit in such a manner during the course of the fall that when she awoke she was extremely clairvoyant. She could tell what was happening in every room of her house at any time by having a clear picture of any room she directed her mind to. She also reported being able to clearly see what another person was thinking. It can not be ascertained that arousal of kundalini was the cause for her sudden remarkable ability since other factors of stimulation can also bring about such immediate results.

Our powers are virtually unlimited according to the process of development we undertake. Attunement with our nature can be achieved by discipline over the course of time through yoga and chakra meditation. The measurement of our success will be the truth we gain from the radiance we exemplify. Harmony is a state of divinity and a result of employing proper methods with earnest efforts. ★

MYSTERIES OF THE TAROT

"Of all oracles, the Tarot is the most astounding in its answers, because of all possible combinations of this universal key of the Kaballah give oracles of science and of truth as their solutions."

Transcendental Magic- Eliphas Levi

The tarot is a hieroglyphic representation of our subconscious and covers the broad spectacle of life as we may experience it. Studying the symbols in conjunction with the Qabalah allows us to become aware of incidents before they occur as well as advance us in the spiral of learning secrets and mysteries that pertain to our chosen course or destiny. The tarot represents facets of our subconscious mind, our material existence and the relationships we seek in our ever-changing evolution. It relates the microcosm (man/woman) with the macrocosm (the universe) in a totality of balanced forces.

Tarota or taro-rota means the 'Wheel of the Law', and as such we can relate the symbols in the cards in conjunction with our hopes, desires and concerns, from the past, present and future. The Wheel of Life revolves, and is ever changing and fluctuating as it turns in the cycle of life. Life's ceaseless events and potentials are masked from our ordinary consciousness but through studying the mysteries of the tarot, a realization occurs which expands our abilities and awareness of what is and can be.

Court de Gebelin, an illustrious French scholar of the eighteenth century, stated that there are three words of oriental origin preserved in the significance of the pack. Taro, he affirms, is from the Egyptian word Tar or Path, and Ro, ROS or ROB, refers to Royal, thus it can be approximately translated as 'The Royal Path of Life'. Another group of words he associated were MAT, meaning overpowered, and the PAGAD from PAG (chief or master) and GAD (Fortune). Some interchanging of the letters would give us the following: TORA (Hebrew)=the law; TROA (Hebrew)=gate; ROTA (Latin)=wheel; ORAT (Latin)=speaks, entreats; TAOR (Egyptian)=Taur, The Goddess of Darkness; ATOR (Egyptian)=Athor, the Egyptian Venus. All these words have great significance in knowing the keys, which assist in unlocking the greater mysteries. It is from the works of Gebelin, and in particular, his Monde de Primitif (1773) that the popular Marseilles tarot decks have been fashioned.

Every author on the tarot holds particular beliefs as to where the cards originated from but the true origin remains a mystery. China had sorts of playing cards in the tenth century, as did India but their designs are quite dissimilar to the known tarot varieties. There is belief that they came into existence in northern Italy in the valley of the Taro River, which comes from the Po. Thus the name tarot may come from the Italian 'tarocchi' and the French translation of that becomes 'tarot'.

Controversy arose in parts of Europe when the subject of the tarot was brought to the foreground. In 1423 St Bernardino of Siena, a Francisian preacher, debunked them as being works of Satan. Such ridiculous statements arose time and again and before long the cards were subjected to being ridiculed and set as taboo. The tarot cards are no more works of Satan than a common hammer and saw. It is pitiful how society has shaped and narrowed the mentality and potential for evolution, by instilling fear into spiritual advancement and constantly replacing it with artificial values. Belief is an important stronghold in most religious dogma however may have no greater purpose than a sense of security and attachment. Naturally it can be a superior tool in giving the mind repetitious instruction and positive feedback, but if belief is abused to narrow our perspectives and weaken our abilities then the spectrum of life and reality can be blindly damaged. Belief, in short, can be a very brainwashing mechanism with no way out. It can certainly thwart the ability to memorize through understanding the 78 cards, but if reversed, then belief may be used to realize and interpret the cards and connect with our inner world to find answers to our life mysteries.

The simplicity in design of the cards in some decks may be almost childlike whereas others may appear to be an intricate and complex array of artistry. In either case the symbols are the important factor and should be studied earnestly for their true meanings to dramatically evolve in our mind. Being timid and inviting fear, as with anything, can create delays and problems. Like any great and practical instrument, the tarot can be and has been misused for every purpose under the sun. There is nothing evil about tarot cards, they simply signify specific components of life and have no relation with hearsay taboo.

Classical mystery religions, mythology, paganism, the philosophies of Plato and Neoplatonists, hermetic traditions and the Qabalah are all invaluable guides for reality enlightenment. The study and assimilation of the tarot is amongst those bearers of truth in realizing the labyrinth of which humanism has adhered. If we are plagued by an over-abundance of research and study, our methods may require a healthy adjustment for joyous experience. If the scales are leaning too heavy on the Saturn aspect of life, then some experience of love and harmony through Venus, the Sun and Jupiter may be in order. This cosmological reference is as useful as it can be applied. Image magic works through visualizing and channeling energies through the cards, as gateways to states of consciousness and experience, and become an invaluable instrument in development. Natural precautions and devoted study are essential in the gradual process of these efforts.

Associations between the tarot cards and the structure of time have intrigued scholars over the years. The basic fifty-two cards have been associated with the fifty-two weeks of the year. The four trumps were comparable with the four seasons, the twelve court cards ascribed to the twelve months of the year and signs of the zodiac and the thirteen cards per suit to align with the thirteen weeks in each quarter of the year. If the numbers from 1 to 13 are added together, the total yields 91 and by multiplying it by 4 (for the four suits) we arrive at 364 and adding the Fool card we end with the number of days in the year. True enough, someone must have been quite bored to concoct that arithmetic, however it does give examples of how some scholars sought affiliations.

There are seventy-eight cards in total, four suits of fourteen cards each and twenty-two symbolic numbered trumps. The four suits are as follows:

English Titles	French	Italian	Modern Cards	Representations
Wands, Scepters, Staff	Batons	Baston	Clubs	Spiritual, Metaphysical Being, Will, Energy
Cups, Chalice, Goblets	Coupes	Coppe	Hearts	Emotional, Pleasure, Love
Swords, Daggers	Epees	Spade	Spades	Intellect, Imagination, Mind
Pentacles, Circles, Pentagrams	Deniers	Denari	Diamonds	Physical, Material, Worldly

The 22 major arcana cards represent cosmic forces and subconscious energies, and the 56 minor arcana represent people, relationships, money, action, and circumstances that happen during the course of living. The total gives 78 tarot cards representing forces and events, emotions and material objects that are always in our path. It is not within the scope of this book to give detailed interpretations of all the cards, as there are numerous great books available on the subject. It is highly recommended that the reader acquire a few good books on the subject and use a few minutes each day meditating on a different card until the meanings of all cards have been absorbed. This will help us to connect many facets of life together and heighten awareness of all that we come in contact with.

Before doing a tarot card reading it is advisable that we cleanse our hands and just prior to handling the cards to shake our hands energetically to rid any tension and allow free flowing energy to occur. The left hand is the one usually used to draw the cards from the deck, as it is the hand associated with the intuitive and subconscious part of the brain. The cards should always be kept in a box and wrapped in a solid color cloth when not in use. During the initial stages of studying each card, it may be a good practice to sleep with them under a pillow at night, after meditating upon a particular card. This establishes a strong connection between them and us with an astral energy attachment to bring us closer and deeper to help reveal mysteries both ancient and future.

As with the practice of yoga and meditation, a clearing of the air is always appropriate when working with our tools of spirituality. This can be done magically by invoking an elemental force that is in accordance with the divination at hand. We may hold our tarot deck in the left hand while directing our will through the right, stating: "Through the divine name of IAO, I invoke Thee, Great Angel HRU who art set over the operation of consecrating this secret and sacred wisdom. Lay thine hand invisibly on these consecrated cards of art, that thereby I may obtain true knowledge of hidden things, to the glory of thy transcendent and holy name. Amen."

When we ask specific questions using the cards, it is through the subconscious that we direct the question. Being overtly serious is not necessary when doing a reading as long as we direct energy and concentrate upon the question. Every person has a different perspective and interpretation from what is revealed. The symbolism on every card has general meanings and slightly varies from one tarot book to another but our knowledge combined with an intuitive perspective will be the greatest guidance for any revelation. When consulting the cards on a question we may perform a reading more than once but should be conscious of not asking the same question over and over again. If the answer is not apparent, it may not be the perfect time to know it. Consistent nagging for answers is similar to a child bothering parents when the parents know it is best to avoid a direct answer.

Freud's collaborator in the early part of 1900's was Carl G. Jung. While advancing in the field, Jung studied archetypal images and the symbols of the mind. During his work with the Yi Ching (Book of Changes) he consistently referred to the subject of synchronicity. It is something that has been experienced by everyone at one time or another. An example would be that if we are about to phone a relative but suddenly the phone rings and it is our relative calling us, an experience of synchronicity occurred. If we were dreaming of a tragedy and the following day on the news we hear that it happened during the night while we dreamt it, we would have again experienced this phenomenon, which is outside the logical explanation of co-incidence. It is an interesting conjecture that foreseeing the future by the practice of divination can become a consciously directed act of synchronicity.

Changes occur each and every moment in life but we still maintain a special affinity and connection to the material world as well as our inner world if we subtly recognize it as being particular to our manner of living. The school of Jungian thought accepts the tarot as Carl Jung considered it to agree with the archetypes of the collective unconscious. The diversity of it becomes a harmonious balance of the elements that make up our individuality, a synthesis of clarifying and cataloging an age-old system that has proven to work. The corridors of our unconscious have a fine mesh interwoven that separates our subjective experience of life. This mesh becomes the paths as a collective arrangement of our internal order.

Some writers declare that the tarot can be traced back to the ancient Egyptian Book of Thoth, considered to be perhaps the oldest book in the world. Thoth is the Egyptian Ibis-Headed God of Wisdom, Knowledge and writing. He was the scribe and is to the Egyptians what Hermes is to the Greeks and Mercury to the Romans. In ancient times it was thought that the knowledge of medicine, astrology, language, art, mathematics, engineering and other sciences came from Thoth. Thoth was also considered to have written the original chapters in The Book of the Dead. The Book of Thoth was scribed on tablets in pictorial form but was long lost to wandering gypsies during their travels. They later transcribed the pictures onto cards which became known as the Major Arcana. The earliest known cards distributed for fortune telling were around A.D.1390. It was during this time that printing is said to have first come into existence through the west. As years passed, great mystics incorporated the tarot cards into the Qabalah. There appeared to be an invariable connection between the 22 major Arcana and the 22 letters of the Hebrew alphabet. The original methods of divination with the cards appeared to help people learn more about their future and illustrated that they had a free will and were able to steer their own destiny. When incorporated into the Qabalah it was seen that the tarot could be used as gateways and doors to gain access to the inner realms that lay dormant from normal conscious recognition. Another extent of its' stratagem was with the capability in fulfilling yearnings and liberating the psyche from subconscious drive mechanisms.

Initiation through the use of the tarot was also a common practice during ritual. The three cards of the Tower, the Moon and the Star, for example were used in an initiatory experience for attaining the grade of Practicus in the system of the Golden Dawn, which is attributed to Netzach or Venus. These particular cards are gateways along the paths that lead to Netzach and therefore symbols and interpretations of them were of great importance in realizing the objective that the psyche was to attain.

The cards were also used in the Hermetic tradition to confer to the candidate rising into a new initiatory grade or level. In the Golden Dawn rituals, the first grade in rising on the Tree of Life is that of Theoricus. The card or emblem associated to that path is The Universe, as it is the card of the 32nd Path joining Malkuth (Material world of 4 elements) to Yesod (Astral world of the Moon) and Yesod is the sphere associated with that grade. Symbols in the card, such as the 4 beasts of man, eagle, lion and bull represent the 4 elements (earth, air, water, fire), and are slightly different than the ones in use with the 10th card or key called Fortune. Also, the oval surrounding the lady in the Universe card has 72 small circles (referring to Schemhamphoresch, the 72-fold name of the Deity). In essence it represents the physical manifestation of the present period in Time of Consciousness, and like the gods, angels and beings in existence, we strive to evolve and fulfill our existence in the universe. When using the cards as doorways, however, it is sincerely cautioned that we become familiar with what we are doing and know the subject well, as in all cases. In this particular matter the reader is referred to Israel Regardie's *The Golden Dawn*, Vol.4 Book 7, to the chapter entitled Clairvoyance where he instructs on the usage of tattvas.

The Moon card can represent the alchemical process of 'solution' which involves being self-critical and psychoanalytical by digging through the reaction and emotional patterns of the psyche. As analyst Carl Jung puts it in Mysterium Coniunctionus (p.256), "…to discover behind one's lofty ideals narrow fanatical convictions, all the more cherished for that, and behind one's heroic pretensions nothing but crude egotism, infantile greed and complacency." In this respect, the card is used as an evolutionary experience by breaking down the inner walls of convictions and ostentatious mental barriers that inhibit greater progress. It is a distressing ordeal but one necessary for valid spiritual excrescence. It becomes a journey of dread through midnight, as the card signifies with nine droplets of blood in the form of Yods, falling from the moon stirring our emotions and vivifying our instinctual energies. The wolf and dog in some packs, for this card, illustrate the wild and domesticated parts of our instinctive nature while the two towers in the background serve as our defense mechanisms of morality and intellect. The Moon is here in the waning stage and it is also the card assigned to Pisces on the Tree of Life. Through meditation on this card we can come up with a variety of interpretations and meanings that will undoubtedly assist us if it comes up in a reading. It could refer to a subconscious struggle, or some manner of testing or rising to new realizations through burning off karmic debt. It is the 18th card, and 1+8=9, illustrating to us that it is the 2nd card referring to "9" as a number of initiation, in the tarot pack. The first initiation card of 9 is the Hermit. In this analogy the Moon becomes the second initiation for the individual. Nine becomes a number representing initiation (3 + 3 + 3…the Three Triads) and through the Hermit (9th card) the Path becomes lightened for all with his lamp and he is independent of others through the wholeness he achieved. Within his lamp is a six-pointed flame, uniting the microcosm with the macrocosm and creates anything that is required, out of necessity, through the trinity of manifestation.

The components of each card suggest it's overall nature and ultimate meaning derived from it. Taking the 5 of Wands as an example, we associate Wands with the Lord of Fire and subject it to the sign of Leo as well as the planet Saturn. The card represents Strife and is a personality issue insinuating unfulfilled desire, vane, and blockage of the creative power as Saturn is in Leo. It may also mean that the person has to go step by step and take things a little lighter and look at the situation before moving onwards. There are also two angels associated with it, as all 36 small cards have, constituting an angel during the hours of light and one during darkness. There are in total, 72 Angels covering the small cards who are derived from the "Great Name of God" of the 72 letters called Shemhamphorasch, which means the divided name.

Using the tarot for invocation, aspiring to the highest, and evocation, a more objective outlook in associating oneself with other Beings, can be an invaluable mirror by reflecting the image of our soul. If we enter a museum and see a complete arrangement of little bottles labeled as individual chemical parts that make up the human anatomy they are far from being an actual functioning human but each component is totally significant for the construction and completion of that person. It is likewise with the cards in that their individual representations comprise something specific to the whole of mankind and life as we may experience it. When combined together they reflect an intricate, organized picture and map of the collective unconscious. Our physical body may be referred to as a Temple and the life therein as the inner dimensions thereof. The cards would be the pictorial representation on the etched stained glass, surrounding the temple of the inner life and energies, which perpetuate that life. Numerous psychoanalysts have incorporated interpretations of the tarot in revealing subconscious activities sprouting from the psyche. Writers such as P.D. Ouspensky in *A New Model of the Universe*, Charles Williams in his *The Greater Trumps* and T.S. Elliot in *The Waste Land*, have made references to what similarities the tarot have with our inner psychological make-up.

The Wheel of Fortune card is the cosmic wheel of Ezekiel, holding symbols and mysteries regarding the circuit of karma. The Wheel itself is s symbol of change and was saved as a classical emblem through the middle ages by Boethius in his classical work, *De Consolatione*. This early treatise on paganism illustrated the rise and fall of mankind upon the wheel of life. The goddess of nature rotated it and was blind to the desires of man. The result was to show the vanity and emptiness in worldly possessions since in the end we have only our God representation to face, and karma. Upon the wheel we may rise to the heights of success and contentment towards the summit, but as it revolves there comes the time to fall to the depth, perhaps of despair or death. It can also represent spiritual ascent and descent, the cycle of life, the zodiac in motion, seasons coming and going, changes of the tides, action and reaction, or simply day following night and so forth. Evolution as with most things can be looked upon as working in a circular motion, similarly as breathing in and out, expansion and contraction. Madame Blavatsky's famous treatise, The Secret Doctrine, mentions the law of periodicity which theosophists later connected to the Indian concept of Karma. It basically stipulates that there is no activation of chance in the world as all things are linked and that which occurs is a result of action and reaction. As we evolve and abandon our linkage to the lower planes, the Wheel of Fortune no longer dictates our outcome as karmic reaction.

The serpent, which is seen descending on the wheel, is Typhon, the Egyptian god of evil. Some refer to it as Seth, the counterpart of Anubis (or Hermes-Anubis) who is seen on the opposite side, ascending, and in Egyptology led the soul to judgement in the Hall of Truth after death. These forces seem to indicate dualities as well as the struggle with aspiring and climbing as opposing forces often do. The eight spokes represent universal radiant energy, called Ahrimanic forces and are linked to the rest of the card with the lunar-mercurial change and our struggle between divinity and materialism. The center of the Wheel represents the Sun, the origin of creative energy and seat of our spirit, Tiphareth. The planet associated with the card is Jupiter. The four animals (1+2+3+4=10-YHVH) in this 10th card can be a winning formula for success (monkey-flexibility; crocodile-creativity; snake-shedding old and non-attachment; sphinx-stability, wisdom, power to change with equilibrium, unifying the 4 magic virtues of knowledge, will, daring and silence.) It's divinatory meaning suggests success, with a turn of luck, changes in fortune and things coming for the better. A great breakthrough is thereby evident and possible. We should consider it and if it is not feasible then we should write down all the things we feel about what Fortune means to us in our present situation and what is hampering us from having such potential great fortune. This card teaches us manifestation, principle, praise, honor, life, regeneration, energy-in-motion, change and amongst so much more, self-realization and creativity. In another sense it helps us to remember not to bind to our possessive nature in a material way and to use forces appropriately towards prosperity.

It is amply illustrated in many great books on the tarot that the cards are significantly linked with the Qabalah, besides being used for purposes of divination. Divination is primarily linked to the Astral Light, the subtle light permeating the astral plane which enables the diviner to foresee visions filtering from higher planes. The most instinctive mind will capture not only specific words from divining an outcome but also visions. Those who analytically reason the most are not easily linked to the Astral Light for obtaining answers. As it is, their minds query and analyze without flowing with the natural ebb of the cosmic energy that tides from the astral realm. The more our interest is excited the greater is our confidence and intuition in obtaining a clear picture and vision. Autosuggestion plays a role in focusing our mind for intelligent interpretations with these oracles as they deliver us a message for our quest as a true seer.

To the ancient Magi, the taro was somewhat of a primitive Bible and honored for the mysteries of synthesis and antitheses with the mélange of revelation it provided. With diligence we may discover answers of universal significance. The tarot is a means to scientific and psychological realization, a wealth of practical knowledge. It's symbols go back to the beginning of time, to ancient parables, stories and the fashioning of spiritual history. The acquisition of the principles of truth through these means may develop and nourish our soul. There comes a sense of liberty, of useful knowledge that we gradually comprehend with studying the tarot and it coincides with evolving, self-discovery and awakening. We have moved away from nature in her purest form. Her laws have turned to mysteries that so few people are interested in discovering. The mind constantly fluctuates each moment with instability and a clear vision of our particular path has become veiled over time. The unveiling occurs by painstaking efforts and focused desires to reveal the knowledge of our particular road of inspiration.

Symbols are abundant in every card. Doves may represent religious ideas, spiritual conceptions, just as the laws of equilibrium and luminous motion keep us on our path in life to realize that we are Stars emanating Light. The man, lion, bull and eagle represent parts of our inherent nature and alike the four horses of the Sun in Greek myth, provides us with the knowledge to free our mind and body from the bondage of material consciousness. Also, as the servants of Wisdom were Adam and Eve, all force and life resulting from two polarities at work, the union of opposites (yin and yang) leads us back to our Identity. The number five (pentagram) represents the soul in the union of the four elements (Earth, Air, Water, Fire), of the ancients, and is associated in the 5th card, The High Priestess, who decides our eternal destinies within ourselves. The tarot therefore appears to be a magnificent and alluring spectacle of artistry and in conjunction with the qabalah can become a self-initiating experience.

It is important to have a certain respect for our pack of tarot cards and not ignore important messages they give to us. Ask clear and concise questions and be ready to receive answers that may not always appease personal emotions. The mind should be clear of prejudice, anger, fear, love and worry in order to employ the clairvoyant and intuitive faculties, which are within everyone, and are the faculties to bring messages for questions asked.

The sixth card, The Lovers, is associated to the sign of Gemini and pertains to attraction, connection and the feeling of fulfillment in the qualities of a loved partner. Psychologists often note that partners mirror the mental, emotional and spiritual qualities of one another. In the Lovers card, Cupid is stringing his arrow and as such card may signify the coming together of a relationship or moving apart of one. It is dependent upon other cards surrounding it and the issues at work with it. It can also denote an interactive, communicative involvement in the material world or an integrating, unity in the spiritual. It may mean something regarding choice, temptation or simply attraction. Six is an even, passive, feminine and perfect number in itself. Perfect in the sense that it equals the sum of it's devisors other than itself ($1 \times 2 \times 3 = 6$, $1 + 2 + 3 = 6$). The next perfect number is 28, followed by 496, then 8128… and so forth. When the name of a person adds to six, the person is often considered as peaceful, somewhat well adjusted and harmonious. It is said that years adding to six are good for settling down, marriage, establishing a home and setting up business ideals. This however adds more to superstition conviction and belief. In Genesis, chapter one, it states that on the sixth day God created man and woman. In the Qabalah, the sixth Sephiroth is that of the Sun, the giver of life, energy, and harmony. The hexagram has six points and is composed of two interlaced triangles, unifying God (The Macrocosm) and Man (The Microcosm), the great Universe in unity with its micro-mirrored image.

Eliphas Levi (born as Alphonse/Abbe Louis Constant, 1801-1875) expanded upon the secrets regarding the connection between the 22 tarot and the 22 paths of the Tree of Life. He was the first to ground-break the importance of the tarot in the occult arts in his books *Le Dogme et Rituel de la Haute Magic* (1856), and *History of Magic*, where he states the importance of the tarot as an alphabet and to be of Jewish origin, "The basis of hieroglyphical science was an alphabet…"

The tarot held a labyrinth of hidden secrets amongst the Hermetic Mystical Orders, and Levi diligently fragmented it out of sequence through his writings, but intentionally so. He was born in Paris in 1801, became a Roman Catholic priest at one point, worked in the left-wing politics of journalism and was a master of Rosicrucian interpretation of the Qabalah.

Using the twenty-two major Arcana as Subjective paths or doorways, with a working knowledge of the

Tree of Life associations, may help us regain a direct link to Objective cosmic forces, the ten spheres of the Tree. Using the cards as doorways to the enunciated regeneration of cosmic reality, we can be in touch with the circle of life and elements that transpire to make all things occur. Assimilating them in a balance between past, present and future will reveal intelligible ideals and provide a compendium of keys along the path of Inner Awareness. ★

NATURAL HEALING TECHNIQUES

"Vainly do mesmerists and healers invoke the testimony of the deaf, the lame, the diseased, the dying, who were cured or restored to life by simple manipulations and the apostolic 'laying of hands'…Newton, the well known American healer, has performed more instantaneous cures than many a famous physician of New York City has had patients in his life."

Isis Unveiled- H.P. Blavatsky

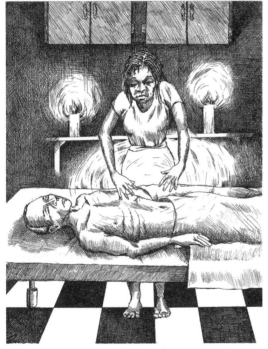

The mystical and transcendental path of pursuing esoteric arts leads us to abilities beyond general recognition. Some of these abilities involve healing our physical body and transforming our awareness to deeper insights, causing changes in many respects to our life. Students that follow the works of Paracelsus and Aesculapius and ancients before them, who were spiritual priests as well as physicians, have come across methods, which have immeasurably advanced modern therapeutics. Each level of manifestation has to be reckoned with and a person being of a sevenfold nature, all levels have their particular disposition. Working with the laws governing each plane and sub-level to those planes is efficacious for personal therapy. The laws of the next level and plane above it rule each plane directly below it. Therefore in healing the physical body, we have to tend to the etheric level to affect certain changes besides the normal physical properties involved in healing it. Physical surgery and medication have their requirement in healing, but there is also a natural tendency of the etheric to mend itself and to mend the physical body with the proper flow of vitality that it accepts from life in the atmosphere.

Maladies in our astral body require us to use particular mental level laws, most of which may be found in psychiatric therapy techniques because the mind is the level above and within emotions and affects cures for distraught feelings. Focusing on the direct area of an ailment is the first step, allowing for the tissues and bodily functions to take their natural course in the healing process. All physical ailments require, first of all, physical treatment and some ailments may not become untangled or rectified with the mere use of mental healing or forces applied. If there is a kink in the intestines, the most logical thing to be done is for a doctor to surgically open the body and untangle that kink because no amount of force otherwise will allow food to go through a twisted tube. Modern medicine and prognosis with blood tests and electro-cardiograph equipment generally details the malady for a doctor's diagnosis to be formed. Physical treatment is always the first step for treatment of physical illness. A true physician should diagnose any ailment before working natural healing techniques in order to know from modern medical practice what are the exact problems and the prescribed course of physical treatment.

A spiritual healer may cure ailments that stem from emotional disturbances by inducing the transmutation of energy levels causing a metamorphosis to ensue. The repair of injuries, physical, emotional or mental in nature, induces changes on all levels of our inner bodies. Each Inner Body is affected by a malfunction and by recuperation.

There are several kinds of healing and not all of them are directly spiritual originated. Ab-reacting karma to free someone from the after effects of forces they have put into operation to create the problem is for the most part mental healing using the powers of autosuggestion. The suggestion is instigated by the healer and creates a momentum in the mind of the injured to re-direct consciousness and thereby remedies the injuries with emotions causing an effectual change. The mind cannot manipulate matter directly, but it can manipulate the emotions to cause effect upon the etheric level, which is the outline that physical matter is directly attached to. The effect of willpower promotes recovery by the power of mental images inducing change in emotions and then in the etheric threads which in turn affect the physical change.

Spiritual healers may channel alternative emotions through mystical trance to enhance healing. Psychic healers bring similar effects through telepathic transference of healing images. In all instances the subconscious mind of the patient is affected such that it sends messages to the etheric body to cause physical changes to occur. It requires the work of a professional healer when the ailment is complex and entangled within the subconscious mind of a patient. If the patient suffers from an influence of excessive life force that is knotted or congested, it would be less than wise to pour more life force into them.

There are fewer harms done in admitting to the limitations of our ability than to raise the hopes of someone that has put all faith into those abilities. With any serious work on spiritual and mental manipulative healing a scientific knowledge of the mechanical functioning of the body is most necessary. Someone who is not susceptible to the change in consciousness that is being channeled to assist in cures will not heal very well. The physical needs of a person must be addressed as well as those on the other levels. As the father of surgery, Ambrose Pare would dearly admit: "I dressed his wounds and God healed them."

Once the mind has been broken and torn from psychological smashing, it is hard to reshape it back in the once delicate form it originally developed from. Science requires the aid of spiritual techniques to bandage the pain, cure the suffering and heal the delicate composure of our complete existence. Suggestions that are put into the mind become the hygiene at work and even if meant to be of no harm, can create changes that bring a line of negative effects into play. Instruments of methods that are not sterilized affect the level of which they are put to use. Upon completion of any technique great care should be given to post treatment such that the patient can apply, willingly on his or her own behalf.

A vigorous person emits vital emanations and when they feel depleted of energy due to an injury within their body such as the spleen improperly functioning, a healer can augment the replacement of energy. This can be done until such time as the person recovers sufficiently to continue manufacturing their influx of prana. Directing the energy flow to the portion of the body that is unhealthy will assist in flourishing it with the cells located in that area for proper functioning.

By putting our hands about two inches apart and revolving them around one another, we can feel the energy transferring from one to the other as we move them in a circular fashion. Bringing our hands closer together then further apart enables us to feel the energy surge and diminish as distance is changed. Focusing and directing this energy strengthens it even if we further separate the hands. Concentrated effort will develop this energy to project healing. Developing it can be done by the practice of feeling it, being sensitive to it and performing rhythmic breathing exercises while pushing the hands away from the body and then pulling them back towards the body. This develops what martial artists and practitioners of tai chi know as the power of Chi. Do some research on this energy and develop it with constant practice to promote healing from your hands.

Nervous conditions as well as sleeplessness and digestive difficulties cause a jangled problem in the etheric body. Headaches may come as a result of congestion of the blood or vital fluid caused by a misalignment of the magnetic principles within the body. Either directing a current of energy to the head from a strong outflow of the hands, or by the method discussed later are both palpable. Using mental imagery, we can make a mental picture of the organ that has a problem and then another picture of it as it should be in perfect health. With this projection imprinted in the mind of the injured, and emotion set to work with it, the etheric body will bring the necessary prana to that area and begin working on the tissues for recovery. Persistent practice in molding the organ with the matter of each plane is required by image building its final replica from the gases, liquids and solids which comprise the actual organ to be refurbished. This concentrated effort is to be followed by directing energy to the area in sustaining a recovery.

Centers of holistic medicine may also include courses in "psychic self-defense". That is a term Dion Fortune used in a book she titled with that name. There are many influences at work around the world and some of them are very negative, almost injurious to those who are sensitive and susceptible to them. Some of these forces may enter the aura of a person and subject them to unexplainable feelings, loss of vitality, outbursts of anger and so forth. Road rage, air rage or winters rage... every day there is a new rage happening somewhere. This is characteristic of someone not using normal rationale and for this reason it is important to consider the construction of a shield against such forces or influences that can bombard us without recognition.

In large cities it is not uncommon to run into people who seem to draw the energy out of others for their own subconscious reasons. That is why it is not a good idea for those people to be around hospitals and people who are ill and unable to fend off the energy draw from such individuals. People who are ill are susceptible to more damage being created because they are not functionally strong or capable of protecting their seemingly limited vitality. The vitality that they have is enduring the busy process of repairing internal damages. The old concept of vampirism holds true in these instances and it is a very known fact that they do exist everywhere, not the blood-thirsty kind but the energy thirsty kind. Some evil influences may propel them to suck life energy from unwary people and use it for their own cravings. There are other types of so-called vampires who cannot use or assimilate the energy they thieve from other people and end up simply dissipating that energy without being aware of it. This class of person suffers from leakage within their etheric body and requires special treatment so that the elasticity of the etheric is restored thus ceasing the perpetual suction and drainage of vitality. It goes without saying that being paranoid about such possibilities can end up being severely traumatic and possibly cause more harms than if ignored.

In creating an etheric shell or shield for personal protection it should be realized that such a shell would not only protect from outer influences but keep in everything that is present in the etheric double. This can be a problem as some of our own emanations are poisonous or contaminants and must be dissipated through the pores and out of the aura on a constant basis. The shell is made by an effort of concentration to create a denser outer layer of the etheric body. The etheric covers an area just outside the perimeter of the physical body, and through concentrated efforts a hardened outer substance can be visualized and made.

Another method is making an additional layer of etheric matter is by concentrating the surrounding particles of the atmosphere and conglomerating them around the body. This method is better but it takes longer to accomplish in learning how to mould the physical atoms and maintain it as a shield or outer lining for the etheric body. It is important to know the difference between each type of matter when working with this material. If an astral shell is made by mistake the astral body would simply float away in it and with it during a projection of consciousness. It would therefore be protecting only the astral body and leaving the etheric and physical body entirely unprotected.

Making an etheric shield is the preferred method because certain areas can be protected such as the hands when they are used in shaking the hand of someone else. Negative magnetic charges can then be prevented from entering. Such shields have been made and employed for fire walking ceremonies in certain religious sects, as the shields become a protection to the physical body against any heat sources. These shields are not capable of protecting against astral or mental influences and for such protection the use of particular matter on those planes is required.

There are methods of magnetic attraction and repulsion that are also efficacious in healing people who have an illness. A simple practice of passing the arms over the body of another person repeatedly with concentrated effort to withdraw congested or diseased etheric matter from the person can bring results. In this case the healer has to be slightly elevated and draw out from the other person negative energy. I have used this method personally in clearing a person who was in the process of vomiting and quite ill from congestion. It proved successful and as can experienced, the healer may capture the influence of the illness and must quickly dissipate or fling it off to the side. I say this for the fact that I began to vomit myself, having drawn their illness into myself at the time and not quick enough to discharge it. Therefore when an infliction is pulled from another person ensure that it is thrown off and discarded by throwing your hands out into the air after you have pulled or drawn from the suffering area. Rinsing the hands in water helps to clear away the "negative" magnetism.

Another variation is to place both hands on the person, one hand on each side of the body that is affected. In the case of the stomach, place a hand firmly there and the other hand on the lower back and proceed to direct the energy from one hand, through the persons' body discharging the congestion, to the other hand. Using a strong concentrated effort, project magnetic fluid from your etheric into the person, directing your healthy force from the right hand to the left over or through the inflicted area. This method is generally done without clothing over the area because materials are a partial barrier to the energy field, silk being the worse.

Magnetic cure is useful in many areas of healing practice. Certain forms of insanity are a result of the etheric brain not functioning properly to deliver the impressions from the astral (emotional) and mental (intellectual) bodies within the person to the physical level. In such cases the use of magnetic energy for treatment has been exceptionally useful.

Physical exercise and general well being is important for health in all Inner Bodies. Muscles that are not regularly exercised may deteriorate and cause congested magnetism resulting in weak spots in the etheric body and potentially resulting in an infection in the physical body. As with all things that are not regularly maintained, such congestion may result in nervous conditions and diseases.

Using the hands to induce the magnetic fluid though a person with illness was developed as mesmerism and got its name from Frederick Mesmer (1734-1815). He gave the name of the forces that pass through the hand and effected cures as "animal magnetism". By removing the etheric matter that is causing or is part of the illness, the link between the physical body and the astral body is broken in that specific area and therefore no feeling is experienced from the etheric removal. Through mesmerism complete sections of the etheric have been dismembered from a body location similar as that when amputation or surgery is performed and can be done without any feeling in that area whatsoever. Dr. Esdaile had compiled extensive operations in this particular field, which are documented in his book Mesmerism in India (1842).

Other instances of the magnetic fluid from the brain being removed from a patient and replaced by that of the operator has been accomplished such that the patients body is in complete control by the operator. In such cases the operator felt what was happening to the patient may in some instances cause sensations to be passed from the operator. This relationship is known as magnetic sympathy when the sensations are linked from one person to another. Success in transferring the magnetic fluid from person to person depends upon the receptive and active force of one another's will. Mesmerism only affects the conscious cerebra-spinal mechanisms and therefore can not make changes to vital processes in the body such as breathing and circulation of the blood.

In transferring magnetic fluid to another person, the exchange of prana energy and mental and astral emanations are taking place. It is therefore incumbent that the operator be physically as well as mentally and emotionally healthy. It is a perfectly curative function for treatment and should not be used in any profane manner. Successful results have been amply documented in historical records and proved especially useful before the implementation of chloroform. Hospital clinics were better known as places of intense torture in the 1800's and such practices that involved mesmerism were a welcomed aid. The results prove more efficacious when compared to the mere use of "willpower" directed treatment in which case the illness may find its' way back into subtle planes and result in later harm mentally or emotionally to the operator or patient. Although willpower is used for the concentrated effort, it is the recognition of magnetic fluid/force that serves as the treatment.

Mesmerism may be applied to many things such as plants to receive stimulation from their growth as well as nature-spirits, which have little sense of responsibility and can be easily dominated to perform missions within their capable means. The difference between mesmerism and hypnosis is quite distinct and are in no direct relation to one another. Hypnosis is a practice of putting a person into a subconscious state by having them induce it upon themselves through suggestive commands. Hypnosis has its place in therapy and often lends to the person feeling no pain from the mind control techniques and upon reviving them they remark feeling at ease and well rested, unless otherwise programmed. For positive results in self-hypnotic work I refer the reader to Laurence Sparks *Self-Hypnosis*, from which I derived much practicality in earlier years of training.

Concepts of Reflexology

Reflexology, also known as zone, spot, or reflex therapy has been a therapy practice for 2000 to 4000 years. It was practiced in Egypt (records date back to 2500 BC with this practice), India and China where they practiced zone therapy for 4000 years. It continued throughout history to be used but not until Dr. William Fitzgerald established it in 1913, did it have such widespread recognition. Unfortunately society began to seek the wonder pill to alleviate pains and such holistic practices went to the wayside. It is a natural

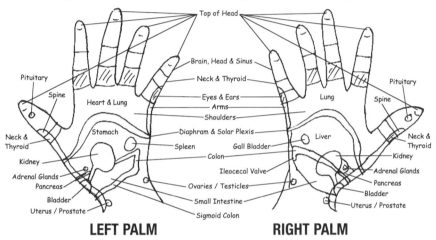

healing art and works with the principle of hands, feet and ears, which are said to have connection to every gland and organ of the body. The inside bone curvature of the foot interestingly enough, corresponds to the curvature of the spine on a smaller scale, and as most body energies go through the spinal area, most body functions end in the nerve endings at the hands and feet. We bite on our fingernails as a brain reflex, rub our hands as a circulation reflex and squeeze our hands as a solar plexus reflex, all of which sends messages to the body to activate a particular function. The hands and feet have ties to other regions of the body and we apply pressure to our hands and feet when irritated in other regions.

The body's energy is sometimes obstructed by crystal deposits under the skin and the energy can be blocked, but with use of pressure at reflex points, the electric current through the body assists the meridian lines and the nervous system to clear the blockage away. Reflexology is a safe and comforting practice and serves as a preventative measure for future problems with many parts of the body. It also works with the central nervous system and relieves a majority of PMS symptoms. Its work in relaxing the muscles, normalizing the body, increasing circulation and opens the way for fresh vitality to freely flow. There are 7200 nerve endings in the hands and feet, which represent particular areas throughout the body. By applying appropriate pressure to one of those points, the reacting stimulus is sent to the area it is associated with and relieves congestion, tension and provides better circulation. The blood circulates, removes waste products, the area becomes normalized and healing begins. It also puts us in contact with our body such that we begin to know what is wrong and what should be done to eliminate an oncoming problem. It relieves sinus congestion almost immediately, relieves tension, and assists in cleansing and de-toxifying the body. It has been a proven technique in removing bronchitis, asthma, gall bladder problems as well as gastric ulcers, nerve inflammation and arthritis.

A proper treatment lasts about an hour, with the last ten minutes concentrated upon working with the hands. Drink plenty of water after a treatment and if a bath is taken, a capful of hydrogen peroxide or some

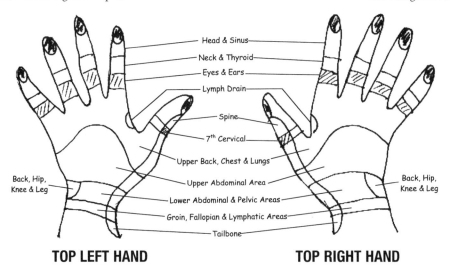

TOP LEFT HAND   **TOP RIGHT HAND**

Epsom salts will help to take out any remaining toxins in the skin of the body. Enclosed is a set of diagrams to illustrate the relative points on the hands and feet that are associated to body organs and areas. A trained practitioner should be consulted in order to learn the amount of pressure properly used to perform body reflexology.

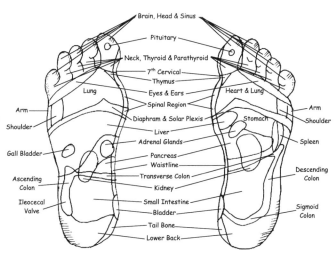

BOTTOM RIGHT FOOT   **BOTTOM LEFT FOOT**

Herbs

Herbs are a high quality food that contains vitamins, minerals, and elements in a natural harmony that are curative for body ailments and assist in providing better health. Some people may have adverse reactions in consuming certain herbs and some herbs are very potent. Herbs provide a cleansing action in our body but some may cause nausea, aches and diarrhea if the body is not conditioned to them during the cleansing process. They are not harmful but it is recommended to always begin with a small dosage and increase it to your particular needs. Some herbs may require taking up to five or seven times as much in curing an illness opposed to the amount recommended for maintaining proper health. Homeopathy declares that it takes a month for every year of illness that has set in to rebuild the body to its natural condition. Herbs can relieve certain problems like congestion and constipation within a day, but other more serious ailments may take weeks to notice favorable results. A person should not stop taking required prescriptions and put herbs in their place without consulting a physician. Some people take herbs in the morning and before bedtime, and others take them any time during the day or with meals, as they are simply a food. Information is very accessible on herbs and their uses. Here is one example using thyme. Thyme is the herb used to curb a cold because it causes us to heavily perspire. It has long been used to remedy headaches due to colds, sore throat, cough and fevers. (That sounded like a TV commercial) Adding thyme with other herbs that are commonly used as a cough remedy can act as a catalyst. You may also use peppermint with either, elderberry and yarrow, or with a touch of ginseng or cayenne.

Color Therapy

"Imagination is more important than Knowledge"   ....Einstein

There is a theory that everything in life contains energy vibrating at different frequencies, including colors. Lighting colored candles creates not only an atmosphere but stimulates previous stored associations we have to those colors. Color therapy recognizes these principles and plays upon the effect that colors have to sooth or change the emotions within us. If we desire to gain knowledge, lighting a yellow candle is said to induce the retrieving of knowledge from our subconscious. If we wish to send feelings of love, lighting a pink candle associates purity from our heart, and it is the heart which is a giver. Blue is used to resolve a spiritual problem whereas lavender is good for the sensation of healing. Silver is good for building protection. We may also use a lamp and a colored light bulb to induce color therapy. Basking in a particular colored light generates feelings within us. The colors we wear in our clothing affects our mood and causes impressions on those we come into contact with. We generally choose to wear a certain color of clothing on important occasions, just like wearing green on St. Patrick's Day. We could even match our clothes to the days of the week, just to test reactions. Monday = Moon (purple), Tuesday = Mars (red), Wednesday = Mercury (orange), Thursday = Jupiter (blue), Friday = Venus (green), Saturday = Saturn (black), Sunday = Sun (yellow/gold).

The colors in our home also have an affect on our mentality and moods. A pleasing atmosphere is a relaxing one psychologically and so contains relaxing colors, opposed to fast colors that are, for instance used in fast food restaurants to get people in and out quickly and keep things moving. Changing the colors around us, for instance at our work place, or adding certain colors may help to inspire us or keep us reminded of something pleasant. Inside of our car we may like to have a color that is attractive yet preventing us from day dreaming while driving. Selecting the color for a bedroom is important as it may help in a better sleep. Eating foods of certain colors can assist in balancing our internal energies and is important in a proper diet. Orange, green, white, yellow, purple and other food colors are plentiful in vegetables and fruit and have certain affects upon us besides their nutritional value. The same goes for consuming refreshing liquids of different color, which generate feelings within us.

Placing colored edible gels into clear water within a jar and then putting the jar in view of the sun to absorb the vitality and later drinking from it becomes an interesting experiment. The sun is well known for its' healing capabilities. I have placed red, yellow, blue and green nutritious liquids into sunlight and used them for healing potions. As the sunlight passes through the spectrum of the colors it yields to the certain qualities of that color and has healing properties associated to illness or injuries becoming a benefit in recuperation. Churches have stained glass windows which when the sun goes through brings a certain healing energy and peaceful ease to those it touches.

As we breathe, we can imagine certain colors coming into our lungs to cause a re-energizing sensation. This can be done during chakra meditations while becoming more in tune with their resonance. With the mesmerism practices of the magnetic fluid emitting from the hands, we may put a certain color to it and direct that color into the person we are healing. Practicing this on our pets provides a willing victim for the practice of our mental projections. Remember that they are on another life-level and their magnetism may also affect you.

The qualities associated to particular colors may vary to some people and cause different reactions. Red is Geburah, a fiery color with energetic powerful vitality. It may be used in drying sores, burning out cancer from cells, and healing circulation and blood disorders. Red may help in sexual potency, digestion, chest and kidney problems. It should not be used on people with high blood pressure, anxiety types, but it can assist in cases of depression. Too much red can end in an aggressive or agitated behavior pattern, so be careful of this and in projecting too much of any color in particular.

Yellow is used for intellectual stimulation, quick decisions, and clearing the mind. It is a stimulating color and must be used sparingly. It can assist in curing skin problems, dermatitis, etc. Green helps mend the heart, brings ease to tired nerves, and has peace and harmony within it. It helps with healing broken bones and torn tissue on the body. There are many tones of green, but light green may bring the feeling of peace and is good for pregnant women to have in daily view of because it assists in growth. Blue brings honesty, harmony and relaxes the mind. It helps in fevers, nervousness, burns, and bleeding since it is a chilling color. Therefore too much of it may cause a sensation of coldness. Purple connects with spirituality and is good for any mental diseases, epilepsy, rheumatism, pain, and healing in the bones. Lavender also is associated with spiritual aspects of healing, equilibrium, replenishing energy and is like a potent drink for the body to rebuild itself. White helps to take pain away and gives a sense of purity in higher levels. Gold is one of the best colors to cure most illnesses. It strengthens energy fields around the body but we can become gradually susceptible to its' powerful emissions. Silver is persistent and helps to remove things with the force it radiates which is always direct. It is a good color for cancerous tissue and blood healing and taking recurring problems away.

Black is not often used in color therapy but brings supreme quietude and silence gracefully as the person contemplates the Higher Light coming through.

Reiki

Another method of healing that has widespread use is that of Reiki (ray-key) which means "universal life-force energy". It uses the feeling of the Reiki going through the hands to heal and rejuvenate, by releasing and transforming the energy within.

There are many forms of training in Reiki and the beginner may gradually develop to reach higher degrees of Reiki credentials should they wish. Emotional energy can be released to such an extent that the person enacts their feelings using the energy to express the occurrence of healing. Working with chakra energy is another avenue, which Reiki incorporates in synchronizing the healing ability. Channeling is also discussed amongst Reiki participants, as well as coming in touch with their guides, invoking angelic forces beyond the physical level, all in assisting the transformation and healing process to greater levels. Workshops sometimes delve into third eye awareness to develop clairvoyance and the ability to see the chakras and the aura in other people. Healing through quartz crystals and mineral stones, incorporation of colors, specialized breathing techniques and pendulum induction are all principles of balanced forces and are all touched upon in the Reiki therapy sessions of today. All these positive steps are influencing the new age system and creating harmonious social interaction with a sense of longevity, rejuvenation and higher energy achievement.

Highly qualified instructors may also bring the earnest person through concentrated meditations of arousing the kundalini force below the root chakra to begin opening the gateways through proper integration of the inner bodies and their gentle, gradual evolution. This of course, should be done when knowledge of personal karma is undertaken and accepted to let go in order that the awakening of the kundalini force opens the chakra centers in a properly prepared student.

There may be blockages from earlier life issues that are not resolved and through guided meditation practices they can be released such that the person may move on with greater comfort and ease. Troubled emotions, temperamental conduct, tormented dreams, nervous conditions, negative influences are all facets of reality in someone's life. Resolving such perplexities sometimes require turning to the spiritual path and seeking a harmonious insight from learned professionals. The pursuit of these practices provides some order of contentment from daily stress or responsibilities. Some days we just wish we could squeeze out more energy and create more fulfillment from meeting our harmonious dreams with disordered reality. Positive direction is a practice through aspiration with realized improvement. Reiki may supply guidance in the proper use of energies, be they mesmeric or other, and with an earnest effort we can use this system to manipulate positive changes thereby moving in a positive direction.

Spiritual Transformation

We do not have to look far to find lectures, seminars, workshops and institutes devoted to training people in the art and practice of spiritual and natural healing techniques. It could be quite a gratifying experience but the important thing is that we are healed before considering healing other people. This not only facilitates the ability to heal others but also prevents us from giving parts of our uncontrolled or negative energy to others. The practice of meditation brings certain awareness regarding the potency of energies and provides us with a harmony that naturally affects others. Personal healing is efficacious and necessary in the pursuit of healing others.

I have always acknowledged the words that "when the student is ready the master will be there". Like the process of falling in love, there is no requirement in a long search for a teacher to obtain enlightenment and spiritual progression, because the greatest teacher is the one within us. That is to say that the search is most times in vain because we have to do the work on our own to achieve anything of worth. Resource material is more than abundant and communication is what we make it. At the end of each phase we seem to attract the right person to further our training by experience one way or another. The answers come with plenty of homework and equivalent experience. The art of healing, like spiritual enlightenment, becomes an earned understanding and wisdom gained by natural transformation. It can not be purchased or given but becomes an attainment from insight, experience and the process of working for it.

Many of today's holistic organizations may assist the seeker in a direction of well being. They may guide us to make a disclosure with those unresolved emotional traumas, clear away unconsciously driven cellular programming, bring awareness to the negative ego, shadow self and sub-personalities, but the effort is really upon the person if anything is to be accomplished. People are seeking more than ever to become aware of their multi-dimensional, higher self-aligned inner life. They want to transmute like the alchemists did, to the higher octave of awareness and shift their outer world, or collective reality with that transformation. True visionaries like Flammel, Paracelsus, and the Comte de Saint Germain realized the purification process and psychological transformation required in beginning any serious work in alchemical pursuits.

There must exist a process or an approach to destroy or rid negativity or influences that perpetuate illness other than common preventative measures. There is a method of distillation known as separation, where we graduate clearer thoughts and refined feelings thereby causing an uplifted sense of being. Becoming aware of the life essence of prana and its influx through our body accounts for this occurrence. Meditation upon this process will bring an awareness of colors, brightness, and assist in clearing away all dreaded matter that lingers and attempts to shroud our Higher Life from shining through. Becoming in tune with our natural harmony, our cellular physical nature, etheric double, astral, mental, and causal inner bodies will eventually bring us in touch with our nucleus, our core spiritual body. This process of separation is not only the acknowledging of what constitutes our existence but making efforts to develop those characteristic components. The next process used by the alchemists was sublimation or purification. This occurs when we are free from physical limitation, free from the restraint that holds us from communion with those Inner Bodies and inter-action on the higher inner levels of their respective planes. With this second process we are not escaping physical life but rather climbing deeply within it to the higher planes and using laws governing those planes to affect changes upon their respective levels. Our awareness in the purification process cannot be deterred by physical plane distractions because the operation of such a process comes only after such concentrated effort has been achieved that it cannot be dissuaded. Acute awareness is distinguishable by the fact of what changes are affected on those planes. Life in the physical world often shadows the special significance of our inner life and natural harmony for progression. Consciousness in the physical world is often sidetracked but upon persistent work of being our own masons on the inner planes we can unify consciousness to achieve the process of purification. The process of coagulation occurs next and is a recombination as the psyche has been elevated, acknowledged and condensation of its' purity occurs. It is somewhat like a holographic realization when we come to realize our Higher Life and True Self with the limitless capability attached to it. We become grounded to the earth plane again but realize that many previous desires that our earthly consciousness held so excitedly are perhaps more of hindrances and we have gained a true vision of the harmony which our Higher Life contains. That is not to say that previous interests and lifestyle has become useless in this elevated stage of spiritual awakening. Our view of life simply altered with prominence and ability in dealing with life issues from a "more" spiritually inclined perspective. We realize the true connection with our soul and over-soul processing on the inner planes and guided by the True Self to see the path as a spiritual road. This process may take years; it may take more than a lifetime, or it may take months. It is significant to note that this state of harmony attunement coincides with life principles and laws on all planes while we embrace our True Will as a realization and thereafter guided by it. Love, as a word, becomes the essence we breathe as we are guided by the will of transformation and the light from the influence of our unveiled spirit.

It may appear complex at the outset, but life is sublimely simple at its roots. It is the myriad of complexity that we add to our quest, boggling our mind and preventing experiences that could lift the veils and subsequently allow the inner light to shine for us to see and communicate on those inner planes, a reality of life which can be intricately beautiful. Poets and singers may express the greatest of passions and they are the ones who know the power of words. The evocation of feeling brightens our soul and uplifts us to a capability of choice and direction. Our feelings in the astral world can be enhanced, they can be tools to convey our inherent divinity. Refinement in the crucible of life transfigures us into communicating Intelligence with great ease and objectivity, passionately so. Our microcosmic representation is the coming to awareness of the microorganism we are of a higher oneness, a realization that we are a combination of elements and perfect as a six-rayed ignited stardust amongst the heavenly spheres. We are capable of causing change to occur in our world, we can transform and we can heal. Each individual is unique with a combination of essential elements molded yet radiating, stimulated yet capable of being refined. Our connection to the forces of nature and Mother Earth is without question as we become solved and coagulated. Making the exodus out of the material grip of existence begins the process of refining the matter energy in each inner body where purified energy counts the most. With this in mind, it is time to enter a subject that pertains to preventative illness and a method of learning relaxation as a healing antidote.

Relaxing to Gain Control

One of the most important things to be able to do at any given time is to relax. It is not an easy thing to accomplish successfully as during these days of having so much to do and think about, people seldom know how to fully relax. Forgetting problems and easing feelings is not a method that will allow a person to truly relax. A child has a natural ability to relax the whole body, but as maturity occurs, responsibilities, concerns and worries encompass daily routine, and we forgot to relax certain muscles and began to develop acute neuromuscular tension. This develops into prolonged tension throughout the body and thus hardening muscles that require massages as often as possible. Headaches result from such tension and wasting energy that is obtained from food to recuperate also becomes inevitable.

A basal metabolism test would define how much energy is consumed in the vital bodily functions. When we are at rest, our heart uses about ten percent of the entire energy intake to force blood though the circulatory system. The chest muscles use about twenty percent to maintain oxygen through the lungs. Therefore about one third of the energy in the body is used simply for respiratory and circulatory functioning. Another ten percent is used for digestion and glandular activity and thirty five percent for muscular contractions to maintain body heat. Finally about twenty to thirty percent is for other vital functions. How much energy is therefore used when a person is worried, concerned, or tensing muscles that otherwise would keep their supply of energy in use for other more meaningful purposes? That is why I say that much energy obtained from food is wasted if we do not know how to functionally relax at any given time and use more appropriate responses to counteract our concerns.

It would be beneficial to have a friend in assisting you with the following exercises in relaxing to gain control. Begin by gauging the amount of tension residing in your body. Lay down on a flat surface and have a friend hold your leg by the ankle about halfway up in the air, above a pillow. Then the friend is to let go and see how easily your leg drops to the cushioned surface below without any hesitation. Next, let the person hold a spot under your knee in the back of your leg and at your ankle the same time. Then after a minute they are to let go of the ankle portion and see how easily your leg from your knee to your foot drops to the cushioned area below. If you found that there was a pause to relax and drop your lower leg, that your leg was not completely relaxed, then you have involuntary tension. You must learn to relax the inner pressures so that it becomes a natural ability to relax under your command at any given time. You can practice with other parts of the body also, and feel how much tension resides within each area and how easy it is for you to let it all become released. Let out a comforting sigh as you practice doing this and do not be afraid of your feelings at how wonderful it seems by realizing that tension is not required to live each minute of the day. It steals your energy away and you should not allow that to happen.

Practice laying down on your own and paying attention to your body as you voluntarily relax each part of your body in turn. Listen to your body as it sends any messages to you. It may seem strange, especially reading about it on paper, but we all have to listen to our body to know what it requires as well as our mind and feelings for what they request. With a sincere effort in doing this you will realize that your body is the most loyal person you have ever known, and that it has always taken care of you, brought you where you wished to go, and done as you requested. It's a true friend!

If you wish to live long and use energy in abundance as you want, and have an energy reserve in storage for any moment required, you had better take care of the needs of your body. One of those needs is proper relaxation. Other needs are obviously proper diet, nutrition and exercise. None of these things are too time consuming or expensive to accomplish on a daily basis. In fact they are all less expensive than anything else we do in life and much more rewarding. Two hours per day would more than satisfy preparing all the meals, exercising and performing relaxation practices. Enjoy everything you do and learn to humor your body as well as anyone who seeks to cause any unnecessary stress in your life.

If you have tense muscles that cause kinks it is from resisting gravity constantly and can be eliminated through awareness of your body. That is the first step in truly relaxing. By increasing your awareness of each part of the body you begin automatically to loosen that area and feel more at ease, more in tune and sense an additional storage of energy within. Sit in a position such that your knees are bent up towards you as though you were going to cross your arms and rest them on top of your knees. Have a friend force your knees apart with you applying resistance to that force. Then suddenly the friend stops to push them or pull them apart and notice how your effort is still there fighting the force. That is what your body does with gravity. That is also what you do in exertion and continue to do after the exertion is complete until such time as your body relaxes to a state that it feels comfortable. You carry this additional struggle of resistance and exertion with you and it becomes a habit. It develops into tension and is accordingly relieved as stress.

If complete relaxation became a developed routine there would never be a requirement for stress. If your body is not a complete comfort to live in, even better than the best recliner on the market, then you need to learn relaxation techniques. Have you thought of more ways for your friend to check and gauge your relaxation ability? Have the person press on your chest as you lay down, not too hard, just in a slow firm manner so as not to damage anything internal. Then the friend is to let up on your chest after a few seconds of pressing down. Feel the ease upon their sudden release. Become aware of your chest area as fully as you can. Do such exercises with all parts of the body. With the neck, have the friend move it back and forth easily then pull up and down slightly just enough to loosen it. Feel how wonderful it is when they let go and you compare the difference of the tension that was there, and became shook loose and how the sensation is afterwards. After several practices, have your friend press on your chest and forehead firmly, at the same time, as you feel yourself becoming heavier and heavier. Literally feel yourself sinking into your lying posture and going through the bench or bed from a sense of heaviness. Then they release their hands from you and you begin to feel the ease your body takes on as it seeks to sink further. You would almost feel like going to sleep for a little while after such practices and surely the resting would be peaceful and so more enjoyable.

You can do such exercises alone as well. While lying down, lift your leg to a certain height about forty-five degrees upwards, and then slowly lower it back to the position it began from. Do this a few times and each time lower it slower than the time before. Then lift it and let it drop suddenly to take its natural course downwards. Do this several times with intent on relaxing it more and more as it relaxes in the fall. With your arms, lift one at a time until the hand points towards the ceiling, and allow your hand to go limp as you do so. Lower it to the resting position. Do this a few times then once upon raising it let it drop by itself. If properly relaxed it should begin to fall from the upper arm to the elbow slightly before the elbow to the hand, as it goes back down. In each exercise with the arm or legs, as they hit the resting area (of your bed or practice bench) there should be a tiny spring as they hit by seeing them slightly pop up and then down again. The springing motion is dependent upon the health of the body. You may also do head lifting to a few inches and then dropping on a pillow. Use your imagination and safety such that there is nothing to worry about, as any part falling will end on a cushion surface from the height of a foot to where it falls.

There are always rewards when you treat yourself properly. The reward in true relaxation is that the energy which otherwise would have been wasted in nervousness, tension and stress is used for another capacity. It has to be used somewhere, and generally it sharpens the mind, intellect and brings you into a better state of being alert. Your posture will even change and other people will notice something new about you. People may wonder if you achieved some instantaneous personal magnetic powers. You will have gained better control through not wasting energy, and definitely express yourself more clearly and fully. It is an awakening process that occurs when you really know how to relax and to be able to retain the vital energy that pours through you constantly. It is really amazing!

If you ever compare the difference in how a child sits and how an elderly person sits you will see that the younger of the two are always flung about with an added expenditure of energy. The older person however has their feet crossed and hands crossed and interlocked. They are conserving energy from constant concerns that they grew up with and tension that became habitual so they feel that there is not a whole lot of energy to spare. It also provides them with warmth, as they are not allowing heat to escape and feel more bundled and comforting by crossing parts of the body and conserving their energy. This is also a position for meditation. By sitting down and crossing the legs and interlocking the hands you are closing the circuits and arousing more energy in such a posture. That is why there is an abundance of energy after a meditation and can be used for any purpose, transformed into any idea you desire.

It is strongly suggested that you begin all of the following practices with a meditation and rhythmic breathing. Sitting comfortably with the closed circuit concept, breath in for a count of five, hold for a count of five then exhale slowly for a count of seven. Sleeping may relax a person if there is no psychic tension that is working in the brain during sleep, but usually there is and therefore sleep is not a true relaxation state. Tissues are rebuilt, toxins are eliminated, metabolism is being performed, oxygen is being transformed, heat is being distributed, and everything is taking place, as the body is a busy factory during sleep. If you do not make certain time to REALLY relax, it may never happen on its own and you could be caught up in most unhealthy lifestyles allowing stress to run your mental, emotional and physical responses. Our body is an emotional bondage and once our skill at relaxing improves we come to realize that we are separate from our body, that we are not tied to it, but that it is a function we use. It will be a truly uplifting feeling, a separation from the physical part that has long enslaved us with its baggage called tension. I certainly wouldn't say that I am my body because months after it is dead I would look down at it and testify, "Nope that's not me!" Therefore we can become aware of our body as a temporary facet and expression of ourselves instead of the totality of our nature.

Begin concentrating on each individual part of your body starting with your feet. Feel the muscles in your feet and think of nothing else but each foot. Imagine them clearly with all that is inside them, nerves, tissue, fiber, veins, arteries, everything that is there. By doing this more blood will flow there, you will become conscious of a warming sensation. Do not rush any of these practices. The more time spent on them the more that will be gained. Do the same for each part of the body, the lower legs, upper legs, stomach, chest, neck, shoulders, upper and lower arms, hands, face, head, back, etc. You may tense each part fully then relax it and tense it and relax again. There will be a feeling of relief as you relax it and you can then set your mind to concentrate on that particular region. You will develop your imagination in these exercises, such that sooner or later you should be imagining your brain, your inner features and how they connect.

You will feel how your eyes are connected inside of you, how your nose and ears are connected and learn to relax every muscle that is at work in order to really know what it is like to truly relax. You are learning to flow blood to all parts of your body by doing this and in so doing you cleanse those areas. This process normalizes the functions of the body and thereby heals any areas that become inflamed from tension and over exertion. Just imagine no more muscle relaxants in old age! You have just discovered an art of healing yourself simply by learning to relax.

You may even extend this to feeling an abundance of energy flowing through to any particular organ or area and it will decrease blood pressure throughout the body. Try to put your concentration on the stomach area as once you relax there you can more easily relax anywhere else. Then go to the other areas to work on them. Freud used the term Id to surmise the activity of the unconscious that deals with instinctual aspects inherited from the past and have emotions attached to them. In the course of studying the chakras, you learnt that feelings and sexual instincts reside in the stomach or abdomen area, the root and spleen chakras. If you learn to relax that area you can be one up on your emotions and their responses. With effort you will be able to relax any part of yourself at any time, wherever you may be.

Extend these practices into meditations such as the following. Feeling very relaxed and imagining the size of your body, you begin to sense the immediate area around your body with your eyes closed. See yourself sitting there at the place you are, from a distant view above you, and all the surrounding area that is miles away from you. The image of yourself there should be getting smaller and smaller. Keep the focus on you as a small light while your consciousness extends, viewing it from above the planet. Your consciousness being way up there, it can sense the cosmic rays and light sources from everywhere above the atmosphere coming through to the earth. You are no longer thinking of your self in terms of personality but a source of light, which becomes aware of other light sources that are coming through to you. Feel the purity within those light sources and bring them into your body that is meditating upon the surrounding vastness. Recall that everything is connected into higher dimensions and you are becoming in tune with that connection.

During all of these developments you should be breathing in deeper and deeper into your lungs so that they expand with your expanding awareness. As the rays enter your body from all directions, giving you energy and vitality, feel yourself becoming larger physically and growing to encompass all that you have hitherto imagined. Feel the world, the planets, the solar system and all stars that your imagination has taken to, to be within your body. By breathing in deeper you are using more of your lung capacity, and while relaxing as you do it, your heart also relaxes, as it does not have to work as hard to produce blood flow and achieve oxidation and thus relieving strain on the heart. Thinking causes variations in oxygen intake, and therefore results in changes in the body. That is the key to this part of the visualization process. As you expand your mind, breathing deeper, the influx of energy and oxygen does repair to your body. It heals areas not previously aware of, and produces positive reactions to functions within the body mechanisms.

One final exercise will be noted to culminate the development of self-healing. While relaxed in a meditative posture, become conscious of one particular area on your body. It could be a spot on your lower arm. While visualizing that spot with your eyes closed, try to see the pores of the skin there as tiny holes that are entrances to within your body. Continue this with the rest of your body until you feel that your body is completely full of tiny holes which are held together in its frame by a matrix of skin. Feel streams of energy like the soft warm winds flowing into those pores and into your body. Allow your mind to flow with what this life producing oxygen is doing for your body as it enters and begins to relieve all areas it contacts. Feel the onrush of energy flowing up from your feet into your lower body and in from the top of your head to fulfill the upper body with renewed vitality. With these efforts you will learn to relax your body and send new biological sensations to places in it that dearly require it. Your body should feel much lighter, cleansed with a burst of energized enthusiasm empowering it.

You have learnt to free your mind and emotions from thinking and feeling that your body is a burden and an incessant mould that causes suffering and pain. You have worked with conscious efforts to rejuvenate all areas of your body and have touched the secret of an ever-increasing passion, an ability to transmute your body by mental alchemy. Your life can mend itself as much as you put forth effort to do so. You can become master of your temple and use these developed energies to direct and channel them in furthering your mystical and magical experiences throughout life. ★

FOOTSTEPS AND FOLLOWERS - THE IMPRINT OF A MASTER

"Aleister Crowley, as we have seen is no Christian, neither is he a gullible spiritualist, nor a gross materialist. Seeking an answer to a mystery, he first finds it in the anthology of the Qabalah, and then finally through Mysticism and Agnosticism, to their reconciliation in a neo-Hermeticism, a neo-Rosicrucianism- which we have already called Crowleyanity."

The Star in the West (1907)- Captain J.F.C. Fuller

This book would not be complete without a simplified overview of one of the greatest influences that caused the spiritual movement of today. Rumor and innuendo is not what is required here so much as presenting a favorable light on the footsteps of such a knowledgeable master, as was Aleister Crowley. His endeavors paved the road for modern scientific research into esoteric studies for western civilization. Although some ill-read, profane writers have misallocated his name to negative connotations, the truth of the matter remains in the black and white of Crowley's own words. His multitudinous writings clearly illustrate the spiritual concern and integrity he had devoted to the cause of loosening and ridding the restriction's that history has imposed upon mankind. Freedom for the soul to attain spiritual awareness and live with that freedom is amply portrayed throughout his words. Just as any rumor gets out of control, malicious rumors from earlier tabloids have been exaggerated beyond belief. The chances of what the average person hears on the street about Aleister Crowley contains about two percent of truth.

This little essay is an introduction, a mere fractured glimpse, of a master of the English language, his works and influence upon other people during and after his life presence. His accomplishments have been more fully detailed in many other books, some accurate and some not, but his literary skill excelled beyond the bondage held by the Victorian era mentality, which he painstakingly lived through. Some of his footsteps will be recalled, and photographs provided to recount the magical journey that his life so depicted. His autobiography, which he called his autohagiography, *The Confessions of Aleister Crowley*, contains a lengthy and most illuminating study of his character, experiences and extraordinary adventures with an accurate account of his lifetime achievements.

He was born as Edward Alexander Crowley at 30 Clarendon Square, Leamington, Warwickshire, England on October 12, 1875. His father, Edward Crowley was a follower of John Nelson Darby, founder of the Plymouth Brethren. His mother, Emily Bertha Bishop, had the inevitable blind faith in religion that got her caught up in rules, regulations and restrictions ultimately impairing her from the ability to attain her true inner nature.

As a child of age four, Aleister, nicknamed Alick, was capable of reading perfectly well, and soon thereafter able to sit with his devoted family and recite, from memory, any passage of the Bible. What intrigued him most were the long Hebrew names like Enoch, Arphaxad, and Mahaleel from the Bible that perhaps contributed to his early progress in poetic proficiency and comprehension of the Hebrew Qabalah. His admiration for his father was undoubtedly praising as he honored the eloquent persuasion projected of his father's refined manner while travelling and preaching the word of God throughout the countryside.

At the age of ten, Crowley left the school of St. Leonards to attend one by the Plymouth Brethren led by an ex-clergyman named H. d'Arcy Champney. Two years later his father passed away, the night of which the boy coincidentally dreamed that his father was dead. From then on his life took a new and more personal route, no longer did he use the nickname of Alick, but endowed himself with being a fully feathered Aleister. His life swiftly churned with changes while exploring and searching for ultimate truth. He enrolled in Trinity College, Cambridge, in 1895 and became endowed at chess, mathematics, chemistry and poetry with rock climbing as a sideline enthusiasm.

Upon visiting Wastedale Head in the Lake District of western England to take video footage of places Crowley climbed and met with Oscar Eckenstein, I met up with Alan Hankinson for an interview. In his book *The First Tigers*, he outlines the great climbing relationship between Crowley and Eckenstein.

Eckenstein made outstanding technical contributions to the sport of mountaineering and developed the commonly used climbing crampons. He became a long time climbing companion of Crowley throughout their expeditions from 1898 at Wastedale to Mexico in 1900 and 1901 and in 1905 up the rigorous Kangchenjunga in the Himalayas. Crowley's admiration for the athletic Eckenstein can be seen in his own words: "He was a finished athlete; his right arm in particular was so strong that he had only to get a couple of fingers on to a sloping ledge of an overhanging rock above his head and he could draw himself slowly up by that alone…He could endure the utmost hardship without turning a hair. He was absolutely reliable…He knew his limitations to a hair's breadth…"

Alan Hankinson provides a great historical account of the fellow climbers and incidents that brought innovations into the sport of mountaineering. Alan Hankinson sums the disdain Crowley had against some members of the mountaineering group called the Alpine Club: "Crowley's contempt was withering and wide-ranging. He accused the Alpine Club of falsifying records, claiming ascents that had not been made and ignoring the real achievements of non-members."

In all fairness, this was typical of Crowley not to allow a program to cheat competent people from their rightful attainments, including himself.

In 1898 Crowley met with George Cecil Jones (a metallurgist, chemist and accomplished magician) who introduced him to the London Order of the Golden Dawn. From this magical organization, Crowley met such noteworthy people as the poet, W.B. Yeats; writers such as Arthur Machan and Algernon Blackwood; the beautiful actress, Florence Farr (who was intimate with Bernard Shaw), and the novelist J.W. Brodie-Innes. There were also Maud Gonne (whose beauty inspired Yeats), Mrs. Oscar Wilde, Samuel.Liddell MacGregor Mathers (who headed the Order, wrote and translated important occult volumes and subsequently died from the influenza epidemic in 1918) and other noteworthy personalites.

The **Order of the Golden Dawn** became established in England after Dr. William Wynn Westcott, who was an Occult and Freemason scholar assisted the deciphering of a manuscript in 1887. A man named John Trithemius coded the manuscript in Polygraphiae. W.W. Westcott was capable of unraveling and translating it and did that with Mathers upon receiving it from a clergyman named Woodford. It contained an address and note to write to a lady named Frauline Sprengel who resided in Stuttgart, Germany. Westcott wrote to her and she responded, revealing that she belonged to a German magical order. She gave him permission to found a branch of the Order in England. In that year, 1887, he began a society called The Isis-Urania Temple of the Golden Dawn. The combined efforts of all magicians brought together ancient traditions of

Hermeticism, Qabalistic teachings and Enochian magic. Such texts as *The Key of Solomon, The Sacred Magic of Abra-Melin the Mage, Grimoire of Pope Honorius* and others were utilized to further perpetuate the magical workings within the Order.

On November 26, 1898 Crowley joined the Golden Dawn and rapidly progressed through the magical grades or degrees of the Order. During the year of 1900 he achieved the high grade of Adeptus Minor, having met all pre-requisites. He got an apartment on Chancery Lane, which he shared with an Adept named Allan Bennett (who later became a Buddhist monk and played a role in establishing Buddhism in the west). Under the Adepts tutelage, Crowley became introduced to the system of yoga.

In August 1899 Crowley began renting a house on the shore of Loch Ness, in Boleskine, Scotland. It was there that he commenced working with the *Sacred Magic of Abra-Melin the Mage*, and magical formulary of Dr. John Dee. Crowley would soon achieve the ultimate aim of all magical workings, the Knowledge and Conversation with his Holy Guardian Angel. The Angel was a praetor-human intelligence, and Secret Chief on the Higher Planes, and named Aiwass.

The Golden Dawn had a falling out and split up in 1901 after its thirteen years of culmination in the magical arts, and some members began offspring orders from it. A.E. Waite had lead one such sanction for another four years. Dr. R.W. Felkin led another with W.B. Yeats, Florence Farr, Arthur Machen and other members until 1905. What followed after that was the dawning of the magical order called Stella Matutina (Morning Star).

In the following years Crowley's mastery in magic and mysticism led him on adventurous pursuits around the world. He climbed mountains in the Himalayas and explored volcanoes in Mexico. He wrote voluminously while in America and travelling across Europe. He published his *Magick in Theory and Practice* in France, became a Yogi in Ceylon, walked across China and the Sahara practicing magical ritual and ultimately altered the course of world history from an event in Egypt. His efficiency must have been astoundingly profound to write so voluminously on every topic of magical and mystical pertinence.

In 1903 he married Rose Edith Kelly (sister of the painter and eventual President of the Royal Academy, Sir Gerald Kelly) while in Scotland. In 1904 he and Rose traveled to Egypt, using the names of Prince and Princess Chioa Khan, during their honeymoon. While in Cairo, Crowley did several rituals with the intention of invoking the Egyptian god Horus. During three consecutive days (noted as April 8, 9,and 10th) in Cairo, Crowley's Holy Guardian Angel (named Aiwass) transmitted a book using his wife as the medium. Each day at noon a chapter was recited through Rose. Crowley rushed to write down every word that was uttered in exact detail. The book is known as Liber AL vel Legis (The Book of the Law) and reveals universal truths and mysteries, which Crowley would spend the rest of his life commenting upon.

The important factor in the teachings and discipline of Crowley's system is rooted in Thelema, which is a Greek word and essentially means 'True Will'. This is signified by the number 93 because Thelema adds to 93 using the method of Gematria with the Qabalah. Significantly enough, the word Love in Greek is Agape and also adds to 93. Crowley's system of initiation incorporated "love under will" as a formula for living.

A new era for mankind had arrived, the past 2000 year Aeon of Osiris was at an end, and the age or Aeon of Horus dawned on that day in April, 1904. Major world changes were set in motion, beginning with the force and fire of destruction by way of wars and rapid technical advancement. The effect of wars, economics, and winged achievements in all facets of science are evident from the early 20th Century until the present day. Crowley was heralded as the Prophet of the New Aeon or age and set about earnestly to detail the course of events that would lead mankind into an esoteric maturity of psychological-magical self-realization for those who were ready to acknowledge it. The essence from The Book of the Law declared that ever individual is a Crowned and Conquering Child and to understand the incorruptibility of:

"Do what thou wilt shall be the whole of the Law."

And

"Love is the law, love under will."

This doctrine is synchronous with balance on the inner realms and stipulates that every person has a true WILL and should love under that true Will, opposed to being swayed by mere desire, wants and corruption. Chaotic behavior is said to result from inner and outer conflict ultimately from not discovering and doing one's True Will and using love within the formula. The "True Will" does not mean do what we want and please, as so many occult strays have led others to believe. It is, of course, easy to pervert words and not acknowledge true meaning in them, however that is left for the reader to appropriately decide. The "True Will" signifies that every individual is a radiant Being, a star in an orbit, and coming to realize it through self-initiation is a matter solely upon the individual. It does not require following hearsay and putting faith in any leader, spiritual or religious. It does not state that God does not exist, but affirms ones identification with the principle of "God" on the spiritual level. Developing latent dynamic powers and becoming self-fulfilled is simply a result of personal success. Crowley did not want followers; he wanted everyone to follow their own Path, their own Truth, and their own Will. The Book of the Law also states:

"Every man and every woman is a star."

"There is no law beyond do what thou wilt. Do that and no other shall say nay."

Can we adequately place a label on Aleister Crowley? We most certainly cannot call him a Satanist, Devil worshipper or Atheist. We most assuredly cannot title him as a Christian or give him another common religious epithet. His literature was "well" written but unfortunately not often "well" read. What title do we give a man that makes statements such as these? -

"It is therefore almost legitimate to say that pure mathematics is our link with the rest of the universe and with 'God'."- Magick,p.149

"…every true name of God gives the formula of the invocation of that God." Ibid. p.179

"The laws of Magick are the laws of Nature." Ibid. p.202

"The Devil does not exist. It is a false name invented by the Black Brothers to imply a Unity in their ignorant muddle of dispersions. A devil who had unity would be a God." Ibid. p.296.

The only way to turn the Light on is to reach some lofty level through a spiritual quest, the road to which can be tread any number of ways. Perhaps then we find that Mr. Crowley does not require so much a label as he does a bit of respect, just like other prophets and saints before him. Causing undue harm to another person is not part of the Thelemic doctrine, as it would be going against their True Will, causing unbalance in them and us in turn. Thelemic literature implies that every person is a star on a particular orbit, and that when two orbits align with their respective natures they go with that tendency and assist one another. That is enough of my rambling; I refer to reader to the writings of Crowley for the verity on these matters.

In May 1906 upon his return excursion from America with wife Rose and their child, Crowley wrote *Rosa Coeli* prior to reaching Liverpool aboard the ocean vessel, Campania. He had managed to write out, mostly from memory, the bulk of Liber 777 and in October began *Clouds without Water*. Crowley quickly summed his position thusly: *"For ten years my life had been a delirious dance to the maddening music with incarnate passion for my partner, and the boundless plain of the possible vibrating with the fervor of my feet. I had come through a thousand crises to the climax of my career. I had attained all my ambitions, proved myself at every point, dared every danger, enjoyed every ecstasy that earth has to offer: the rest of my life recedes from romance in the boyish idea of what romance should be."*

It was perhaps momentarily in his mind at that point in writing, but most certainly his life rose to more challenge, more endurance, more adventure and more prose. The boyish romance may have stayed with him, but there was still a lot of work to be done. In the summer of 1911 he wrote no less than nineteen books of magical and mystical instruction (see his Confessions.p.672-3). While travelling once again across America, he began writing short stories, sonnets, essays and poems constantly. The character in his short stories entitled Simon Iff came bustling to life. The main character is a detective who is capable of solving crimes and finding solutions by calculating the mental and moral energies that are subtly displayed from the dubious characteristics of the villains and personalities he investigated.

Crowley's sexual ecstasies with women, he called Scarlet Women (a term from The Book of the Law) focused his energies to greater height. In *The Vision and The Voice*, attainment of the grade of Master of the Temple, (attaining self control surpassing the Abyss and annihilating the false ego) was symbolized by the Adept pouring (pouring may be replaced with the word sacrifice, as throughout Crowley's writing sacrifice is used in such a context as meaning giving) his complete individual life into the Chalice of the Scarlet Woman, who represents Universal Impersonal Life. His *The Vision and The Voice* originally published in *The Equinox*, (Volume 1, supplement to Number 5) contains the experiences of evoking the Angels of the thirty Aethyrs with the use of Enochian magic. His first two attempts while in Mexico in 1900 were "mysterious and terrific" but he was unable to surpass the twenty-ninth since he had not yet achieved the grade of Master of the Temple. This Magister Templi grade is required to penetrate the shield surrounding the essence of the Aethyrs at that level. These apocalyptic evocations subsequently describe the mysteries of the Qabalah.

Aleister Crowley founded his own magical Order in 1907, called the A∴A∴ (Astrum Argentium, meaning Silver Star), and devoted the remainder of his life to establishing that Order with further writings. The Order was not merely one on the physical plane but existed upon the inner planes as well. The majority of his writings for that spiritual Order are published in his The Equinox Volume 1, numbers 1-10, as are many writings, called Libers, from his Golden Dawn experiences.

In publishing some of his writings, he knew the importance of colors from his Golden Dawn adventures and chose to elaborately fix the covers of his original published books with colors that played significance upon the psyche. Some colors automatically bring up the opposite colors to mind and in the change of colors, referred to as the flashing colors; visions upon the higher planes will divulge akashic perceptions. His Heart of the Master (1938) was bound in yellow cloth and inlayed in purple (similar color as the magical Dagger of Air); The Equinox, III, 1 (Detroit 1919) was bound in blue and inlayed in orange (similar as the Cup of Water). There are several other examples, such as Konx Om Pax (1907), sub-titled as Essays in Light, and was bound in black with white lettering (thus affirming Light arising out of the darkness). Konx Om Pax are Greek words that some authors declared were shouted during Elusinian Mysteries with the descent of Light during initiation but also have origin from the Egyptian words Khabs Am Pekht.

In 1910 Crowley divorced Rose, who had become alcoholic, indulging frequently with her "hereditary disorder of dipsomania".

Crowley definitely honored friendship and acknowledged learning from so many other people. The reader should understand that Crowley used the term God in the context of such versatile height while benevolently bestowing gratitude to those teachers he deeply admired. He gave a place in history to those who assisted him along the Path as can be seen shining through his words:

"Pollit… made a poet out of me: Eckenstein a man: George Cecil Jones and Allen Bennett a God."

The World's Tragedy, 1910

In 1911 he joined another ancient magical order called the O.T.O. (Ordo Templi Orientis, Order of the Templars of the East). He had written *The Book of Lies* (1913, falsely co-called as it consists of statements that are as nearly true as possible using the English language) and upon the following year the head of the German O.T.O., Theodore Reuss, was harshly knocking at his door. The O.T.O. head accused Crowley of writing about one of the secrets of the 9th degree, and opened Crowley's book to the section: "Let the adept be armed with his magic rood and provided with his mystic rose."

Reuss did not realize that rood meant rod in old English literature and therefore crucifix, but Crowley assured him that he did not attain the 9th degree of the O.T.O and thereby could not divulge its' secrets. Intuitively, Crowley came up with the conclusion that the 9th degree had to do with sexual practices and to the astonishment of Reuss, they began to discuss links between magical and sexual practice. The intensity of the connection deeply intrigued the Master who came to utilize sexual energies from then on to further the 93 Current of Thelema. Reuss allowed Crowley to begin an English branch for the O.T.O and invited him to Berlin for initiation, where Crowley took up the magical name of Baphomet (the name of the idol, which the Knights Templar worshipped). Karl Kellner, a rich German, brought the O.T.O alive in Germany at the turn of the century, and Reuss became his successor. Kellner had great interest in the Hindu system of tantra, which dealt with developing and heightening sexual energies between two partners and consecrating talismans with those energies, known as the elixir, to achieve the results that were aimed for.

The various rituals that involved such works in the O.T.O were not to make a debauchery out of the pleasures of love but to make the act sacred for the ultimate purpose desired opposed to wasting sexual energies for simple gratification. Other practices of the magician would involve divination, to seek answers upon the quest, and rituals of evocation and invocation. With invocation, the magician is identifying him/her self with the gods and goddesses of ancient mythology, qabalistic representations of the divine manifested. By bringing the influence of the god/goddess into the working circle, the consciousness can connect with it for the chosen work. If the Egyptian god Horus was invoked, its' Greek equivalent god would be Ares, and the

Roman equivalent would be Mars, all gods of war. Crowley's book *Liber 777* brings together many qabalistic correspondences, which are most practical for magic and the study of the Qabalah. In such a magical working one would unite all things associated with Horus. The number appropriate would be 5, associated with the fifth sphere on the tree of Life, Geburah, thus using five candles, and the sign of the pentagram. The color for that sphere is red, the sacred plant to the working being oak, the precious stone as the ruby, the magical instrument as the sword and so forth. The ultimate goal upon the Path is to achieve the Knowledge and Conversation with your Holy Guardian Angel. Misuse of magical means deters us from the ultimate goal and incurs more karmic debt. With evocation the magician is calling forth an entity, spirit etc. to do work for him/her. If this is performed, it should be towards the ultimate goal. Again I stray, but this illustration is to let the reader know such valuable information can be obtained through the tables listed in Liber 777.

Crowley labored inexorably to find out what was false and what was true. The press and tabloids poked at him, as did many people during the turbulent Victorian era. Rumors flew out of hand but to Aleister it was part of causing such change to occur while walking through town, known as the most infamous man alive. The system was not about converting anybody, but about transforming the souls that knew where they stood and where they desired to end. He did write contrary statements towards Christianity but not in vain of the actual Adept, Jesus. It was to illustrate how the teachings were perverted and that mankind was put into a prison system of belief through religious dogma, without an inkling of self-initiation. The debauchery of using spiritual symbols in religion without spiritual acknowledgement didn't excite Mr. Crowley. Furthermore, he fashioned his name after the Beast in the apocalypse and was soon deemed The Great Beast 666. The number 666 is generally misallocated with the Devil for the most ridiculous of reasons. In the Bible (which is a Greek word, meaning group of books, thus written by several people over time), the number 666 is the number of a man, and is associated with the anti-Christ. That is another term, which is wrongfully associated with the Devil. Anti essentially means "other than", and does not mean Devil. But leave it to the profane use of a "saleable" concept with movie writers to make people believe in all sorts of things.

Dramatic media, lame folklore and preposterous superstition have been the result of our language being perverted as much as our minds. (But it's never as bad as it seems!) Now we are at the stage where the great magician (poet, writer, and explorer), Aleister Crowley, The Great Beast 666, has tolerated the "majority" of the sarcastic population that has not read into what he wrote, and thinking him to be the Satanist of the era. Perhaps he found it amusing, perhaps a bit pitiful, but the obvious fact is that he painstaking produced hundreds of striking writings the world would ever know. Writings that illuminated the way for many to achieve their higher genius, education of comparative religion, realization of the Inner Path and coalition of numerous spiritual concepts, explanations and associations. This is the important measure of a human, the applications that are used and the results obtained for a positive movement, not just for self but for others after self. Crowley met face to face with the challenge and succeeded where others turned away.

Crowley always insisted that you "do not believe me, find out for yourself" which is contrary to most world teachers and leaders. He did not want followers in that sense of the word, but to see true aspirants that would share and develop in the work at hand for their own Enlightenment. The aim of the Astrum Argentium was to further mankind and to assist in the development of humanity. It brings one to the Knowledge and Conversation with one's Holy Guardian Angel. Just as the Angel of Jesus was Christ, so to was the angel of Crowley, Aiwass. Everyone has his or her own inner divinity to aspire towards. The route can be twisted and winding, or clear and direct.

Crowley incorporated the letter "k" into the word magick. He added the k at the end to symbolize the importance of that letter, being the eleventh in most alphabets and eleven being the number of magick itself. Since then many writers have added a k when writing on the subject of magic (k).

The Book of the Law also reveals the word Abrahadabra (adds to the number 418 using Hebrew Qabalah) and replaces the corrupted old word, abracadabra, in magical art.

Crowley often had fun quoting Tennyson in *The Book of Lies*, and he amusingly makes opposites quite apparent in his masterful verse as in this extraction from that volume:

69

THE WAY TO SUCCEED - AND THE WAY TO SUCK EGGS!

This is the Holy Hexagram.
Plunge from the height, O God, and interlock with Man!
Plunge from the height, O Man, and interlock with Beast!

The Red Triangle is the descending tongue of grace; the Blue Triangle is the ascending tongue of prayer. This interchange, the Double Gift of Tongues, the word of Double Power - **ABRAHADABRA!** - is the sign of the **GREAT WORK,** for the **GREAT WORK** is accomplished in Silence. And behold is not the Word equal to Cheth, that is Cancer, whose sign is 69?
This Work also eats up itself, accomplishes its own end, nourishes the worker, leaves no seed, is perfect in itself.
Little children, love one another!

Each section of *The Book of Lies* comes with a commentary. Normally the red triangle represents fire and ascending, and the blue triangle represents water and descending. In this case Crowley asserts the significance of the god Horus as descending (the red triangle) upon the altar with the occurrence of the Equinox of the Gods and the blue triangle, symbolizing devotion, as directed upwards. It is a combination for the meaning of the Hexagram, the accomplishment of the Great Work. It is well noted in his commentary on that verse in that book.

While giving a lecture on "Magick" in New York during the early part of 1918, one of Crowley's listeners in attendance was Alma Hirsig. A few months later she appeared for a visit at his studio near the corner of Washington Square, with her thirty-five year old sister named Leah Hirsig. Leah had an illegitimate child named Hansi whose father was Edward Carter and who had simply took off. Leah had later taught at a school somewhere in Harlem and supported her child who began residing in Florida. Crowley gave him the nickname, Dionysus. Leah remained in New York until completion of her courses in law while residing near New York University. For the following six years Crowley and Leah would travel and consummate the establishment of the Great Work. Leah became known as Alostrael throughout Crowley's writings. During crossing the Atlantic with Leah and Hansi, Leah met a girl aboard ship named Ninette Shumway, also with a child, whom Crowley later nicknamed Hermes. Completion of the voyage had them all team together for some future plans while Ninette, named Sister Cypris, settled in Paris as Leah briefly resided in Fontainebleau.

Crowley often consulted the Yi King for answers on perplexities. On March 1, 1920 he received the answer from his divination to set up house in Cefalu. In the spring of 1920 Crowley rented a house on a hillside in the town of Cefalu, Sicily. His printing of cards for their address said:

Collegium ad *Spiritum* Sanctum.

The new residence was established as the Abbey of Thelema where some thelemites would come as a retreat and learn instructions in yoga, magick and the doctrine of Thelema under Crowley's guidance. Ninette Shumway (Sister Cypris) and Leah Hirsig were living there with him. Jane Wolfe, who was a flourishing Hollywood movie star, wrote him of her intention to come and it was agreed they would meet in Tunis. On June 22, 1920 he left for Tunis to meet her, but she never showed up. He returned a few days later and on June 28 stayed up the night at the Abbey and wrote *Leah Sublime*, a pornographic poem dedicated to Leah, who was also called "Alostrael" within that poem and elsewhere. On July 23 he received news that Jane arrived in Palmero so he went with Leah, to meet her. Jane was warmly welcomed, settled into the Abbey to begin initiation into the A∴A∴ and took the magical motto of "Metonith".

On November 21, Cecil Frederick Russell, a naval hospital attendant during the war, arrived at the Abbey. (Crowley and Kenneth Grant {Frater Aossic} later gave him the nickname Godwin.) He took the oath of Frater Genesthai (the flowers - that are coming into being) and commenced initiation into the Order. He later returned to America and in 1970 began publishing his three volumes, *Znuzz is Znees, Memoirs of a Magician.*

There were many editorials to which Crowley contributed such as The International magazine in New York. He assumed several different identities within the magazine, which was always the way, changing his name, using a new magical motto in aiming to set another goal. The English Review and The Occult Review were other editorials he had written for. The following portion of a letter to the editor of The Occult Review appeared in the June 1910, volume XI, edition:

...Apart from this there is a type of mind that gets its best results from a dynamic rather than a static concentration. Few western minds are capable of forcing themselves into the dreary discipline of the East, and for such a person ceremonial magic, with all its illusions and disappointments may prove the shortest way. It is, moreover, no essential part of the question to show that ceremonial is absurd. It is easy to laugh at the wig of a judge, but the point is that he can send you to penal servitude, which is no laughing matter, and the test of a method is whether it works or no. I find few persons who really understand the nature of ceremonial magic complaining that the results are unsatisfactory, Bar Mathers.

I am Sir,
Yours obediently,
Aleister Crowley

Francis Israel Regardie was born in London, England on November 17, 1907 and went to live in America in August of 1921. In 1928 he returned to Europe to work as Crowley's secretary. His career in the field of magic quickly developed under the schooling he received from Crowley and in 1932-1934 he prepared and published, *A Garden of Pomegranates* and *The Tree of Life*. Both books are exceptional volumes on the study of magic and the Qabalah. In 1934 Regardie began magical operations with the **Stella Matutina Temple of The Golden Dawn** at which time he wrote *The Art of True Healing* and part of *The Philosopher's Stone*. He returned to America in 1937 and with his compiled information produced the first edition in four volumes of *The Golden Dawn* (1937-1940). From this author's perspective, Regardie's writings are considered as essential works on magical and Qabalistic instruction. He graduated Chiropractic College in New York in 1941, then served the military during war until 1945. He later moved to Los Angeles where he opened a chiropractic practice and also taught psychiatry. In 1970 he produced *The Eye in the Triangle* which is one of a few biographies he worked on as an intricate interpretation of Aleister Crowley. Concerning Crowley and the Golden Dawn, Regardie wrote:

"This elaborate Golden Dawn system became part of Crowley's own inner world…He carried it further than even the Golden Dawn principals had envisaged. I know of nothing within the Order documentary that even hints at the kind of visionary and spiritual experience Crowley managed to get out of it."

In ancient Egypt, Thoth was worshipped as the scribe, the God of writing, knowledge, and the messenger, as was Hermes for the Greeks and Mercury for the Romans. Thoth represents Wisdom and the Word and the tarot cards are the material representation of that Word/Wisdom/Knowledge. In 1944 Crowley finally published a major work on the tarot, *The Book of Thoth*. The Masters from above sent him an articulate artist named Frieda Harris, who painted all 78 cards under Crowley's guidance. What was to take some months extended into a five-year project. The outcome was mystically amazing. The cards illustrate a magnificence of interpretation and are in widespread use today. The Egyptian god Thoth conveys Ancient Wisdom while holding the Style in his right hand and in his left the Papyrus with the on-looking Ape behind him. The Ape is the mocking image of Thoth, the originality of which it follows in shadow. Crowley received much of the ancient Thoth information from his Golden Dawn days but made several additions including rearranging two of the cards on the Tree of Life and renaming some the cards from the old traditional names. In *The Book of Thoth* he also included another important faction on the tarot, which he discovered while in Naples, Rome and became known as the Naples Arrangement. There have been several books written on the interpretation of Crowley's Thoth deck since his original one, assisting the tarot enthusiast in the use of their symbolical allegory.

Kenneth Grant says that the Book of Thoth "is a collection of magical formulae in pictorial form which contains the mysteries of Time and the Oracles of Eternity".

Crowley wrote numerous rituals for the magical practitioner to perform and graduate in the mysteries, invoking forces, the deities of the planets and other influences constantly at play in nature. The Gnostic Mass, *Ecclesiae Gnosticae Catholicae Canon Missae* (which takes at least forty minutes to perform) is one such sacred ritual. It involves a priest, priestess, deacon, virgin, two children and a chorus. A common ritual amongst magicians is that of the Lesser Banishing Ritual of the Pentagram. It is performed primarily as a protection against forces of nature, astral entities, and other influences while essentially practicing yoga and magick. The magician recognizes the forces of nature through the four winds from East (Eurus), South (Notus), West (Zephyrus) and North (Borus) with the corresponding Hebrew god names of YHVH (form of Jehovah), ADNI (Adonai), AHIH, and AGLA, while visualizing appropriate images associated to those "earthly" directions. Vibrating the names of the Arch-Angels (Raphael, Michael, Gabriel, and Auriel) for those quadrants is also employed in that ritual while tracing the sign of the pentagram in the air. Such a ritual is efficacious and emblematic of modern magical practice.

In the early 1940's Kenneth Grant had picked up a copy of *Magick in Theory and Practice* at Charring Cross Road and found Crowley's explicit teachings fitting the style of an ideal Guru. He finally met Crowley

Gatehouse entering driveway to Boleskine House

Front view of Boleskine house, Loch Ness, Scotland
Once owned by Jimmy Page of Led Zeppelin and later resold.

Graveyard across street from Boleskine House

Rear View of Boleskine House

Inn at the Lake District where Crowley met with Alpine
Members, and Oscar Eckenstein to make ascents.

Beach Head, Southern England, where
Crowley practiced scaling.

Abbey of Thelema, Cefalu, Sicily

Author at Abbey

Rooms are in decrepit shape within Abbey.

Inside Abbey side entrance room is adorned with murals done by A.C.

towards the end of 1944 after attempts to send him a letter at a failed address and finally to one that forwarded the letter on. Crowley moved from 93 Jermyn St., London to the Bell Inn, Aston Clinton, Buckinghamshire on 8 April 1944. While resident there, he worked on compiling the book known as *Magick Without Tears*. Grant went to the Bell Inn, where Crowley was residing in ill health to receive magical instruction in trade for being Crowley's secretary, nurse and factotum as it were. Crowley moved to a boarding house called Netherwood in Hastings, Sussex the following January 17th, 1945. It was here during Crowley's last months, in ill health, that Grant brought him biscuits and tea, from the downstairs kitchen area, during the meager end of the war era. Grant left in June of that year, apparently never to occasion seeing Crowley again. Frieda Harris was there to care for the aged mage as did others stop in from time to time, such as his literary executor, John Symonds. On the night of Dec. 1st 1947 Aleister Crowley died of myocardial degeneration and chronic bronchitis, he was seventy-two years old. There was a nurse and a man named Mr. Rowe in the room as Crowley passed on. On Dec 5, he was cremated at Brighton, and a service held in the chapel with friends such as Frieda Harris, Norman Mudd, Gerald Yorke, Kenneth and Steffi Grant, and the poet Kenneth Hopkins. Louis Wilkinson recited the Hymn to Pan and passages from The Book of the Law were read as newspaper reporters looked on. Years later there were people professing to be Crowley reincarnated, as you can well imagine, with the treasures of history the mage left behind.

In the years to follow Grant published several books a few of which are: *Aleister Crowley and the Hidden God*, and *The Magical Revival*. He continued to establish the O.T.O in England and in an interview with his publisher, SKOOB, replying to the purpose of his books he noted, "The main purpose is to prepare people for encounters with unfamiliar states of consciousness." The nature of the rituals practiced at the New Isis Lodge between 1955-1962 was expressed in another of his books, *Hecate's Fountain*, which in a letter to me from Mr. Grant, dated Jan. 1991 he anticipated it's publication later that year. It was published as predicted and was a part of a trilogy that soon accompanied it.

A few other distinct claims to the "rightful head" of the O.T.O cropped up around the world as well. Marcello Motta of Brazil began publication of some books with much of Crowley's material in them and titled them as The Equinox volumes (distinct from Crowley's original Equinox volumes). Motta established the S.O.T.O. (Society Ordo Templi Orientis) which grew in parts of America, Australia and abroad.

Within the United States, a young war soldier named Grady McMurtry (with the magical motto Hymenaeus Alpha) met Crowley after correspondence, during his last days in Hastings, and took what he could to further establish the O.T.O throughout America. From that, Lodges, Oasis and Camps of the Order sprung up with affiliation across the U.S.A. and eventually throughout the world. Upon the death of Hymenaeus Alpha a new Head of the Order, William Breeze (Hymenaeus Beta), was anointed and continued to expand and rectify the Order. Hymenaeus Beta earlier worked with 93 Publishing of Montreal, Canada which published some of Crowley's writings, namely *The Book of the Law* and the edition of *The Magical and Philosophical Commentaries of the Book of the Law* (93 Publishing Montreal, 1974). I yield to a short quote from that book with reference to Chapter one, verse 52 of The Book of the Law, to allow the unfamiliar reader a brief insight into the incorporated commentaries:

"…We have accepted Love as the meaning of Change. To us, every act, as implying Change, is an act of Love. Life is a dance of delight, its rhythm an infinite rapture that never can weary or stale. Our personal pleasure in it is derived not only from our own part in it, but from our conscious apprehension of its total perfection's. We study its structure; we expand ourselves as we lose ourselves in understanding it, and so becoming one with it. With the Egyptian initiate we exclaim 'There is no part of us that is not of the Gods'; and add the antistrophe: 'There is no part of the Gods that is not also of us'."

Many of the Lodges, Camps and Oasis of the O.T.O in America and abroad have since published Newsletters, Periodicals, Journals and republished Crowley's books. In a letter to me from Frater Leoviridis in May 1989 he wrote about The Magick Theatre Camp of California with their upcoming Journal as: *"We plan it mainly as a vehicle for publishing some of the unleashed Crowley material which the Order has in it's archives, as well as material by Grady, Achad, Bennett, Fuller, Parsons and other important writers within the Order."*

It is with a continued effort to establish Thelema, the law of Do what thou wilt, that all these organizations and their offspring have made effort to publish and continue to release material relating to furthering mankind in this new age with the doctrines of Thelema (discovering one's True Will).

Not all organizations are purely devoted towards our best interests. There have been countless cults and sects that have delved into brainwashing techniques with the promise of enlightenment and attainment into artificial degrees to appease a hungry ego. Danger is always a potential to the unwary victim seeking to make their spot in the world. Because there is a banner at the door, does not mean the door goes anywhere of worth. There are many true aspirants who quietly study and practice the teachings of Crowley. Sometimes this is best rather than being misdirected with a false sense of belonging. G. M. Kelly of Pennsylvania, USA, is one such aspirant, although he is not so quiet. He produces The Newaeon Newsletter with numerous supplemental Encyclical Letters, from 1977 to the present illustrating the importance of "reading between the lines" and not believing everything you read. His book reviews give ample examples of where some authors have erred in calculations of Gematria as well as content. The importance of his work and others like him is in keeping the radiance of Thelema as Crowley envisioned it from becoming perverted into secular cults with misinformation and harmful practice about the original teachings.

It should be apparent that there is not one system in the world that is going to work for everyone. Every person is at a different level in life and interests. The hard working rice-picker or midnight janitor may be a Thelemite without acknowledging the term. It is essentially One seeking and performing their True inner Will. Crowley's writings make constant reference to other writers throughout history. There is an order to his system, but it does not stipulate that the practitioner can not be of another system to use it functionally. In essence it is all systems, all truth, all that is relative to our growth and awareness with edification. Theosophical teachings (Theosophy was established the year Crowley was born, by Madame Blavatsky) are of benefit for the study of Crowley's systematic chronology in understanding theory of the inner planes and life elaboration through them. It becomes an ascension in education of the Higher Life, realizing the mysteries of creation, evolving to where the Angels reside, the Genii coincide and the Masters work.

The Crowley influence flowed up the road of time as many pop artists assimilated some of his concepts into their expressions. The Beatles were amongst many whom were intrigued by Crowley the great magician, and his vocation. They put a picture of Crowley on their "People We Like" record sleeve of their album Sergeant Pepper's Lonely Hearts Club Band. Sting, from the original "The Police" music band, Mick Jagger, Jimmy Page of Led Zepplin as well as David Bowie (mentions Crowley on his Hunky Dory album) were all enthusiasts of the labors of Aleister Crowley. Also, Ozzy Osbourne recorded the song Mr. Crowley. Genesis P. Orridge was deeply influenced as can be seen in his music and videos. Lyrics in "Shake Her Shake" by The Cure, "Hate and War" by The Clash and "Gloria" by Patti Smith are other little examples of the effect aroused by some that have heard of the legend and incorporated what they heard into their lyrics and inspirations.

The Self-Attainment process is solely an individual call. There are countless others who have been inspired by this unforgettable Master of Magick, the Mahatma Guru Sri Paramahansa Shivaji, Aleister Crowley, Logos of the Aeon, who Fathered the Word of Thelema into this phase of mankind. Operating upon rumor and slander is not the goal of spiritual achievement. Objectivity is hard to come by and the misuse and misappropriation of another individual soul is not an incorporation of Crowley's magical system. If the author may be so bold as to add a personal opinion before departing a complex subject such as this, please bear with me. The topic of "Crowley" is a very touchy subject and can cause severe blows to the "personal ego". Many "followers" of the Master's work deliver their personal impressions and claim it to be their will, even upon others. The focus of this book intends for each person to discover their inherent enlightenment and not requiring the use of leaders, masters, self-proclaimed Gurus and the like. Knowledge can be a dangerous commodity, even more so when we rely upon others to have it. Be yourself, and you have no one else to blame. It is hoped that this simplified introduction serves to disprove some blatant rumors about Aleister Crowley and that his writings and memory are acknowledged for the objective values any reader may find throughout them. ★

PRINCIPLES of WICCA and MAGICK

"The quest for alchemical gold is the further processing of consciousness by techniques of prayer, meditation or magic...Finally there is the great experience of unification in the mysterium conjunctionis. At its individual level this is a manifestation of the divine spirit completely expressed in the personality ...In religious terms this might be expressed as transfiguration."

A History of White Magic- Gareth Knight

Wicca and Magick incorporate similarities and maintain distinct differences in their respective practices. Each has their place in spiritual progression and each lends us significant principles to harmonize the way. Aspiration and inspiration work together and regardless of the methods we use, spiritual insight and fulfillment tend to mirror our achievements. Wicca is based upon natural practices that incorporate energies of the Moon Goddess and Earth Mother whereas Magick is a solar oriented practice that concerns energies and deities from the planets, Sun, stars, and a wide spectrum of inner life research, comparative analysis and practice. The two become intermingled with practices of near similar nature as their practitioners borrow principles from each other. Progress in either of these spiritual practices can be achieved without following a rigorous routine. That is to say, they are self-propelled, self-tailored practices capable of fitting to the needs of any person. Some authors may have us think otherwise, but each system is diversified enough that we may use any combination of principles to suit our tastes and particular requirements for a rhythmical and well-balanced exploration in life.

Wicca is the most commonly followed of the pagan paths and sprouted in the nineteenth century from generations of witchcraft. It asserts the existence of the Inner Bodies and seeks to find that life-principle in all of matter. It is very receptive to the currents and rhythms of the immediate surroundings, which have their result from the Goddess(s).

Pagans regard the higher Deity as not being a "thing" somewhere up there, separate from down here, but rather in all living organisms as an integral part of existence. The word Pagan comes from the Latin, 'paganus', and is a word originally meaning peasant or countryman. We have advanced a little since then, in some ways, but still carry on age-old traditions, which bring us a certain harmony and balance with nature. The divinity and spark of matter is a result of polarization as it manifests itself into physical creation. To be lost in a completely material life "consciousness" can result in total lack of awareness for anything more, anything divine, and anything stable. It is with this primary realization that many have sought to return into a life of acknowledging the reality of the Goddess as a spiritual momentum. It is with individual experiences that the development and rediscovery of the Goddess tradition, in whatever culture, has transmuted knowledge that paved the way for this affluent culture to continue as effectively as it has.

The Mother principle dates back to earliest Egyptian times, as a priest once told Cambyses, King of Persia: "It was Neith, the mighty mother, who gave birth to Ra; she was the first to give birth to anything; she did so when nothing else had been born, and she herself had never been born."

Neith is Nuit or Nu the Goddess of Infinite space. Ra is the Sun god, and so it seems astronomically correct that space existed before the Sun came to exist. The symbol in fact, of the Sun is that of a circle, with a point in the middle, which also signifies life. The circle being infinite, the feminine principle, and the point being the male principle, the directed energy, injected within the circumference of the infinite female. This can also be associated to the metaphorical creation in the Qabalah. The supernal Mother, Binah (Understanding) from her influence of Chokmah (Wisdom) gives form to the mental world below the spiritual/ideal and causal levels, to Chesed (Mercy), the first actualized entity of creation.

The Great Mother nourishes the seed into Creation. She has been vanished from some religions (Judaism, Islam, Christianity, etc.) and for some reason there was the Father, Son and Holy Ghost but no representative for procreation, the female principle, in the religion(s). Even on the physical level (in Christianity) the mother (Mary) is virgin and not recognized for her principle in creation.

In the human brain it is likened to the left and right sides. The left is the linear-logical male psyche but requires the right, intuitive and instinctive creative principle of the brain to complete its idea and formulate an initial desire. This biological integration is the emphasis of creativity in life. The principle of polarity is essential to evolve a concept into a tangible system that works. Without the subconscious the conscious would not be able to accomplish anything because it uses the latter for all resources. It is with their interchange and functioning that all things happen in human life. There is no harm in calling the creator of this dual-force, God, but the opposite energies exist as manipulative entities to cause creation. The polarity of both formative and fertilizing, synthesizing and analytical, monolithic and mobile countenances are the feminine and masculine principles of the One coming into Being, manifesting to Mother and Daughter Earth.

In 1975, Dr. James Lovelock and Dr. Sidney Epton complied research which they titled their Gaia Hypothesis. Lovelock later published a book *Gaia: A New Look at Life on Earth* (1979). The hypothesis stipulates that for 3,500 years life has been poised with the temperature, salinity (or humidity), acidity, and such life preserving conditions at a relative level such that if they swayed out of that level life would have become annihilated. Another point to the hypothesis is that life is not passive and finds ways to keep and force those conditions of nature within tolerable means to sustain life. The Earth receives between 1.4 and 3.3 times the amount of solar energy that is required and the atmosphere has been altered in just the right way to keep the temperature within living conditions (15 C- 30 C), otherwise sudden changes in either direction could begin to cause catastrophic results. Their results went further into the study of the oceans and how everything ends up staying within its narrow life-supporting limits despite all odds against it. Their conclusion from the complete study of the Earth, biosphere and system surmised that it - "…seemed to exhibit the behavior of a single organism, even a living creature." They hence called it the Gaia Hypothesis (the name Gaia comes from the ancient Greeks and was their Earth goddess). The Earth provides almost everything for us, but primarily a place to live, food to eat, shelter, and the experience of life. She is an entity in herself. Earth has long been called Mother Earth from the roots of paganism and was adored with worship and respect for that reason that she is a living entity. Qabalists generally refer to the earth as the Daughter and maintain Saturn as being the Supreme Mother tenet.

As there is good, there is an equal and opposite force that we call evil. As there is positive there is negative. With light we become aware that there is darkness. This principle holds true for the Earth Mother as well. She has her opposite as the Dark Mother with all that is not regenerating. Fear of that prevents us from seeing that she does rejuvenate herself. She takes humidity from the earth and returns it as rain; she takes life into death and returns it to life. She has to destroy in order to renew, as all things come to their fruitful end and revitalize to the next level or stage as a process of the life cycle.

The Dark Mother is not necessarily equated with evil but She is the force that brings us back to the bright Earth Mother, thus providing a required turn of events. She is the menstrual cycle of the female that ends a time of fertilization (a chance for impregnation) only to begin anew again. She is the New Moon, ending the waning of the old. She can be associated with the unknown within us, that part of the subconscious, that we are not familiar with out of fear of it. It is from our inherent illusions, our independent limiting ego that prevents us from openly acknowledging the unavoidable fact of life, death and change as it is and living in accord with that.

The ancient Assyrians practiced worshipping of the Moon on the day of the New Moon and the seventh, fourteenth and twenty-first day thereafter. Each seventh day was called the sabbatu and is from that principle that the Sabbath falls on every seventh day and has been falsely considered to something of a taboo. It is only relatively taboo on the first Sabbath as the menstrual cycle would then begin, but only out of fear is that a negative or taboo notion. It is one thing that is unavoidable for a growing woman, and she not only menstruates on the physical level, but within her other bodies as well (etheric, astral, mental) as a cycle of completeness for her nature. In the Sabbath worshipping, the nineteenth day was also recognized as that closest to the peak of ovulation. The waxing moon was used for constructive Magical and Wiccan workings and the waning moon for destructive and banishing practices.

A name that has often come up during discussions of witchcraft is that of Gerald Brosseau Gardner. He was born on 13th June 1884 in Blundellsands, near Liverpool, and was of Scottish descent. He had long been interested in esoteric and occult studies. He moved to the Far East where he worked many years as a tea and rubber planter as well as a Customs officer in Malaya until he finally retired in 1936. He had made a substantial amount of money during that time and did pioneering research into the early civilizations of Malaya. He published a book from his first hand experiences while pursuing the study of the native Malayans, which was titled: *Keris and other Malay Weapons* (Singapore 1936). The history and folklore of the Malay Kris was well documented through it, which soon brought him into contact with great archaeologists, anthropologists and eminent researchers of folklore.

After retirement he moved to the Hampshire area of England and upon the start up of the war he wanted to do everything possible to help his country. He wrote a letter to the Daily Telegraph, which suggested that all people of England should be able to bear weapons to protect themselves against invasions from the Nazis. The article of the newspaper found its way to the Frankfurt Zeitung (newspaper) and the Germans there were furious, stating that it was an "infringement of international law".

Gerald Gardner contacted a witch cult in Britain and commenced affiliation while assisting in their efforts. He also met Mrs. Besant-Scott (the daughter of Annie Besant of the Theosophical Society) and shared interest in her sincere efforts with the Co Masonic movement (which was begun by Annie and enabled women to share in the tradition of the Masonic Rites). Witchcraft was still an illegal practice in England (The Witchcraft Acts of England's parliament were not expelled until 1951) and so the craft of the wise had to be secretly practiced behind closed doors.

In 1940 several of the coven's members practiced the big Lammas Rite in the New Forrest not far from where Gardner was living, to raise the Cone of Power against Hitler's threatened British invasion. Occult powers that Hitler had in use against other countries are no secret either. Over five members participating in the Rite had died by the time the ritual was enacted four times, no doubt having taken the remaining life energy out of them. It is not an uncommon practice that when one country is in trouble, members of all organizations inaugurate practices to alleviate the possibility of catastrophe. Prayers, projections of positive energy, magical wiccan and other spiritual enactments are benevolently practiced to summon hope, strength and assistance. There are so many great folks out there!

Gardner found that there was a traditional resemblance between the Craft and Masonry. The Three Degrees of initiation have similarities that stretch back in history. The Craft use of the terms "the working tools" the "Charge" and "properly prepared" are similar to words uttered in the halls of the Freemasons.

Gardner met Aleister Crowley during the final year of the latter's life while residing in Hastings. A friend had taken Gardner there to meet Crowley, which ended in several subsequent visits. Crowley made Gardner an honorary member of the O.T.O. Gardner had used several quotes from the works of Crowley in the Rites he performed because he recognized particular gaps in some of the wiccan rites which necessitated additional fervent machinations for the correct atmosphere to be present. He had added some personal experiences combined with his knowledge of magic and traditions from the East to make an imprint on the future of the Craft. The theories of magic and wicca are continuously evolving and intermingling as everyone dips in and broadens the spectrum with practice.

Modern day witches and wiccans are thankful for the fact that Gardner defended the Old Religion against the adverse slanders of blood sacrifices, devil worship and perversion. These misrepresentations caused years of hate propagation towards a practice that pertains not to evil and harm but to the joy of harmony and bringing love into world consciousness by proper use and recognition of the powers of nature. By observing the bright glow around the moon during different periods of the month we can get the feeling that many focused wiccans are in "contact".

The old belief of witches flying on broomsticks, staffs or other objects has some merit. The ability to do so has been pointed out by different writers that a certain unguent was made from a special recipe and is used on the body of the one in flight. This reputable capability was remarked by Abraham the Jew in the book, *The Book of the Sacred Magic of Abramelin the Mage* (original publication circa 1458), which was translated by S.L. MacGregor Mathers and published in 1948. He mentions that he met a young witch in Austria upon his many travels in search of the mysteries of magic, which were revealed to him through his encounters with the mage Abramelin, and subsequently accounted in that book. The witch gave him an unguent, which he rubbed on his feet and hands, while she did the same enabling them to travel in the air to any desired location. After another experience he inquired about the ingredients of the special unguent but she did not disclose the recipe. Later writers and experiments found the recipe of the unguent or flying ointment to work with any proper combination of various ingredients and was documented to be successful.

The use of herbs is in large part of the practice and life for every true wiccan and witch. Plants, trees, and flowers have not only medicinal purposes but also hidden properties of which their use lends to the Craft. Special use of herbs goes back to the ancient Egyptians whose Lady of the Moon and Mistress of Magic was Isis. Herbalists and witches alike use elderberries, mint, squills, poppies, aloes, myrrh, colchicum, pomegranates and so forth for designated recipes. Hippocrates used over 400 different herbs during his time for remedies and about 200 of those are still used today. From the first century Greek physician, Discorides to the sixteenth century works of Cornelius Agrippa, usage of plants and herbs in natural magic and remedies became an extensive study.

Some flowers were found to have narcotic effects upon the person they were applied to. The great mullein that grows in hedgerows has been called the Hag-taper (from the English word haegtesse meaning 'witch') and is refereed to as 'the witches candle'. Periwinkle is known as the sorcerers' violet and became the Provincia of the great occultist, Albertus Magnus, who considered it to be the most powerful flower in producing love. For protection, the herb, St John's wort (Hypericum perforatum) and the rowan tree (also mountain ash) have often been utilized in workings to banish evil spirits and dissolve spells.

Of particular importance in meditations and most magical workings is the use of incense. The aromatic gums and scented substances were used in old times to carry prayers and used as an emblem of sacrifice in magical operations. Incense and candles are used not only for their physical stimulus but for enticing the mentality just as perfumes may do to develop the required aromatic atmosphere. Incense comes in two varieties; that which burns itself and the kind that require a charcoal substance to keep it burning. The best kind comes from the resin-gums of tropical trees. The ancient Egyptians sent expeditions to southern Africa to collect special quality incenses and spices for their magical workings of embalming and communicating with the gods. Experimenting and noting the influences of any particular incense helps to decipher the psychological affect they produce. Some people may find that frankincense is most appropriate during rites of the Sun whereas sandalwood heightens arousal during workings of Venus and so forth.

Traditionally witches work as groups that are called covens. The number of members in a coven should be thirteen (which has long been associated with the thirteen full-moon Esbats throughout the year) but less than thirteen in a coven is also fine. Advanced covens usually have eight members and are involved in more important, worldly matters which require years of devoted aspiration towards. There are typically six men and six women in a coven with one additional person as the leader. Their nature rituals harvest positive energy for life and luck while venerating occasions throughout the year. Nicknames are usually given to develop the personality in the role that best suits the individual. The name is usually changed at an initiation ceremony to reflect the change in personality and growth of that individual.

The use of the circle in wicca and witchcraft connotes not only protection for the practitioner against hostile forces but also to concentrate the power that is raised within it, referred to as the Cone of Power. The high pointed hat traditionally used by witches has evolved as a symbol of raising the energy from the combined efforts of the coven.

The Circle

The circle is an established attribute in pagan and Wiccan heritage. It depicts the linking together and forming of completeness. Collections of beads upon a string to create a necklace or a group of people that form a bond are representations of circular power. It is a very significant form represented in all walks of life. The zodiac is circular and is a particular cluster of astrological signs that the sun goes through each year while bringing particular qualities associated to each sign as it passes through it. Cycles are represented as circular by being renewed properties that work as a recurrence. The old fashioned "ladies sewing circle" and the popular "social circle" are examples of the power that is gained from circular formations. Clocks are generally round and depict repeated occurrences and routines with time. In magic the circle is a boundary of sacredness protecting against forces and influences outside of it. The Babylonians made a circle of flour around the bed of a sick man to keep out demons and negative forces. The East Indies and the Assyrians used circles, called usurtu, in ancient times for protection. In ritual magic the magician stands inside of a circle for protection against spirits, demons and forces during evocations.

The circle is drawn deosil, or clockwise, moving to the right symbolizing good and the direction of the Sun, opposed to counter-clockwise or widdershins (an Anglo-Saxon word meaning to walk against). When tracing the circle either the Athame is used or the consecrated knife (magicians utilize the sword). It can be painted upon a piece of carpet so that when not in use it may be rolled up and stored away. A convenient circle may be nine feet in diameter and can be drawn with a sword, knife, charcoal or chalk. Inside of the circle another one should be drawn eight feet in diameter. Within the rim may be placed bowls of water, crosses, words of power, names of god, and pertinent plants like vervain (which demons detest). This reinforces the barrier against any hostile or disturbing forces. There are different formulas employed in drawing a circle, according to the nature of the operation. Dion Fortune, in her book *Psychic Self-Defense*, gives a modern interpretation of the circle with the magician standing and facing east, making the sign of the equal armed cross designating the four elements and cardinal points. The four cardinal points and center altar can be likened to the symbolical allegory of the mandala, which signifies spiritual balance between the person, God and the Universe. Carl Jung has written on the significance of the mandala and how it relates to the collective unconscious.

When entering the circle we are taking control of our personal universe. We are identifying with the True Self, thus becoming the objective center of all. In essence we are no longer our ego or false self, but affirming connection with the True Self by surrendering the lower part of our nature and ego before entering the circle. If this surrender is not adhered to the circle is dysfunctional, things can go wrong, people argue, and covens become disorientated from the true objective. Relinquishing the lower nature before entering the circle affirms that all becomes united as one, as a fraternal gathering of brothers and sisters upon higher planes. Ulterior motives are non-existent and shall in no way affect the operation.

Once we are within the circle we are never to lean outside of it. We are affirming our identity with the infinite as a balance of the work with all points on the circumference being of equal distance from the center. We are affirming our devotion to the work without question and with utmost focus. Candles (of beeswax or other appropriate ingredients) may be used and stand upon pentagram candle holders around the circle to provide further protection by representing the microcosm, the four elements crowned by spirit with aspiring Will, perfected and conjoined to divine forces. Generally there are nine candles used to attract forces and to signify to those forces that they must obey the spiritual laws and that they also partake in the Great Work.

At the center of the circle, a small table is used as an altar. Upon the altar is placed the items for the working, such as a censor of incense, candle, and magical tools and instruments for the high art. Anything that is placed within the circle should be balanced with an appropriate object, keeping all points from the center outwards in some reflection of perfected harmony. If an object is placed somewhere to the right then it must be balanced with an appropriate object on the left. Every object has an astral counterpart and so becomes an instrument of use upon another plane. Each instrument has an identity and another physical object to represent a balance to it. Clutter becomes a burden in all respects and reflects an outcome in most. Each object should appropriately adjust mental and emotional issues to create equal and balancing values.

The circle is like the line separating yin and yang within its circle, dividing the outer from the inner, or pronouncing a boundary just as the present separates the past from the future. It divides the known from the unknown, the outer universe from the personal universe. The True Self is symbolically represented by the center of the circle. The center is the smallest of possible circles and identifies our truly focused Self with our spiritual core by separating it from perception of the ego. Stepping inside of the circle is like removing our clothes or personality and coming to terms with our truth and reality. The circle is a psychic and ethereal armor for the practitioner.

Cleanliness is next to Goddess-ness and purification of the circle is imperative. A study of construction, purification, banishing, invoking and proper consecration of the circle and use of the instruments is important for any ritual working. Gerald Gardner's book, *High Magic's Aid* and Aleister Crowley's *Magick in Theory and Practice* provide details on constructing the magical circle and all related implements.

After constant practice with and devotion to the circle, through powers of visualization, we may encompass it within our aura so that when we travel anywhere we maintain a certain amount of protection. The ancients used a ring on the right index finger to represent their portable circle. Rotating the ring represented tracing the circle and a counter-rotation meant withdrawal or dissolution. Balance is everything and if something is gained that is not rightfully ours, we must prepare to sacrifice something of equal value. This follows with the "threefold law of return" which specifies that "as we sow so shall we reap". Also, the law of karmic return or the threefold law, states that what ever is done, weather it is for good or ill, it shall be returned to the person threefold. Holding trust in ourselves with all our heart because "it is for the good of all and the harm of none" becomes the practice associated to the Bright Mother Earth.

MAGICK

The secret of magical success is the practice of *Noscere, Audere, Velle, and Tacere*. To Know (an Air principle), to Dare (a Water principle), to Will (a Fire principle), and to keep Silent (an Earth principle). These are the four powers of the Sphinx. Knowledge must be followed by the courage to use it without audacity and direct it with the energy summoned through the divine will, but without talking about it. True silence has great power and assists in functionally balancing all the other forces that go into the performance and creation of the act. Energy that is developed should not be dispersed and depleted with idle discussion. This is one reason why secret teachings are not idly discussed because the societies and organizations practicing them follow the To know, dare will and keep silent sanction. Their success partly depends upon not dispersing the forces that have been summoned in the work. They are not simply a secret organization, but an organization with *secrets*. The Adept Jesus also preached this rule by stating to his disciples not to cast pearls before swine or they would turn again and rend them.

With the combination of all four elements and their multiple correspondences, there arises a fifth, called Spirit. Spirit is the power of evolutionary progression, to go forth and accomplish, ABRAHADABRA, and become balanced in the use of the pentagram forces, the power of man and woman in creation.

The practice and discussion of magick is like that of any other occult subject, and has not been without persecution throughout the ages. Governments followed the rules of the Church, which detested magic stating that its practice unleashed diabolical forces into the world. If we can have but a glimpse of what occurs around the world at any particular minute we would see that there are numerous diabolical forces at work. Most of these forces, in fact I would wager 95% of these diabolical, harmful, utterly negative occurrences have nothing whatsoever to do with magick, wicca or any form of spiritual practice. These forces at work are in all cases a result of not practicing these spiritual subjects. The knowledge of Magick allows us to become aware of our self-control, of forces that are at work and how to prevent them from controlling us. It allows us to study our mind clearly, to practice spiritual aspiration, to gain insight and to become creative. It defines proper preparation, it sorts out the vast subconscious; it becomes the partner of yoga and avoids harm, failure, and the deterrence from righteousness. Magick is a means of clarification and does not justify causing harm in any form to other people. Aleister Crowley gave the fine tuned definition of magick as: "The art and science of causing change to occur in conformity with will."

Magick is a subject used with artistic hands and a scientific mind. It is an active form of yoga and provides a positive evolutionary leap for those who wish to acknowledge it. Every act we do may be considered as an act of magick. Brushing our teeth and cleaning our house are acts of magick. In both cases we supply an amount of energy, use mental projection and desire to have clean teeth and an uncluttered home. With magick, we are learning to use the proper force and ingredients to cause a certain outcome. If we are practicing high magick, we should have an advanced working knowledge of the laws of the inner planes and a very astute understanding of the elements of nature. It should be a refined and workable, very tangible and conscious realization of the connections that nature holds and the systematic functioning of beyond worldly forces. It provides a framework of direction, meaningfulness and a process to achieve that, which for so long has been intangible and idealistic under normal automated conditions. Magick is not, nor is it meant to be a social convention to flaunt the conscious ego or to hide anguish and fears under a mask of illusion. Magick may cause an outpouring from the Unmanifest, an opening for Divine Light to come through. It may help in rapid development of the Inner Bodies, which receive and become nourished by that Inner Light. It is a Light resulting from inspiration, of purity and the expression of realizing the True Will.

Magick is sometimes categorized into three allegorical types according to the purpose and outcome. White magick is performed to cause a change to occur that brings the magician into obtaining the Knowledge and Conversation of his or her Holy Guardian Angel, or towards that aim. Grey magick is performed to cause physical or non-physical good to come to you or to another person. Black magick is performed to cause some physical or non-physical harm to our self or others. Grey magick can begin as such but turn into black magick if the results are for achieving money or some material object and in the pursuit of such desires may bring harm to another person. There is nothing completely wrong with increasing material success, provided it is utilized solely towards the ultimate aim of white magick.

Self-Initiation or becoming initiated by a group is the advancing to a new stage and higher level of achievement and responsibility. It essentially becomes a death and rebirth experience of the personality such that a new dawning is realized to undertake new tasks for the candidate without hindrance of thoughts that previously lingered in the mind. It is not the splitting up, as in schizophrenia, of the mind, but an awakening from one level unto another. A new magical name or motto is usually assigned to signify the challenge and wisdom that the candidate is undertaking. The beginning may seem like a seed has been planted without any discernable results for some time. With time and effort a new realization dawns and new ordeals are faced for greater advancement and achievements.

Self-initiation has the advantage of being wholly artistic without the interference of other people. If the rite has been fully charged with aspiration, the Light delivers corresponding inspiration. It is the individual who ultimately initiates their self. Belonging to a group for initiation can be dramatically inspiring and may provide additional assistance and advice in times of turmoil or difficult barriers provided the group comprises truly sincere aspirants and are spiritually communicative.

Upon personal purification and dawning the magical robe, a magician enters the circle and draws the circumference with the sword while invoking the guardians of the four quarters. These guardians are represented by the Angel, Eagle, Lion and Bull, as depicted in the tarot. The circle is then purified with fire and water, developing a center vortex while calling down the Light of the divine Holy Spirit. The intention of the working is vibrated clearly and becomes the sole thought purged within the mind as prayers containing divine names heighten the consciousness to realize the influential powers of divine intervention. This routine is common amongst many rituals and may require extra time for appropriate preparation.

The outer temple of a magician should reflect the sanctum of inner aspiration. It should be clean, orderly, and decorated with few, yet effective emblems to awaken the subconscious into focused activity. The magician enters and leaves the temple at will, but always upon entering brings radiance from above and within. The instruments of magical art within the temple represent powers that are developed within the psyche. They call upon subconscious forces of those powers, which are utilized and directed towards work on the inner planes.

The four basic instruments are the sword or dagger, the wand or rod, the cup or chalice and the pentacle or shield. They represent, respectively, the four elements of air, fire, water and earth. These are the four basic elements of the physical plane of which all other elements are developed from. All instruments should be kept in a clean woolen cloth when not in use, preventing lingering influences from contacting their surfaces.

The Sword

The sword represents Air, the intellect, mind and swiftness. It is used for command and sometimes punishment. Substitutes or in addition to it include the dagger, knife or pin. These are thrusting instruments and represent piercing through an obstacle and are sufficient to replace the use of a sword. It is essentially a symbol of justice, retribution and control of forces that are of any threat. Pointed upwards it signifies separation, dividing the crown upon the head and thus should never be lifted. Directed downwards it symbolizes expended energy as a human force and used to control forces, demons, or entities that require to be put in their proper place. The sword is an analytical and dividing weapon of art and is generally used in lower forms of magick. It should never be used in invocations, as it is an instrument of vengeance more than peace. The blade represents Mars with the warrior aspect of its steel and directness, whereas the hilt is of

Venus, (Netzach), Victory and Love of which influences and directs its use. Etching upon the blade of the sword is often done. Crowley suggests that the sacred word 'AGLA' be etched which are the initials for: *Ateh Gibor Leolahm Adonai*, 'To Thee be the Power unto the Ages, O my Lord'.

The Wand

Sometimes referred to as the rod, staff, scepter or club, the wand is a phallic symbol representing the force of the Will. It is used to direct positive energy or forces, construct forms and is an extension of the oath taken by the magician. During initial stages the magician does not comprehend the extent of the True Will and to what it entails. An oath and motto may be taken towards an objective with the aspiration to know the True Will. The oath should be allotted a particular time frame to be completed, for example at a particular initiation, before commencing a new oath. The oath then becomes a stage of development and obedience for the higher objective of the magician. The magician directs divine force through the wand with the success already visualized. Pride is a rather useless emotion and generally used to appease the material-consciousness. Such emotions are more of an indulgence than assistance. The purest of aspirations should be acknowledged with direct and concentrated energy when commencing the word of the Will. The construction of the wand and indeed all instruments is best if done by the hands that use them. The power that goes into making an instrument can be harnessed in its use and results. Marcus Aurelius, stoic philosopher, once wrote: *"No longer talk about what a good man ought to be, but be one."* Foresee the result while maintaining a pure will, use the fire of immaculate desire, observe the direction of forces and the outcome, and entertain no idleness or flattery.

The Cup

The holy cup, chalice, or grail represents the contents of divine aspiration. Nothing should be put in the cup that is not totally pure. It is the inner symbol of nurturing, love and acceptance. Its' symbolic element is water and from it strength can be drawn to wash away evil influences that disrupt the mind. The higher form of the cup is Spiritual Understanding. It can represent the contents within the personal subconscious that can be pulled from memory. It also contains the life force that has always been held as sacred and ideal in sustaining existence. The cup may resemble an emanating chakra collecting energy for expression but should not be used for other than the Highest of invocations. That which filters through the veil of the cup from the absolute limitless love of the infinite shall intoxicate the innermost senses of the magician with purity of perception. No one should ever touch the sacred cup and it should not be moved once set in place upon an altar.

The Pentacle

The shield, disk or coin is used for protection against hostile forces and may have a pentagram or other holy symbol etched into it by the holy dagger. It is symbolized by the element of earth and is sometimes made of pure wax. It becomes the storehouse to take from it what is vital like a refrigerator or cupboard that contains food for sustenance and proper diet. It should contain the symbols that are most representative of the connection between nature, God and man and be paired with opposites that are in relation to and balanced with those chosen.

The pentacle is not unlike the amulet or talisman we may wear on a chain around our neck. In this case our affirmation with karma is projected through its' use. It is part of the oath and can not be broken once directed with intention. It becomes a magical symbol of unification upon the Path by uniting the microcosm with the macrocosm. It must contain just the right elemental essence so as not to over bulk the journey. Illusions are cast everywhere and within the shadows of the mind; enlightenment unfolds the barriers to see what is relatively true and what is relatively false.

There are other items that can be used by a practicing magician, namely the crown (representing attainment), the bell (used to summon and alarm) and the lamen (containing the secret keys of power). There are also the book (of conjurations and spells), the lamp (self-lighting the image of the pure soul), the ring (holding creative and protective forces, balancing the wand), the oil (for consecrating) and so forth.

The summoning of forces and spiritual influences within the magic circle is invocation (to call in) and may be called within the body of the magician to receive the arousal from that force. It is a dangerous practice to allow any entity to inhabit our body. When working with deities attributed to specific spheres of the Qabalah, we are working with exact and detailed states of objective consciousness. We begin by invoking the god for that sphere who may send the appropriate Archangel and thereafter commands the appropriate angel to be sent to us by our effort. The power of the god then sends the Intelligence of that Sephiroth to aid in the authority of the particular spirit to manifest. Invocations are for divine aspiration.

Balance is the essential cornerstone with magical practice. White magick seeks to affirm Self with God. White magick is the attainment of Samadhi by methods of magical practice. If proper balance has not been developed in the course of the work, the realization of Truth will be incomplete. All the necessary elements must be put in place beforehand. Invoking Isis, in the case of a male magician, would prepare him to realize the female spiritual principle prior to achieving Master of his spiritual Temple. Similarly, scaling the Tree of Life, we must maintain balance towards the supreme goal. If poverty is a condition in the material world that hampers the achievement of the aim, then Jupiter is invoked to provide the goods necessary for the accomplishment of the Great Work. Keeping in mind that "equilibrium is the basis of the Great Work", it is easy to lag, falter and forget unless we keep a leash on both our mind and emotions.

If we invoke a deity, we come into contact with the life force of the deity and are thereby influenced. Devotion to the aim is essential in any ceremonial practice. Methods vary but basically we are enacting a particular rite or mass, as in the life-story mythological representation of the deity. It is similar to how an actor assumes a role by learning about the characteristics involved and eventually becoming one with the character of the role.

Outside the boundary of the magic circle a triangle is usually constructed for the purposes of evocation (to call forth). Within this triangle forces or entities manifest and can not leave the triangle or enter the protective circle of the magician. The triangle is the first representation of three dimensions in form. There is the point, the line, and with three points comes into being the triangle. This becomes an allegory representing manifestation by the force of the father and acceptance of the mother resulting in the child principle. All sides of a triangle are equal and when rotated any point can be the apex and any side can become the base. If it is rotated very rapidly, that is to say a spinning triangle, it resembles the circle. All three points have likeness and balance to the other, as the child grows it becomes an image of the mother or father or combination of both. The child holds within it, impressions given by the mother and the father. Looking at this analogy, we can see that the triangle has spiritual principles, not only of ascension and descending but also of holding within, that which we project from the inner worlds and our inner self.

Improper and sloppy employment of magick is better left undone. It is a scientific, calculated art of pure aspiration. If we err into the direction of black magick and contact the qliothic forces, most vile and negative energies can run the better course of life with madness and insane actions. This is primarily the greatest downfall I can presently think of. Magick is a sublime use of energy and power, but when used for selfish motives and unconnected to divine aspiration, it can quickly resemble other abuse of powers that are rampant amongst society. The Kings of Edom and Lords of unbalanced forces exist as influences upon the lower planes. By dabbling with negative forces, it becomes an inevitable change of personality and eventual lose of purified ambitions. Each step in life becomes part of the ones we left behind. Direction is all that need be concluded on this matter.

Proper preparation, purification, and consecration should go into every magick ceremony. Preparation may require many days of concentration exercises, practice of the words to be used, and personal examination to ensure everything is subservient to the one directed purpose. Abstaining from certain foods and such that distract the attention from the ordeal goes without saying. Preparing the temple of working means absolute cleanliness and everything properly constructed such as talismans, instruments, and props that are suited to the rite.

Prior to any ceremony of invocation, a banishing ritual of the pentagram must be performed to rid any influences and at the same time the circle becomes protected by the Archangels and their hosts. The Angels are constructed from pure consciousness and are, "sexless" Beings. Archangels however are real Beings and operate as specialists for specific purposes. Descriptions of the Archangels and their responsibilities will vary from one viewpoint to the next, however as a basic presentation, here they are.

Raphael is the Intelligence of Air and one of the great Four Archangels. His work entails the instructing to humanity special capabilities including the healing of wounds. If we were to imagine Raphael from historical data that we may obtain we would see a mighty traveler holding a flask containing healing ointment, carrying a staff and wearing a hat to signify his adventurous nature.

Michael is the Lord of Fire and the Archangel personifying right and reason triumphing over the ignorance and wrong of humanity. He provides the Intelligence of how to rightfully use the inner Fire of our nature. He is depicted as holding scales to weigh souls upon death to separate the worthy from the unworthy. He also restores the unbalance in organic nature and heals diseases. His crown has an emerald that has been likened to the image of the Holy Grail such that solar energy transmutes through it and brings the energy to the green fertile fields, which produce herbs for healing. His spear is the rod of fire and when we light a candle we are using that energy which he transforms to the material plane for safe use. Whenever we turn on anything electric we should think of this Archangel. Prolonged efforts with concentrating upon these associations will prove advantageous during the invocation of Archangelic forces. The practice of invoking once a month will allow us to recognize the force of any particular deity.

Gabriel is the Archangel ruling the principles of Water. He carries the consciousness between the divine and human intelligence. He brings force into form and is powered by love, as the Life-Bearer. He also resurrects life from death, producing the change with the medium of water for its continuation. Gabriel is linked with the ancient fertility attributes of the moon and the lunar tides. He is also linked directly to the force fields and charges of energy above the physical plane and is capable of being both the male and female principle. He is the potent one personifying the Divine Power that is expressed as Love. The cup holds the water, which becomes its form. The cup and pentacle are both female principles as the sword and wand are both male. When handing a cup, or cupping our hand to hold something, or when looking at the stars in the vessel of the universe, imagine the ever-flowing energy of Gabriel. Our human body is a cup holding the consciousness of life. Similarly our blood vessels and cells are miniature cups or pentacles as our bones and nerve endings are wands and swords. To everything there is an attribution, a connection and a symbolic reference that guides us into understanding the subtle fabric of life.

Auriel is the Archangel of Earth, and faces Michael across the magic circle. He can put the "fear of God" into the hearts of everyone. His energies are personified in avalanches, earthquakes and other natural disasters that can be most frightful. He controls the forces of the earth's nature and is depicted as holding a Book of Wisdom. All of our knowledge becomes proof on the earthly plane and it is through this great Intelligence that the keys to penetrate the secrets of laws must be held with respect. We are reminded of the significance of the drops of dew (wisdom) upon the petals of the Rose-Cross as distilled essence, as the distillation of our essence comes into divine contact. By combining the four elements in the shape of a proportional cross we are reminded of the Emerald Table of Hermes wherein states "it ascendeth from Earth to Heaven" and the golden Light from the Sun raining Knowledge and Life as personified by the Light of Auriel. This concept brings us to the ancient magical one known as the Operation of the Elements where fire was applied to the cauldron (symbolizing earth) and the water within became steam (air) and condensed into a sacred single drop. Cosmogony suggests that the Creation began from the utterance of a single Word of power. From this developed the waves and vibrations to create consciousness and begin diversity. This was the expression from the One (Golden Drop of Dew). We must collect and re-form our energies, purge and refine them to receive the true essence into the higher bodies, and work with those in a harmonized way to scale the Tree of Life (see section on Qabalah) thus directing towards the higher accomplishment of contacting our Holy Guardian Angel. In doing this we surpass the actual world and enter the spiritual level eventually returning to the One, upon the higher planes from whence we originated and become "as Gods" to begin the process anew into a higher evolutionary chain.

Charging an object with energy and influences has always been an important practice in the development of any magician. It is with that purpose that a short discussion on the principle of talismans will be addressed.

The Magic of Talismans

Working with the four elements as they are in relation to one another and their composition is the preliminary requirement in making successful talismans. Earth and Water are the active heavy elements. Fire and Air have the qualities of being passive and are the lighter elements. Fire has three significant qualities and they are brightness, thinness and motion. Earth is significant to darkness, thickness, and quietness. Air is predominantly thinness and motion. Water has also three distinguishing features and they are thickness, darkness, and motion.

Inner Abbey Order

A Spiritual Order to Provide Truth through Life

Dear Reader,

Your Enlightened Soul has been a true labor of love under will. It is a book designed to primarily transform the reader through its formulary into an evolutionary progression. The formula is presented throughout the book in a subliminal and objective manner. It clearly dictates that you take control of 'your' life and move harmoniously inward with the process of purification and contemplation. Our daily burdens or concerns generally mask us from clear, intuitive realizations however with practice we are capable of heightening our consciousness repeatedly to touch upon the boundless, limitless energies that pervade life from within. Spirituality may be an expression of communication, celebration and sanctification, each to their own, and can be realized by filtering these energies with effort through the objective spheres of the Tree of Life. This process enhances life, rectifies fallacies and allows us to be 'above' the mundane subjectivity of wants and desires that may cloud the Vision of Understanding.

With this in mind, I hope you take full advantage of the principles outlined throughout your new book and bring your spiritual aspirations to the forefront. The twenty-two short stories should be an inspirational adventure for you to contemplate as well as a source of useful knowledge to work with. Each story relates to a specific tarot card and path on the Tree of Life, in order, as do the first 22 poems in Part 2.

In my next book, 'Sanctuary of the Spirit', you will once again meet all of the main characters of the short stories you are about to read. In this next book, available by the end of 2002, I will present a bizarre yet fascinating connection with a new model of subconscious affiliation for the Tree of Life, utilized to illustrate an intensely important faction of life. I wish you safe journeys and eternal success.

Love, Light and Blessings,

Paul Bear

The elements that are incorruptible and not compounded are pure elements and are of the first order. Those that are compounded, changeable and are impure, by the art of transmutation can be reduced to their pure simplicity, and are of the second order. There is a third order of elements, which are an infallible medium by being twice compounded and are the soul of the middle nature of things by creating the effect to the end result. They provide the binding, loosening and transmutation of everything through alchemical means by making those that are impure to become pure and the compounded to become single.

The element of Fire provides heat and light for life. All ceremonies, religious and personal use the light of candles and torches to deliver their consciousness to another level. Fire is used upon the altar to deliver the sacrifice unto the higher plane. The sacrifice IS incense, which takes the place of blood (from some ancient ceremonies), and is of equal potency. The foundation of all elements is Earth. It is the receptacle of the celestial rays to nourish the seeds of growth and seminal virtues of life. It is composed of the animal, vegetable and mineral components. Earth is the Mother of all things to flourish and grow. It is purified by fire and reduced to its original nature by water to the essentials of the principles of the Philosopher's Stone. Particular aspects of the element earth can be subdivided just as all other elements have their classifications. Things that are heavy are earthy Earth, like lead and silver, while those that are transparent like crystal, beryl, pearls are of the watery Earth element. That which is sophous, and capable of floating above the water like a sponge, plastic, wood etc. are airy Earth and those such as thunderstorms, volcanic, and asbestos are fiery Earth. The concept can be extended indefinitely to all things material. Plants are a mixture, like all other material objects, of the elements. Their roots are earth of Earth, their leaves are water, their flowers are air and their seeds are fire (for their multiplying factor).

Water is the seminary virtue of all things and provides growth. It is the dew that nourishes the continuation of life and without it spiritual regeneration would not exist. Its' magical ability washes away disease and sorrow. Air is the vital element passing through all beings and is a medium to which all is held together. If receives the influence of everything celestial and transforms those into the proper place. It hides things that are not seen by the naked eye. Air holds impressions and can be felt and sensed by intuitive psychics. The average person may sense impressions from the air, especially while asleep. Thus it is that during times of dreaming, surrounding impressions enter to develop those dreams to become what they are by our accessibility to the impressions and sympathy to them from the air that holds them.

The elements of our character can also be justified by these principles. The slow and firm motions of a character are significant of Earth, the reminiscence, sluggishness and fearlessness are of Water, cheerful and amiable disposition are of Air, and quick, aggressive, fiery are of Fire. With these elements and combinations thereof the nature of our personality is made. The elements diffuse through us continually and are programmed into our memory, become our daily enthusiasm and our expressions of how we feel at any instant. We contain a certain mixture of all the elements and no two people are identical. Although several people contain similar personality dispositions this allows psychologists to label them as particular personality types. A well-balanced person is such that they do not have too much or too little of any prominent characteristics that are of one particular element classification to weigh them down or make them flighty.

The orders of spirits and angels are also classified with the four elements. Seraphim's are fiery, Cherubim's are earthy, thrones and archangels are watery and dominions and principalities are airy. The Universal Spirit, God, gave all things their seal, character, mark and figure entrusting them with the ideal virtue as officers unto his Name. Manifestation through the planes comes from the original idea then to the governing and ruling Intelligence's residing to those ideas, then from the aspects of the stars which rule those concepts and finally to the elements where they are formed with temper and disposition. In the multiple elemental mixture of plants (herbs) and minerals (stone) are the qualities that mutually correspond to the originality from which they descend. Invocation then essentially becomes a magical practice and formula used by magicians to call upon beings higher than that of human nature in the hierarchy, such as angels, archangels, demi-gods etc. Evocation is the practice used for summoning beings lower in essence than the human being, such as demons, arch-demons, demi-devil entities and so forth.

Therefore are all things connected through a medium into the planes of existence, with a spirit that brings them forth and ends in binding them together, as within every person the medium of their spirit brings change and sensations that cause such change. To be able to separate this spirit from the elements would be of great advantage. To transform anything into anything else would then be possible instead of allowing it to go through the natural systematic infiltration to eventually become what it is, as we would call destiny per-say. Thus is the great value in constructing talismans and in touching the required medium for the change to occur by a directed desire.

It has been mentioned that the vital use of incense represents a sacrifice and creates an affect in the consciousness. I must point out that human or animal sacrifice is of no good in magical ceremony. Dabblers in the art have misemployed it, but like all arts, magick has its rights and wrongs and such sacrifice as to harm another living organism defiles the rite. Incense does the job and has been in times of old called the herbs of the spirits and in their use particular forms appear when rites performed according to them. Such strange and remarkable tales and stories of occurrences have been told from its use. People of folklore used to burn the hoof of a horse to drive away mice or burn feathers of a peacock to bring serpents together and the like. This is mentioned so that in the creation of the talisman, the result will be more efficacious if the appropriate incense is used accordingly with the planetary influence associated with the working. In all good matters concerning love and divine nature, the scent of the incense is most pleasant and refined. All the planets and signs of the zodiac have their particular suffumigations.

The role of numbers also plays significantly upon the construction of a talisman. Although of more formal than natural, their affect has great power with the essential principles working in life. The number of elements employed, the time of day and constellation influence, and the Sephiroth of the talisman operation are all designated numbers by the virtue of their representation. Numbers work upon the soul as objects do upon the body. As all things proceed from one, they ineffably endeavor to return to that one. Upon manifesting through the planes they become infinitely connected in their spread through the extent of influences. But it is that all things honor unity and that which is one in essence.

Just as animals have a dominating figurehead, so do humans in their leader of a country or religions in their supreme deity and so forth until the effect of a pyramid is created to manifest divisions and subdivisions from the original one. All of our senses, qualities, virtues, motions, words, deeds and so much more is contingent upon the proportions and scales of numbers that affects them. There are magic tables of numbers associated with the planets, which unite the extremes of the matter for the medium associated in the talisman to the will of that influence. Through the affection and soul of the operator is this medium harnessed and applied in fitting with the energy by virtue of the associated number(s) within the talisman.

The Intelligence's are the presiding angels that are connected to their respective planets whose seals or characters are fashioned on the talisman. Observing the signs and degrees of the planets and especially that of the moon brings more powerful results in conjunction and in accordance to the influx instilled within the talisman. When any planet is joined with the fixed constellation of their nature, their power is significantly augmented. We must seek not only the external aspects of the planets or Sun, but also the internal energies and representations from where those qualities are endowed. In placing fortunes to the ascension of those planetary influences they will in turn return that fortune significantly. The motions, declinations, aspects and rising of the planets and constellations have great effect upon the outcome of directed force. With this in mind, and the creation of that which we entrust with power to do work for us, be it on parchment or leather, ring or metal, table or altar, clothing or other substance, may success be endowed for purposes true and divine.

Acts of magick may involve the use and practice of instruments, movements, gestures, images, amulets, consecrations, enchantments, mirrors, unguents, potions, ointments, incantations, imagination, charms, lighting, blessings, candles, pictures, orations, vows, oaths, passion, imprecations, all under preparedness and directed with concentration to energies carrying them for an accomplishment. It should be evident that the practice of magick has nothing to do with evil but rather an understanding of the laws of nature and how to apply them towards achieving harmony and thus Unity. It is with the theory and practice of magick that all of our actions are accounted for and realized towards a desired outcome. The answers to the complexity of the hierarchical system or chain of command through the inner worlds come as stages of growth and self-initiation. As sentient Beings, our place in the Universe must be realized and our potentials acknowledged so that we may open the doors to step back into our connection with the beginning. If such preponderance is undertaken, the mysteries of life will become unveiled as required for an education of our Higher Life. Our evolution will move forward and move humanity towards a greater care and concern for direction. Physical limitations and mundane problems such as environmental, starvation, money, gratification, and all such disabilities of the physical plane would become capable of being solved so that the next step may be taken. It would be a giant leap for mankind, but equally as important, is that it becomes a giant leap for the individual, who eventually ushers others by pure example and subtle influence. A relatively perfect world may never exist but the work towards its' accomplishment with such realizations as wicca and magick principles do provide, will enlighten the soul and bring the individual to another proscenium of human evolution. ★

VISUALIZATION
-FOR-
MATERIAL SUCCESS

"What is a weed? A plant whose vartues have not yet been discovered."

Fortune of the Republic - Ralph Waldo Emerson

Maintaining a successful inner life is not nor should it be limited to having the very basics of material necessities. Wishing to obtain material objects is a natural desire in this ever-changing and growing world around us. Taking particular steps to achieve our material desires can coincide with the harmony we uphold for our "well being" in life. Physical "well being" involves not only material achievements but also how we feel about our health, body and appearance. When we wish to change particular physical, emotional or mental aspects of our life we take certain steps to do it. We make it a routine to physically put our body into shape, to rid our emotional disturbances or to keep our thoughts in a positive frame of mind. All glitches that come into our life involve work, routine and usually at the same time some form of entertainment or pleasure to replace them with happiness and contentment. Step by step we can make efforts to achieve that which we most desire to have. A **positive outlook** is only part of the formula in obtaining what we want most out of life. There are many important ingredients to put into the formula to achieve success and in this chapter we will look at the importance of ten ingredients.

Creative visualization is an art of applying efforts of desire while obeying certain principles to manipulate an outcome of that which we envision. There are scores of books on achievement, personal growth, positive thinking, goal setting and direction. Many of them will instruct us with methods on focusing for success and managing our life better. That is not the aim of creative visualization in this chapter. It is presumed that you can already think for yourself and apply your own principles for your own happiness. We will rather focus on the art of being creative and applying it to visualize our desires and make them materialize.

Channeling our energy is one of the key ingredients in the success of creative visualization. We begin by being creative no only on the physical level but the emotional and mental levels. The intensity of our desire and the strength of our thought provide us with the channeling capability. The strength that we put into our physical activities, such as exercise, develops greater energy, awareness, stamina and enthusiasm for creativity. Creating a positive atmosphere around us keeps our emotions strong by vitalizing them and therefore keeps them focused. Maintaining this positive atmosphere feeds our desire to strengthen it like a habit, a positive feeling habit with focus.

There are several words in just about every letter of the alphabet that impress positive thoughts upon us. When we think of those words, they generate positive feelings. That is what we want to do when we think of what we desire to have. We have to generate positive feelings and feel at the same time that we have what we need before we obtain it, in order to obtain it. When we hear words that associate positive images to them they trigger emotions inside of us. We have to impel or **stimulate emotions** for successful creative visualization. As an example, feel the emotions that are triggered while thinking of and conjuring images to the following words.

Achieve, Attain, Acquire, Astonishing, Awesome, Astounding, Believe, Benevolent, Confidence, Celebrate, Charitable, Cheerful, Dedication, Delightful, Enjoy, Enchanting, Excellent, Eager, Fabulous, Fulfill, Fortune, Fantastic, Generous, Grand, Good, Happy, Hope, Influence, Invent, Jovial, Joyous, Kind, Luck, Magnificent, Marvelous, Miraculous, Nice, Outstanding, Perfect, Pleasant, Prosperity, Reliable, Riches, Splendid, Startling, Spirited, Skillful, Stupendous, Trust, Unity, Vivify, Vitalize, Wisdom, Wonderful, Wealth, Zealous.

Those words can have power by influencing us if we allow them to. They are simply words but words contain power because they generate feelings from images. These images can make us feel good from the emotions that they excite or stir inside of us. They **trigger images to emotions** and that is our next key ingredient for successful creative visualization.

The true test of any system that we use for advancing ourselves is shown over time. If we look back and see what principles we've used to obtain where we are at today, we can see what worked and what apparently did not work so well. An honest look will tell us how far we've come in achieving what would make us most happy in life. Without creating alibis or excuses to appease our setbacks, we should do a reality check and then become determined to work towards our goals. It may be useful to keep a record and check the steps and progress made towards those goals. Effective visualization is when we see results. There are certain considerations we should keep in mind in order to make visualization a simple and effective everyday tool in our life. First of all, we should gradually build up to the things we wish to obtain. We should concentrate and work at gaining **one thing at a time** in our life. That becomes a developing process of building or enlarging our circle of material possessions. We begin by obtaining one thing at a time that best suits us and increase our possessions with this useful art. This is the **gradual building of our circle of suitability**.

Begin by desiring the thing you need now, the item you need most. There may be any number of things you really want or need. If it is a certain job opportunity, you should be ready to handle that job. You may receive it, but could loose it if you are not sufficiently prepared to DO IT. Remember that you are working with physical laws as well as mental and emotional ones. We have to be in sync on all levels to handle the outcome of our desires. If, for example, you wrote some stories or collection of poetry and wanted to publish them in some magazine, you could easily visualize that accomplishment. I think we have established the concept of need, so that the thing you are going to work on having will not interfere with your life but rather help it in some special way. With this, keep in mind that a gradual progression to greater things or larger items will increase the size of the circle of suitability. Do not imagine winning the lottery, AT FIRST!

By gradually increasing our circle of suitability and obtaining what we need in progression, it will seem that things will come naturally and easier as time goes on. This will make you more proficient in manifesting the things you need through life. If you try to reach for something you are not ready for and is beyond your present scope, it may not come until much later in life and by then you may find that it is more of a hindrance than an assistance. It would have past its time of requirement. Therefore the thing you desire should be something you feel that you need either now or soon. Some people may claim that they are content and that they do not really need or want anything now. If they wanted something they would simply go out and buy it, if they have the money to do so. That is fine, but understanding the principles of creative visualization is a useful knowledge to comprehend the functioning of the Inner Planes. If there is something missing in your life, something you feel that you need and would love to have, utilize this system.

Do not designate from where the item will come from. For example, do not visualize someone leaving you an inheritance of some kind and thus be praying upon his or her earthly departure! Allow the visualization to take what course it will in order to manifest on the material plane the item you seek. That way the source of the achievement is left open and it would be as if nature provided you with the acquired possession. Aptly apply common sense with your desires while using this system.

After we put desire-energy into what we want to obtain, we should leave it at that and forget about it to allow it to work for us. There is a tendency within the inner planes that once a force is in motion it will continue to be in motion. We do not want the forces that we have set in motion on our behalf to keep continuing to bring us the same thing over and over and affect our judgement and life wrongly. That is to say once we obtain our object, there may be the chance that the situation will repeat itself over and over. That is why we concentrate on having JUST that one thing and stop there.

Creative visualization is a process of habitually focusing desires and then allowing them to work for you. It also requires specific stages to become engaged and essential steps to become triggered. Once you begin, and see success occur before your eyes in a short period of time, you can observe your achievements and know intently that you have applied magic into your life to accomplish a goal. It involves the creative construction of a desire chart, which will be elaborated upon after this summary of a few experiences.

When I was twelve years old I noticed a man standing on a doorstep across the street. I went over to talk with him as he was staring at the stars in the sky. He talked to me about the planets and it wasn't long before he invited me in for a deeper discussion on subjects that I expressed interest in. I told him that I wanted a bicycle for my birthday but was not sure if I would get one. He told me to get a picture of the bicycle I wanted to own and glue it on a piece of paper and to look at it every night and say to myself- "I will have a bicycle. I feel myself riding on MY bicycle. I can see myself riding it where I want to go."

I did exactly what he suggested and it worked! I received a bicycle without even asking my parents for one! I must have visualized very hard to achieve the bicycle because a few years later when I came home one day from school my father looked at me sternly and ushered me outside with him. In the back yard he presented me with a brand new mini-motorcycle. From that day forward, I began visualizing the things I desired to have. I learnt to apply the principles in more detail to many other parts of my life. It seemed that material possessions would come into my life more and more as I applied the ingredients to achieve them. Not only material items came to me but other important things like adventures and meeting very interesting people that I may not have otherwise met without developing and graduating my circle of suitability.

Travelling was put into my enlarging circle and before long I visited and lived in beautiful locations across Canada and around Europe. It suited me just fine! I also worked with television stations and began making videos in countries I only dreamed of visiting one day. I did not stumble into wealth but made gradual creative visualizations towards each and every goal and attained them sooner and sooner each time. I enlarged my circle so that the things I visualized to have soon became more and more within my reach to achieve. This is a marvelous ART that does and will work for every person. These are only a couple of my true experiences. You probably have a few of your own that stand out in your mind, after having thought of something and seeing it come true for you.

It does not matter if we end up obtaining what we need by mere coincidence or confidence, as long as we obtain it. By attracting what we desire with channeled energy we are extending and gripping the feeling to work for us. Just like when a billiard player focuses on a shot with a pool cue, energy is exerted and aimed to accomplish a desire, and the desire causes the ball to go into the pocket.

Another example where I used creative visualization was two months before finishing High School. I really wanted to own a car and drive to New York City to visit some people I knew. I made a visualization chart on cardboard and pasted a picture of a car from an auto magazine. It was a cool red car and on top of it I wrote this- "By July 1st I will own a beautiful red car. I will pay maximum $2000.00 for this car. The car is mine!"

I should have begun saving money, because that much money was a lot for someone who was in school and worked part-time sanding paint off of automobiles in an auto-body shop. At the end of June I basically had only enough money to purchase my schoolbooks for upcoming college. I lagged, I faltered, but I visualized! I did not properly save for my dream vehicle, but every night I looked at my chart and imagined having that hot red car and envisioned driving it to NYC. Every night, for two months my mind worked on what I desired and my dreams increased with those desires. It just happened that on the last day of June, while I was enrolling in College and purchasing textbooks at the College bookstore, I overheard a computer professor behind the counter talk about getting rid of his car. I quickly asked about it and he said it is a 1976 Toyota Corolla and it was mechanically a very sound vehicle. "How much will you sell it to me for?" I asked with a quiver. His reply was: "$200.00, do you want it?" I only had $50.00 left after buying my books but he was not concerned about having all the money right at that moment for it. He said I could pay him the rest later. The car was mine on July 1st! It was a perfect and wonderful car, which served my needs for years and it was coincidentally red in color. I made that NYC trip and beyond! The opportunity came on the date I envisioned and desired to have the car, and I was ready to ACCEPT and ACT upon that OPPORTUNITY.

The similarity about these examples is that they were all within my range of acquiring them and suitability of fitting my needs. I did not reach for the moon or the stars, although my head was sometimes there. I gradually developed my circle of material items that I had need for. The first thing I always think about is what do I really need or what do I really want that will improve and ease my life or particular crisis.

If we need something bad enough, chances are we will have it sooner or later if the efforts are concentrated and applied. There is more emotion and thought attached to something we need than something we simply think would be nice to have. If you think about having a great sum of money, all at once, it may work, but will it cause problems that will be complicated to handle? Would it make you lazy, thoughtless and careless? Would it become more of a distraction from what you are to learn in life? Most people may respond - "No, no and no, I would be just fine being RICH!" Anything that we need may be obtained when energy is channeled/directed towards acquiring it whole-heartedly. When energy is focused it must manifest some kind of result. The results that manifest in the physical world are generally in accordance with how clear and intense our mental energy is building upon our desires.

Another important principle that always affects life physically and otherwise is the dual nature of every single thing. Everything has TWO sides to it. Our clothes, a wall, a door; every item has two sides, an inside and an outside. Forces also have two sides. When we go jogging there is a force exerted forwards and an opposite force exerted backwards. We work against the opposing force as efficiently as we can in order to accomplish the action. Using this analogy we may comprehend that on the Inner Planes, one side of the force brings us the item we desire and the other side of THAT force works at taking it away. It is an inevitable equal and opposite force at work. Think of dreams you may have experienced where you felt stuck and unable to move, as I mentioned in the astral chapter. There are forces holding us back, but with effort we can spring or virtually fly forwards. If the opposing force does not cancel our effort then something takes place, whether we realize and see it or not. We therefore have to **restrain and secure the opposing force** so that it does not cancel our effort to materialize that which we desire.

A little example of this is when I was an excited entrepreneur at the age of thirteen. My brother-in-law finally allowed me to play poker cards with him and his friends. I only had about $4.00 in my itchy pocket but the desire to win was flaming within me, so I played poker with the brutes. Within the hour my financial gain had skyrocketed to $32.00 on the table in front of me. It was very exciting and I wanted to quit but they beckoned me to continue. Sure enough I did continue and with in the next hour I was down to a measly $2.00. The forces gave, and the forces took away! It happens every day in life, in one form or another. It is a matter of perspective and the results affect us and may make us decide to quit while we are ahead, but it is a matter of experience. Moderation can help us to hold on to what we have before we loose it. If we work on obtaining something really big, the chance of loosing it is always there when the reaction force comes into effect, just as the wheel of life rotates.

Self-Communication should be a very positive experience. FEEL and THINK that you already have that thing you desire so much. Imagine yourself using it, enjoying it, and know that it is already part of your life. Send clear, concise, proper messages to the other side, to the astral world, the world of emotions and channel those energies to obtain what you need. Attach those emotions to the image of your objective. It is stated in the Bible, Mark 11:23 - "Therefore I say unto you what things so ever ye desire, when ye pray, believe ye have received them and ye shall have them."

Feel the pleasure of using the object of your desire. Connect the feeling with the need of having it as you visualize using it. Desire is a creative energy and a great emotion to work with.

A dear friend once said to me: "Give me the spark of natures fire, that is the learning I desire." I believe she requested the energy of life! Holy prana! Use your life energy! Build it! Be aware of it, harness it and channel it appropriately.

Desire is an exciting emotion and fiery energy to make things occur in life. It makes things HAPPEN. It creates more potential. Use It, Build It, Live with It!

Take pictures from magazines and make a chart on a bristle board for you to visualize upon. Write beside the picture(s) that you will have that item, and even describe when you want it, what you will do with it, how it will make you feel using IT, all in a brief outline on your chart. Make it like you would design and create a craft that is personal to you. Everyone in business makes charts for one purpose or another. It is a marketing strategy or a means to promote and sell something. They advertise using the media, television, and newspapers. Their advertisement appears attractive, captures attention and is designed to work on our emotions of need. Ancient Egyptians used charts to create effects by writing on the tombs of Kings/Pharaohs. They illustrated the Pharaohs as having a prosperous life and afterlife. Magical priests did the artwork and directed energy to the inner planes, creating success for their Pharaoh.

Here are a few ideas for your chart. You can do it any way you wish but be inventive, be CREATIVE. The work you put into it reflects the results obtained. Make your desire visually attractive, just stunning! Be happy with it. It may be made on a piece of cardboard, bristle board, about 2 feet by 2 feet large. Draw a fancy border around the edge of it so that you limit your vision to everything within that border. Remember that physical objects have astral counterparts so you are in effect making an astral border for it at the same time. Try to prevent anyone from seeing it because it is your private work of art unless you are working in collaboration with a partner. Do research, and find things from books, magazines and so forth that will excite and stimulate your mind when you go to concentrate on your chart each day and/or night. You may wish to look at it twice a day, devoting ten minutes each time.

You may also wish to divide your desire-chart into sections for whatever reason. An example would be dividing it into three sections from left to right. The left side could contain pictures of your future, the center contain pictures or drawings of your present and the right side may represent things that were in the past or are passing away from your life now. In such a case it would be similar to the three pillars of the Tree of Life. This way you can compare the past and present while envisioning your future. Items that you once had and items that are in your life now and a certain thing that will come into your life to make it better. Whatever uplifts you most with inspiration tends to work best. Imagine or simulate your chart as your own pictorial tarot card creation. Use it as a doorway for your consciousness to enter the astral plane and build your desire to materialize your goal. **Concentrate routinely through the doorway to your objective**. With the inspiring pictures that you put on your chart you will be able to mentally enter it and envision already having and using the object that you want. Visualize and memorize your chart so that you can recall the images on it at any time.

Every person will have a different approach and different resources at their disposal therefore results will vary and are also dependent upon the effort put into them. It is good to have an idea where you want to go with your life and the goals you are working towards. Your circle of suitability should be increased towards accomplishing that objective. Each step taken may be noted so that you are aware of progression. Your chart is a FORM of the forces that you are putting to work for yourself.

In the example chart that is illustrated on this page, my friend Carl depicted the desire to have a house

or a car. It gives you a very basic desire-chart idea, and although the car he drew is not of today's highway standards, he was nonetheless practical in what he drew and desired.

To recapitulate, the ingredients for creative visualization are:
  1. Develop a Positive Outlook.
  2. Channel Energy by Intensifying Desire and Strengthening Thought.
  3. Stimulate Emotions and Channel them.
  4. Trigger Emotions from images to build Energy.
  5. One thing at a Time.
  6. Gradually build the Circle of Suitability.

7. Do not designate from where the item will come from.
8. Restrain and Secure the Opposing Force.
9. Create an appealing Desire-Chart.
10. Concentrate Routinely through the doorway to your Objective.

Keep these creative visualization ingredients in mind next time you hear people talk about positive thinking. You must hold on to the positive incoming force of your desire and not allow the other SIDE of that force to catch up and take it away from you. You will observe that this happens in life but it is not something people pay much attention to, just like they don't think about the inside of their shirt as much as the outside. You can even state on your chart that you will not allow the opposite force to interfere with obtaining the object of your desire. That way, the magical fingers of your astral body grip the astral substance of your desire, be it an object, experience, job opportunity or whatever. By realizing the potential opposing grip you can weaken it's threat as you strengthen the incoming astral force of your desire.

Work with a promise to yourself, a decision towards developing your life and furthering your goals to ultimately achieve your blessed dreams. Procrastination is the opposite of decision and slows down the energy in our desires. Procrastination results after negative opinions are formed. Opinions are the cheapest commodity and we all have them. If we allow other people to form our opinions then our desires will be weaker than if we formed them by ourselves. This causes a sense of inferiority in some respects and also prevents us from empowering our energies for accomplishments. Do not tell other people what you intend to do when developing your creative abilities. Show them by the great examples of living life as an Art through your Practice. Action is what makes things happen. Put these principles to good use and remember that emotion does not exist in the future or the past. It exists when it is felt. Emotion is an event in the NOW, the present. Live in the NOW and USE your e-motions. Begin with your well-planned thought, then develop emotion towards it, connect with the vibrations out there/in there and manifest to your hearts deepest desires!
★

OUR PLACE IN MYTHOLOGY

"This is in myth a perpetual theme, in the voices of the prophets a familiar cry. The people yearn for some personality who, in a world of twisted bodies and souls, will represent again the lines of the incarnate image."

The Hero With A Thousand Faces- Joseph Campbell

Mythology is a collection of legends and stories from the history of cultures. The stories may associate particular powers to deities, heroes and gods, holding them responsible for principle occurrences in life. Interpretations of ancient folklore tend to affiliate greater powers than what people have immediate control over and are designated to these higher, majestic beings that influence changes in our life. It becomes an interesting study of fables past down through generations and cultures. The mythological experiences represented between women and men have been an invaluable learning tool throughout history. The woman is usually depicted as the nurturing, maintainer of life whereas the man was the defender of territory. In some cases the roles were exchanged but in most mythical scenarios there is a figurative hero that we can count upon.

Nearly five million years ago the hominidin resided in Africa and became differentiated from the arboreal ape because he released his hands as he ran, enabling him to use them for greater accomplishments. His brain increased in size from the use of his hands and his developing thoughts began crafting tools and performing actions that were superior to his ancestors. Then about four and a half million years ago, man ran without his knuckles dragging on the ground and was called the Homo habilis, having a brain slightly larger than a male gorilla. The next evolution of man began making useful tools around 500,000 BC and is called the Java man or Pithecanthropus. Some of the tools were used for ritual purposes. The next order of man is the Homo sapiens or Neanderthal man, dating back to 200,000 BC and ending his period in history around 40,000 BC. During this era mythology evolved with man making associations and stories relating the forces of nature to figurative representations.

Around 60,000 BC the first known burial had taken place and was at Mount Carmel, now known as Israel, and was done with the aid of instruments or tools. Sacred burials and worshipping of cave bear skulls had taken place during this flagrant period. The people of those times respected animals and thought them as another equivalent species but required them as food and worshiped them. The animal continually returned to the hunter's ground, as its purpose in life was to become instinctively a 'willing sacrifice'. The people during that period paid homage to nature and the animals for their life, knowing that resurrection will return the animal to life again by the process of reincarnation. Today we generally thank our Divine Being for the food we consume and not the food itself. The whole mythology has changed form, from changes in thinking and perception to recognition and respect. Thanking a particular higher deity or the local grocer is now the average person's way of being grateful for food instead of thanking the life and spirit of the animal.

As the Cro-Magnon man evolved, making sculptures and carvings in caves became part of culture. Depictions of women were often illustrated with her having short legs and no facial expression in the pictorials. She was the creator of life, giving birth and nourishment to the meaning of life. The construction of ceremonial huts took form thereafter as a symbol of rebirth and sacred ground upon which man lived. Upon entering their ceremonial sanctuary he was going into the body of the mother, wherein everything was magical, holding mysterious powers. That is what churches came to signify later in life, as the field where the essence of life would be felt and a role played to reenact teachings that represent life. Paintings and tattoos on the body became a form of permanent role playing to decree the mythological representations that were sacred or had special meaning to the person. Women became known as the initiator as she was the one closer to nature and represented the significant magical connection to higher forces.

Greeks evolved this rationalization with Zeus as the father who fell in love with Thetis, a beautiful nymph. She was a goddess but Zeus thought it better for her to have a human husband so she married Peleus and they had a son named Achilles. When they married she transformed into several objects of nature such as a lion, fire, water and a serpent (all symbols representing parts of her temperament). The serpent sheds its skin to be reborn just as the moon does its shadow and is a symbol of lunar consciousness and reawakening. The lion represents the sun and is absolute life, a true giver, yet capable of being fierce and strong. The goddess therefore symbolizes the mother with all of these energies as being engaged or disengaged dependant upon how she reacts. She is the dimension beyond the physical, beyond forces of good and evil, the yin and yang, by representing the totality of opposite forces. Crete was the culture that most predominantly endowed the woman in murals and art because the mother goddess role held great significance with them. When a goddess is represented or sanctioned in a cult, the instructions generally depict spiritual aspiration and ascension due to her initiating principles.

Different cultures began forming pictorial keys to represent that which they held as being sacred. The formation of mandalas came into existence always with the eastern end of it open and pointing to the top because the east was considered to be sacred and it poured in radiance from above, figuratively speaking. The sun rises or is perceived coming from the east and Buddha is said to have faced east when he achieved Enlightenment. Also, the New Testament is a teaching performed on Sunday, the day signifying the eastern Sun and rejuvenation. The belief of the transcendent light arriving from the east and going around the south to set in the west is cultivated in many traditions. The north has long been considered as being a mysterious place, dark and full of uncertainty, concern and suspicion.

Many of the stories in mythology are portrayals of life as a joyous recurrence with adventurous dramatizations. It illustrated the world as a stage whereon the gods and goddesses are playing a game of principles and laws controlling life. Animal fables became quite popular, always being portrayed in dancing roles and playing parts that humans would normally decree. Languages became associated with one another such as Sanskrit, from India having similarities with Latin, Greek and the Celtic Germanic lingua. The people of these nations became known as the Aryans (Sanskrit meaning noble). The Indo-European people assembled in tribes and conflicts soon ensued with their neighboring adversaries. This resulted in the rise of warriors and references to gods that portrayed violence with spears and thunder hurlers such as seen in myths of Yahweh, Zeus and Indra who early man prayed to for victories in war.

Alexander the Great commenced his voyage to India in the fourth century BC and found that the gods and deities worshipped there were similar to the ones from the mythologies of his native land. Indra was to Zeus as Krishna was to Hercules and so on. But in Judaism one can not say Ezra is similar to Yahweh, because there are no other deities that exist and they have kept the faith in one Supreme Deity, which carried on throughout the Western traditions and contributed to the future religions. We can not compare two distinctly different systems and so different cultures may in some cases be like different worlds. In India people are not in expulsion because god is within them. They have their universal deities and lower deities, which are composite to the facets of their life in a grander system. In Western tradition a person is faced to come out of displacement and their God is a hidden mystery figure and people must pay for their original sin. Eastern religion and western religion are completely different life styles and have dissimilar feelings about their deities but all seems to be converging and gradually assimilating to what may be styled as a universal truth opposed to personal bias.

Egyptian religion can be a deeply fascinating subject with the sacred images associated to the afterlife and the multiplicity of gods that have left a legacy of historical wealth. Around 2600 BC the first of the great pyramids were designed by Imhotep and called the Step Pyramid, constructed for King Zoser. The pyramids become a different branch study of Egyptian religion. Some recent anthropologists hold that the three pyramids of Giza correspond to the stars of Orion's Belt and the Nile River to be a figurative representation of the Milky Way Galaxy. It has become a branch unto itself.

The King represented the incarnation of the power of the Pharaoh, who was Osiris personified. The power of the Pharaohs' rule is demonstrated by the image of the sphinx. The lion-goddess Sekmet got impregnated by a moonbeam and gave birth to the mythical sphinx. The moon-like god that caused the birth was Ptah who is usually typified as a mummy. The pharaohs were the mediators between the people and the sun god, Re or Ra. Re was considered a Great God and his name was applied in various forms as the dynasties changed. In the Old Kingdom he was worshipped as Re-Atum in Heliopolis and the pharaoh was his representative upon earth. During the reign of the Middle Kingdom when the political capital was in Thebes, the worshiped god was Amun and became the sole state god with his solar name as Amun-Re, or Amon-Ra.

The higher deities are Isis and Osiris, the Great Mother and Father who are the children of Nut and Hem. The younger brother and sister of Isis and Osiris are Set and Neftis. The heaven goddess, Nut, or Nuit, is the infinite space and stars, the Universe, and the earth god, her consort, is Hem. This is candidly opposite of the Mesopotamian concepts that held the higher god as male and the earth as the goddess. The great sky boat is that of Ra, the sun god who takes the souls to the mouth of Nut to be reborn in the East, instead of descending into an underworld where Osiris awaits.

The prevalent story of the Egyptian's reveals that Osiris slept with Neftis one night, thinking it was Isis and the result was that she bore a child named Anubis who had the head of a jackal. Set did not appreciate this so he had a sarcophagus made exactly to fit Osiris. They had a celebration and during it everyone in attendance had to step inside the sarcophagus to see who would precisely fit into it. When Osiris stepped in, seventy-two attendants rushed in and locked it shut wrapping it with iron bands and threw it into the Nile. It was later washed up at a town in Syria and a tree grew around it. Osiris was encased within the tree and meanwhile Isis had begun to search for him.

The Prince of the town liked the aroma that came from the tree and had it cut down to be made into a pillar for his new palace. He had a newborn son and accepted Isis as the nursing maid when a worker brought her into the palace after meeting her while out getting some water at the drinking well. One evening Isis puts the newborn into the fireplace to burn off his mortality and to make him immortal after which Isis transforms into a swallow and flies around the pillar knowing her beloved husband, Osiris is within it. The mother enters and begins to scream seeing her child all alone and in the fire. She abruptly decides to rescue him whereupon Isis turns back into the maid and explains the situation as the King enters the room. Isis asked for the pillar saying that her husband is locked within it and the King wisely and politely abides by giving it to her. It is transported on a barge with Isis and she opens it and comforts down on her dead husband and conceives a child named Horus.

She does not want to return to the original fortress because Set has taken control so she gives birth to Horus in the papyrus swamp area. Amon and Thoth arrive to provide assistance for her. Uncle Set happens to go out hunting and while chasing a wild boar finds Isis and Osiris and becomes completely outraged. He rips Osiris into fifteen pieces and scatters the body portions all over the land. Neftis and Anubis come to assist the devastated Isis again in finding all of her husband, but they only find fourteen pieces of him. They have him pieced back together and Anubis embalms him. The piece that was missing was the genital organs, which were swallowed up by a fish. This is said to be the origin of eating of fish on Fridays as a sacred tradition, because it was a sacrament of symbolic consummation of the sacred flesh, the production of life and has long ago been passed into religions that incorporated much from Egyptology.

Osiris became the judge of the dead in the afterworld as his son Horus grew older and became fraught with battle against his uncle, Set, the patron of Lower Egypt. Horus lost an eye during the battle, which was a sacramental offering that brought his father back to life. He defeated and castrated his uncle Set, sending him out into the desert forever, and he then became known as Heru-Ur, or Horus the Elder. When he conquered Set (3100 BC) the Upper and Lower Egypt became a unified kingdom. In the city of Behdet they worshipped a form of Horus that was represented by a solar disk with a magnificent set of wings attached to it. This winged globe figure is at the top of many sacred steles of Egyptian religion and is also associated in occult academics as Hadit, the center of the solar deity.

In the judgement scene Osiris is upon the throne as the judge of the dead with his two queens, Neftis and Isis behind him. From the waters of eternal life the lotus blossoms with the four sons of Horus upon it. The four sons were Amset, Hapi, Duamutef and Qebhsenuef. They protected parts of the body of Osiris and became the guardians for the body of the deceased. The goddesses Isis, Nephthys, Neith and Selket continuously guard the four sons from harm and detriment.

When a person becomes deceased they are identified with Osiris, so if their last name were Seagul, they would be considered Osiris Seagul in reconciling with the process of death. They are identified with the father and they and the father become one. On their journey they consume all of the gods which are mystically representative as expressions or projections of their energies. All of their bodily parts may be associated with some particular god but within the underworld they maintain keeping their own heart. They must be properly prepared so that they come to the permeating realization:

"I am yesterday, today, and tomorrow. I have the power to be born a second time. I am the source from which the gods arise."

While in the underworld the heart is weighed against a feather on the scales of justice. If the heart is heavier then a monster will eat the soul, but if it is lighter than the feather then they will enter spiritual life. Anubis, the god of mummification, does the weighing while Ani is escorted to the weighing before sent to the throne of Osiris with Horus escorting him.

There were eight primordial deities created by other, higher god forms. They were Kau, Kauket, Nun Naunet, Heqet, Heq, Amen and Amenet. Matt is an important deity also and is associated with truth and justice. Hathor is the goddess of love, birth and death. She is a solar sky goddess with maternal characteristics of the night sky. She is a beautiful goddess with a headdress having a sun disk and two elongated cow horns protruding. She is sometimes referred to as Hwt-Hr or House of Horus when she is connected with the Elder Horus from her life giving house or womb. This Mistress of the Sky also rules and influences Ra or the sun god and the king(s) of the earth as the Living Horus. She seductively dances in front of the sun having it follow her through its daily cycle from dawn to midnight. Her characteristics change through the day and during the afternoon she becomes the Daughter of Ra. This distracts the penetrating and increasing daily heat of Ra, the Sun, to become calm and cool so that he does not burn up everything during the course of the day. This has become a mystical saving grace in more ways than one.

Sobek is the crocodile god or the Lord of Faiyum who brings Isis and Nephthys in the afterlife to protect those who become deceased. He assisted with the birth of Horus and in the ultimate destruction of Set. He also represents the four elemental gods of Osiris (water), Geb (earth), Shu (air) and Ra (fire). Geb, is also known as Seb and is a masculine identity with the earth and is the father of Osiris, Isis, Set and Nephthys. He is the husband and brother, in a spiritual manner, of Nut or Nuit, the goddess of infinite space.

Amulets, crowns, jewelry, animal figures, statues and many other such emblems were important implements for transferring magical potency. Each object represented some special force that was delivered from another world within. The ankh, representing life with its T being the male energy and the oval on top the feminine quality shows the vitality that is awakened when combining them as one energy for regeneration. Similarly the pharaohs' eye called the udjat, gives power to see everything and brings prosperity and fertility to that which it is directed.

The magical assimilation of preparing the dead to meet Osiris in the afterlife was meant to spiritually ascend the soul so that a resurrection just as Osiris experienced, would occur. The inner sanctuary of the temple had daily offerings to the deceased by the appointed priests. They would burn incense and provide offerings of food to the image of the god, which was anointed and set upon a shrine. All of these ancient legacies were used to in the development of other religious practices and customs in one form or another.

Judgement day and the weighing of the heart upon the scales in the Jewish Book of Proverbs found its wisdom from the Egyptians. Much of Coptic Christianity's after death concepts were inherited from knowledge collected out of ancient Egypt. Hermetic literature has also assimilated, over time, the value of relationships between the deities of different religions and folklore, which had origins in Egypt.

Particular communion with the synthesis of glorified principles may cause mystical experiences for people that emotionally thrive on worshipping of deities. This ecstatic phenomenon usually results after fasting and prolonged meditation and contemplation upon a particular deity. People that are driven to contact with the energies of certain deities have performed acts of devotion and recited repetitious mantras with particular movements of enacting sacred rites. It has been compared to the rapture experienced in complete sexual union when normal worldly senses are abandoned and surpassed. Some claim true ecstasy to result from transcending earth consciousness while being united with a deity and having their mind uplifted to that level. Still there are others who think it to be a heightened awareness from a mystical experience of attaching to the knowledge of a deity and gaining wisdom that they would under normal conditions not come to know. In such an experience, people are unresponsive to normal sensory stimuli such as pain or pleasure.

Some followers of religious sects are known to pierce parts of their body with hooks, pins, and other objects without feeling any pain. The level of ecstasy is totally irrelevant, as the term has become widely used for a conglomerate range of subjective, social and religious convergence. The experience, however is remarked by ravishing rapture such as initially was intended upon with the idea of unity, marriage, love and fulfilling glory. This peaceful release and repudiating of worldly awareness is usually experienced for a short duration, such as an hour while frenzied trance states, religious experience or mystical states dominate the conscious awareness of the devotee. These experiences have converged in western civilization as a voluntary practice but have their roots in ancient cultures.

On the other side of the Mediterranean, the antiquated Greeks worshiped the twelve gods of Olympus collectively rather than giving great praise to any one of them in particular. They include Zeus, Hera, Athena, Poseidon, Demeter, Apollo, Hermes, Artemis, Ares, Hephaestus, Aphrodite, and Hestia. Sometimes Hestia's place is also taken over by Dionysus. Hestia discovered the building of houses and is a guardian goddess. Prayers and sacrifices are often given to her since she resides over altars and hearths and she was the first to be born of the great Olympians. She remains in her home and never partakes in feuds, wars or struggles amongst men or amongst gods.

Zeus is considered to be the father of men and gods, having the greatest wisdom, highest spirit and being a supreme Lord of Justice. He provides persuasion to the good and punishment to the evil of men. The Greeks considered Zeus to be the Father Sky and consorting the Mother Earth, providing rain, thunderstorms and changes in climate. The father of Zeus was Cronos and in turn whose father was Uranus. In a myth based on the concept that the earth and sky were once joined and became separated by Cronos castrating his father, Uranus, he caused the life principle of reproduction to become the material plane of earth and the father figure to remain in the sky. Uranus is a Greek word and means 'sky' and he disliked his children of the earth because they contained negative influences as being impure creatures causing similar affects. The Roman equivalent to Zeus was Jupiter and he, like Pitar, Dyaus, and Pater all mean 'Sky Father'.

The Queen of Heaven is Hera who formed the Milky Way while giving milk to Hermes and had pushed him onwards. She had many transformations and assumed the form of other important figures. Her jealousy is a mark of her character, as she would persecute the children that her husband had with other women as well as the women themselves. Such was the case with Semele whose death is blamed on Hera. When Heracles sailed to Troy, Hera caused terrible storms, which outraged Zeus so much, that he hung her from Olympus with anvils restraining her feet.

Athena is recognized as the goddess of wisdom and a virgin goddess. When she was a little girl she had played with another girl named Pallas. She killed Pallus and upon grieving her death made a wooden figure of her likeness called the palladium. During the first king of Attica, King Cecrops 1, Athens was adjudged to Athena who developed the arts, the olive tree into existence and the development of clothing.

Poseidon was given the trident by the Cyclopes and became lord of the sea and tamer of horses. He rivaled Zeus for the love of Thetis but Themis told both that the son of Thetis would become greater than his father, so they both left her.

Demeter is known as the goddess of farming, cultivating corn and taught mankind to sow and reap a harvest. Hades took her daughter, Persephone, and Demeter looked for her all over the planet with torches in the night. She left Heaven and came to Eleusis disguised as a woman where she met with Imabe who made her smile by the telling of jokes.

The god of light, Apollo, was born on the island of Asteria (Delos) and learnt from Pan, the art of prophecy. He introduced healing, the bow and the lyre to mankind. He killed the Cyclopes because they gave Zeus the thunderbolt, which Zeus used to kill Asclepius. Apollo was sent to Thessalia to serve the King as a servant and fell in love with Daphne who turned into a laurel tree when she ran from him.

Hermes is the messenger and herald of Zeus who is recognized for his characteristic of intelligent speech. When he was very young he stole some of Apollo's cattle while the latter was distracted with his love for Hymenaeus. He protected Dionysus from the torture of Hera and gave the ram with the Golden Fleece to Nephele. While Argus was guarding Io, Hermes killed him and received the name Argiphontes.

As the Watcher over streets and harbors, Artemis is known as the goddess of the hunters devoting herself to the chase. She also has an affect in healing young children and the creation of foods for babies. Ares is a warrior and the god of war. His sons are Phobus and Deimos (Terror and Fear). Pelion and Ossa confined Ares to a brazen jar for thirteen months but Hermes rescued him. Aphrodite loved him and during the Trojan War Athena wounded him and he gave his horses to Aphrodite who was injured in war and subsequently returned to Olympus.

Hephaestus is the god of metalwork, engineering ways to work with copper, iron, gold and silver. He was married to Aphrodite but she loved Ares. He chained Prometheus to a rock in Mount Caucasus with the assistance of Cratos and Bia (Power and Violence). Such names given to the gods and idols represented powers that came into play through the forces of nature and emotions of a person, on varying scales.

The goddess of love and beauty, Aphrodite, was in charge of weddings and great passion. She helped the Trojans during the war and saved the life of Paris so he could be with Helen. She won the apple of Eris (Discord) as she intervened with the judgement. Paris and Aphrodite are recognized for helping young people falling in love.

In the stories and fables of historical mythology there is in use a type of logic that is not ordinary, not random, not even consciously coherent. It is a language unto itself that works with symbols, allegories and analogies that are part of our imaginative history. It becomes poetic in thought and involves fantasy in dealing with the path through instinctively recognizing the meaning for interpretation.

Legends and myths have been passed down through the centuries by poets and scholars and have a special appeal perhaps not because they all actually occurred, but from the truth they contain about human existence and life as we can fathom to understand it. The fascination of good triumphing over evil, the villain being put in a proper place by the hero and the attribution of qualities to a particular facet of nature are all marvels that are entertaining as we learn from them and experience through them.

There are superstitions that we abide by at times for no apparent or particular reason, yet they come from our subconscious mind and make us react, perhaps to avoid calamity or to gain something through the instinct associated with it. The number three is a superstitiously lucky number but for what possible reason? The Christian "Trinity" has roots in our subconscious mind, the triangle has a significant relation to being a positive form, and also the father, mother and child have a sense of completeness and accomplishment in our mind as a fixed triad. German folklore once declared that stabbing a werewolf three times at the brow reveals the true identity of the monster. The Spanish royal family believed in calling the dead King three times by his name before burying him. The Pythagoreans believed that three was a perfect number because it had a beginning, middle and end. Even in erotic symbolism three is often used in love charms for its connection to the male genitals.

Numbers, names, and images have an impression upon our mind from their historical roots. They have been past down from generation to generation, as a mythology of the ages and became an imprint of life. Knowledge and associations are stored in our mind, and connect to instincts that influence our behavior. That becomes the significance of mythology and our connection to it, rooted as part of the psychology we are made of, given to us from our ancestors and implanted within the complexity of our growth and DNA.

Specific names were given to mythological deities because those deities represent those names. Everything that is given a name is tangibly connected to the meaning of that name. A cat is not given the name "cat" because it has disquieting eyes, four paws and a tail. It was given because it fits all particular features that make it a cat. The same is true of gods, angels, spirits, demons, people and every form in life. People ponder over names before naming their newborn baby because it will affect the character of the child as it grows older and the parents want the best possible life for the child because the name attracts the and builds qualities it represents.

Mythical deities have certain characteristics and depictions that are sometime enacted within social circles. We often imitate performances that originate from some ancient mythology. An old principle of magic, called mimicry is when a person imitates an event in the hope that it will occur. This is often done socially when one person imitates and gestures in hope of seeing a certain outcome. As a passenger in a car while a driver is speeding we may press our foot into the floor mat wishing the driver would press onto the brake pedal and slow down. In effect we are mimicking the action to send an impression. Sport fans sometime become tense when they want their athlete to perform the greatest, so they strain their muscles sending a hope that the athlete will feel it and accomplish the desired outcome. Through such actions we are practicing mimicry and enacting our desires. Tales of mimicry are ageless and some rooted in mythology by the very actions that we perform without realizing why we do them.

In Buddhism the belief in gods, lesser spirits, demons and the forces of nature exist and all are subject to the law of karma. Their religious concerns are based in the Buddha's Dharma or doctrine such that should material gain or misfortune fall upon them it is not a matter of spiritual concern. It is more the result of a powerful force from one of many gods subject to moral actions from justifiable karma and higher forces. Gautama Buddha held the work of the gods to be significant even when the king of the gods placed Vishnu as the protector of Ceylon. Ceylon was the city that the Buddha declared on his deathbed to have a greatest stronghold on his religion. The traditional belief is that the last person to attain Nirvana had lived some 2000 years ago and the next to attain it will come when the next Buddha, called Maitri arrives. In Buddhism, people are responsible for their own salvation and mundane affairs are not associated to their specific religious dealings except on occasion of or after someone becomes deceased where monks would then chant a collection of the Pali texts called the piri or words of protection. Secular events such as birth and marriage are not incorporated into their spiritual practices as traditional.

Indra was considered Lord of the atmosphere between the heavens and the earth and was recognized by the Aryans as having fought successful campaigns amongst the demons that represented the inhabitants in the Aryan invasions. Varuna (meaning sky) was another Aryan god and corresponds to Uranus as the all-seeing and all-knowing sky above, who growled through the sounds of thunder and sent his force of breath in the winds across the earth. In Egypt, Horus was revered as the dominating power in the sky through the

Sun. This sun god was represented with a falcon head and renowned as the fiercest of birds that soared in the Egyptian skies and had the all-seeing, penetrating eye.

We tend to feel a great affinity in reverence to the sky and often discuss the weather, planets, stars and things "up there" which leaves wonderful mysteries about what exactly is out there in the vast sky. We sometimes ponder if there are any superior beings, life forms that exist in the billions of star systems in the Universe or did we just happen to be the only lucky habitable planet. Sky deities still exist to the present day by being passed from ancient lore and are held responsible for the orderly flow throughout the Universe on a cosmic scale. The movements of the stars and planets have great influence upon things in our daily life as can be validated through the study of astrology, being the logic of the stars. Life is constantly expanding and there appears to be an order to it opposed to ultimate chaos. It appears that through knowledge and experience there are greater powers associated to deities homologous with life beyond this planet. Through some intricate way their characteristic creativity plays a role in the procession of our life. The expression of mythology and our place in it has been our forefathers attempt to explain those forces.

Slavonic tribes that existed around the first and second centuries AD stretched across parts of Europe as far as Spain. They were hospitable to strangers and very strong with the capability of enduring the cold with few human basics such as clothing, food and fire. Some of them resided along the Baltic shore and on the island of Rugen, which became an area involving Slav pagan worship. They were very akin to nature and created gods that became expressions of the life they endured and things they most depended upon in their environment. Ovinnik, Yarilo and Kupala were some of the deities used in ritual for worshipping fire. They held their pagan beliefs for some time until Christianity eventually replaced it with the premise of angels and saints. Their magical rites with fire were from the belief that it cleansed and assisted in healing but later that it was a protection against unclean forces. Every predicament was associated to relevant forces and developed legendary mythology as a road of concern and sagacious belief.

Slavs believed that spirits and demons were everywhere and that their ancestors returned as such to either assist or harm the descendants. Offerings of food and clothing were left with the burial in the coffin beside the deceased, as they thought such items were needed in the afterlife. They had offerings, laments and a meal at the funeral in honoring their cult of the dead, so the ancestral spirits would come and help in protection of their home and land thereafter.

The concept of evil evolved from attributions of pain and death which the people of Mesopotamia described in their mythical representations. The Sumerians, Assyrians and Babylonians had a pessimist view of life thinking that the gods put mankind on earth as a sport for their amusement along with plagues, diseases, and people causing increased suffering. Although the gods purportedly caused all this in the beginning they were never questioned about the justice of it all. This gradually brought about the idea of dualism in religion, which is quite distinct in Zoroastrianism. It began in Iran from the teachings of Zoroaster who was born about 570 BC. The two principle deities causing such affect in life were Ohrmazd and Ahriman. Ohrmazd was responsible for all that was good in life and Ahriman caused all that was evil resulting in demons, pain, and even death.

In India, the Hindu gods Vishnu and Shiva were both creators and destroyers of life. Judaism had a modified conception of duality in the first century AD with Yahweh or Jehovah as the only deity who existed and embodied both good and evil. Demonology evolved during the sixth century BC accounting for demonic forces from the work of the devil, which stems from the Greek word diabolis, meaning dual or duality. The Christian gospels and the Dead Sea Scrolls both give this representation of duality within their writings. Jesus is said to have been tempted by the "Prince of the world" and the devil/dual force in many instances of his noble life.

The Orphic myth of the Greeks shows the son of Zeus being eaten by the Titans causing mankind to manifest as a physical vehicle inhabited by an immortal soul. From then on the term, having a 'Titanic' body became known as a soul that longed for its return to the Divine. The Orphic cult expressed the need to ascend back into the heavenly world and escape the bondage of material restrictions. The idea arose in most cults and religions thereafter including Gnosticism in the 2nd century AD that attested to the fall from heaven. The rise of Manicheism had such views as well and taught that the opposing forces of nature were good and evil, spirit and matter, lightness and darkness. It became a plague for mankind through time that the soul must ascend back into its rightful order of divinity.

There appears to be some illusory life that we are put value into and everyone tries to explain it in different ways and how to overcome it or live with it using various practices. Why some religions pronounce their doctrines to be sole truth is a bit of a perplexity. It appears that when they denounce other forms of worship they are in fact stating that others are wrong but who is to say since it is all relative and partial to the whole. We seem to be gradually opening to embrace more of a cosmic reality than a personal one as civilization grows and as science walks along with spirituality in hand. This material world is seen in most religious contexts to set us back instead of move us forward into spiritual awareness and ability. We have used abstractions of myth and magic through the ages to explain phenomena and life. All religions incorporate ideologies from the past, handed down by ancestors. We are fractions of a vast system and when an attempt to explain one thing is concocted, innumerable other references come into play. There seems to be only a little bit of truth to anything and a vast amount of relativity to everything.

The soul has been considered through many ancient myths to be capable of leaving the body, similar to what we conceive when we think of projecting consciousness with the astral body. Some fables reveal the protecting the soul by temporarily disengaging it from the body. It was thought that transferring the soul into a material object outside of a person's body would render the person safe from dangerous enemies. The body was considered to be capable of continual functioning without the soul in it by virtue of a sympathetic "action at a distance". It was also thought that the body becomes immortal if the soul is deposited in some foreign object because life does not inhabit it and therefore the body cannot be killed or aged. Although this reasoning is not justifiable it played in several fables from various cultures. Some of the Hindu fables contested that magicians and ogres told their comrades that they projected their soul inside of a bird or other chosen object and that they would be protected while physically absent from their soul. While at some distant location, the bird was locked in a cage, incapable of being found, stolen or injured by enemies. When the object was found and destroyed, subsequently the so-thought "immortal" person became deceased. James G. Frazer mentions these and similar stories in The Golden Bough - The Roots of Religion and Folklore.

Another story, of Cambodian origin refers to the King of Ceylon who left his soul in a box hidden away at home so that when he went to battle he could never be killed. During a war against Rama, the King left the box with a hermit named Fire-Eye and while in battle he was struck by an arrow but remained alive. One of Rama's allies knew of the Kings secret and transformed into the likeness of the King and went to the hermit and asked to return the box. The ally brought the box to the battle, squished it to pieces in front of the King and watched as the King fell lifelessly to the ground.

In an old Norse story, a vulgar giant mentions to the captive princess that his heart is on an island, next to a church where there is a water-well. In the well there is a duck that has an egg and in the egg he had transported his heart. The hero of the story retrieves the egg and demolishes it whereupon the giant bursts and the princess becomes rescued. These and other stories in myth and legend exemplified primitive faith for protection of the soul. The soul of important people and kings of ancient times being bound within particular sacred objects is not uncommon. Carlos Castenada makes similar pretensions in his recent story relating a spirit in a bird that has been passed down through generations. There are countless allegories relating myth to magic and religion to folklore, all with attempts to explain some mode of powers being transferred or supernormal capabilities being employed.

Our efforts to study and unravel some of these mythologies are a sign of gratitude for the history they endured. It is a complicated subject when we wish to find the origin of any one myth. The cultures through civilization have and continue to borrow from their neighbors and cause the stories and memories to change hands and views. We may say that Typhon was a story built upon the eruption of a volcano, with borrowed thesis from older civilizations than Greek. We may say that vampires do not exist and that they are merely pale, distempered people with sinister and evil interests having physiological disorders. The critic may insinuate that werewolves are a rare skin disease, which caused irrational behavior in the person who contacted such a disease. Whatever our hypothesis, there is always another explanation.

Regardless of the interpretations and explanations, mythology holds certain social truths and can be construed as playing a part in modern lifestyles. It is a system of thought, which has been impressed upon us since and before birth. We may relate it to aspects of our moral character, superstitious beliefs, fundamentals of theology or even as forces and principles in an array that reflects spiritual relevance. It is important to hold originality as mythology evolves into new hands. Historians sometimes study myths to help place events and locations of eras gone by. Occultists may extrapolate symbolical allegories from myth, psychologists may explain behavior and disorders relating to myth and philosophers may coin logical and moral justifications from mythical experience. There are many different views to the same story in mythology and the point of view will vary from one account to the next. Mythology has a place in our life and we have a place in it. Our view of how it affects us is as equally important as remaining flexible with our interpretations. ★

TOUCHING THE QABALAH

"On penetrating into the sanctuary of the Kaballah, one is seized with admiration at the sight of a doctrine so simple and at the same time so absolute. The necessary union of ideas and signs, the consecration of the most fundamental realities by primitive characters, the trinity of words, letters and numbers…such are the primary principles of the written word, shadow of that Spoken Logos which created the world!"

Eliphas Levi

The widespread promulgation of the Qabalah (also spelt Kabbalah, Kaballa, Qaballah, and Cabala) since early secretive traditions has suffered with the persecution of mystic Jews during the Spanish Inquisition. Qabalah became incorporated into Astrology, Yoga, Magick, Tarot, Gematria, and other esoteric assemblies throughout time. Qabalah was most prominent in the twelfth century but existed before that by practicing mystics. During early eras it went against the formative dogma and hierarchical structure of organized religion and was therefore not an accepted practice in religious circles. The mystical Qabalah was a more personally customized approach to the needs of individuals in their search of mapping the chain of creation's command, and opened itself to comparative religion.

The creator in biblical terms is God but with the Jewish Qabalah having been employed mystically and magically for centuries, that fathomable "God" that we comprehend contains particular limitations and is subordinate to a higher, limitless and unknowable God concept, which is referred to as Ain Soph or En-Sof.

The origin of the Qabalah system was derived from the three Hekhaloth books, known as the Sepher Yetzirah, the Sepher Zohar, and the Sepher Bahir. The Qabalah is a pictorial representation of the world in creation and is divided into ten spheres called Sephiroth. The Sephiroth are emanations, and together comprise the Tree of Life, the divine macrocosm, which is mirrored within each person and represents the composition of diversity of worlds from the Ain-soph or limitless light to the physical plane.

There is a speculative side to the Tree of Life, which contains all of the philosophical considerations and there is a practical side that is magical and refers to the Hebrew words, letters, and attributions assigned to the Tree. The conception of it began, as it is said, when Moses (1194-1270) had received the written law (the Torah) on Mount Sinai. He was a Spanish Talmudist and Bible commentator who studied the Qabalah. It contained the sacred names of God which when further divided and analyzed prove to be facets of the body of God as represented in the Tree of Life. The word Qabalah has been translated as meaning "from mouth to ear" given that the oral Torah was taught from mages and scholars through the ages as secretive interpretations since written documentation of it often caused some form of persecution.

An esoteric discipline or study involving cosmology and cosmogony, called the Maaseh Bereshith (History of Creation) was responsible, according to many authorities, for the writing of one of the most influential books on the Qabalah written in the sixth century. Maaseh Merkahah (History of God's throne-chariot) is the practice of meditation and ascending to higher spiritual realms and Bereshith in part refers to aspiring to a mystical state through meditative practice. Rabbi Jochanan ben Zakkai is said to be the father of Merkabah mysticism and Rabbi Akiba the father of Berashith mysticism.

This one particular book that was issued from the Maaseh Bereshith contains important Gnostic material and was called the Sepher Yetzirah or Book of Creation, which claims to have been received from a vision. Great preparations were done with talismans, seals, amulets, and magical incantations from the Jewish mystics prior to the ascension of the soul for retrieving certain illuminating information on Creation. The book details the ten Sephirothic spheres of number and establishes the Hebrew alphabet to the Tree of Life as an explanatory instrument of Creation. Mystics who worked with the Sepher Yetzirah developed telepathic and telekinetic powers and were able to alter natural events, which feats appeared quite magical to bystanders. Commentaries on the Sepher Yetzirah first appeared in the tenth century. There were different versions of the book translated. The short version contained nearly 1300 words and the long version nearly 2500 words.

Several early authorities attribute the writing of the book to the Patriarch Abraham who was born in Mesopotamia, later living in Egypt and known as the greatest astrologer and mystic of his time. He sent his gifts of the occult mysteries across Asia as it is said in Genesis 25:6:

"…to the sons of the concubines that Abraham had, Abraham gave gifts, and he sent them away…to the lands of the east."

The Tree of Life, or Otz Chiim, is the most fitting name to the expression and work of the Qabalah as it is the map of creation and image of Gods perfection through creation as an organized file-system of transcendence and manifestation. It contains ten spheres called Sephiroth and twenty-two paths interconnecting the spheres. The Sephiroth may also be considered as paths. In total, the 32 paths are states of consciousness and the 32 times that God's name Elohim appears in the account of creation in the first chapter of Genesis. The ten Sephiroth (Sepher means "text" or "book") are considered to be Objective and the 22 paths as subjective experiences, in one context.

The 22 letters of the Hebrew alphabet are assigned to each of the 22 Paths.

The Hebrew letters become a pictorial text, as for example the letter Shin, has three heads that are separated and suggest 3 flames of a fire. It is also the dominant letter in the Hebrew word 'Esh', meaning fire. The other letter in fire is aleph, which is air because fire cannot exist without air. The letters can also be used in their complete written form, for example ALEPH or in a numerical form called Gematria where they are added up, as in numerology, and equated to other significant and associated words deriving new interpretations. They can also be vocalized and are vibrated as the holy names of God. Vocalizing the Hebrew letters has been of great importance to magicians (ie YHVH, ADONAI, AGLA, EHEH) and Qabalistic healing techniques through the dynamics of their vibration.

The 32 paths have been associated with the 31 nerves through the spinal cord; the 32nd one being the combined complexity of the 12 cranial nerves. The Paths are a two-way street; in descending order they exert control over properties of manifestation or creation and in ascension they become a mystical expression of experiencing realization of their forces. In this context, worlds refer to the four worlds of the Qabalists, as well as the four levels of being (material, astral, mental, and spiritual). The four worlds are known in descending order are Azilut (the Divine World of Emanation/Spiritual), Beriah (the World of Creation/Mental), Yezirah (Formation or Formative World/Astral; the human psyche) and Assiah (the World of Action/Physical). The four scales of these worlds are depicted in the paintings rendered in this section as the King, Queen, Emperor and Emperess scales.

Significantly enough, the 32 paths correspond to the amount of apexes located on a five-dimensional hypercube. To imagine this, think of a line as having 2 apexes, one at each end of the line, and a square as having 4 apexes, one at each corner. A cube represents 3 dimensions and has 8 corners or apexes and a four-dimensional hypercube would have 16 apexes and lastly, the five dimensional hypercube has 32 points or apexes. Difficult, perhaps, for the mind to fathom at first, but the concept is indeed intriguing concerning how higher dimensions contain a conglomeration of other dimensions within them. The first three dimensions comprise that of space, the fourth is time and the fifth dimension may be likened to a spiritual affinity encompassing all that we can know.

The Hebrew word for heart is Lev, which numerically adds to 32. The heart is required in the ability to understand, as a receptive and purifying substance traveling the paths. Also, through the heart, Understanding channels Wisdom from Divine Nature, into all emanations. The 32 Paths as mentioned, may be divided into 10 main Sephiroth, and its 22 subjective paths as 3 Mothers, 7 Doubles, and 12 Elementals.

The study of these paths of wisdom has been associated with both esoteric and exoteric doctrine. Esoteric refers to the heart doctrine where information exudes from the heart-center. Without the heart the physical body would be dead matter and the mind would cease functioning. Thus when communication comes from the heart, expression is esoterically produced. When information is derived through the mentality, it is considered as exoteric since it is divulged exclusively from the intellect and reasoning faculty.

Wisdom, Chokmah (the Spiritual/Supernal Father principle called Abba) represents nonverbal thought and has its great power within its silence, whereas Understanding, Binah (the Spiritual/Supernal Mother principle called Immah) becomes its verbalization and expression through the heart of each Sephirah.

Chokmah is a sacred Wisdom that is without words in an infinite and boundless abstract sense. Bringing that sacred Wisdom to Binah, conceptual understanding, it unites and begins creation on the mental plane, into the next world of creation and mentality, called Beriah. It is for the following reason that the words understanding and wisdom are used emphatically throughout this book.

"With Wisdom a house is built, with Understanding it is established, and with Knowledge its rooms are filled." - Proverbs 24:3,4.

It is through the Sephiroth that God and man communicate. The Tree of Life is the route map of all possibilities for that discourse to occur. The Tree may be likened to a delivery service and not meant as an emblem of worship as such. Learning attributions to the Tree of Life develops a conscious awareness of the subconscious filing system that exists and helps to categorize all things and harmonize the information processing with data and relationships in life. As all objects in life are composed of certain elements, qualities, and substance, everything can be placed somewhere on the Tree. Also, for example, if a person wished to have an object, they may do a particular magical operation or mental manipulation by using principles of the Tree to bring that object into their life. Similarly for learning, writing poetry or expressing an emotion, the Tree can be used for anything imaginable and beyond.

Knowledge is attributed to the so-called false sphere titled Daath on the Tree and is not really a Sephira but is sometimes alluded as one for it's position and confluence between Wisdom and Understanding.

The Three Mother letters in Hebrew are Aleph, Mem, and Shin and are primary letters. Aleph is the first letter of the alphabet, Mem is the middle letter and Shin is a double letter. These letters are called Mother letters because they are derived from Binah, the Great Mother of Understanding, the primary feminine principle. Pronunciation of these letters has been a practice of mystics for transcending into the Chokmah State of consciousness. This is said to be accomplished by passing through the Chashmal into their corresponding domains of breath, water and fire and achieving a completely receptive mode with the AMSh and finally within the creative practice of YHV, where the so-titled creation of descendants occurs.

The Tetragrammaton is abbreviated as YHVH (Yod Heh Vau Heh), and is intricately associated to the pentagram. It symbolizes the 4 elements and spirit dominating over them, representative as man the microcosm. Qabalists affirm that the letters YHV are derived from AMSh. Yod is derived from Mem, Heh from Shin, and Vau

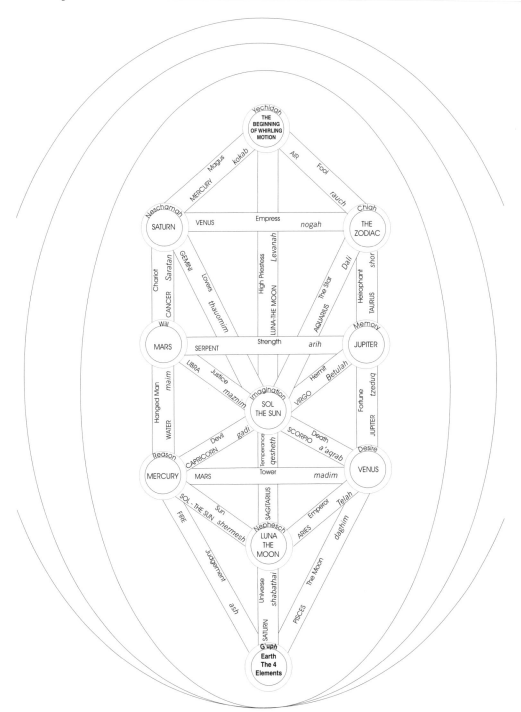

Tree of Life:

10 Sephiroth with planetary attributions. 22 paths with astrological, planetary and element attributions.

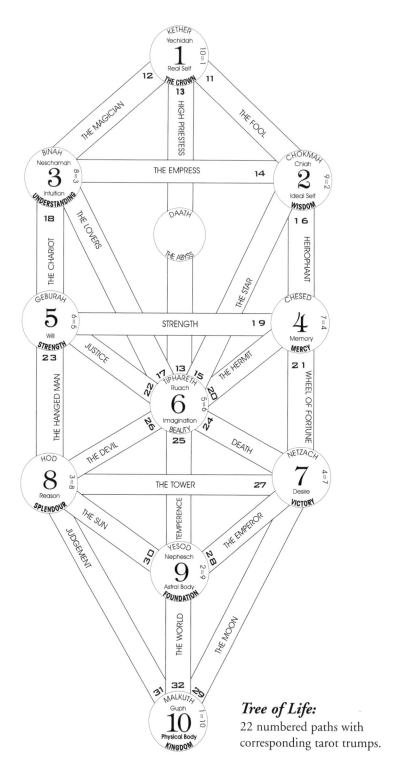

Tree of Life:
22 numbered paths with
corresponding tarot trumps.

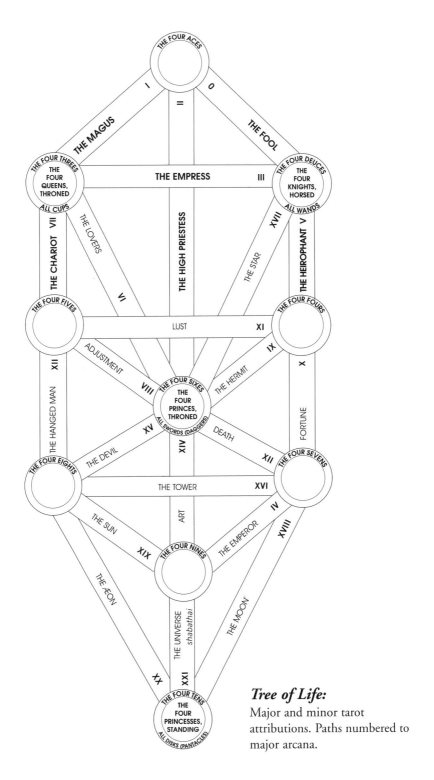

Tree of Life:
Major and minor tarot
attributions. Paths numbered to
major arcana.

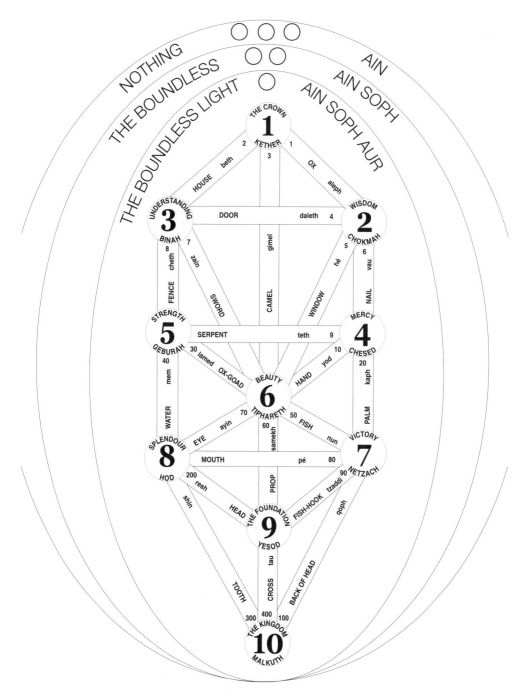

Tree of Life:
Divine meanings of the 10 Sephiroth. 22 Paths with Hebrew letters, meanings and values.

from Aleph. The 3 Mother letters are the roots of the letters of the Tetragrammaton and are an intriguing mystery. The Mother letters also spell out the Hebrew word Emesh (yesternight) which is the gloom before Creation, before the Sephiroth were brought into existence. These letters represent the mystery of the reconciliation of opposites, which normally cannot be reconciled therefore they transcend the concept of logic. One can literally and figuratively walk on fire with this secret, and as Jacob said: "And Emesh gave judgement" - Genesis 31:43

The Mother letters also represent cause, effect and their synthesis between the two opposites. They correspond to the three elements of air, water and fire and with the 3 pillars under Kether, Chokmah and Binah (Present, Past, Future). The first triad is dielectric and exists as "Creator", the next as the object of creation, and finally the act of creation. From this supernal triad the next triad comes into existence and is composed of love, judgment, and mercy. It is responsible for defining the three pillars of past, present and future into our world.

From the 3 Mothers (the horizontal lines) arose the 3 Fathers (the three columns) of YHV which caused space to come into existence and creation to thereafter follow. Here it may be fitting to mention the six rings of the King's name, YHV, which represent the six directions (Up, down, left right, back, front), and the source of physical speech, as they have also been accrued as "the six rings of the throat" in the Zohar. These rings were sealed as YHV, worn on six fingers and represent the six Sephiroth and directions which become transcendent of speech and uttered in the word of Creation. Awareness is concealed in the physical dimension of space or Olam (universe) but can be transmuted with the permutation of AMSh.

The seven double letters, Beth, Gimel, Daleth, Caph, Peh, Resh, and Tau (BGD KPRT) can be pronounced hard or soft but the six letters BGD KPT are usually pronounced hard at the beginning of a word. The hard sound refers to an active running and the soft to returning into a meditative state. Initiates use the hard sounds for climbing or scaling up the tree and the soft for returning, as it were.

The six days of creation have been likened to the six directions in that it took one day to create each direction and transform into three-dimensional space. The seventh day being that of the Sabbath by representing the connection between Malkuth and Kether, similar in this sense as Adonai is connected to Malkuth from above, and rejoiced as the center point. Thus the seventh day denotes perfection in creation while entering the eight denotes a transcendental influx.

One of the functions of the seven letters therefore is to climb the seven lower Sephiroth since there are seven vertical paths associated with them. There is not an eighth vertical path, but if one existed, it would likely be from Kether to the Infinite Being. The seven planets of Saturn, Jupiter, Mars, Sun, Venus, Mercury and the Moon (the Romans named the days of the week by the planet dominating it during the first hour in each day) are astrologically connected with the seven letters and their corresponding angels guide their influence. The angels exist in the world of Yetzirah, and were created from each word spoken by God. "Every word emitting from God creates an angel." -the Talmud

The angels work through the planets and stars, as they are somewhat like souls connected to those celestial bodies. There are permanent and temporary angels, the latter being without actual names. When a person is born, the date and time are of importance towards their destiny according to the angelic influences associated with the cosmic bodies at that time. It is also said that the angel Laylah oversees the moment of birth and has an influence in whether the person will be of weak or strong character, wealthy or poverty stricken, and basically foolish or wise in major decisions.

The twelve remaining letters are the elementals, connected to the remaining paths, and have a singular sound. The twelve signs of the zodiac and the twelve months of the year, as well as the twelve permutations of Tetragrammaton, (which are used in mysticism to extend beyond the realm of time and space to the 'eternity of eternities') are also identified with those paths. Meditating upon the twelve diagonal boundaries provides a grasp on the complexity of infinity and a proficiency at moving along the paths diagonally, which is an easier method of ascending the Tree, opposed to vertically. Through these infinite lines of diagonal boundaries, the link between physical and transcendental, as an integrated flowing energy from the Tree of Life, develops our cognizance of the Universe.

Nullifying the ego by transcending its limiting effect allows for the realization of God as a force perpetuating Creation to illuminate through the transparency of the Self. This attainment comes after ordeals, experienced states of consciousness and trials of initiation into enlightenment. It is not something that is recognized or believed by someone that has not had the experience. Belief is not the fulcrum of the Great Work, so much as results are reality for the truly sincere aspirants. A true mystical experience is an attainment of surpassing the self-image and realizing the ALL as it is, connected through the higher dimensional framework of combinations from the Divine.

These four worlds and four planes of existence are said to have occurred simultaneously resulting in the final physical, material manifestation, which we know and are "somewhat" trapped consciously within. The first world, as mentioned, is Atziluth or world of Emanation. God manifests himself in the form of Archetypes in that world. His inexhaustible energy created ideal or archetypal representations that would become higher models of everything made manifest. The union of God and his Shekkinah or feminine counterpart takes place in this higher, inner world. The following three worlds become the result of this unification of the higher world such as is illustrated in the yin and yang of Chinese philosophy. The next world called Briah is the world of Creation. Pure spirits and the highest of angels reside in this world and herein are revealed the holy names of God. The next world is that of Yetzirah, or world of Formation. Within this world are ten angelic hosts named: Malachim, Arelim, Chajoth, Ophanim, Chashmalim, Elim, Elohim, Benei Elohim, Ishim and Seraphim. The Prince of the world, called the great Metatron or Angel of Presence, resides over these angels. The final world is called Assiah and is the world of humanity and nature upon the physical plane. In this world impurities of the planes above it were/are filtered but the density and multiplicity of combinations, causing much imperfection. Negative forces such as called the Qlipoth and evil entities came to be formed and for this reason it is considered as the 'world of making'. The ten Sephiroth appear in each of these four worlds creating a tree within a tree according to the level one is referring to.

The Adam mentioned in the Bible can also be placed upon these worlds. In the first three worlds he is androgynous, first as the heavenly man, then as he appears in Genesis I, 27, then as Adam of the Garden and finally the Adam of the flesh. In the world of Assiah he is no longer androgynous and can begin his reproduction. The Adam in all these worlds becomes the symbol of the universal man, or animus mundi, with his brain in the first world, heart in the second, breath in the third and genitals in the fourth.

The original Adam was Adam Kadmon who had concentrated beams of light emanating from his eyes. All souls that existed were within him, but being cast down in his fall to the physical plane, his soul was exiled or became separate from his body and this separation is the original cause of ours. That is to say it is the logic behind the division we have as humans and require the hard work of reunification to become self-realized again. Our conception of darkness relating to the density of matter in absence of light upon the material plane is the world of shells and Qlipothic realms. The job becomes the restoration of recovering the original unity, by transmuting our lower world back to it's originality so that we are not capable of being influenced by those forces and misled into ultimate chaos.

Ain-Soph is the limitless or boundless unity beyond comprehension. It is the no-thing which cannot be described in terms of being or non-being and simply exists in its non-existence. It is the non-entity vehicle, which many have tried to explain by stating what it is not. It is neither eternity, nor time, nor truth nor is it essence as it is beyond any rational explanation. Ain-Soph comes before God and although through yoga we can develop ourselves to comprehend no-thing just as the concept of infinity in the science of formal logic, it is beyond scope to presently explain Ain-Soph. It is not the Creator of the worlds as it has no desire and is without form. However at the same time it is affluence in the universe, through the Sephiroth, but in no tangible, comprehendible way. The only activity that could be discerned from Ain-Soph, if there could be one, is a ray of light but that is provided there was/is/will be the desire to perform on Ain-Sophs' part.

Creation results from contraction as a concentration of energies at a center requiring to expand. The concentrated form becomes a beam of energy that is sent outward as an original expression. If those energies flowed back into itself, the contraction of the Ain-Soph would be assimilated. As one Chinese text explains *(The Secret of the Golden Flower)*, the withdrawal or return flow of the senses are required to create the flower, or subtle body. In this limited sense we can conceive that Ain-Soph can create itself or be itself without creating any other thing. It is one of the great mysteries that scientists attempt to unravel in seeking the origins of the universe.

The first triad is composed of Kether, Chokmah and Binah. This archetypal model may be considered as the first principle in Creation.

1. In Kether, the universal plan contains what intelligence may convey as the Primordial Point or Monad. It is also referred to as the White Head, the Ancient One, The Inscrutable Height, Macroprosopus (The Great Countenance), also called The Vast Countenance. It is the first expression of God's will and contains all potential opposites in complete harmony. It is the Crown and also the fulcrum for the next two forces on the spiritual level to maintain equilibrium. The crown is a symbol of that which is above, supreme power in the immortal Spirit, the beginning or root of all life forms. It is the First Manifest, the Ancient of Ancients as the other side of Kether is Unmanifest and is a living Being that is considered to be conceivably timeless. The Archangel that resides there is Metatron and communication is direct with the Spirit rather than to our mental and emotional levels, which to that Being is like a substance similar to what we think of when we see a material object. We look for more convenient ways to communicate than carving our ideas into objects such as stone, and so the Higher Order of Beings similarly transmits the message to our living spirit. The order of angels is the Holy Living Creatures, which astrologically correspond to the zodiacal signs of Taurus, Leo, Scorpio, and Aquarius. The Egyptian Atum-Ra is best equated with Kether, who lived within Nuit before anything else came into being and signifies the alpha and omega, beginning and end, dual aspect of the Manifest and Unmanifest. All Sephiroth are influenced by the ones preceding and proceeding them. The only two that are not so affected are Kether and Malkuth because they are the beginning and end. Therefore Kether is completely masculine and Malkuth (The Earth Mother) completely feminine in this particular respect.

2. Chokmah is Wisdom, the masculine Father and the willingness to express the Will. It looks at the Divine and sends that wisdom or dynamic thrust of spiritual force to mankind through the worlds to teach what is there. Chokmah has influence from Binah (feminine) on one side and Kether (masculine) on the other. The spiritual experience is the Vision of God face to face as the omnipotent perfection of ideal Truth. Its' virtue is Devotion and anyone claiming to be in this sphere would be drawn into Union with God and no longer exist physically unless they be a living Christ or Angelic Being using the material plane for some divine purpose from the Word. The associated Archangel is Ratziel with the title Ab or the coming forth of power (aleph, beth) and its' reflection, Abba. Its' order of angels are the Auphanium, or Wheels giving rise to the Zodiac and its' whirling motion of power.

3. Binah is Understanding, and feminine in nature as the Great Mother, the first form, Imma, and represented by

Saturn. It is from her union with the Father that Daath (Knowledge and Reason) is formed but is not a Sephirah in itself. From Binah, the next seven Spheres proceed, which coincide with the creation from seven days as given in Genesis. The Crown, Wisdom and Understanding have been associated with the three Fire symbols above the Hebrew letter Shin. Deeply concentrating upon these higher forces can cause problems when the initiate is not sufficiently prepared. That is why the lower seven Sephiroth are within our grasp of comprehension to sufficiently develop the moral and spiritual character of a person prior to the great step over the abyss to the fiery archetypal realm. The Jewish initiate is said to wear their kippah (Yiddish) or skullcap during worship because of the pure energy that's radiated from the spiritual plane. The spiritual Understanding here is the emanation of Faith with its' roots in Amen (So be it) and is the highest level of mentality that can be attained. Its' Vision of Sorrow is the involution and evolution along the Path, not to be confused with the sins of man which are within the Pit of Qlipothic forces as distorted images of the Holy Tree. The Archangel Tzaphkiel has been called the Keeper of the Records of Evolution and is associated with the Akashic Records of karma in the great Cosmic Akashic Consciousness, which is the finest of subtle matter in life. Binah is the great principle behind all moon forces and with Saturn having many moons, it is a fitting association along with its power to draw down the Limitless Void to the worlds of form. Its' virtue is Silence which is required on all levels if Binah is to be the Archetypal Temple of forms for heavenly forces to indwell.

4. Chesed is the Mercy of God and is considered a masculine force and represents the first day of creation. Its planet is Jupiter, but ruled by Zeus as the ruler of gods and men. It receives all of the Holy Powers that come from the Supernal Sephiroth and emanated through Daath to cohere as forms in Chesed. Intuition and the abstract mind have their formative aspects in Chesed and is the sphere where Masters' correspond together in abstract form.

If a person has actual conversations through the Treasure House of Images, Yesod, they are performing astral psychism and are contacting those forces from the abstract worlds. The problem is in translating their information without distorting the originality of the messages and so raising the level of consciousness to their level is part of the developmental process. Otherwise, hallucinations and schizophrenia could result from a person not sufficiently prepared to use the information gathered and assimilated. The doctrine in Liber Legis is best portrayed in the nature of Chesed: "Love is the law, love under will." For it is the law of love under God's Will that Chesed is attributed.

5. Geburah is the Severity or power of God and exists in harmony or balance by being opposite of Mercy, Chesed. It is feminine in nature and is symbolized by the planet Mars, the force of Aries. It is the second day of creation when the waters were separated and caused the firmament to appear. Its power resides in the principles of adjustment and assessing standards of Truth. Working with these forces can upset physical circumstances and emotional states if a person is not adequately ready. The magician here should be skilled in working with building forms for the spiritual forces to indwell.

6. Tiphereth is the Beauty resulting from the marriage of Chesed and Geburah. It is also called the Lesser Countenance, Zair Anpin; the Microprosopus that is both manifest and unmanifest. It is represented by the Sun and is the third day of creation when the waters gathered in one place, dry land appeared and the vegetable kingdom began existence. The Archangel Raphael is situated here and revitalizes the auras of people that come into contact with him. The Malachim, Kings, are the order of angels that are in Tiphereth which bring healing and life-giving agents. This important Sephiroth resides in the center of four others and like the Sun itself, sends it's rays, energies and life to those through the interconnecting paths. With this accomplishment in the natural order of life, the next and final triad was given form.

7. Netzach is Victory and is recognized through the qualities of Venus. It also represents the fourth day when God created the Sun and the Moon. Some attribute it to the seventh day of Creation as victorious but can be misleading if the simultaneous developments of the seven spheres under the abyss are not considered. It takes the sunlight of Tiphereth and divides it into beautiful arrays for the next lower worlds. In Netzach there are many Creative elements that come to fruition in victory. There are two aspects of many forces employed as working in polarity through this sphere. The relationship between brother and sister in the physical sense and the spiritual sense as form and force is what is meant. They work together as streams of energy to communicate and flow in an even and recognized balance. Esoteric fraternities, student and teacher, child and parent, all have this manner of polarity at work. Lucifer, the Light-bearer is associated with Venus and as with all spheres, victory is not accomplished without struggle, firmness and great valour.

8. Hod is the Glory and is represented by Mercury, Thoth, and Hermes in differing respects. It is the fifth day when God created the creatures of the sea and air. In Hod the Hosts are the forms that clothe the forces emanating from Netzach. Its' Archangel Michael works with unregenerate forms and forces by purging with his element of fire the ignorance that come from the base mind of Hod. This Sephiroth represents esoteric philosophy and magic by way of Hermes in the Hermetic Light. Hermetic philosophers such as Plato, Proclus, Synesius, Olympiodorus, Plotinus, Heraclitus and Hermes Trismegistus are associated here for the profundity of learning that they shed upon mankind.

9. Yesod is the Foundation and represented by the Moon. It is the sixth day when God created Adam and Eve which represents the reproductive organs. It is the final sphere of the third triad and stabilizes the opposites that precede it to represent the universe as we conceive it in its multiplicity of forms. Yesod is the storehouse of Images for

everything that exists on the physical plane and is the etheric representation of this world. Gabriel is the Archangel of Annunciation who gives the visionary images of pre-physical manifestation of the higher bodies through the influence of the Moon. The moon and sea powers emanate through Yesod. This may be likened to a great energy source that is switched from Yesod to you through the process of Visions such as by clairvoyant or clairaudient receptivity. The Kerubim through this sphere are the order of angels that build force and knowledge in the etheric levels and are greatly responsible for the healing energies to be transmitted into the physical.

10. Malkuth is the Kingdom of God and is the feminine receptive principle symbolized by the four elements working on the physical plane. It is identified with the Shekhinah as the final development of Godhead from Ain (no-thing) to Ani (I or Being) in the completeness of Adam Kadmon. It is a tremendous and wonderful place, this material world, and should be used to the greatest advantage while holding the key to spirituality. Milton described poetry as being "simple, sensuous and passionate" and it is with this feeling that Malkuth should be embraced without the sensual greed and anarchy that leads one away from recognizing the Divine. Malkuth is connected with Binah, the Great Mother, which is the experience of Sorrow through its Gate of Tears. The cause of sorrow being desires, it can be imagined that throughout the physical plane there is great sorrow held and tears shed. Sandalphon is the Archangel for our planet and as the Guide and Intelligence, carries the bridge between what should be accomplished, called the planetary Entity and the stresses of the etheric levels, called the planetary Being, to the higher levels of humanities responsibility. Persephone and Demeter were of the greatest examples of mythical deities in the Eleusinian Mysteries that personified the Earth Cult and concerns thereof. The spiritual experience associated with Malkuth is the Knowledge and Conversation of the Holy Guardian Angel, which becomes the awareness of one's true destiny.

The Pillars

The Tree of Life can be configured into three pillars as well. It is as though the downward stream of creation spread into opposing or balancing forces and from this originated good and evil, adjustment and balance to create life, as we know it. By tasting the fruit, or touching the Sephiroth, the Paths of the Tree of Life, the Knowledge of Good and Evil, the eyes of an individual become opened and aware of the creative forces employed in or through Life. The subtle forces of Ida and Pingala entwined and revolving around Shushumna is apparent here. They are the solar and lunar forces within the body that cause harmony when properly and actively employed. Acknowledging these forces of nature, from both sides of the tree, the process of growth and enlightenment of our soul takes its first step as is plainly stated in Genesis: "For God doth know that in the day ye eat thereof, then your eyes shall be opened, & ye shall be as gods, knowing good and evil." - Genesis xxx, 5

Responsibility is acknowledged when such a state is achieved and that responsibility completely avoids acts of destruction and harm upon one's fellow man. The opposing forces are a mediating factor, which make up the Mandala of Eternity, having assimilated the past and future in perfect balance for the present.

The Right Pillar is called Mercy and comprises Chokmah, Chesed and Netzach. It has been associated with the Past, Light, and the Tree of Good. It has its' name from Chesed as being Merciful with an enduring obligation towards Wisdom. From Chokmah to Netzach the prominent gods are Zeus, Jupiter and Aphrodite-Venus. Chokmah is the elemental combination Water of Air. Water is condensation and air is movement which, when combined, the idea of motion in an existing place as an abstraction of the Past may be realized.

The next sphere down the right pillar is Chesed, ruled by Jupiter and one of its responsibilities in a past tense is dealing with banks and money. Gambling is also referenced in this sphere because it is a form of the past at work for a future. That is to say, in order for gambling to exist in the present, some form of wealth previously existed to bank on. Chesed is Fire of Water, which is expansion and condensation, or the development on a form that already was there and is now set in motion.

The next sphere down the Past Pillar is Netzach, which is Water of Water, condensation of condensation. Aphrodite is pictured as having great luxury such as jewels, silks, clothing, furnishings and becomes the consumption of the past principle, form upon form that was already in existence.

The Middle Pillar is Kether, Tiphareth, Yesod and Malkuth. It is the power of the soul in all levels, the feminine counterpart of God as the Shekhinah, and is associated with the Present. Kether is the Spirit and always exists in the present.

The God of Love and the Sun is named Apollo, as Tiphareth. Apollo is the etheric of the physical Sun, just as the older Greek God Hyperion, is the astral counterpart of the Sun. Apollo is a God of the Present, being in the now, and a leader of Muses whose activities are in the now. Drama, dances, festivities are all considered as things happening and as such are in the present form.

The Yesod influence of Diana, Hecate and Artemis, in the sphere of the Moon, are quite intensely interesting. Combining all that has been said of the moon and this dynamic trio the imagination can be quite appalled with their affects. The elemental is Air of Water, which brings mobility in condensation as an action. Malkuth is the four quarters of Air, Fire, Water and Earth. It has Air of Earth, Fire of Earth. Water of Earth and Earth of Earth, which can readily be seen in the multiplicity of action occurring on the physical plane, called Malkuth.

The Left Pillar is the Pillar of Judgement or Severity, composed of Binah, Geburah, and Hod. It has been associated with the Future, Dark forces and the Tree of Evil. It receives its name from Geburah but can contain majestic qualities when its power is received from Binah, the Great Mother or Understanding. Saturn was linked to the Golden Age in mythology, which was a time when death and sickness did not occur. The future is something of a projection from our consciousness through desire, as a mirror of the past that becomes a pictured place to be, to happen, to occur. Saturn is Fire of Air, or expansion in movement and is associated with Time.

Geburah, which is Fire of Fire, has Mars and Aries as powers representing strength. Here we have expansion of expansion, which is a strong driving energy and future desire atmosphere. The police are ruled with this sphere, as is the justice system, which as a result of being in this particular area of the Tree, and will aptly illustrate why corruptness has crept into those systems in some instances when a blinded, abstruse, non self-examining process is at work. Undoubtedly this occurs in human nature, even under the jurisdiction of Justice, when forces are misapplied. This is the place where future force is used, so care should be considered when employing this energy.

Hod is a mercurial sphere with Thoth-Hermes as a force of magical operations. These are operations using the emotion of desire, and desire is a future emotion. Desire in the present is generally for something in the future to occur, and desire that exists from the past is memory. The mythical Gods are forces upon the tree, which rule something of a physical nature. Hermes as the messenger of the Gods conveyed information between those forces, information that would be enacted upon in the future tense.

This elementary essay on the Qabalah is to form a basis for the beginner and review for the advanced, as the Tree is not simplistically one in number to everything it relates, but is within another Tree and another. It is given here in a basic dimension, but engulfed within it is tree after tree, having multiple influences and manifestation principles attached to every living thing. To better grasp some of the aforementioned attributions, sketching out several Tree of Life pictorials and attaching all the qualities, combined elements, influences and attributions on each of your separate diagrams will allow for a simplistic method of meditation for these forces to better comprehend such vast knowledge. It may sound complex at the outset but assuredly it is divinely simplistic in nature.

The Thirty-Two Paths

Some basic attributions to the 32 Paths will be given and provided for correlation and meditation. There are different Gods, deities, and heroes from different religions and mythologies that are associated to each Path. There are also certain metals, perfumes, flowers, plants, trees, animals and numerous other things that are distinct to the nature of each path, as everything is connected like a multi-dimensional web through our subconscious and conscious realization of the world. Learning these and other attributions provides a filing system whereby we come to know and organize our subconscious mind and relate everything in it. The traditional system of having the tarot card The Star, the sign Aries upon the path Tsaddi has been changed with that of the letter Heh, The Emperor and Aquarius to Tsaddi accordingly as mentioned in *Liber Al vel Legis*.

1. **Kether.** The Admirable/ Concealed Intelligence. The First or Primal Glory where no living being is said to be capable of fully attaining to. Arik Anpin, The Vast Countenance. Gods- Ptah, Amon-Ra, Zeus, Jupiter, Brahma. Archangel-Metatron. God-name- Eheieh. Astrological: Neptune Tarot Cards: Ace Wands- Root of Fire. Ace Cups- Root of Water. Ace Swords- Root of Air. Ace Pentacles- Root of Earth. Stones: Diamond. Associated legendary animals: Swan, Hawk. Perfume: Ambergris.

2. **Chokmah.** The Illuminating Intelligence. The Second Glory and Crown of Creation exalted above every head. Ab, Abba. Tetragrammaton. Gods-Thoth, Tahuti, Pallas Athena, Minerva, Matt, Uranus, Hermes, Yang, The Zodiac (Mahat, Cosmic Ideation, Kwan Shi Yin), Vishnu, Ishvara, Memrah. Archangel-Ratziel. God-name: Jehovah. Astrological: Uranus. Tarot Cards: 2 Wands-Dominion. 2 Cups-Love. 2 Swords- Peace restored. 2 Pentacles-Harmonious change. Perfume: Orchitic Musk. Plant: Amaranath (immortality). Stone: Star Ruby, Turquoise.

3. **Binah.** The Sanctifying Intelligence. The Creator of Faith and Foundation of Primordial Wisdom. Ama, the dark sterile Mother and Aima, the bright fertile Mother. Gods- Kronos, Saturn, Frigg, Sakti, Kwan Yin, Yin, Kali, Mulaprakriti (cosmic root substance). Archangel-Tzaphkiel. God-name: Jehovah Elohim. Astrological: Saturn. Tarot Cards: 3 Wands-Established Strength. 3 Cups-Abundance. 3 Swords-Sorrow. 3 Pentacles-Material works. Stone: Pearl. Plants: Cypress Lily, Opium Poppy.

4. **Chesed.** The Cohesive or Receptive Intelligence. Contains all the holy powers and emanates the spiritual virtues. The Will of the individual is aligned with the Will of God. One is magic. Gedulah, Love, Majesty. Gods- aspects of Jupiter and Zeus, Poseidon, Indra, Amoun, Thor (with thunderbolt in hand, Scandinavian). Archangel-Tzadkiel. God-name: El. Astrological: Jupiter. Tarot Cards: 4 Wands-Perfected Work. 4 Cups-Pleasure. 4 Swords-Rest from Strife. 4 Pentacles-Earthy Power. Plants: Pine, Olive, and Shamrock. Metals: Tin. Stones: Amethyst and Sapphire. Perfume: Cedar Plant: Jupiter

5. **Geburah.** The Radical Intelligence. Resembles Unity by uniting with Binah. The Hall of the Lords of Karma. Fiery Serpents of Seraphim. One is fully skilled in working magic. Gods: Mars, Ares, Nephthys, Thor (Norwegian God of war) Archangel- Khamael. God-name: Elohim Gebor, the Mighty Gods. Astrological: Mars. Tarot Cards: 5 Wands-Strife. 5 Cups-Loss in pleasure. 5 Swords-Defeat. 5 Pentacles-Earthly trouble. Plants: Tobacco and nettle. Metal: Iron. Sacred tree: Oak. Stone: Ruby.

6. **Tiphareth.** The Intelligence of the Mediating Influence. Multiples the influx of the Emanations. Zoar Anpin, the Lesser Countenance. Gods- Ra, Apollo, Adonis, Iacchus, Asar, Rama, Dionysius, Balder, The Sun. Beauty. Archangel- Raphael. God-name: Tetragrammaton Aloah Va Daath. Astrological: Sun. Tarot Cards: 6 Wands-Victory. 6 Cups-Joy. 6 Swords-Earned success. 6 Pentacles-Material success. Perfume: Gum of Olibanum. Stones: Topaz, Yellow diamond.

7. **Netzach.** The Concealed or Occult Intelligence. The splendour of the intellectual virtues from the contemplation's of faith. Archangel-Haniel Gods- Aphrodite, Hathor, Bhavani, Venus. Victory. God-name: Jehovah Tzabaoth, the Lord of Hosts. Astrological: Venus. Tarot Cards: 7 Wands-Valour. 7 Cups-Illusory success. 7 Swords-Unstable effort. 7 Pentacles-Success unfulfilled. Perfume: Red Sandal, benzoin. Flower: the Rose.

8. **Hod.** The Perfect or Absolute Intelligence. Archangel- Michael. Gods-Mercury, Thoth, Hermes, Anubis, Hanuman. God-name: Elohim Tzabaoth, the God of Hosts. Astrological: Mercury. Tarot Cards: 8 Wands-Swiftness. 8 Cups-Abandoned

success. 8 Swords-Shortened force. 8 Pentacles-Prudence. Sacred Plant: Moly. Stone: Opal. Perfume: Storax. Vegetable drug: Anhalonium Lewinii.

9. **Yesod.** The Purifying Intelligence. Purifies and corrects the emanations and filters that above to Malkuth. Gods- Shu, Ganesha, Diana. Archangel- Gabriel. God-name: Shaddai el Chair, the Almighty Living God. Astrological: The Moon. Tarot Cards: 9 Wands-Great strength. 9 Cups-Material happiness. 9 Swords-Despair and cruelty. 9 Pentacles-Material gain. Sacred Plant: Mandrake, Damiana. Perfume: Jasmine.

10. **Malkuth.** The Resplendent Intelligence. Provides the influence from the Prince of Countenance, Angel of Kether and illuminates the splendors of all the Lights. The Gate of Justice, Tears, Death, Prayer, Garden of Eden and Daughter of the Mighty Ones are some titles attributed to Malkuth. Gods- Seb, Psyche, the lower Nephthys, the unmarried Isis, the Virgin or the Bride, Persephone, Ceres. Deities: Sphinx, Lakshmi. Archangel- Sandalphon. God-name: Adonai Malek or Adonai ha Aretz. Astrological: The Earth. Tarot Cards: 10 Wands-Oppression. 10 Cups-perfected success. 10 Swords-Ruin. 10 Pentacles-Wealth. Perfume: Dittany of Crete

11. **Aleph.** Meaning: Ox. The Scintillating Intelligence. The Cause of Causes that formulates the order of superior and inferior causes. Gods- Hoor-paar-Kraat. Zeus, Jupiter, Maruts (Vayu). Animal- Eagle. Stones: Topaz, Chalcedony. Perfume: Galbanum. Symbols: Swastika. Element: Air. Tarot Card: The Fool.

12. **Beth.** (Bes)- Meaning: House. The Intelligence of Numinosity. It images Magnificence and is the source of visions in apparitions. Gods- Odin. Perfumes: Storax, Mace, and Mastic. Stone: Agate. Plant: Vervain. Animal- Ibis. Astrological:

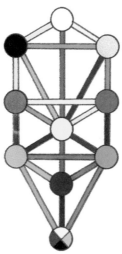

Sephiroth in Queen Scale
Paths in King Scale

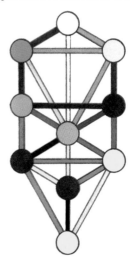

Sephiroth in King Scale
Paths in Queen Scale

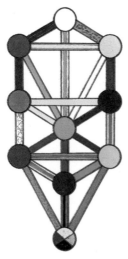

Sephiroth in Emperor Scale
Paths in Empress Scale

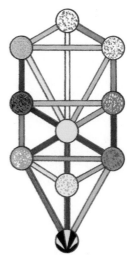

Sephiroth in Empress Scale
Paths in Emperor Scale

Mercury. Tarot Card: The Magician

13. **Gimel.** -Meaning: Camel. The Uniting Intelligence. The essence of Glory that reveals Truth to spirits. Gods- Artemis, Chomse, Chandra, Hecate. Perfumes: Aloes and Camphor. Stones: Pearl and Moonstone. Animal: Dog. Astrological: The Moon. Tarot Card: The High Priestess of the Silver Star.

14. **Daleth.** (Dallas) -Meaning: Door. The Illuminating Intelligence. Concealed ideas and basis of holiness. Gods- Venus, Freyja. Stones: Emerald and Turquoise. Flowers: Myrtle, Rose. Birds: Sparrow, Dove. Astrological: Venus. Tarot Card: The Empress.

15. **Heh.** -Meaning: Window. The Constituting Intelligence. Fashions the creation in the world's darkness. Gods- Athena, Shiva, Mars, Minerva, Mentu, Tyr. Stone: Ruby. Flower: Germanium. Astrological: Aquarius. Tarot Card: The Star.

16. **Vau.** (Vav) -Meaning: Nail. The Triumphant and Eternal Intelligence. The Delight of Glory in paradise for the just. Gods- Here (Goddess of Marriage) and Hymen (god of carrying nuptial veil). Adonis, Attis, Mithras and Tammuz have associations with Vau also. Perfume: Storax. Plant: Mallow. Stone: Topaz. Astrological: Taurus. Tarot Card: The Hierophant.

17. **Zayin.** -Meaning: Sword. The Disposing Intelligence. Perseverance for the righteous for receiving the Holy Spirit. Gods- Castor and Pollux of Greeks and Rekht and Merti of the Hindus. Apollo, Janus, Hoor-paar-Kraat (summing the Lord of Silence and Lord of Strength, Harpocrates and Horus in one deity). Bird: Magpie. Stones: Tourmaline and Alexandrite. Plants: Orchids. Astrological: Gemini. Tarot Card: The Lovers.

18. **Kheth.** (Ches) -Meaning: Fence. Intelligence of the House of Wisdom. The great arcana and hidden meanings are retrieved. Gods- Khephra (midnight sun), Mercury as messenger and Apollo as Charioteer. Hermod (Norse). Animal: Sphinx. Flower: Lotus. Perfume: Onycha. Stone: Amber. Astrological: Cancer. Tarot Card: The Chariot.

19. **Teth.** (Tes) -Meaning: Serpent. The Intelligence of Spiritual Activities. Gods- Pasht, Mau, Sekket. Demeter and Venus (as agricultural), Ra-Hoor-Khuit (representing the Sun as ruler of Leo). Animal: Lion. Flower: Sunflower. Perfume: Olibanum. Stone: Cat's Eye. Astrological: Leo. Tarot Card: Strength.

20. **Yodh.** (Yod) -Meaning: Hand. The Intelligence of the Will. Individual personalities are prepared for the Primordial Glory. Gods- unmarried Isis and Nephthys, Hindu Gopi cow girls, narcissus, Adonis, Balder. Flower: Snowdrop and Narcissus. Stone: Peridot. Astrological: Virgo. Tarot Card: The Hermit.

21. **Kaph.** (Caph) -Meaning: Spoon. The Intelligence of Mediation. Influences existence from receiving the divine benediction. Gods- Pluto (blind giver of wealth), lower plane attributes of Brahma, Indra, Zeus and Jupiter. Njord (ruler of storms). Plants: Oak, Hyssop. Perfume: Saffron. Stones: Amethyst, Lapis Lazuli. Astrological: Jupiter. Tarot Card: The Wheel of Fortune.

22. **Lamed.** -Meaning: Whip, Ox-Goad. The Intelligence of the Faithful. Spiritual virtues flow from it fulfillment to what is beneath it. Gods- Themis (abstract law, equity), Maat, Nemesis, the Hindu Yama. Plant: Aloe. Animals: Spider, Elephant. Perfume: Galbanum. Astrological: Libra. Tarot Card: Justice or Adjustment.

23. **Mem.** -Meaning: Water. The Intelligence of Stability. The source of consistency in all numerations. Gods- Auromoth, Ptah, Tum. Poseidon and Neptune (as water gods). Plants: Lotus and water plants. Stones: Beryl and Aquamarine. Perfumes: Myrrh and Onycha. Element: Water. Tarot Card: The Hanged Man.

24. **Nun.** -Meaning: Fish. The Imaginative Intelligence. The model for likeness of the beings who are developed with its aspects. Regeneration through Putrefaction. Gods- Ares, Mars, Apep, Kundalini. Stone: Snakestone. Animal: Beetle. Perfume: Opoponax. Plant: Cactus and poisonous plants. Astrological: Scorpio. Tarot Card: Death.

25. **Samekh.** (Samech) -Meaning: Prop. The Intelligence of Temptation or Trial. The first temptation which God tries his creatures by. Gods- Apollo and Artemis (as Hunters), Diana (celestial Archer), Ares. Stone: Jacinth. Perfume: Lignaloes. Astrological: Sagittarius. Tarot Card: Temperance.

26. **Ayin.** -Meaning: Eye. The Intelligence of Renovation. That which is renewed and capable of renovation by God. Gods- Khem (creative principle, Yoni+Lingam), Priapus, Pan, Bacchus. Stone; Black Diamond. Animals: Ass and Goat. Perfume: Musk. Plant: Hemp. Astrological: Capricorn. Tarot Card: The Devil.

27. **Peh.** (Pe) -Meaning: Mouth. The Natural Intelligence. Everything within the life of the sun is completed to perfection. Gods- Ares, Mars, Horus, Mentu, Krishna, Odin. Metal: Iron. Animals: Wolf and Bear. Stone: Ruby. Plants: Pepper, Rue, and Absinthe. Perfume: Pepper and pungent odors. Astrological: Mars. Tarot Card: The Tower

28. **Tzaddi.** (Tsaddi) -Meaning: FishHook. The Active Intelligence. The energy and activity which is displayed by the spirit of all beings being created. Gods- Juno, Athena, Ganymede, Ahepi and Aroueris. Plant: Olive. Animal: Eagle. Perfume: Galbanum. Stone; Chalcedony. Astrological: Aries.

29. **Qoph.** -Meaning: Back of Head. The Corporeal Intelligence. The force behind the growth or corporeal portion of all bodies. Gods- Vishnu, Neptune and Poseidon (as governing over the waters of fish), Kephra. Animal: Dolphin. Stone: Pearl. Astrological: Pisces. Tarot Card: The Moon.

30. **Resh.** -Meaning: Head. The Collective Intelligence. The perfection of the science of astrology, movement of the stars and the speculative influences that arise from that motion. Gods- Solar gods of Surya, Apollo, Helios. Metal: Gold. Perfumes: Olibanum and Cinnamon. Plants: Laurel, Sunflower, and Heliotrope. Astrological: The Sun. Tarot Card: The Sun.

31. **Shin.** -Meaning: Tooth. The Perpetual Intelligence. The assurance of the motions of the sun and moon. Gods- Agni (fiery Hindu god), Hades, Pluto, Vulcan. Egyptian gods Thoum-aesh-neith, Kabeshunt, and Tarpesheth. Stone: Fire Opal. Perfumes: Olibanum and fiery scents. Element: Fire. Tarot Card: The Last Judgement.

32. **Tau.** (Tav) -Meaning: Tau Cross. The Administrating Intelligence. It directs the motions of the seven planets and is the lowest part of the astral plane. Gods- Pan, Brahma, Vidar, Sebek., Gaea, and Saturn (as an early Italian god of agriculture and civilization). Perfumes: Assafoetida and evil scents. Astrological: Saturn. Tarot Card: The World.

Daath

There is the invisible Sephirah called Daath (Knowledge) that is not directly part of the Ten Sephiroth system of the Tree. Its Archangels are those at the Cardinal Points and the spiritual experience is the vision across the abyss.

The Deities associated with it are Sirius (the Dog Star), Sothis. Gods associated with it are Isis, Janus, and Balder. It is a relatively new addition to the Tree and is a unity in the world of force taking on forms. To it is ascribed an abstract knowledge beyond human mentality that brings about the mystical experience with absorption and realization. Revelations such as what Moses had on Mount Sinai with the Tables of the Law are acquired through the abstract mystical consciousness of Daath.

There is enough to meditate upon, become creative with and learn such that one does not have to be engulfed in the so-called false Sephirah of Daath. There are certain harms that have been attested to in meditating upon its Justice aspects. The rate of vibrations in the planes associated with those concepts are seen as strange reds, speckled brown and white, greens, and electrically charged blues. They are said to be colors that can cause damage to our inner vehicles. This sphere is not our personal subconscious but the Universal Subconscious, which contains much of past history and the stresses of the Logos and so there is potentially great harm to the individual soul in messing through that door.

Mythically, Daath can be attributed to similar dangers that were experienced by Prometheus, Perseus and Galahad. When Prometheus took the Fire from Heaven as a symbol of primitive man making a rapid advancement from the near animal level, he was chained to the mountain for his action. An eagle then ate his liver. This event caused Zeus to come down as a result to enact a kind of justice for Prometheus's premature act. Galahad being the perfect Knight had but one request upon completion of his Quest, which was to die, and it was granted. A favorable side of Daath is exemplified when Perseus assisted by Hermes captured the head of Medussa, which otherwise turned all into stone who looked at it.

It is for this and other purposes that Daath should be left to do it's job unless the practitioner is MAGIC, (this does not mean that the practitioner simply knows magic, but IS MAGIC!!!) as in an Adeptus Exemptus in the Magical Grade assigned to Chesed and is rightfully prepared to cross the Abyss into the greatest responsibility life can ever challenge as Magister Templi.

The potential of growing an inflated ego with such valuable life knowledge as one may obtain from occult studies goes without saying. That is where Yoga complements Magick and Magick balances Yoga with assimilation of exoteric knowledge and esoteric methods. Great changes may eventually occur in the study and practice of the Qabalah by using it as a convenient filing system. It allows us to do much research and experimentation upon the inner planes and through daily activities. While rising on the planes, or skrying, one endeavors to seek the experience of one Sephirah after another as the soul traverses each path and brings back knowledge to record in our personal diary. Self-realization and an uplifting of the consciousness become the result of cared and planned ventures into this avenue of cosmic and psychological research. Aleister Crowley wrote: "The Universe is a projection of ourselves; an image as unreal as that of our faces in a mirror, yet, like that face, the necessary form of expression thereof, not to be altered save as we alter ourselves…discover ourselves by means of a sequence of hieroglyphics and changes…It enables us to see ourselves, and therefore to aid us to initiate ourselves by showing us what we are doing."

The aspirant to these studies should endeavor to master the weaknesses opposed to being concerned about how magnificent are the powers to achieve to influence other people. Sometimes having higher goals overcomes lower weaknesses and to this end setting the sights for achievement may safely be altered. Weakness in some respect may only serve as a channel for evil forces or energies that cause an unbalance in the nature of the individual who is disguised as a perfectionist and thrilling at the strength the ego has gripped upon them. Taking the slow, sure route with esoteric studies will build a firm foundation such that conflicts arise less and less, and the process of a higher life education becomes established. The travesty of misuse with the Qabalah is not unlike that of any other system, for it can be used and abused. The mysteries should not be hidden from those earnestly seeking enlightenment. Qabalism is most certainly the groundwork for a natural process of spirituality to unfold. The reader is referred to Israel Regardie's The Tree of Life- A Study in Magic, and to The Mystical Qabalah by Dion Fortune for a more developed and excellent synthesis on the subject. With this outlined study, Dr. Israel Regardie's book The Middle Pillar is above any in its field and herein will some information be extracted from its invaluable program.

The importance of psychoanalysis in working with magic can not be underestimated, as one is dealing with the mechanisms of the mind, and prior to a serious practice in the field of magical operations it is practically required to know those mechanisms. In that regard Israel Regardie delivers the opening to his Middle Pillar exercises with a solid foundation on the subject. Anything from childhood memories to traumatic events have their seat in the recesses of the subconscious and should be exposed and treated accordingly. Analyzing, facing and accepting the events that linger in the mind from the past which cause little patterns in behavior and personality reactions is the beginning of cleansing that attic which houses the memorabilia responsible for the matrix of the personality. The Buddhist system of Sammasati meditation is a practice of memory, which releases a great deal of tension from raising earlier experiences. Nervous energy is often tied up in those rooted memories and by cleaning house a great sense of freedom and satisfaction can be gained.

The Freudian psychological term of Id is the deepest aspect of the unconscious and relates to the point of Kether on the Tree. It is the Es of Dr. Georg Groddeck's system in his Exploring the Unconscious, and is also referred to as the Monad or Yechidah. This pure Self is the kernel of the Self, or core of the consciousness, which is placed in the same morphology as the Tao. The deepest parts of the feminine and masculine, Yin and Yang, qualities in a person reside in the anima and animus, or Neschamah and Chiah. Within the deepest part of the soul, there is a masculine bias of a woman, which is termed the animus, and a feminine bias in a man termed the anima. The animus is related to Chiah, the Will, also meaning life and the anima is Neschamah, the higher soul principle of understanding and love. The greatest feeling of true love is placed within one object, which a person seeks to be identified with. This harmony of beauty and love is what is implied with the anima. Within it resides intuition and insight and with this greatest feeling of love comes realized understanding.

The Ruach dominates the conscious ego through the mind. Ruach is comprised of the fourth to eight Sephiroth on the Tree of Life. This is an aggregate of memory, will, feeling and thinking surrounding the ego, which bring us into a mode of adaptation to the world around us. It has been surmised through psychology that the unconscious does not harbor explosive motives but only becomes so when the Ruach and conscious mind represses its legitimate activity. Actions are not always consciously directed but are generally involuntary compulsions enacted upon from a feeling of permission from the psyche. Focusing upon the pathways and being free of the lingering relics allows us to ascend with conscious intention towards the pure essence that Unity provides.

The Sephirah of Yesod is the Nephesch or animal soul that contains the urges and emotions referred to as the Freudian Unconscious. Routine actions and behaviors that we are always doing without thinking about them, and those thoughts and feelings that are lingering there are situated in this area of the unconscious. It is the sex instinct as well as the activity of the cerebellum, which drive this Nephesch mechanism within us.

Malkuth is the physical brain and the active physical body. It may be associated as the action of Yang in material and tangible life whereas Yesod is a filter behind the scenes acting as its Yin counterpart. The Ruach may also be considered as the Yang principle to the higher order of the Supernals of Kether (Yechiah), Chokmah (Chiah) and Binah (Neschamah) as Yin, working behind the conscious expression of the Ruach.

The qabalistic cross places the ego under the protection of the Yechidah, divine will, and makes it susceptible to the higher order of influx from the unconscious. The lesser banishing ritual of the pentagram gets rid of the undesirable elements within the psyche.(See page 66 for Divine Names to this ritual) By this method the libido is increasingly flowing to disintegrate the undesirables by banishing them away with the power and resonance of the divine holy names. With this accomplished the Sephiroth of the Middle Pillar are to be visualized within the aura as radiating light spheres in the center of your body. Arousal through this visualization allows their magnetic fluids to circulate into operation and contacts dormant corners of the psyche and thereby releases revitalizing energies that are in harmony with the framework of the mind. Such meditations bring intuitions from the higher self down the central Pillar of the Present into the aura of the individual as a result of transmuting the conscious levels. The higher archetypes bring calmness and serenity to the lower mind and will be recognized in dreams during such exercises. General superficial experiences will not occur in dreams but rather a draw from the creative and archetypal world of the animus which great poets and mystics of the past have gathered their material and inspiration from.

Israel Regardie brings the aspirant through these exercises and techniques and continues with a further elaboration using the Vibratory Formula as an extension of the Middle Pillar visualization which he states as: "The theory here is that by awakening a power or level of consciousness within man's own sphere it is possible to contact the corresponding force in the external world or similar level of perception and experience in the Collective Unconscious. Its intent is not only the development of the individual by rendering him conscious of his other principles, but to transform him into a willing vehicle and instrument of the Universal mind, of that great and uniform substratum common to the whole of mankind. It is within the power of man, by these methods, to associate himself with the almost omnipotent vitality and spiritual value of those divine powers which as an aggregate comprise the universe."

It should be quite evident that magic does not exclusively deal with ceremonial practices to contact higher forms and forces within the universe. It is also through elaborate meditation exercises and mindful awareness that the person gradually uplifts into higher experiences of becoming Adept in the illustrious arts.

It is through these arts of personal magic that one begins to vibrate the divine names of God and connects with the formulas of the pentagram and hexagram as spiritually endowed symbols in structural synthesis. Invoking the Archangelic forms into the four quadrants with this practice allows the grosser elements within the soul to be ejected and prevents reentry of them. A gradual uplifting through the Middle Pillar is achieved with the practice of bringing the higher energies down and into you and thereby you ascending up and into them. Expanding consciousness using the lesser banishing ritual of the pentagram and visualizing the Qabalistic Cross as a radiating light from within, while invoking the Archangelic guardians has much greater purity in results than embarrassment in shame. This endeavor increases vitality, brings awareness of inner powers and abilities and should prove a greater bind with the soul by clearing the mind from any neurosis that may be hidden in the corners.

Every person is different and may view these concepts in ways that are quite foreign to them, and in some cases there may be glitches that are unforeseen. That is why psychoanalytic techniques are vital to commencing such serious work with the unconscious territories. Some prefer to have a mildly simple life and not be boggled and complicated with the knowledge of such a vast system of cosmic organization. However, for those who quest and seek earnestly, there are innumerable jewels to be found by using the Qabalah. Study and practice will prove this art to be as limitless and creatively fulfilling as anything could be. Universal Cosmic Connections to all that pertains to life are on and in the Tree of Life and through practice the reality of Inner Light becomes a realized phenomenon. Nourish the soul with higher energies and purer projections then watch the growth occur. ✶

Path	Eng	Hebrew	Meaning	Astrological	Tarot Card	Titles of Tarot Trumps	Egyptian God	Greek Gods	Roman Gods
11	A	Aleph	Ox	Air	The Fool	The Spirit of Aιθηρ	Nu,Hoor Paar Kraat	Zeus	Jupiter
12	B	Beth	House	Mercury	The Magician	The Magus of Power	Thoth, Cynocephalus	Hermes	Mercury
13	G	Gimel	Camel	Luna	The High Priestess	The Priestess of the Silver Star	Khonsu	Artemis,Hecate	Diana
14	D	Daleth	Door	Venus	The Empress	Daughter of the Mighty Ones	Hathor	Aphrodite	Venus
15	H	Heh	Window	Aquarius	The Star	Daughter of Firmament,Dweller between Waters	Haroeris, Hapy	Athena,Ganymede	Juno (Aeolus)
16	V	Vav	Nail	Taurus	The Hierophant	Magus of the Eternal	Asar,Imsety,Apis	Hera	Venus (Hymen)
17	Z	Zayin	Sword	Gemini	The Lovers	Children of the Voice, Oracles of the Mighty Gods	Rechti,Merty(twin Gods)	Castor,Pollux,Apollo (as Diviner)	Castor, Pollus (Janus, Hymen)
18	Ch	Cheth	Fence	Cancer	The Chariot	Child of Powers of Waters,Lord of Triumph of Light	Khephra	Apollo (As Charioteer)	Mercury
19	Th	Theth	Serpent	Leo	Strength	Daughter of the Flaming Sword	Ra Hoor Khuit,Pakhet,Mau	Demeter	Venus,Attis,Ceres,Adonis,Vesta,Flora
20	Y,I	Yod	Hand	Virgo	The Hermit	Prophet of Eternal,Magus of the Voice of Power	Isis(as the virgin)	Attis	Jupiter (Pluto)
21	K	Caph	Palm	Jupiter	Wheel of Fortune	Lord of the Forces of Life	Amoun-Ra	Zeus	Vulcan(Venus,Nemesis)
22	L	Lamed	Ox Goad	Libra	Adjustment	Daughter of the Lords of Truth,Ruler of the Balance	Maat	Themis,Minos,Aeacus	Neptune (Rhea)
23	M	Mem	Water	Water	The Hanged Man	Spirit of the Mighty Waters	Asar,Hekar,Isis (Hathor)	Poseidon	Mars
24	N	Nun	Fish	Scorpio	Death	Child of Great Transformers,Lord of Gate of Death	Typhon, Apep, Khephra	Ares	Diana
25	S	Samech	Prop	Sagittarius	Art/Temperance	Daughter of Reconcilers, The Bringer-forth of Life	Nephthys	Apollo	Pan,Vesta,Bacchus,Priapus
26	Ay	Ayin	Eye	Capricornus	The Devil	Lord of the Gates of Matter,Child of Forces of Time	Min, Khem (Set)	Pan, Priapus	Mars
27	P	Peh	Mouth	Mars	The Tower	Lord of the Hosts of the Mighty	Horus	Ares	Mars,Minerva
28	Tz	Tzaddhi	Fish Hook	Aries	The Emperor	Sun of the Morning, Daughter of Firmament	Mentu, Ahephi, Aroueris,Nuit	Athena,Ganymede	Neptune
29	Q	Qoph	BackofHead	Pisces	The Moon	Ruler of Flux and Reflux,Child of Sons of the Mighty	Khephra,Anubi	Poseidan	Apollo
30	R	Resh	Head	Sol	The Sun	Lord of the Fire of the World	Ra	Helios, Apollo	Vulcan,Pluto
31	Sh	Shin	Tooth	Fire	The Aeon	Spirit of the Primal Fire	Mau,Horus,Thoum-aesh-neith	Hades	Saturn
32	T	Tav	Tau Cross	Saturn	The Universe	Great One of the Night of Time	Mako, Sebek	Athena, Kronos	Ceres

ELEVATIONS OF LOVE

"It is claimed that the preliminaries to sexual intercourse involve sixty-four elements,
probably because they were originally described in sixty-four chapters."

The Complete Kama Sutra

Love has many levels and affects us with the exchange and transformation of energy it entails. It is capable of soothing our emotions, stimulating our mind and changing our body. When we connect with a partner through the feeling of love, our soul is proportionately molded and invigorated with the channeling of energy that is shared. Our partner in love also feels the exchange of energy and experiences it according to the their ability to flow with the feelings as a metamorphosis when the **energy exchange** occurs. When we no longer appreciate the other person, for whatever reason, the radiance within one another seems to diminish, to lack that shining, magnetic substance and elevating with love becomes limited. The doors may then be closed to greater experience and the unlimited energy within is either dissipated unconsciously or kept dormant.

Having **a deep feeling of connection** with another person is essential to elevate love. **Communication** opens our heart and draws us together simultaneously with expressions of affection and passion. This arouses emotions of weightlessness and all of the world's problems seem to not bear much conscious weight. Stress is relieved and butterflies bring out the beauty and coherence, creating a unity between two souls.

Cultivating the energies that are built up allows us to channel and regulate them so that awareness of the harmonious flow throughout our body is felt. The pituitary gland transforms sexual energy into a refined substance, which nourishes our soul. Nerve centers throughout our brain receive pulsations from this energy, which excites us into spiritual rapture by releasing chemicals. We become invigorated with balance and sexual dynamism from activating this chain reaction. We are thereby repairing bodily chemistry that has been diminished through previous situations involving stress and at the same time evolving our inner nature and patterns of behavior. The heightened sexual energy from one another is experienced on all planes and by channeling that energy we can realize it as a remarkable assistance for greater performance. When efforts are combined and in unison between two partners, this energy can be directed and very useful.

If a great attachment between two people comes to an end, either voluntarily or involuntarily, it feels like an invested emotional energy has bottomed out and everything shared suddenly becomes lost. Time is required to recuperate and repair the damage of hurt emotions, anger, dependency and we must focus our sight with a renewed future outlook. How much damage is felt and done is entirely a personal decision from attachment and karma, through our emotions. It is certainly best to take the most advantageous aspects of the relationship and use that energy to move forward to evolve further into the nature of love.

This is easier accomplished when love of self is in a cosmic scope with the right amount of self-worth and self-esteem to know our importance in life. That is not to say a selfish, introverted, arrogant and vain state of mind is adopted, since that would only lead to further selfish motives and afflictions. Self-love is required before truly loving another soul and if we do not have love of our true nature, then we are most likely just lusting with the other person and living on dependency. Self-love is a harmonious insight that we gain from feeling our life-essence and being able to appreciate our body, soul and spirit for the qualities they provide in keeping us alive. Our magnetic attraction to another person is stronger and more affective when we can express our true nature through love. Our yin and yang characteristics become an adventurous and ecstatic interplay of our testosterone and estrogen levels. Our collective chemical make-up gives and receives what is required for active and excitable interchange.

The aging process hinders efficiency in our hormonal functioning and reduces the required electromagnetic reactions that provide strength throughout our body. Learning to cultivate the sexual energies and developing what the Taoists term the Chi power throughout the body will prevent this from occurring at the usual rate. When we become aware of this internal power flowing through us, we can develop it so that it flows to and fills the cranial cavity. It would then stream through our body with life force to increase strength and invigorate our immune system in addition to decelerating the aging process.

For the male, the method begins with directing and controlling the hormonal vitality within the body opposed to ejaculating and loosing it. Life force is lost when ejaculation occurs and as time goes on the body cavities increase in size and depletion of this vital energy causes pollutants and enlarged fatty tissue to reside in their place. The result is that life slows down, activity decreases, aging speeds up and illness gradually occurs. An ancient secret of Taoist masters is in cultivating this energy and delivering the resultant chi power to the bone marrow where it becomes greatest in fighting diseased white blood cells throughout the body. In turn, it cultivates our youthful expression and keeps the body free of diseases.

Attitude plays a role in this and indeed in all nomenclature of spiritual activity. Attitude is a facet of personality and capable of changing in any given instance. It can either hinder or assist a process and our determination. It is, like almost everything we are conscious of, a mental and emotional tool at our disposal. During love, we wish to feel an unlimited source touch us, some genuine higher ecstasy beyond our emotional normalcy to shine through and fill us with joy beyond excitement. That boundless source of energy, sense of freedom and cosmic avenue of potential is always available for any purpose, if we allow it to be. If we are free from personal restraints and personality confrontations that shadow the light from entering our field, it simply occurs.

Returning to **controlling the life force and directing it**, let it be reminded that everything has life to it. A single male ejaculation ends up killing up to 500 million sperm. That amounts to approximately half a billion potential lives. It takes roughly thirty blood cells to create a single sperm cell which in turn contains twenty-three chromosomes, ions, trace elements, prostaglandins, enzymes mixed with other essentials, ready to create a life form when attached to the female egg. The prostate gland propels the sperm with an additional fluid as it makes its way through the seminal vesicle through the male organ. Learning to control this fluidic motion and obtaining an orgasm without ejaculation is the focus that begins prolonged ecstasy.

We only have so much life force and energy reserved inside of our body, to keep our immune system, organs and vital parts functioning throughout life. If more energy is expended than obtained, then the reserve of energy in the vital organs is gradually depleted. For an example, we may require 1500 calories of food energy per day for the energy we expend through sexual intercourse, working, playing, poor dieting, habits that consume our energy substance, but perhaps we only have 1000 calories at our disposal. In this simplified elucidation the additional required energy is depleted from other areas of our body. As time goes on, this depletion weakens those other vital organs resulting in reactions of illness, chronic fatigue, lack of life enthusiasm ad infinitum. If we learn to habitually reverse this process so that we increase the store of energy, life force and dynamic potential always at our disposal, we may keep it as a reserve. When awareness in fulfilling this precious energy is achieved, it can be directed anywhere in our body, through concentrated efforts.

Building this storehouse or internal reservoir of force and learning to channel it provides greater quality and experience in elevating sensations in the body and emotions of love, as well as personal well being. Sharing the moment consistently, flowing with combined, channeled force and reaching peaks of ecstasy simultaneously penetrates the heart of passion. Loving partners can share and negate the affects of stress in life, or they can increase those affects negatively. Communication, enthusiasm and passionate interests can be put into a personality as easily as we can put on our clothes in the morning. It is all a matter of whether we wish to make the effort, and obtain the magnificent affects from the endeavor.

It is normal for a young person to be fully energetic, with a seemingly endless supply of dynamism. It is also normal that it becomes expended within years down the road and they are more often than not, fatigued and problem burdened, confused about issues and repeating their history. Properly channeling energy in the early stages and learning how to use it and not abuse it allows for longevity and wise decisions throughout life. Getting to know our partner, their rhythm and cycles, and working in harmonious fields of shared and developed energy is important. Seeking continual gratification without putting refined efforts to work for one another causes relationships to deteriorate. Jealousy and dependency result from immature, self-centered cravings for sexual pleasure and thinking of the partner as a personal property. This creates destructive tendencies, insecurity and boredom in what could otherwise become a flavorful loving alliance.

It is incumbent therefore not to deplete the sexual energies that in the beginning feel immense. The seminal fluids should be raised towards the heart center so that sexual energies are not dependent upon lower extremities. Retaining the fluid prolongs lovemaking and elevates the emotions to higher centers that are more subtly shared. Love has higher, deeper meaning and carries on after the sexual appetite flows with lasting pleasure. Becoming in tune with the stimulation that your partner feels while raising these energies from the navel to the head increases the enthusiasm to perform it. Our chakras become whirling with emanations of purity in passion, sensuality in subtlety, and light in love.

It takes months and years to learn one another's system, cycle and abilities. There are subtle energies within a woman and man that do not flow during every intercourse session. At times they may be peaked, at other times very sluggish. Greater and refined energies can be felt from a woman over time. Patience is the key to many inner secrets such as these. While peaking interest and excitable emotions, life becomes unconstrained and filled with exhilaration. Out of the blue, the most remarkable things can be said and experienced while experiencing rapture. The greater we make the other person feel, the greater it can come back to us. **Bring out the radiance in the person you love.** Making our partner feel beautiful while rising their intuitive nature with passionate explorations can perk up life tremendously. Don't expect your partner to always do and say the most wonderful things. By balancing the actions, by partaking of the giving, we can grow stronger, faster and deeper with love. Heightening pleasure together is an outgoing; giving experience that is not self-directed. Every good thought and feeling that is produced flows into the stream of life, on respective planes and brings harmony into the web of existence. We should give our ALL and make it a habit to do so.

If we are without a partner, elevating love principles are still very much applicable. Each person has positive and negative, male and female qualities within their nature. This may be considered to be a hermaphrodite nature of the emotional-mental layers of our life and is partly responsible for our chemical balancing and attraction to other people. Chastity is of equal importance in spiritual progression. Some forms of Taoism instruct on the cultivating of sexual energy while feeling the male and female expressions within our body. To use the analogy of yin and yang within our psyche, we can harmoniously project our energies towards those inner characteristics of ourselves. We can develop, excite, nourish and experience inner growth through manipulating our own sensual drive mechanisms. This is an emotional and mental experience of applying the interplay of yin and yang, female and male elements within our soul. It is the fire (yang) of the intellect and the water (yin) sexual fluids and all of their corresponding connections at play in the fulfillment of the joy of life. It does not refer to lustful self-seeking pleasures of raising incubi and succubae through the practice of masturbation. It refers to the feeling of self-fulfillment, joy, encouragement, love and harmony within and using the energy from those feelings to uplift us to the heart center for further and deeper realizations.

Controlling the biophysical energy or **sexual essence** by raising it instead of discharging the seed extricates pranic energies, vitalizes the body and excites the higher emotional centers to uplift the powers of kundalini into spiritual awakening. It is not enough to simply retain the semen but we must unleash the energies from it, and raise them. As accumulation in the testes transpires over time, it is consumed by the kundalini power and begins strengthening the astral and other subtle bodies. The energy from this life force goes to nourishing the inner bodies, our inner life, which is why so many sacred societies teach about retaining and channeling this life energy up the medial nerve of the spine to realize enlightenment. The heat and pressure that is built up in the prostate has to be released inwardly, raised by the will power to higher levels in the body otherwise the prostate gland can eventually have a breakdown.

The term "the perfect love" or the "twin flame" is used in context to represent how we become capable of sensing and feeling the strength in passion and love with one other particular person. The "twin flame" is said to be the original result of the manifestation of two souls upon earth, one being male and the other female and have descended from an ovoid that contained both as one. This is our originality state, or first incarnation, that long ago existed when we had our first life existence on earth and simultaneously, someone else was born as our twin. Since that original birth, karma, (defined in this instance as energy and consciousness in action causing retribution through causes and effects; also considered as the law of the circle as each action creates an affect and comes full circle through inter-life levels) has taken affect though our existence. Lower octaves, vibrations etc. on the physical plane prevent our awareness of what was and has occurred to affect our awareness of everything we deal with. Many past and past life relationships created such and such obligations that a myriad of mental and emotional commitments have occurred and we came out of touch with our original "twin flame" that we began existence with. Thus, our divine counterpart has been lost over experiences and time but in each person we see qualities, some of which we are attracted to and some that are apparently revolting to us. There may be a longing to come in touch with the one that we are most closely affiliated and attracted to on every level. There are certain qualities that bring us closer to a true rapture with our original birth mate so that we may recapture the original essence together once again. In order to work with karma, however, we have to foremost fulfill our responsibilities and complete that which we have created as unfinished business. It is a process of purification so that we come into contact with our inner and Higher Self, living a freedom of harmonious motion while maintaining our work that we realize is part of the path we tread.

Having worked with another soul in parallel with our destiny for a long time, perhaps one life after another, is having what is commonly termed a "soul mate". It is two people that have shared a common bond of development and fundamental aspirations linked as close or closer together than a brother and sister. The feeling of truly loving them comes from sharing that intrinsic mutual relationship over a long period of time. An evolutionary progression has been shared together through the seat of the soul chakra that resides just above the base chakra.

Deep within, however there may a voice that whispers this person isn't as close as the "twin flame", the original counterpart that we began time and originated with. This may be part reason why many people go through a number of relationships as though they are complimenting one another with an assistance until they grow awareness and seek a closer complimentary expression of who they really are. They may also be going through karmic marriages or relationships for the purpose of completing the karmic ties to another person that began long ago. There is also the common notion that, in the case of men, they want to sow their seeds, have abundant experience and fulfill cravings that are perhaps a bit rampant.

The end of the age of Pisces is sometimes attributed to balancing aspects of past karma that are required for further spiritual progression. Therefore coming into realization of our inner polarity has great affect upon the person we choose to be a partner. Sometimes it doesn't matter since our original "twin flame" is no where to be found, but then we may feel a life-long loneliness and being entangled in additional karma relationships makes us feel further from a sense of divine reality and Oneness. If our original twin has worked out all their karma and ascended to higher inner planes then we may feel a stronger sense of that Oneness as it can still affect us through the veils of the inner planes like light passing through a curtain. If they are still on the physical plane we may never know it unless we come to know ourselves as a part of the divine Oneself and master the ability to see through the octaves of light and illusions to find our original mate from the vibrations they send. The strangest of circumstances may happen in our life when we reach out as we reach within.

Meeting who we believe to be our "twin flame" may not always be a pleasant experience because they may find certain quirks of unpleasantness in our character and vice-versa. They may be with another person or we may be happily married. There may be astrological influences, psychological differences, and evolutionary changes, causing either conflicts or amity when we find our original mate. Life isn't a perfect rose and can be attested to by the changes and direction we take at the end of each street. Sometimes we have to make a little sacrifice to become emotionally untangled. In either way, the identification of true love is within true liberty and not in bondage. Love sets us free, it unites two people as one, focused on a path of fulfillment without the suppression of spiritual functioning. It is a spontaneous and ever enlightening awareness that stirs within us when we are aligned with another soul in the experience of love.

Soul mate and twin-soul theories may have some foundation but having a greedy fever for finding our significant other may be filled with fallacy. There is another ground to work from and that is the one that is more plausible, more efficacious and more readily rewarding. The person that we presently share our life with, our love, dreams and hopes with is the best candidate to fulfill our ecstatic love elevations. There has to be a developed communication, a line of truth and an interest with compatibility otherwise any development may seem separate and difficult. Negative vibrations attract one another and thrive on one another, devouring the schisms, which they attract. Therefore to have an emotional swamp of negative energies may be more distracting than progressive. Generally, it is incorrect to create any karma but bad karma becomes more of a chore to resolve.

In some unique balance we may be wishing to speed up our life and yet slow it down simultaneously. Slowing down the negative and speeding up the positive is done partly by resolving past issues quickly and transmuting our energies to higher levels to remain focused and create new positive cycles and perspectives. This speeds up our inner life progression, as we become aware of using and developing potentials towards one goal after another. It is safe to say that building a reservoir or bank account of positive energies can be very useful in strengthening those energies and giving them life force to make things happen. That is essentially what is occurring when the fluidic essence of seamen is cultivated and delivers the resultant chi power through the body. Everything develops through practice and effort and refining the rapturous intensity of love is no exception. The exchange and focus of energy between two people can produce the deepest desires and make ambitions come true. Inspiring our significant other to feel and become aware of greater shared potentials releases further energies that may be channeled to what we wish to accomplish in life.

The exalted heights and tragic depths of love have been represented historically and through mythology. In the case of Psyche, she could not resist temptation when it came to Cupid as her curiosity in the true identity of her lover lead to her demise. Ulysses was drawn home from his wanderings through Penelope's faithful caring of the flame of love. Launcelot and Guenevere and so many others in and out of fables display the sanctity of love between two aligned souls. This also is a difference between a relationship and marriage that is transformed to share success and one that is a based on physical concerns without direction for anything greater. An experience is either shallow or fulfilling and it is up to us to decide how much of either it will become.

If we make it a pleasurable experience to share intimacy with several people instead of just one significant partner, we may take on vibrations and emotional ties that become karmic baggage and additional burdens thus hampering true freedom and focused progression. On the other hand purity and honesty in love with one particular partner can be focused stronger, more efficacious and make progression an easier task.

Enhancing the qualities of one another through guided arousal of the sacred fire, kundalini, stimulates the chakras into activity thereby transmuting consciousness into a deeper or higher sphere of love. Surrounding the kundalini at the base of the spine is an egg like substance called the kanda. It has some nadi which are little subtle flames that bring energy into the kanda. The central energy channel along the spine, as previously mentioned in the Meditation chapter, is the sushumna. It also has a nadi attached with it. The nadi is a supply of energy for the kanda or egg as the kundalini power is raised. Positive energy should be directed into the kanda because it sustains and nourishes the kundalini power for proper and healthy arousal. This can be achieved through proper massage techniques and particular exercises that should be in most good books on kundalini and the chakras.

The first, second and third chakras awake our passions on all levels and ignites love into heightened states. When the heart chakra is aroused through the fiery power of stimulation it opens portals within us to experience the divine influx of emanations. Divine visions are experienced through stimulation of the fifth and sixth chakras. The crown or seventh chakra above the head has nearly a thousand petals enshrining it and filters Inner Light to our soul, filling us with radiance from the Divine. When our soul is immersed in such purity through heightening love the experience lends us to be in contact with divine forces. The road begins by plunging our karma into a subtle chemical solvent to relieve the entire negative atmosphere that shrouds us from attaining. When we dissolve the covers of cynicism that have been plastered from multiple vibrations preventing us from seeing our true colors and feeling our refined vibrations so much more becomes possible.

Relating procedures of sexual arousal and elevating love consciousness with the Tree of Life can help us to resolve some of our inhibitions and allow love to flow without restraint. Our logical and reasoning faculty is attributed to the sphere of Hod. This is the machinery of the mind that may house inhibitions in a personally rational manner. It is also the seat of images that may be controlled to begin arousal in the brain to work with its neighbor, the sexual, sensual love-sphere of Netzach. This sphere is that of Venus, the goddess of sexual love. The next higher sphere is Tiphareth, which houses the Higher Ego, and dominates the Lower Ego, which is the frail ego that hampers our potential for performance. Transcending into this Higher Ego is not so easily accomplished. First of all the Lower Ego has its grasp upon the emotions and mind. It is the ego that clings to habits for gratification and basic comforts. It is that part of our consciousness that wants to be constantly rewarded as mentioned in an earlier chapter. Generally, habits are difficult to break and when breaking them is attempted we may feel withdrawal, stress and create a feeling of illness. That is how strong the Lower Ego has a grasp upon our actions with the construction of habits. It is the same with depression, anxiety and all emotions that have their perks in our life. They are all hard to break because of the attachment and functioning of our perceived "self" through the Lower Ego.

The practical side of all this realization is simply that we can cause a chemical reaction to occur in our body and overcome the Lower Ego desires that prevent us from becoming fulfilled. It all begins in the brain through the sphere of Hod, which we may refer to as the functioning muscle that imagines sexual pleasure. To be rid of any habits, drug related alcohol affiliated or simply negative emotions, we must become involved in a greater pleasure to stir our chemicals into activity. That greater pleasure is sexual activity. Not an orgasm, but rather the building up of one. By focusing our mind towards being turned on for as long as possible we can overcome anything that the Lower Ego demands of us. As we begin to feel "turned on", we do not have any negatives bothering us. We are becoming excited and that provides us with the feelings to replace anything the ego previously demanded of us. During this excitement, we haven't the time or interest in other cravings and we become increasingly excitable and in a positive mood for thinking and feeling. It is a powerful tool for creativity and realizing greater potential within us. The trick is not to orgasm, to loose the sacred seed and thereby feeling complete and satisfied. We should endeavor to work with that heightening of excitement for at least forty-five minutes while preventing an orgasm from occurring. The energy feels so good that we can carry it with us as a stored feeling, slowly opening the gate to release it through our body bit by bit throughout the day. Having sexual activity with a partner or alone can accomplish this. The ability to do it mentally is possible by solely using our imagination and strengthening our capability of sending sensations through our body without normal physical contact.

Music is a wonderful asset to enhance sensuality. It is used throughout society to sell, promote and influence the mind of shoppers. Harsh sounds are more irritating than pleasurable, however soft nature sounds like that used to induce meditative states are tranquil and allow the mind to relax. In yoga, the great Patanjali said that the word "Om" is the most powerful word to induce balance and harmony in mind and body and is manifested through the Anahata Chakra. In the Vedas there are said to be 50 sacred "Bija Mantras" or seed sounds that are the base of creation. Interestingly enough there are also 50 gates to the activator of our higher self through Binah. There are also 50 letters of the Sanskrit alphabet (Matrika- Shakti) and there are fifty and one half coils of kundalini. Fifty is a common number in religious and esoteric lore. Sounds can produce majestic affects such as when performing invocations during a magical ceremony by directing vocal energy to produce and command an affect to occur. Invoking the cherubim as the guardians of love upon the physical plane is accomplished through vocalizing ritual. Sounds can assist in summoning and raising the powers of kundalini from the Maladhara Chakra. Sounds and music are the result of inspiration and aspiration and become the creative outlet for art and entertainment and can be enticing in sexual rites to strengthen the atmosphere.

Expanding awareness with ecstasy is an adventure of love. Techniques are as endless as the imagination and beyond. Unity is the one supreme state we all seek to achieve. Unity with the divine, with cosmic connections experienced through our partner becomes as arousing as our desires to create it. We want more love, more ecstasy and more bliss in a relationship and the methods to do it are not difficult.

A walk, a bit of entertainment, playing a sport together, just being active brings energy into a relationship. A non-active relationship may become tiring, boring and produces tension, despair, and the separation of feelings. The etheric river of our soul can be kept clean and free of debris with honesty, gratitude and a giving nature. Armed with a sensual imagination, our appetite grows with fervent passion. In keeping our conscience as free as the winds yet strong as the planets, we can flourish any relationship into the greatest nurturing embrace. Sharing our energy with our partner by using all of the elevation principles highlighted herein can enhance our spiritual insight and renew our body, emotions and mind. ★

MYSTICAL ORDERS AND PERSPECTIVES

"In moral terms there is little, if any difference between the aims of science and the aims of prayer and magic.
It is simply that the modus operandi differs…All three modes of action can be abused, or used for trivial ends."

A History of White Magic - Gareth Knight

Esoteric and intuitive knowledge evolves our spirituality and may become enhanced when we delve into the mysteries of ancient orders that resurrected and practiced sacred wisdom. From the early centuries AD, the Gnostics, "those who know", have passed teachings from the gnosis (Knowledge) through individuals that were initiated in grades of advancement. One such person was Valentinus, who in the 2nd Century AD wrote that a Guardian Angel accompanies a person throughout life and would reveal an intuitive knowledge to the individual through the enlightened awareness of their Being.

It is said that Valentinus possibly wrote the Gospel of Truth, which is a "knowledge of the heart" opposed to something created through philosophical reasoning or scientific comprehension. This Gospel contains Valentinian Gnosticism and expresses the nightmare of life in the physical sphere and the connection that a person holds with their Guardian Angel. When one comes to hear the calling from the Guardian Angel, the person can enter into a level of great realization when the "gnosis" is revealed through the Angel. Altered levels of obtaining such mysteries through the revelations is claimed to be received through the Angel, according to the Valentinian School, since there is no other rational explanation for the acquiring of such articulate knowledge.

Gnosticism is not directly linked with ancient Greek or Egyptian religious concepts or any other fundamental doctrine. It was a revolutionary movement that went against the mainstream beliefs and professed the view within its religious philosophy that there is a struggle for God, for man, and for the realization that the inner Self is of the same substance as that of God.

The idea that Wisdom was the instrument of creation and descended into the lower realms to fulfill creation for the powers of the angels to be born is a Gnostic concept of Jewish and Samaritan belief. Simon Magus from Samaria illustrated this from the idea that wisdom stems through God attributed to the name of Helen, and descended into the creative world, establishing the furtherance of life. This is similar to the dissertation of descending with the principles of Chokmah and Binah in the Qabalistic system.

Meander, Simon Magus, and the Samaritans Dositheus are considered to be among the first Gnostics, which is rooted in Judaism. They were opposed to believing in the Jewish god as the highest source of creation. One sect called the Magharians, distinguished between God and an Angel that governs the world and who is responsible for the descriptions of God throughout the Old Testament.

Simon Magus was a Samaritan magician and teacher of Gnosticism. He requested payment for the transmission of power, which is why Peter, the apostle, reprimanded him to be doomed. During this time Peter and John left Jerusalem to seek converts. By the year circa 150, Simon was regarded as the founder of

Christian heresy and it is said that he claimed to be 'the first God' in the human race. Most Samaritans had worshipped him and within the years 41-54 Simon had practiced his magic in Rome. His abilities were noted as being astounding and capable of great accomplishments. His art of invisibility, animating statues, transforming into an animal like a goat or sheep or moving through a mountain and appearing on the other side were some allegations sent through the ages about his magical talents. It was also attributed to him that he was born of a virgin mother and that his character was associated to that of Faust in the 16th Century, which was first published in Frankfurt in 1587. The original Faust is not alike the more philosophical Goethe version wherein this later version of Faust was associated with selling his soul to the Devil. The Simonians augmented questions regarding the religious framework that did not gather favorable acclaim from their Christian oppositions. Concerns such as the powers that controlled nature and the function of the female principle in the process of Creation were propagated against mainstream religious belief. The degree that biblical ethics held as a product of conventionality was another question that the followers of Simon Magus raised during these early times.

The primal sources of religious and spiritual ideas are hidden in the initiated interpretation of mysteries and traditions. There are many obstacles and morals to overcome in the Inferno of the material world. Through ethical spiritual enlightenment the veils upon the path unfold for truth to be discovered. Uncovering the veils of mystery to see the truth that is within, is an education of sacred wisdom and understanding that governs our attunement with what 'IS' opposed to what we wish to believe.

The original Gnostic concept was gradually Christianized by Valentinus who brought the idea of duality into creation. This became the foundation of the Occidental School as followers of Valentinus, which were different from the Ptolemaeus views of the time. The former believed in Christ as having only a spiritual body whereas the latter stated that Christ has also a soul and psychic body. The confusion in terms was common during that era. Valentinus and Gnosticism were the fertilizer for the soil that dominated western civilization in Neoplatonic philosophy and Christian theology for centuries to come. They became the spiritual ancestors of many formed beliefs and mysteries, which spread out into different schools and Orders of spiritual aspiration. Secret societies have dawned through the ages to shed light on the path of mysteries attempting to resolve the quandary of creation and complexity of God.

The oldest Latin name for God is Ju or Jovis, which formed into the father and the male principle called Ju-piter. Pitar comes from Sanskrit meaning 'father', just as Juno is the feminine aspect from the Phoenicians meaning 'rest' and 'comforter'. Another ancient name attributed to God is Yaho from the Hebrew, which is written in Greek and may be translated as Iao. An old religion of the Chaldeans whose beliefs are amongst the Neo-Platonists, ascribed Iao to be the Divine, above the seven heavens, and is attributed to the Demiurgus, the knowledge of which is said to be revealed only to the highly initiated.

The mystery of IAO, as a trilateral unity has been connected to Isis, Apophis and Osiris in the Egyptian form, as earlier recounted. It is the alpha and omega, the beginning and end, with the middle event of Apophis. It represents the inner sun, called "the eternal Sun-Abrasax", and represented by Tiphareth (the Son) on the Tree of Life. It is the veil to the Shekinah of Ain-Soph (En-Soph) and is also referred to as the "Breath of Life". It is from this central sphere that a cycle is formed and extended as a spiral of circles with the serpent, representing divine knowledge, following up the spiral. The serpent also represents wisdom and eternity as a divine cycle of renewal. The serpent is also the "Shadow of the Light" and from the ancient sect of the Ophites, it is referred to as the Savior. Essentially it is the forbidden fruit, or the Tree of the Knowledge of Good and Evil, whereas the Tree of Life is the spiritual aspect or principle of the Logos. This philosophical analogy associates ignorance to duality causing death and doom whereas receiving the Knowledge of the Divine Light provides the soul with the sacred propensity of immortality.

The original legends of the Holy Grail appear between A.D. 1180 and 1230. The bearer of the Holy Grail was Joseph of Arimathea who heralded magnificent adventures throughout Europe. He traveled from Spain, over to the coast of North Africa, which is a route that was not unfamiliar in the procurement of mystical lore as documented in early Rosicrucian and Freemason legacies.

The German legend of Parsifal being the hero of the Grail comes from the writings of Wolfram von Eschenbach. There are also French and Belgian versions. One of the better known versions is from Sir Thomas Malory, whose book was printed in 1485, which collated the legendary King Arthur and the Knights of the Round Table. It also contained the stories of Sir Lancelot, Merlin the magician, Guinevere, and legends of the Holy Grail. Malory was a knight during the age of the Wars of the Roses and his works made generations of legends come alive. He incorporated the souls of the legends into written form for the western world. It paved the way for folklore and fairy tales as well as initiatory procedures, adventure and spiritual conceptions to become broadened.

Albertus Magnus was the teacher of Thomas Vaughan and together they introduced the astronomy theories of Aristotle to the religion of Christianity. It was these theories that Dante Allighieri used while incorporating the ancient mysteries and white magic principles into his text of The Divine Comedy. Linking the growth of the soul to the grading system of the mysteries, the heavens beyond the Earth, to the Heavenly Spheres was part of the foundation in his book. Dante portrays the Quest for the Soul by overcoming barriers of physical life and his own sins. The Hell in this story is none other than the vast subconscious, which houses its own horror of providing obstacles from complete 'inner freedom' and peace. He makes his way with his guide, Virgil, to the heavenly ladder reaching the spheres of the Moon, Mercury, Venus, the Sun, Mars, Jupiter and Saturn. On each stage of his journey he meets with saints and beings of great caliber. This is none other than rising on the planes with the planetary influences, which are in order with the tree of life Sephirothic representations.

Heinrich Cornelius Agrippa (1486-1535) was born in Cologne and became the famous and simultaneously most infamous man throughout Europe, in conversations on magic amongst secret societies, universities and schools. He lived by his wits as a scholar of occultism, lawyer, doctor, spiritual healer, court astrologer, historian, political advisor, special agent and practicing alchemist. He moved through Europe constantly until his enemies caught up with him and imprisoned him. They tortured him so relentlessly that within weeks of his release he had died.

One of his best known works is *De Occulta Philosophia*, (Occult Philosophy) which was printed in three volumes in 1531, twenty-one years after it was originally completed. His views primarily encompassed the conception that man is a miniature replica of God and the creation of the Universe. He believed that everything that existed had a soul and showed its particular properties through phenomena of nature such as through animals, herbs, metals, and natural dealings. The universe was held to have a soul unto itself. He explained that the relationship between matter and spirit could be expressed through the arts and sciences and everything is connected to the great spiritual whole. He defended magic in his works as being the supreme path to the understanding of the world and God. Magic was the method of investigating the inner aspects of life with the connections between all things and its knowledge was shared through secret orders, of which he had formed a few. Goethe took information from the stories about Agrippa's life to form part of the countenance of his play, entitled *Faust*.

One of the stories told about Agrippa is that he left a key to a secret room at home with his wife while he went out one day. They had a lodging student staying there, and while Agrippa was away the student got the key and went into that room and found a book of spells. He sat down and began reading it and before long looked up to notice a demon standing in front of him. He was shocked with horror and the demon jumped at him and strangled him to death. Agrippa arrived back and was afraid of a charge of murder so he summoned the demon to return and restore the life back into the student, which the demon obliged to do. The student was seen walking through the street but collapsed soon thereafter when the spell from the demon had worn off. His genius may not have been as profound as Paracelsus, but Agrippa had a definite impact and great influence, which was well projected for the social and intellectual ferment of his era.

In 1688, Emmanuel Swedenborg (1668-1772) was born in Stockholm. In 1706 he was initiated in Lund and worked towards higher degrees in the teachings of the Templars. His unusual psychic ability as a child brought him into trance states and later resulted in him abandoning his career in the midst of success. He was very inventive and made drawings of submarines, flying machines, machine guns and mechanical pumps of varying designs. His writings dealt with experimental attempts of communication in the spirit world and a theological construction of explaining them. The original Swedenborgian Society in London was known as the Theosophical Society of the New Jerusalem and they adopted the Rite of Swedenborg in 1721 which made its way to America through Samuel Beswick who authored a document on the Rite titled the *Swedenborgian Rite*. In this way, Swedenborg became a spiritual figurehead of that epoch.

Anton Mesmer (1733-1815) was the scientific pillar of his day with his art of healing and curing. He graduated as a doctor in Vienna in 1766 and began his profession with applying magnetic plates to inflicted limbs thereby influencing the subtle universal magnetic fluid that runs through the body mechanisms. In 1781 he was in Paris and refused a substantial amount of money from the King to teach his techniques, but later accepted 340,000 livres to provide lectures on his findings. He used a tub of water, called a baquet, which had iron rods protruding in it. Patients sat in the tub of water and joined hands and were connected through a cord enabling the rods to touch the inflicted areas of their body. An assistant would go around and touch the patients with another rod whereby they fell into convulsions and were often diagnosed as being cured. The Marquis De Puysegur who utilized a tree instead of the baquet practiced this effect of Mesmerism. The patients were tied around and he found that the patients would enter a state of somnambulism and cures would ensue from the treatment.

Details for summoning spirits and entities with the aid of God were given in sacred texts called grimoires. Grimoire is similar to grammar, and is also spelt as gramarye, which was an old term used to describe enchantments and magic. Since words are of such great importance in magical operations, grimoire or grammar became the name associated with writings dealing with vocalizing and controlling the forces and vibrations through entities beyond the physical level. This kind of text first appeared between the sixteenth and eighteenth centuries with the most acknowledged one being the *Key of Solomon*.

Solomon was considered to be a great magician and to have conjured up demons and worshipped peculiar gods. MacGregor Mathers republished the *Key of Solomon* in 1889. *The Lemegeton or Lesser Key of Solomon* is another grimoire and is divided into four sections. The first section lists the names and powers of 72 chief demons and some directions for summoning them by evocation, into visibility. The date of this grimoire is around the sixteenth century. There are other grimoires that were based upon these two, such as the *Grand Grimoire*, also called the *Red Dragon*. *The Secret of Secrets* is another and was first published in Rome in 1750. The *Grimoirium Verum and the Grimoire of Honorius the Great* are also chief among these texts for harnessing the powers and forces to subjugate demons and entities into obedience by the well trained magician. It should be noted that Aleister Crowley warned in his writings that evocation of demons for whatever purpose should not be performed prior to the would-be magician attaining the true knowledge and conversation of their Holy Guardian Angel. This would appear to make great sense since contacting lower realm entities before becoming spiritually united with the True Self and Will can divert focus and cause reprehensible damage to the psyche by delving into nefarious territories.

Mediums, spiritualists, and seances became an established profession during the nineteenth century. The business of allowing elementals and entities of various astral forms to willingly enter a person to provide information and entertainment conjured notoriety and fame. The unfortunate and misunderstood aspect of this is that it does not imply great power on the part of the Medium. The person is a receiver, allowing the entity to come in their possession so that the will of the entity is furthered rather than the True Will of the Medium. Whether for amusement or investigation purposes, the passive state that is induced during such 'possessive' states incites vibrations that are not akin to human divinity. Cases are documented showing that mediumship may result in hospitalization after a course of weakness ensues followed by oppression, insomnia and ultimately physical deterioration. Such spiritualism is practiced in some secret societies but the negative consequences have been recorded by scientists such as Richet, Flammarion and Crooks, to name but a few. The Society of Psychical Research has much documentation in reference to spirit phenomena and investigative reports in that field.

William Wynn Westcott (1848-1925) was the link for international Rosicrucian-gnosticism to emerge due to his associations with the famed French Hermeticist named Papus, also with John Yarker and Madame Blavatsky. W.W. Westcott had close ties with MacGregor Mathers, which enabled the establishment of the Order of the Golden Dawn. His German O.T.O. connection with Theodore Reuss furthered his groundwork for that Order.

Papus was the Head of the Martinists in France, Reuss and Engel were heads of the German Illuminati and Ordo Templi Orientis, John Yarker was head of the Ancient and Primitive Rite of the Rite of Swedenborg and W.W. Westcott was Supreme Magus of the Rosicruciana in Anglia. Each of these order heads had a significant role in what would come to be a line of magical and mystical orders into the following century.

Westcott was also one of the three founders for the Hermetic Order of the Golden Dawn (12 February 1888). Two other great drives that brought the Order into operation were S.L. MacGregor Mathers (1854-1918) and Dr. William Robert Woodman (1828-1891). The structure of this Order was based upon symbols from the Qabalah. R. A. Gilbert, in his book *The Golden Dawn Companion*, discusses how in the first year the esoteric organization gained 61 members and were spread through its' three temples. Through advertising in the Theosophical Journal titled *Lucifer*, would-be initiates became all too eager to enlist and learn the secrets of the magical fraternity. The temples were filled a year later, in May 1892, with a membership of 150.

Around the year 1900 Mathers was approached by a lady named Mrs. Rose Horos (Crowley made references to her as Laura, the Swami, Soror S.V.A. and Mrs. Jackson), who had arrived from America. She told Mathers of a conversation he had with Madame Blavatsky during a previous year and impressed him by her statements of knowing about this special conversation. She and her husband wanted to set up an affiliated temple of the Golden Dawn and were given permission. Rose and her husband, Mr. Horos had a very dubious past in America and were soon to be realized in England as being devious sexual perverts. They used the Golden Dawn as a front to lure girls into their lodge and committed acts of rape upon the new members. Mrs. Horos not only accepted the fact but also contributed in the activities. Their escalations caught up with them and in December 1901 the Central Criminal Court sentenced Mr. Horos to fifteen years imprisonment and Mrs. Horos to serve seven years. This resulted in bad reputation on the part of the Golden Dawn, and some members were quite distraught over it and left the Order. One reason why many Order documents are non-existent today is that many members burnt their personal documents when they left the Order.

One of the profound personalities that arose through the Golden Dawn was Dion Fortune (1891-1946). Her birth name was Violet Mary Firth and throughout her life she became a prominent writer in western occult and psychoanalytical fiction and non-fiction. When she was about 20 years of age she worked at an educational institute who's principal was very domineering. The principal had repeatedly psychically attacked Miss Firth through a form of hypnotic yoga that she had learnt in India. The episode left Miss Firth emotionally torn and was documented in her book *Psychic Self-Defense* where she noted, "It was the experience which led me to take up the study of analytical psychology and subsequently occultism."

After she became initiated into the Hermetic Order of the Golden Dawn she claimed to have been finally healed of the traumatic experience, which caused damage to her etheric body by leaking energy throughout the years since her psychic attack. In the 1920's, Dion Fortune founded The Fraternity of the Inner Light, which is still in existence as is The Golden Dawn. Near the end of her life she corresponded with Aleister Crowley from whom she received much of the material for her substantial book, *The Mystical Qabalah*.

One of the greatest influences that sprung from the Golden Dawn was Aleister Crowley. He developed the Order of the Astrum Argentium (Silver Star) after the original Golden Dawn had a falling out and separated into other Orders led by different original members. The Astrum Argentium curriculum was developed in *The Equinox*, Volume One, Numbers 1-10, series of books, which Crowley had published between 1909 and 1913. This became an established connection to the Great White Brotherhood in which those who entered began advancement upon the inner planes having the treasures of Golden Dawn and numerous other sources as their reference. Crowley's magical motto of Perdurabo, 'I shall endure until the end', was illustrated by his rapid ascent into this Order in the series entitled *The Temple of Solomon the King*.

His realization that sex could be used ritually and magically came about most profoundly when Theodor Reuss, a high ranking Freemason from Germany had visited Crowley while Crowley lived on Victoria Street, in London. The history of this was mentioned in the previous Crowley chapter, but the previous head of the Order that Reuss had belonged to also knew about utilizing sexual potency in magick. That person was Karl Kellner, who knew of the practice of Tantric sexual magick which the yogis in India called maithuna. It is the ritual of sexual union while the mind, the breath and the seamen are controlled and held still.

Reuss had returned to Germany and expounded upon what he and Crowley had talked about and realized. He mentioned it to other leading freemasons in the Order, one of which was Franz Hardmann, a companion of Madame Blavatsky. In 1902 they began a new order called the Ordo Templi Orientis (Order of the Templars of the East). It had nine degrees within the order that claimed the secrets of the Rosicrucians and Freemasonry. It also has secrets of the Illuminati; the Order of the Hidden Church of the Holy Grail, the Knights of the Holy Ghost, St. John, of the Holy Sepulchre, and of Malta to be all communicated within those degrees.

Madame Helena Petrovna Blavatsky (1831-1891) founded the Theosophical Society in 1875. Her mystical adventure began in 1848 during her travels in Asia Minor where she met with Paulos Matamon who is said to have been a Chaldean magician. She went to Greece and Egypt with him after which she resided in London and in 1856 became an initiate of the Carbonari by Mazzini and was also initiated into the Druses.

In 1858 she returned to Russia to be with her father until 1863 when she went to Caucasus to meet up with her husband, a marriage that lasted about three months. She went on to Italy and in 1866 she was with Garibaldi and accompanied him on expeditions but she was later seriously injured in battle at Mentana. Upon recovery she went to Paris where she met with a Freemason and spiritual magnetizer named Victor Michal and his friend Rivail (Allan Kardec) who became the pioneer of spiritism in France.

In 1875 Madame Blavatsky went to America from Paris. It is here that she met Henry Steel Olcott and formed the beginning of the Theosophical Society in New York that year. She was the secretary and Olcott was the president, while George H. Felt (Professor of Mathematics and Egyptology) and Dr. Seth Pancoast became the vice-presidents. George Felt was also a member of the Hermetic Brotherhood of Luxor, which was a secret society that had a great role in spiritism in America. In 1878 she and Olcott left for India and gradually formed the Theosophical Society Headquarters in Adyar during the year 1882.

Annie Besant met Madame Blavatsky in 1889 through Herbert Burrows, who was also a member of the Stella Matutina. On May 8, 1891 Madame Blavatsky passed away in London leaving behind an organization that fashioned extensive knowledge of the inner worlds and the rise of aspiring adepts to fashion many written texts on spirituality.

Madame Blavatsky collated *The Secret Doctrine*, Volume 1 (Cosmogenesis) piecing the basis of religion with the fundamental and hidden side of Nature, and Volume 2 (Anthropogenesis) with suppositions on the evolution of life from the beginning to the evolving races, symbolism of world religions etc. She also published another 2 volume set titled *Isis Unveiled*. In Volume 1 (Science, 1877) there was foreshadowing of the importance of the atom and the discovery of radioactivity as well as discussions about Huxley, Crookes and Mendeleeff. She also analyzes mysteries of nature, cyclic phenomenon and a host of other incredible paranormal activities. Volume 2 (Religion) covers the pantheons of many religions, sources of Christian and Pagan rites, Rosicrucian mysteries and on through Tibetan, Hindu, Mexican, systems of belief. Madame Blavatsky also wrote *The Key to Theosophy*, concerning man's constitution in a psychological and spiritual states as well as Fate, Destiny, Karma, Free Will and other pertinent topics in the quest for truth. Her *Studies in Occultism* emphasizes the path of altruism, theoretical and practical occultism and the warning about acquiring powers that one is not properly prepared for. One of her great little treasures was *The Voice of the Silence*, which are Golden Precepts that she received from the inner Masters and wrote it mainly from memory.

From particular cogitation of the Theosophical Society arose the Society of Anthroposophy through Dr. Rudolph Steiner. He broke from the Theosophical Society primarily for the lack of Christian content in the heritage and belief with the Society. His writings veered towards the beliefs and system of the Rosicrucians when he touched upon subjects of a magical nature. The school of Anthroposophy gained favorable reputation and opened centers for the handicapped, agricultural stations for farming and introduced eurhythmy into education. Anthroposophy is also credited for the study of homeopathic medicine, furthering the discipline of projective geometry and the application of color theories in present day sciences.

The Rosicrucian Order, AMORC (Ancient Mystical Order Rosae Crucis), formed as an International body in 1915. It is a non-sectarian body devoted to the research and study of natural and spiritual laws to further the evolution of mankind. The Headquarters of AMORC was established in 1927 and is spread on a five-acre lot in San Jose, California.

During the early 1930's a secret society arose in Berlin calling itself The Luminous Lodge or The Vril Society. They were inspired by Bulwer Lytton's (1803-1873) *The Coming Race*, believing in great beings living below the surface of the earth, a subterranean race, that had superhuman powers using the Vril power of the body and able to accomplish magnificent feats. They practiced exercises similar to yoga, believing that this potent force was similar to that of the spinal fire, called the fiery power of kundalini.

Lytton was a Rosicrucian and began an organization culminating occult knowledge for the practice and investigation of ceremonial magic. He recruited Eliphas Levi and others in an organized club and it was documented that during 1853 those members had attempted to evoke elementals on a rooftop on Oxford Street in London. Lytton was considered a member of the Eastern Brotherhood of Adepts, according to Madame Blavatsky. Lytton took part in psychical investigations with D.D. Home and during different instances Lytton was seen moving objects from a distance.

It is not surprising that all of these Orders and many like them have numerous offspring to continue their traditions, thus adding to the long line of fraternal orders and secret societies. There is an abundance of occult organizations propping up and purporting the divulgence of the ancient mysteries in present day civilization.

The occult explosion is widespread and continually expands with fortunate and unfortunate results. There is nothing lethal about a cult or magical order but the deplorable reality is that they sometimes harvest bad crops. The perceived prestige of belonging to a mystical or magical organization lures some very unstable characters into the clutches and produces further burdens in the name of magical prosperity. If the order is sound and true to it's principles, it should automatically weed out such trouble and havoc. This has bearing on some sanctioned organizations but on others that rile in undisciplined practice, their values may be so determined. The positive side of group work is tremendous when all components work with an open-mind, legitimate practice and spiritual aspiration. Outcomes can be very rewarding if the order has guidelines established to prevent lurkers after prey from scouring the righteous intentions. The past has left us with innumerable teachings to gain a positive leap into the future. Cosmic connectivity through spiritual pursuit involves incorporating from those cultures and traditions that have traversed the road and found a way. ★

SECRETS of POWER

"A human being is like a driver in a chariot.
The immortal soul is the driver;
The chariot is the body;
And the reins of the chariot are Wisdom."

The RigVeda

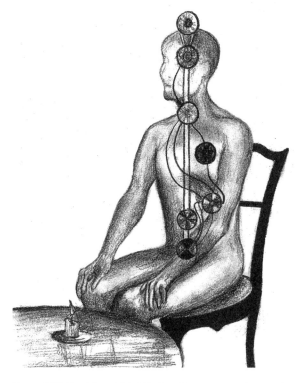

Power is generally associated with authority, strength, great influence, dominance and control. It may be a sense of self-esteem, pride and projected as an abundance of energy or force. There exists a great source of power that is seemingly limitless for some people and apparently impossible for others to tap into and use as a constant flow to achieve consistent benefits. The mind and emotions have enormous ability to connect with energies as tools of power to achieve whatever we channel those energies towards. With spiritual aspiration comes the supervision from an Inner Voice, from a spiritual guide as we employ the forces from the inner world. When we recall experiences that resulted from using mental and emotional energy to accomplish a task, they become recollections of tapping into powers from within, as an awareness that caused us to make something go right in our lives. In some peculiar way we seem to be in touch with something greater than our normal consciousness during certain times in our life. It appears to give us proof that there exists a higher creative power and perhaps "non-visible" guides within life that direct us to make certain achievements.

In nineteenth century Germany, a particular power was given the name of the Vril Force and was defined as an astral or psychic force that may be harnessed and used as a magical force to accomplish feats requiring an uplifted boost of power. It is a powerful energy available for us to use and be aware of when we need to use it. This force has been given other names and numerous new age instructions allege to some magnificent force available for all to harness and use. An exercise for using this particular type of force and storing into an object will be given later in this chapter.

The moral character of the person using power, force or energy that is out of normal context is of great significance. Many people are simply not interested in gaining powers because they either see no purpose in using them or are afraid to employ powers that may be beyond their ability to control. However, there are people who do want the ability to wield more power in their lives. There are also some individuals that simply allow powers to come to them through the sheer virtue of daily activity and employment. Powers should be used with some caution because projecting powers for negative reasons can result in negative attractions, and such misuse will deter spiritual progression. Committing psychic criminality is no less of an offence than committing physical crimes. Psychic attacks may result from misuse of power and amount to certain damage emotionally, mentally and physically. When we realize that someone is doing this, it is to our benefit and theirs to set the record straight before it gets out of hand. The practices and information revealed throughout this book are based upon the balance of energies and the proper focus of forces for enlightening the soul and to unveil its true visionary and powerful potential.

Destiny is controlled by the way that our spirit controls our inner and outer vehicles. When we want something we say, "I want", but when we refer to a part of our body we may say "my foot" illustrating that we are not our body, but rather something greater, inside of it. If life seems stagnant and uneventful, inexperienced and unfulfilled, it may be a sign from within that we should learn more, to become fulfilled and in touch with our spirit. Being in touch with our Self and experiencing life with the needs of the body is a learning process of constructive, positive and natural adaptation. It is something we attain not by running away from and abandoning our problems and responsibilities, but by handling them and stepping outside of our created ruts.

The charade of life has many rules that do not altruistically include our own. As we progress through life, our goal should always be directed towards the unselfish sprouting of our spirituality. Otherwise we may make the same mistakes over and over. Problems that once seemed to annoy and diffuse us will be less of a threat once our consciousness encompasses greater horizons. Rushing about daily to complete routines and functions may be viewed from a more conscious, coherent and efficient level resulting in less error and less worry when we focus our energy.

Such martial arts as Kung Fu and Tai Chi offer incredible opportunities to bring out the power of Chi from within us through special breathing techniques and forced movements. With practice it becomes a flowing energy of ease balanced with tension while simultaneously harmonizing the physical energies at work within the body. Physical exercise is partial to developing any form of energy and channeling it.

Children seem to have simple concerns, simple problems and less complexity than do adults. They learn to make life a complex deal by imitating adults and through social intervention. Their innocence and ability to see invisible people is not always fantasy. They are more receptive to the emotional and astral level because they have not learned to block their intuitive nature with personality. Children do not live a solely material existence. There is a child that remains within us and it is a special key in learning how to make life simple. Our inherent child-like qualities can converse with the inner guides, and find the path back to our godhead. Matthew 18:3 illustrates the importance of our child-like quality: "Unless you turn around and become like children, you will never enter the kingdom of heaven." Working with the eternal youth of the soul allows us to tap into the unlimited power within, the child that wears the crown of godhead and is in the image of perfection as opposed to the physically limited image we wear and eventually wear-out.

Travel brings awareness, experience and development but generally the greatest powers are achieved by conquering our situations in our original environment. When we project energy into our immediate environment it returns to us in different ways. If we nourish those energies and build upon them, they can return in abundance. The beauty in making a garden or growing from original seeds is that an energy flow will germinate rows of achievements like trees yielding great fruit. Our process of growth subtly connects us to further creative skills and ambitions. When we put positive energy into our growth and life we habitually regenerate it and receive it back. This positive energy is extended from us to our immediate environment and in turn we develop from this continuous cycle. Refining our nature involves the projection of mental images driven by emotions to higher planes. Mental images are thoughts and positive ones will ascend our emotional nature to receive divine influences from the spiritual plane. In this respect, the polarity is such that our consciousness becomes a vessel to receive stimulating influences from the depths of our subconscious positive attributes. By uniting our consciousness on higher planes, we assume better control and can focus our higher realized ambitions to a greater extent.

Our present phase of evolution is built up from years of experience and ordeal. Our subconscious is the storehouse of the past. In allowing it to blindly control us we may be bound to a part of our past evolution while struggling to live in the present. Self-initiation is primarily a condensed version of evolution whereby we process ourselves rapidly with techniques to clear most mundane problems away. Furthermore, emanating positive energy tends to lead us on a course of being positive, whereas emitting negative energies tends to make us repeat our mistakes.

Religious and spiritual fraternities attribute particular powers and forces to their higher deity that may reside on any level of a particular plane. Every religion and every person has a different conception and realization of their higher deity. Some esoteric teachings hold the theory that nature forces dwell on the second plane and that Saints reside on the third, inner Masters on the fourth, Angels on the fifth, Archangels on the sixth, and Christ consciousness dwells upon the seventh plane. The "Lords of the Elements" are said to be rulers on the sixth and seventh planes and deeply influence the evolutionary process of our life. They have servants on the lower planes, which are called the Elementals and are a non-intelligence life form. Communication with those servants called elementals may occur through vibrations of our etheric body however obsession may occur if we allow them to mate with our energies. If such an incidence does occur with an invading elemental, although quite rare, our etheric must be sublimated or purified after casting them out. Although they may at first vivify our etheric emanations, they tend to absorb our energy before long. Some cultists have ushered contacting the strata of elementals in the "earth soul" and use such forces in forming weaponry of a psychic nature, however the dangers and misrepresentation involved may not be conducive to spiritual ascension. Whatever plane, sub-plane or level we ascribe our source of aspiration to, our focused elevation of consciousness should ultimately seek to be at one with our Divine-Self and Spirit.

If a teacher of esoteric lore says they can instruct on methods of healing and spirituality, and if that teacher often appears ill or has irregular quirks, an individual should think twice about consulting such a professed teacher. It may be that the teacher is misapplying exercises and their employment of energies and power could result in physical injury. Forces that are used for healing or any other purpose must be utilized properly if benefits are to be achieved. Forces represent particular fire energy and each part of our physical anatomy has its own type of fire energy used for a specific purpose. Similarly, concentration on the chakras without proper gradual development can result in an affliction. The chakras are located near nerves of the physical organs and premature arousal or excitation may cause nerve damage. It is possible to break the surface shield of protection in the subtle etheric body, opening the physical body to further deterioration and affliction. Taking certain measures of gradual development and harnessing of power is sound advice.

The natural acquisition of powers is a result of attainment and not an ultimate goal for a true initiate. Seeking a Master on the physical plane to assist in our evolutionary direction is generally a questionable request. We should, first off, ensure that the focus and direction of the Master is parallel to our ultimate goal. When we are ready, it is a general rule that the Master will be there. Any truly enlightened Master will not want followers but would rather assist earnest devotees that come into contact with them by some natural means. The Master will know what will come of our moves in advance, like a sharp ability to clearly foresee our future. They are capable of seeing the profundity of evolution and our devotional grasp that we have in our pursuit.

It is important to be properly tuned and balanced while tapping into unlimited power. We should avoid tapping into the aura or psychic energy of other people during this particular feat, which would interfere with the process. Thoughts and emotions have vibrations and are projected from every person. As a result, the process of nurturing our inner powers for proper use must be a concentrated effort without interference. In other words, a certain "peace of mind" must be maintained. There will be an exercise regarding observing the energy from people and living organisms forthcoming but that is separate from the tapping into unlimited power. An inflation of the ego and an all-self-important frame of mind is also a severe detriment to properly using and channeling powers from the inner world. Balance, therefore, is key in securing the positive use of such energy for spiritual advancement and for the ultimate reward of attaining "Oneself" and "True Identity". Developing energy to use as power can be done in many ways. We should have no fear of gaining power and using it constructively. It may be focused towards an achievement, healing, material success, knowledge or any area of choice.

Certain powers may have limitations and by realizing this we will come to know the potency and ability of those powers. In desiring to use a power on a specific plane we must give it a form from the plane above that or else the power will be quickly dispersed and nullified. If we want it to affect the physical plane we must give and direct the power to an astral vehicle and outline exactly what is to be done, just as we did with creating a desire-chart while visualizing the obtaining of a material object. Our desire should be connected with the goal in a concentrated effort and with nothing else. Once we have focused consciousness, desires, dreams and ambitions towards our goal, it is time to invoke the power to live within it. This process is done over time with proper preparation so it is incumbent to live it for short time periods and return to our daily activities and progression in spiritual development.

We may increase power by limiting our consciousness to the sole aim that we destine. This does not imply that we have a limited consciousness but a focused one. Consider concentration to be the apex of a triangle and use the extension of consciousness to form the complete triangle from its base. In this way we will derive a secret of power to be the extension of our consciousness on both sides of a force that is working on our behalf. In this analogy, the triangle reminds us to secure the limitation and reverse side of our power supply while extending our consciousness to the point. The laws of action and reaction apply to this principle of limitation. We may safely transcend the limitation principle by knowing it, just as we can transcend our consciousness from the physical to the higher astral and mental planes. The plane above the one we are focused on imparts the creative seed for success because it is the positive influence for creation on the plane below it. The triangle is merely a simile of bringing force into form without lose.

There are people that work in convocations to channel energy as a combined effort. The united conscious effort of a group working together is negative in the sense of the plane that they are working on with respect to the plane that is directly above them. With their aims principled upon the next higher plane, and the efforts of a leader, their work is eventually materialized. They essentially become impregnated with great creativity resulting in an uplifting of their group-mind to that of the leader who becomes the provider to materialize their group work. The leader inherently provides the positive stimulus to transfer their combined power into a physical form.

There are three pertinent personal principles that we may adhere to in tapping into and acquiring unlimited powers:

Disciple and Practice
Drive and Direction through Enthusiasm
Determination through Persistence

We must practice and discipline ourselves to become aware of tapping into what seems to be an unlimited energy from within. We must have a certain amount of drive to do this and be focused energetically to continually realize it. We must remain determined and persistent to reach this Infinity State or awareness of it in order to return to it constantly and bring power to our needs.

The astral plane is the realm of emotion and desire. We require an emanation of dynamic and dramatic emotions in order to tap into the powers that will be directed to function on our behalf. When I was an elementary school student and put on magic shows for the grade one and grade two students, I found that practicing the tricks at home made all the difference in creating an atmosphere of magic and wonder for the little spectators of my age-group. The more practice and visualization I did the more I was able to convey the desired magical effect. As a result, I was able to not only perform the tricks properly, but also control their emotions through the element of surprise that I employed as a trickster. Their energy in turn contributed to my performance. This also demonstrates the truth in the old adages of 'as you sow, so shall you reap' and 'you are what you eat' and 'cleanliness is next to godliness'. Each of these maxims suggests that we gradually become the result of our efforts. Whatever we feel, think, and do will become part of our atmosphere. The degree of success depends upon our energy and efforts with the three pertinent personal principles.

With progression, our mind and emotions work for us as tools. We are no longer slaves to random thoughts and stirred emotions. With effort we sense a rising above the mundane material level of life, and tap into the core of soul essence with an altered ability to influence forces for success. A personal sense of well being on our path in life, attuned with fulfilling our destiny, is a great leap forward. We may employ an imaginary flare and develop our efficiency in such a manner that accomplishing our goals in life will become reality. There are numerous ways to increase our success, and tapping into the limitless powers that radiate through us can speed up the process. It should be proof that we are doing something correct if we obtain some measure of success and self-realization in the process. It also happens to make us acutely aware of how little we really know compared to how much we have yet to know and learn.

Increasing physical stamina and inner qualities involves practice and the development of specific abilities. To pause for a moment, if we get the feeling that someone is using nasty powers on us, drawing emotional turmoil into our life, I have but one suggestion. Ignore it and it will go away! By keeping physically ACTIVE and keeping busy, busy, busy, we strengthen our focus. Whatever influences we feel from another person will diminish and in time die away. If we are "actually" interested in spirituality, then we are always busy and so we will never become concerned or pestered by "negative" emotions emanated from other people. It is when we focus on "negatives" that we feed them and bring them to life, causing eventual outcomes.

To connect with and harness powerful forces we must train our senses, and manipulate the flow of energy with focus. Masters taught their disciples to see without using their eyes, to hear from great distances and to feel without touching. The ability to see without seeing may be trained by a simple practice. Pick an object such as a plant or flower and look at it directly. Do not allow any outside thoughts or distractions to intrude on the experience. Feel the life of the plant, the petals, the colors, the growth and source of its life. Concentrate on it for five minutes. You should be able to close your eyes and still see the flower exactly as it is, in every detail. Once this has been accomplished, use your imagination and visualize walking somewhere in your home to perform a function and then return to where you actually are. Attempt to see every detail in the actions required in accomplishing a specific task. This is similar to the process discussed in the chapter on Astral Achievements. You are radically training your mind over and over to move in a direction under your control and thereby strengthening your willpower. Make sure you do not delay in practicing this, otherwise you might never do it. It will help to discipline your mind and become a habitual practice of intensifying power to your will.

Just as active balances passive, projecting accompanies receptivity and wisdom resides in understanding, we shall begin to broaden our visionary ability to that which is not readily visible. Developing the etheric sight allows us to be receptive to energy surrounding all objects. In the nineteenth century a practice was developed for this ability and it seems to work for most people. Obtain a horseshoe magnet and hang it from some object, using a string. Cover one eye with a hand and stare at the edge of the magnet for a while with the other eye. With persistence you will see the magnetic flow around the magnet from pole to pole. After a few minutes, if you have no awareness of this field, rest your eyes and try again using the other eye. After some practice you will see the field around the magnet, if you quietly and persistently concentrate upon it. Try to see it with both eyes open. Figure out which eye has greater vision capability. Once you have accomplished this, try to see the energy surrounding a plant or tree and then extend the ability to seeing the energy radiating from animals and humans. Do not divert attention to everything but simply choose one object at a time until a magnetic field of energy can be seen. Through this practice, you will tune your vision to see the energy and even the emotions and feelings that surround a person. If we can see the energy sent from another person, we may prepare to deal with it in advance if so desired. There may be occasions in which you will sense that you are psychic to the extent of seeing events and situations on astral levels while you expand these clairvoyant abilities.

Sharpening hearing can also be enhanced with practice as well. Most people have experienced hearing tests during medical examinations. Attempting to hear the higher and lowers frequencies diminishes once the sound waves rise above or fall below an audible range. Listen to one particular sound, such as a waterfall. Sit near it, and listen carefully to it. After a while move back and see how well you can still hear and detect it. Move back again and continue to listen to the same sound. See how far away you can travel and still be able to detect its sound. Tranquility tapes or CD's may work also, with the repetition of ocean waves or similar sounds. By turning down the volume of the stereo, we can test our hearing and attention span to the diminishing sounds.

Once this has been practiced, the audible etheric ability may be developed. Obtain a bar magnet and hang it from an object by a piece of thread. Twist the magnet around several times, then release it so that it will spin on its own for a short time. Listen carefully and with practice you will be able to hear the magnetic field changing like the faint echo of a wind going through a tunnel. Having developed this auditory talent you may hear noises that you were not previously aware of. If you are near power lines you may hear crackling noises from the electricity passing through them since you are now more susceptible to such frequencies of noise. Have you ever thought the telephone was going to ring and then suddenly it did? Was this a guess, was it a psychic connection with the person phoning, or was it that you heard the noise coming to your destination before your ears registered it to your mind?

Practice describing the particular smells associated to different objects. For instance, the peeling from an orange has a strong citric odor and flares the olfactory sense. Examine spices from a spice rack with your eyes closed and smell each one. Once you set a spice down, try to still imagine the smell of it. You may have noticed that it is also possible to smell water, especially if it is chemically treated, but otherwise it has the scent of a clear and clean liquid. To practice the etheric sense of smell you can once again use the bar magnet. Wash it first, as all items should be clean of impurities before examining them in their true or somewhat original form. You will, with practice, be able to detect a different smell from each end of the magnet. The north end will not smell the same as the south end. If you have ever said to yourself that you smell something 'bad' in a situation, you are using a sense of emotionally psychic smell when you detect a distinct danger, fear or negative influence.

We have already exercised our powers of sight, hearing, tasting and smell. Now it is time to practice the ability of sensation through touch. Choose an object and feel it with the palm of your hand. Close your eyes and pay attention to exactly how that object feels. Try to describe it in words such that someone else would be able to figure out what the object actually is. Use the palm of the other hand and see if the sensations are exactly the same or slightly different. This requires special attention as you are sending messages to your brain regarding the object's precise texture and hardness. You can tell how hard or soft the object is, how tightly the molecular structure feels as you compare it to other things and know that it has particular qualities by holding and "feeling" it.

To practice the etheric sensation of touch, obtain two quarters, one that is quite new and one that is much older. Wash the new one in water and dry it with a clean cloth. Set both coins on a piece of paper. Pick up the new one, set it in your palm, and close your eyes. With a clear mind, feel any vibrations that emanate from the coin. You may get a few vague images, but generally you can expect to feel relatively few impressions from this coin. When you are finished, take the older coin and proceed in the same fashion. Feel the vibrations that come from it, through its texture. With this one you may feel many mixed emotions. It may house some of the feelings of a person who previously held it. You may receive some mental pictures that are unclean. These impressions come from various people who held the coin, and you are simply becoming receptive to them. With the practice of these exercises, the etheric senses will evolve and enable you to become aware of life with an extra set of "subtle" senses.

With this keener grasp of energy awareness, you may begin projecting your own energy into an object. It is similar to storing energy into talismans, which has previously been discussed, but here we shall store energy into any object of choice in order to obtain that energy later and to feel it or redirect it. This energy may be referred to as the Vril Force previously mentioned and is projected with concentrated effort. Choose a substance or clean object that you wish to store energy into. You may find that something with a rough surface rather than smooth, and something that will fit into one hand will be easier to send vibrations into. Take a shower and cleanse away all negative energy from your emotions and body. Lighten up by getting into an energetic mood and sitting comfortably with the object that you will store power into. Close your eyes and hold the object in both hands while concentrating on the flow of energy from you to the object, charging it with force. Feel the energy going through your body, through your arms into your hands and into the object. The particular energy you choose to send should be the only thing you are thinking and feeling as you project it into the object. If you wish to store your object with a sense of happiness, serenity or peace then build those energies within you and focus them out of your hands and into your object. If you wish to send feelings of luck and fortune then you must FEEL that energy and charge the object with those quality sensations. It is not enough to do this once or a few times. It must be an energetic exercise performed a few times every day so that the object has the same energy flowing into it over and over, repeatedly. After a few weeks you will be able to feel that energy when you pick up the object. You can then use the object to receive that energy when you feel down, saddened or at a loss. Keep it in a safe place. Do not leave it out in the open for others to see or touch. You may even wish to wrap it in a special cloth. What you are doing in fact is putting feelings that are pure through concentration into an object so that you can strengthen those feelings and use that energy for later convenience. Some people have recorded becoming financially successful by filling a particular object with financial success. But whether you use it for happiness, peace, harmony, enthusiasm or financial success is unimportant, as long as it is sufficiently charged to provide for you. You are essentially becoming a medium between unlimited energy and the object you are transferring energy into.

Self-purification is essential in order to realize and connect with powers that can be tapped into and used for marvelous benefit. If you have practiced meditation and yoga then you may be sufficiently prepared to perform the following lengthy exercise. You may wish to choose a particular day about a month in advance for this main exercise. Leading up to that chosen day, it would be prosperous to cleanse the physical body through a special diet, continually train the mind with focussing, and practice being devoted to spiritual aspiration. Being experienced in daily meditations, breath control, concentration and a conscious ability to project the astral body is important and of extra benefit.

Prior to the main exercise and upon awakening every morning you may do a simple yet effective method of stretching which balances the physical body and is practiced in some schools of yoga. Begin by stretching the arms out sideways and stretching your fingers apart. Bring your arms in front of you and bring your fingers together. Turn the palms towards one another and slowly interlock your fingers. Slowly raise them over your head with the fingers still interlocked. Breathe in the purity from the air. Now that they are above your head, pull your arms apart, but do not break your interlocked fingers. Lower your elbows as you begin to exhale and continue to slowly lower your locked hands past your face, chest and stomach. At that point, release the grip. Inhale, then slowly exhale, releasing all tension. Many practitioners of yoga do this on a daily basis. You can add to it as you wish, and it is a good idea to do it upon awakening every day so that your physical body becomes refreshed through an effort of consciously regaining balance.

The day of a new moon is a particularly good time to choose to generate and become receptive to power. To prepare for your intensive self-control, purification and spiritual exercise, select a room that has nothing in it; or else clean it up so that you can work in it without any interruptions. Purify the room from any influences that linger and construct a magical double circle by spreading salt, as a purifier, around the circumference. According to ancient lore, the outer circle has a radius of 2.72 feet, while the inner one has a radius of 2.56 feet. This allows your powers to be tuned to pass through it and to reject powers from outside of it. Set within the circle a small table with a cloth and a chair. Place on the table a few candles, some matches, a journal and a pen. A bucket should be placed under the chair to use as toilet facilities.

The day before your self-purification process, do not eat any food, providing you are medically fit to abstain. Fasting is an important facet in cleansing. Drink plenty of water and eat fresh bread. Make sure you will not be disturbed during this process. Bring bottles of water and some bread with you into your prepared temple. Plan to remain in your meditation temple for a full 24-hour period doing exercises of meditation, concentration, contemplation and purification. With this you will come to realize the storehouse of unlimited powers within and learn how to tap into them. Write down pertinent information that you discover during this period. If you smoke or drink alcohol, refrain from doing so several days prior to this main exercise and special day. In a sense, you are becoming reborn, shedding off the facets of your old personality and allowing your spiritual Self to shine through. It is a simple, yet effective self-initiation practice. During your period of rebirth you are essentially freeing your mind, emotions and physical body from interruptions so that your Inner Guide will communicate through you.

Perform a cleansing of the nerves of your Etheric Body as a practice of pranayama or breath control. Our consciousness will receive and comprehend the inner voice of communicating vibrations from our Inner Guide through our etheric nerves. To remove etheric impurities, which may take a full month of daily practice, sit in a meditation posture, on a chair, pillow or however best accustomed. With your back and head straight, use the thumb of your right hand to cover your right nostril as you inhale through your left nostril and comfortably fill your lungs. Release the thumb and use your index finger of the same hand to cover the left nostril and exhale through the right nostril. Inhale again through the right nostril, cover it with your thumb, and exhale again through the left nostril as before. Your right and left nostrils are consuming the fresh oxygen and sending it through Ida and Pingala, the two etheric nerves. They will spread the oxygen throughout the etheric nervous system, the counterpart of the physical nervous system, and rejuvenate it by releasing all of the gathered impurities, which prevent the clarity of your inner voice from reaching you through your soul.

Ensure that you are properly prepared for this period and willing to shed your personality aside to obtain the greatest benefit. Through this period of silencing the mind and emotions a tremendous sense of well being will be gained. If you feel or think that this is a difficult task to undertake or that you are not prepared, you can work up to it as a future endeavor. There is no hurry to do this exercise and it may be done in stages to develop towards it. It is a completely harmonious journey of cleansing our nature, moral characteristics, and ego, and allowing the spark of spirit to shine through. It will bring us in touch with our Self and reveal powers and qualities never before realized.

This special 24-hour period becomes a magical adventure. It is a spiritual practice, a cleansing routine, and a consciously expanding awareness and realization experience. It becomes anything we make it to be by the efforts put into it. When we are concentrating, we are fixating our mind on ONE thing, like a point on a pond. When we contemplate, we are thinking about that one thing, in a manner similar to concentration except we are going deep into the pond, following that point upon the pond to its depths as we perform Dharana. When we meditate we perform Dhyana and become one with the pond in totality. We are capable of being one with the whole pond and with the total nature and effect of all points and total depth of the complete pond. In yoga, we are becoming one, in a relaxed and passive state such that our body is not tense, but yet under constant realization and Self-Supervision while heightening our state of consciousness. With magick, we are conscious of our True Will, our ability to extend that Will, as directed by our Higher Self. Magick is the active state and yoga is the passive state, in a particular sense. They are balancing partners for one another. Yoga is our passive chalice of understanding and magick is our active directed wand of will. Together they become implemented just as man and woman.

While concentrating we should always perform pranayama (breath control). Before we begin regular pranayama and concentration, we should do a pre-concentration cleansing, as noted in the meditation and yoga chapter. Breath in for seven seconds, hold for one second, exhale for seven seconds, and hold for one second. Repeat this five times before beginning to concentrate on the chosen object.

During the 24-hour period of solitude any number of directed achievements might be aimed for. Consciousness may be focused towards a specific sephirah of the Tree of Life by rising on the planes through the tree of life paths. Concentration on specific parts of the body and chakra meditations may also be incorporated. Light has an ability to cause change and eventual transformation. By visualizing the Inner Light radiating from the crown of Kether through our body we may induce changes to occur. An exercise for doing this will be mentioned briefly. In any event, this 24-hour period will be a busy one such that it will go by fast in one sense yet may seem much longer in another sense for the work performed and accomplishments achieved. The mind likes to play tricks at times, and you are likely aware of that by now. Being aware that such fallacies and deceptions arise in the mind during extended efforts will help to get around them and ignore them. The funny thing about "material consciousness" is that it seems to want "rewards" for every petty thing it does for us!

Concentration on the heart chakra may be done during the main exercise. Consider a flame residing there, while growing a sense of devotion to purify your heart. Envision the colors of blue, white and pink of your subtle etheric heart center receiving divine emanations from the higher spheres. When all thoughts have been quieted and you are at complete ease and fully aware, the brow chakra may be realized as a flame between your eyes, a radiant eye itself, that receives messages from your Inner Guide as currents of inspiration. When you feel communication in this way, concentration upon the crown chakra will bring an Inner Voice from the depth of Silence, as though you are being clearly communicated to, without flaw. It will be a concise experience without misinterpretation. You may have a vision through the interpretation. You may see a bright Light, a heavenly or spiritual image, a radiant star, your inner eye, or something of similar nature that brings clear, mental illumination. Inner Light brings harmonious awareness and enlightens the soul. It provides insight and inner-communication with an ever-present state of consciousness. Intuition is also enhanced when we strive to connect with our Divine Source through conscious effort. Opening of the inner eye, the Third Eye, releases visions and allows us to be intuitively psychic. The third eye resides between the physical eyes. The physical eyes should be closed and directed slightly upwards and very slightly inwards during any effort to see through the third eye without causing strain to the physical eyes.

The soul is being charged with renewed vitality through the 24-hour exercise. After completion of this main exercise you may feel a completely re-energized feeling and be overwhelmed in some respects yet be exhausted in others. Ensure there is a nutritiously proper meal awaiting you. Enjoy the day in rest and relaxation. Get some fresh air and write as you feel about your post-experience. You may come out of this with some great ideas, solutions, and abilities that you were not previously aware of. The realization of your life being upon a spectacular Path may be the greatest of awakening experiences and realizations.

Experiencing meditation with the Sephiroth, the ten spheres of the Tree of Life, raises our consciousness to the higher planes. In doing so we rise with the tides of energy from the planets, just as the physical body is subjected on Earth with the tides of its subtle body, the Moon. The value of this point can not be over emphasized. Self-initiation is of prime importance if we are to achieve anything of lasting worth before the physical body terminates it material life. When rising our consciousness to the higher spheres of the tree of life, we are subjected to the Planetary Being of the particular sphere we ascend to. This is a normal occurrence and is not a negative consequence. It is essentially the potency of that sphere that begins to arouse us when we contact it and become influenced by the energized influx of its momentum of force.

Working with the forces associated to attributions of the sephiroth is a natural progression provided we learn to balance such forces that come through our consciousness. It is also possible to prevent the reverse aspects of a force from interfering with our goal by nullifying its attachment. When inspired by a force from above or within, we should attempt to balance it with creative efforts so that we are not dragged into the lower and reverse side of the force and inverse of the tree of life called the Qlipoth. In this way we may preserve a harmonious balance and continue the flux of the vital forces from the sphere of our aspiration.

The center pillar of the Tree of Life can be used to tap into a purified limitless energy and has been given as an exercise by Dr. Israel Regardie in his book *The Middle Pillar*. The middle pillar exercise will be briefly mentioned here in my own words in case the reader finds it difficult to procure that book, however it is highly recommended that it be obtained. *The Middle Pillar* book gives much greater and better detail that what is about to be relayed from memory and practice. The power that is unleashed with this exercise may be channeled towards healing and rejuvenation. In performing this exercise a comfortable posture such as sitting up straight or kneeling should be adopted.

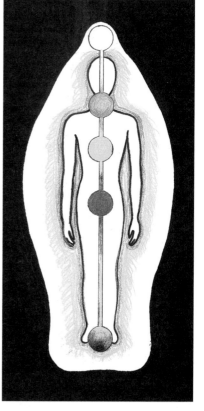

The topmost point is Kether, the crown, and is about four inches above the head. It is a sphere of white brilliant light from our spiritual core of cosmic energy and represents the divine Spark of Spirit. Feel yourself bathing in the stream of white light that flows from above your head into all parts of your body. The next sphere is Tiphareth, the Sun, and is a yellow or golden light sphere at the center of the chest, the solar plexus. Breathe in deeply while visualizing a beam come from the center of Kether that is a concentrated light flowing down into Tiphareth at your solar plexus. Pull the concentrated light into the solar plexus with some effort of visualization and ensure you feel it fill your Tiphareth center. The third sphere is Yesod, the Moon, which resides as a glowing violet hue in the region of the generative organs. Gently exhale and extend the light, as a shaft of energy, into the generative organs in the sphere of Yesod. The final sphere of Malkuth, the Earth, is about three inches below the bottom of the feet and is divided into four colors: citrine, olive, russet and black. While exhaling, continue to extend the light from Yesod to below your feet into the four-colored sphere of Malkuth. Malkuth is the multiple combinations of the four elements on the physical plane. Reduce any resistance that you may have in fully visualizing these four spheres in your body. Do not be interrupted by random thoughts. The key is to flow with the visualization and allow the stream of light to pour through gently on its own accord. You should feel harmony throughout your body if you are doing it correctly.

You must now balance the positive charge coming down from Kether with a negative charge, from the Earth through Malkuth and back up into the spheres. Once again, inhale while visualizing the forces of the Earth in the four-colored sphere of Malkuth rising as an orange light to enter Yesod, continuing through Tiphareth and above the head to Kether. Draw the forces up while breathing in and visualizing the energy from them being filtered into purity and going through all of the cleansed spheres to make their way into Kether. Exhale, relax and prepare to do the process again. You may try it up to five times or else you may do it a few times and see what affect is gained from it. Feel the stream of white brilliant light emanate from Kether and flow down through the other spheres and then visualize the forces of Malkuth being drawn up into the body to Kether, just as outlined. You may then practice the forces flowing down from Kether with the forces flowing up from Malkuth simultaneously. A healthy, balanced feeling of conjoined forces in mind and body should be experienced.

According to the strength of your visualization, this energy may be very potent and should be properly channeled before opening the gates and allowing more to flow through. The energy flowing through is neither good nor bad. It is just energy from vitalized forces and the amount you allow to flow through is of vital importance. An over-abundance of such energy can cause an unbalance and affect the outcome negatively. This energy may help you in becoming very creative and constructive. It can assist in healing and enlivening your ambitions. It is your moral responsibility to utilize it properly as with the acquisition of all powers.

Problems never seem to last forever. They come and go just like the thoughts that accompany them. They either distract us or move us on our way and how we assimilate and handle them becomes part of our personality. Our life and physical body is in constant change and how we take care of it is a reflection of how organized we are on the inside.

There are psychological components that are involved in working with forces beyond the physical level. As Carl Jung pointed out, we can develop "guilt-complexes" such that we feel "cut-off" from the people around us. Keeping this in mind as we work on appropriate levels to maintain balanced with "reality" should not pose any difficulty.

The higher levels of the tree such as Kether represent the unconditional consciousness of the Spirit, the True Self that is the primal source of all power. Tiphareth is the super-consciousness and Yesod is the "personal unconscious" or subconscious part of our mind. Malkuth is the sensory consciousness that brings sensations to our physical self. Each level represents experiences and mingles in the area where the conscious mind becomes aware of them. Each sphere of the Tree has a Tree within it and operates in each of the four worlds as represented by Qabalistic teachings. They become a balance for another force or power and as such require the opposite combination to remain adjusted, which becomes a natural occurrence with gradual progression.

Psychic attunement reveals the fact that we are never completely alone, no matter where we are. The astral and mental worlds are shared by everyone else on Earth and there are people who are exceptionally spiritual and are helping others and assisting our enlightenment on the inner planes. Passing through dark times and difficult experiences may be unavoidable at certain landmarks in life. It is surprising how much more aware we become of what is right and wrong for our way to be made clear while using these secrets for the unlimited source within. ★

HOUSE of YOUR SOUL

"That the difference between creation and conservation is a difference solely in our way of thinking is one of the many things which the natural light manifests to us."

Descartes Philosophical Writings- Trans by N.K. Smith

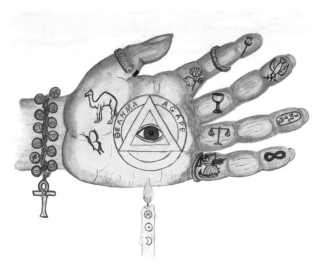

When we search for a house to purchase, we shop around and do research while viewing several until the exact style and requirements are found. It has to be in a certain area for convenience, relaxation, and suitable tastes. It also has to have certain sized rooms and a layout that is aesthetically pleasing. It is then furnished and decorated to make it feel just like home. It is outfitted for functional reasons and may be refinished to reflect a personal fondness and artistic atmosphere. It becomes our creative corner in the world and provides a sense of security and inspiration. It is something we spend money and time on diligently so that it becomes an asset in life. The house that we live in is similar in several respects to our body and soul. Our body is a temple comprising numerous organs and features, which affect our moods and our inner life. We have walls within our mind that separates certain areas comprised of personal thoughts and feelings and provides exclusive privacy from the outside world. We have emotions and desires delicately decorating the pleasures and cravings that appease our particular appetites. They can be connected to memories of good times or warnings of what we should and should not do, linked to our conscience. Emotions cause us to react to situations that could affect our future and comprise a large area of our inner home.

The furnishing of our inner house with positive growth and linking our emotions to greater ideals is an active attempt of becoming fulfilled. Making it a more comfortable and organized place to function, to retrieve information and classify it systematically is essential in using it beneficently. Being rid of some bothersome and useless emotions that hamper open-minded views for further progression is an important initial step in growth.

As we've already outlined, the Qabalah is a system to utilize functional parameters of our inner world. It may be used to classify, organize and differentiate baggage of the mind and forces in nature that we are constantly affected by in daily life. The Tree of Life is the map of the inner world where our inner bodies thrive and it is a glyph of life illustrating the way to consciously create and manipulate manifestation. The inner worlds are for investigation and we as students learn to manipulate life to be successful, primarily in realizing our destiny and accomplishing it. It is not a fanciful dream but an awakened ability to use all of our inner power in doing what we must accomplish through the use of Light that illuminates our path. Working with the forces in life, positive energies from other people, and being rid of built up subconscious complexes that inhibit the full expression of our freedom, is a practice that can change the way we feel and make it easier to adjust attitude for positive outcomes.

Before long, and we have known this all of our life, we become conscious of what is an obstacle and what is of assistance for us to fulfill our perceived destiny. We have a gut feeling, a resonance from within, that something is a waste of time, or that it is a hindrance to where we want to go and what we want to achieve. Harmony is a result of proper adjustment, and when something is in the way it is a responsibility to correct it and express once again the consistency without being enslaved to the storehouse of past programming that may inflict discord.

Sharpening our wits with the tools of inner refinement becomes a great advantage for achieving goals associated with discovering our latent abilities. This way we will not be influenced by the powers of others, and we will not be broken by our own system of beliefs, whatever they may be. Also, in quieting the mind and emotions we can pick up the vibrations of other people around us and know where their intentions are leading to, whether for sincere or dubious purposes. The majority of people may find this difficult to significantly accomplish for one main reason. Distractions are abundant and the gluing effect of media, associates, television and a host of other entertaining conglomerates affects the qualities we inherently have to work with. Distractions are inevitable but the practice of quieting our mental and emotional corridors will prove beneficial in listening to our inner voice. Then inner refinement takes a positive turn in seeing what is within our house and where we should begin construction for certain attainments.

The tools that are available are innumerable and of great advantage in answering our most personal questions about life. Before making any significant decisions it is always a good practice to become quiet through meditation. Meditation should be done not on the question, as we have personal feelings about it that could impair judgement, but upon funneling the Inner Light through us in a selfless, limitless manner. By allowing this pure light to enter, it is like turning on a bright flashlight while in the basement and seeing what obstacles are around us. It provides a clear view of what is, in an impartial light regarding any predicament and awakens us to attentively find answers.

Time is of the essence to use in overcoming internal weaknesses that we have with any particular situation. To close the doors of our inner house is a refusal to be sagacious, for we must be able to enter the rooms of our Ruach, intellect and mind freely and be able to haul out exactly what is required at any time for any dilemma. Wisdom and Understanding shine from the spiritual plane into our functional mind when we meditate upon the compensating qualities required in overcoming weakness. Facing humiliation, knowing our limitations and diligently taking a rational stand provides us with strength in all concerns.

Feeling sorry for our self, having low self-esteem or shyness are all qualities attached to the lower mind. They are attached to the lower self, the selfish, enervating part of our persona. They create blockages and restrictions from realizing radiance. They are akin to sins, preventing the flow of light to radiate through to express in spontaneity our True Identity fully living in the Present.

The world has many sheepish people with tough, demanding personalities, ready to make a point but how limited the point is, can be seen through their colors. Conscious mental action works off our karmic bonds and will free us from thought-slavery so that we are at liberty to see our colors and those of others. Through determined realization we have the ability to break the karmic bonds that tie our mental plane thoughts and emotional plane feelings to any bothersome situation. This is usually accomplished to some extent but we are not consciously aware that we do it.

Any predicament can be reduced to its original condition. The complexity that we make with our problems in life is like the wrapping of a mummy with white bandages around and around, with increasing mental and emotional implements. To contact the Lords of Karma, we must seek the spiritual root of the situation, within the bandages and bondage that have been wrapped around. That which seems incurable can be reduced to simpler terms and modified by applying clear decisions through courage, energy and refreshing perception. Sometimes we do not see the simplicity in matters that shroud our mind unless we pause from it and then review it from a new perspective.

Our fears come from an overworking imagination of what can happen in the course of any event. Fear does not exist in a present state but from worrying about something that may never occur. It is useful as a preventative measure and warning apparatus but too often it results in causing us to not be prepared in properly handling and facing a plight. Positive images and a picture of where we wish to go or what we desire to achieve helps in arriving safely at our destination or choice of outcome. Practically everything comes as a result of some certain effort behind it to drive it there. The best picture we can have on our face during any instance is that of success.

Repetitious problems in our life that seem to shape our personality may be linked to karma that has been gathered in the present or a previous life. When a person dies, their inner vehicles work on the inner planes and gradually disintegrate leaving their subtle essence to pass into the spiritual plane and become part of their Individuality (that which cannot be divided). Anything that really stands out in our life may connect us to the chain in reading the imprint that has been made from our previous life. Recognizing the astute, invariable nature of our individuality may bring images or impressions relating to who we once were on the physical plane so many years or lifetimes previous. The long lived process of reincarnation and present life interaction shapes us into who we appear to be and what kind of problems we habitually bear upon our hands.

There are many fine books with instructions and techniques to discover past life identities, but as a precaution we should never strain our desire of contacting those images that will reveal a previous identity. Conjuring up subconscious images that are untrue may result from such straining and we can loose the verge or cusp of conscious and subconscious transition where factual recollection occurs. A picture will come freely in a spontaneous and intuitive manner from the subconscious, that we do not control with our conscious mind. By having our inner eye open and being patient we will maneuver from one state of consciousness to another and within that verge an image will appear. We will know it is relevant by the emotions that we have for it. It may come during the moment of awakening in the morning, so be prepared to write on a piece of paper or in a journal what is recalled and felt if this visionary experience occurs.

Discerning what period of history to which an image relates inevitably provides information for us to further discover in seeking our previous incarnation. Emotions regarding it may be quite distinct and possibly alarming. Memory will formulate a coherent series of pictures given the proper mood and focus. It is possible to recall more than one previous life and is generally easier to retrieve images of when we were of the same sex as we are during the present lifetime.

Our personal character dictates how our karma functions during the course of life. If misfortune and ruin comes then it is a result of a part of our previous or present character that brought it into action, or as a later reaction. The things we do and the way we do them cause the results to occur the way they happen to. Nothing occurs in life without certain forces putting them into action. If we change our character our karma will change by having altered the direction of the flow of energy expended and thus causing the environment to change its course of reaction upon us accordingly.

Temperament brings out what good karma there is to be given us when we express our harmonized nature with the cosmos. To be clear of karma, we have to be clear of our past debts that are built in our subconscious rooms and to use just enough character and temperament to be in cosmic balance with the present. Too much or little of either is an unbalance and is similar to an over or under dosage of vitamin C or an over or under dosage of a vaccine.

To this end we want to cleanse our house, to have a soul reflecting the light of spirit and to be free from hampering circumstances to pursue our destined Path as a successful course in Life. To have a clean slate, we must accept the working out required through the actions of karma and the perfecting of character such that it does not control our movement on the path. Initiates may speed up their destined karma in order to have it worked out sooner so that they can ascend to spiritual levels. Either way we should look at what occurs in life through clear windows in the best way possible and get through it without creating more havoc and uncertainty if we believe in controlling destiny and evolutionary progression.

Through the mysteries of perfecting and harmonizing our nature, life itself will throw a question at us and if we have long applied spiritual principles in our pursuit then the answer will be automatic. The Veil will open and into the inner sanctuary our soul will enter with utmost devotion and clarity as the words duly express what is experienced therein: "Not my will, but Thine be done." The radiance shines over us and through the core of Being, awakening to the realization that "thou" is mightier than anything preconceived and is partial to the limitless light that created the manifestation principle of our spirit. Awareness of the Higher Self is without question at this stage. It shines through to our inner vehicles providing a conscious realization of it's existence and although the journey is seen as being one uphill, it gets clearer at each step. Fate as it were, is a thing of the past, and belief we are beyond, acknowledging life as reality in an ever-present state. The ability to read the inner layers of life's fabric will be easier, as we will have an unclouded vision of what life is and how it functions. A visionary experience and a link to divinatory competency through the psyche will be enhanced many fold since there will be neither emotional deceit nor random thoughts impinging upon our directed questions in life.

Positive psychic images come from control of our mental apparatus through the voluntary nervous system. Negative psychic phenomenon results when emotions channel images haphazardly and comes through the involuntary nervous system. In the later case subconscious distortion results from previously stored data and brings up images that may not be factual. Positive psychics are developed spiritual people who are not always capable of full image control unless the conditions are right to work with. When we ask a question to a psychic, their response may be slow due to this fact.

Negative psychics may wish to become controlled positive psychics but the relinquishing of the involuntary ability is the price they must heed in working with a higher pictorial conscious state. It is through such higher training that symbols and images make the visions coherent and the study of the Tree of Life to become a pictorial anima. Such a developed framework releases impressions advanced by illumination and dreams become realized experiences during the maturing of a true seer. Inaccurate perceptions should be realized and steps taken accordingly when the collective unconscious yields images to interfere with what the person knows to be untrue image recollections. A sound knowledge of the pictorial Tree of Life is of immeasurable assistance when a vision is suspect of not conforming to what the trained mind knows to be a real vision opposed to a fake and formless illusive perception.

Having a conscious connection to the fourth dimension where there are intervening grades of subtle matter and various entities dwelling in what may be called the supernatural domain of life is an endowment to witness astral inhabitants. It is the supernormal sector termed the astral plane, which will manifest in physical existence or else ascends to a higher plane as the process of disintegration and or refinement evolves. Inhabitants on the astral plane living in the astral-mental world are subject to superior Beings who manifest their presence on that plane from higher or finer grades nearer the spiritual realms. Such inhabitants are not considered human in nature but are linked to the collective unconscious of mankind and have an influence on what occurs and why something does not. This theory suggests that happenings in life occur through a major networking scenario and have many elements and inner plane influences at play to cause them to transpire.

If we as humans choose to believe that existence is only confined to physical perception then the price we pay will be a fragile limitation of visionary scope. Such limitation is not unlike the person who is blocked in the middle of a large city and unable to see what else occurs throughout the world. Their capacity is centered on what is immediately occupying their senses and they have chosen not to go beyond that. The ability to see further scenery, or reality, through psychic ability is the acceptance of shifting consciousness to the "hypnogogic" and "hypnopompic" psychological state where images of the astral light are witnessed. This state occurs in every person at the moment of falling asleep and during that of awakening in the morning. Interpretation through the astral light however, can be totally illusive.

Initiated psychic abilities may be gained from symbol-relationships that are developed in the course of Tree of Life meditations. Psychic information at this level does not occur with images but with relationships that are a result of esoteric training. Assimilation through meditation provides better or unprejudiced identification. Manipulating an outcome is possible with initiated knowledge of the vision relationship and can influence the current of energy that is the source of its power. This ability is incapable of being used selfishly, however those who randomly dabble on the lower end of the scale would have us think otherwise. The lower self sometimes referred to as the persona is a result of social interaction and is the "false ego". It becomes the duty of an initiate to have it refined and calibrated so that it can be released without concern to attain spirituality just as the Ruach becomes a willing sacrifice in achieving the knowledge of our Guardian Angel.

It is towards spirituality that we all eventually aspire even though many people use the term haphazardly without summating the full scope of progress that it requires. To contact our higher nature we must strongly develop the powers of the abstract mind. Mankind has gone through many stages of development through the precession of the Equinoxes, which is the turn of the orbit of the zodiac. Each sign takes roughly 2200 years and the 12 signs take nearly 26,400 years to fulfill the cycle. The Picean age which just passed, commenced just prior to 100 BC and is a water sign representing emotional development and cleansing as is performed in baptismal practice by Christianity. Such water-mixed, "universal-solvent" cleansing traditions were incorporated by religions that involved love, mercy and compassion, all representative of the element of water during the age of Pisces.

The present Aquarian age is an air sign and involves interest in the higher mind, being in control and being mobile. These traits have come into most preferred lifestyles in the past decades. Air corresponds with the mental plane, thought developed intellect, and the higher manas. It may be based upon fulfillment through love but is dependent upon the stage of evolution the person is at and their focus. Prior to the age of Pisces, Zoroastrian religion evolved through the element of fire with purification dominating all that transpired. Confucianism was based upon the element of earth, which relates to grounded, solid, practical applications. Everything is natural in evolution and as it should be according to nature's laws, formulas and play upon time. When wrongful applications are permitted to destroy the natural progression, it affects all planes and causes complexities, pollution in every sense of the term and an unbalanced state of affairs. Adjustment is required when unequal and unstable incidents threaten present and future circumstances.

Everything in nature is rhythmic and cyclical according to the cosmos. Our states of consciousness relate to the power and energies of the planets and our personality relates to the Moon just as our Higher Self is manifested in the symbol of the Sun. The planets reside on the pillars of the past and future (right and left) in the Tree of Life and the states, which we experience, cause us to act in a certain way through our personality. As briefly mentioned previously, the rising of a full moon is good for constructive work through the personality to contact the higher mind and the waning to new moon basically for destructive work such as the ridding of uneasy feelings.

Acquiring information about the forces that planets represent through the Qabalah is the initial step of balancing such forces that we are constantly affected by. Understanding the signs of the zodiac and the element of each sign provides us with the insight of such traits and qualities that are within us and to balance them with corresponding qualities of the opposite sign and element. Balancing qualities of Fire with those of Air and traits of Water with those of Earth permeates a harmony within our personality. The left and right pillars of the Tree of Life are natural polarizing forces within our house. We can not know what hot means without measuring its relationship with cold nor can we describe light without its comparison to darkness. Balance is a harmonious unification of the elements that pervade our house. We have to assimilate the principles of air, fire and water and stabilize them with earth in order to balance the planetary and zodiacal forces and influences for natural progression.

We become like an entrapped bird within a cage or hound on a leash when particular elements dominate our personality and prevent us from exercising our right of true freedom. Tranquility is an elevation to lofty states, without restriction and disarray through advancing an uncluttered mind into conscious spheres of realization. The capability of making positive outcomes in most circumstances by applying conscious effort and quality choices is always within our grasp.

Our thoughts and emotions are transmitted at a particular rate of vibration. We are capable of changing the ratio such that the vibrations we send to another person are felt stronger, purer and more vibrantly effective. This is a distinguishable quality in people of highly motivated characters that portray exuberant energy in their ambitions. Unclogging the overexertion of any particular element that dominates our character allows us to change our emitted vibrations and our aura, the color scheme surrounding our body that represents our character. Assimilating the four elements of character traits in balance alters our thoughts and ultimately changes the colors that express our personality.

Self-communication entails entering to the inner sanctuary, to the fabric of our soul so that we can see from a detached viewpoint and capture a broad spectrum with a clear conscious ability. From this vantage, an infinite source is available from which we can pick and choose. This clarity for inner vision becomes an experience of liberty at harmony in an ever-present state to obtain phenomenal experiences. Words that we use during communication are attached to our emotions but sometimes after using them we wish that we portrayed our true feelings more clearly. This is partial to the elements that cause our emotions to fling words haphazardly. Editing our vocabulary comes as a result of being in accord with our inherent elements and allows us to focus on what we really wish to say and achieve with the power behind the chosen word.

Our inner house should be clear of obstacles that hinder in dept transitions and the free expression of a illuminated soul. Subjective states of consciousness are like hallways that lead to rooms of objectivity. The rooms are the Sephiroth of the Tree of Life and the realization of them are attained through subjective experiences or travelling the twenty-two paths of the Tree. We constantly fathom one subconscious road to another in achieving our goals and realizations. The roadmap of the inner planes reinforces our ability to functionally create success in life. We can harness greater creativity and advance in achieving goals in an opportunistic way if the approach is made with conscious effort.

Intellect enables abstract thought in terms of principles and impressions to form in our mind when we effectively work our imagination, memory and reasoning faculties. Abstract thought comes from the intellect and is more effective and penetrating when we learn to tap into using it. Headaches and mental strain may occur when we are not used to exercising this higher order of mental activity. This region of the mind is where causal thought originates in an elevated capacity. It provides us with greater control over our lower mental and emotional centers and develops our intuitive nature by transcending the Ruach faculty. It allows us to become aware of life in a detached yet internal space. The energies and vibrations experienced from causal thought are quite incredible. Our foundation should be strong, firm and without crevices that allow negative influences to enter and congest our personality. Being filled with exalted moral qualities and having sights directed to higher ambitions helps us to contact the causal realm of our mind. Selfish motives do not expand our causal ability but contracts it. An unselfish nature offers what has been achieved to the further progress of humanity. A clean window gives a great view and should be shared.

Gradual conscious efforts become habitual and before long we may become an outpouring of limitless energy and radiant light in harmony with the cosmic laws of nature. Colossal vibrant emanations may exude from our aura dissuading negative influences that tempt to permeate our inner house when such efforts are made to put our home in order. To accomplish this we must rise above the sensory limitations of Malkuth, the earth plane consciousness. Our consciousness must also be exalted above the Moon or Yesod sphere where astral emotions reside as the sentiment language of our soul but may be used as a springing board to rise with the existing current.

Consciousness is an experienced activity of the present and is the central pillar of the Tree. The right or past pillar corresponds to the passive part of our consciousness and the left or future pillar is the active force of our consciousness. As an exercise, centering our consciousness in Tiphareth, called the sphere of Beauty and Imagination can be a remarkable experience of insight. It is the point within our existence that radiates light and heat to give life energy into all other aspects of our mind, and is represented as the Sun. The sun center sustains the other faculties of our mental plane consciousness and are, according the Tree of Life, Memory as Chesed, Will as Geburah, Desire as Netzach, and Reason as Hod.

It is a reflection of our Spirit, Kether, which has been called the Sun behind the Sun. It is the provider of life, as the spirit is the source of life. The Sun is also an expression of accumulated wealth through work. Its corresponding metal is gold which is the base form for money. Expended physical energy is performed to acquire money or wealth so that we can achieve our material necessities in life. The representative 'gold' of the Sun is the mental plane knowledge and intelligence of earned inner success. The physical aspect of gold is wealth through expended human energy to achieve it.

Through the knowledge and intelligence of our inner Sun comes the ability of natural healing and nurturing. In fact, most of the mythology gods attributed to the Sun are healing gods. Relating Chokmah (Wisdom) as the father, and Binah (Understanding) as the mother, and their unity giving rise to a son, the Sun and their daughter, the Moon, we can correlate this inner family to be representative of our growing, striving and enlightening soul as the spiritual core of our house.

Embracing this center of our Being, which corresponds to the solar plexus and extends luminous energy throughout our body, soul and mind is essential to receive nurturing for inner growth. It may be compared to a plant that requires the physical sun to flourish and provide its full assertion in growth and greenery. Awareness of the Sun within us provides the vision to see harmony in all things. Tiphareth is a switch whereupon on one side it is the lesser Countenance of Kether or a form expression for the higher, spiritual True Self and upon the other side of the switch it is a force as seen from the spheres below it. Malkuth, Yesod, Hod and Netzach look up to it as a great life force and center or seat of divine radiance. The Sun in this respect is the mediator between God and Man. Visualizing this great sphere of energy within our solar plexus region radiating vibrant energy throughout our body becomes an energetic meditation. To raise our consciousness and actually enter the sphere of the Sun within us is a self-initiatory experience providing endless creativity.

In our analogies, we may view the Sun as the source of heat and provider of life for our house of the inner self. It balances and harmonizes all that we must contend with and work through. It is the lack of this expression in our life that fails us to be uplifted into finding beauty in all things. Such a lack also causes negative associations whereas seeking the light would better result in providing armor against low energy fields. Realizing this may help to explain the reasons for unhappiness, melancholy, insignificant progression and unhealthy mental attitudes that dominate as emotional disturbances. Life is a garden, and as gardeners we must share what grows and nourish the roots from within.

Another spiritual experience through Tiphareth is that of sacrifice. As we know, energy is neither created nor destroyed but transformed from one state to another. It is from devotion to the ALL that we sacrifice our lower self or ego in order to transcend to the influence of the Higher through regeneration. In this instance, we devour such selfish attributes as pride so that it does not interfere with the ascending process and is put to the Calvary Cross, as a sacrifice for spiritual progress.

In Tiphareth success gleams through all the tarot cards associated to it. The six of swords shows success having been earned through mental pursuit and the six of cups demonstrates great joy through love. The six of wands is victory achieved from the power of the will and the six of pentacles is material success having put power into balance. All that is within us is at equilibrium so that energy is projected in harmony to all other branches or rooms within the psyche.

Extending our imagination to the fourth sphere of Chesed or Mercy brings us to the pillar of the past, also referred to as a pillar of Mercy. This sphere of the Ruach represents having worked off karma and being free from the wheel of life. The initiate is exempt of life's influences on the lower levels and sees each dealing as one of God with the soul. Through this achievement, the mystical and magical grade associated to it, termed Adeptus Exemptus becomes attainable. Memory is also attributed to Chesed but clearly it is the first touch of actuality from the ideality of the triad above it on the spiritual plane. Our causal nature is capable of seeing the archetypal images in visions as the source from which they spring instead of being fooled by the illusions of apparent apparitions, as may be the case in lower spheres. Illusions are associated with the sphere of Yesod, the Moon. They are neither good nor bad but reside in a lower state as images attributed to Maya, which has a beginning and an end. When our nature ascends to Chesed we may meet with Masters from the spiritual realm. They may be robed in different colors representing the ray of influence that emanates from them and telepathic communication will be beyond any preconceived psychic transmission. Chesed is affiliated with mercy and exalted love. As we break through to this higher stratum we may contact the holy powers and virtues that reside there which come from the crown of Kether or Godhead.

The tarot cards of this fourth sphere interpret the nature of the sphere with the individual. The wands represent a completed cycle and wholeness dawning to make its way into our life or relationship. The Cups portray luxury through treating others and ourselves in a fulfilled, perfected love through devotion with which we should not be totally dependent upon. Swords bring truce into any existing conflict so that we obtain a clear view for our plans. The four of Pentacles demonstrates power and may indicate someone being too rigid or that their character could be better abiding.

When the path of adjustment is tread from the Sun Sephiroth, we embark upon the fifth Sephirah called Geburah. This sphere is associated with severity, power and the will. It resides in the pillar referred to severity and is a pillar of the future. It is a required part of nature and creation just like all other Sephiroth that exemplify the emanations of God in balanced uniformity towards the material world. In this sphere we witness the force of Mars as the warrior, dragon-slayer and dynamic energy through sacrifice towards a greater good. Nature's psychological counteraction against things gone wrong acts through these energies.

The sword is a symbol of an objective state of consciousness, being the power of justice, to uphold the law of nature according to the True Will. In this case, the intellect must be as sharp as a two-edged sword to make changes that may be radical but always with the mercy and love of Chesed in balance under a guiding light. Intellect achieves greater strength to accomplish objectives when it is balanced. The power and forces employed are swift and without hesitation as is symbolized by the chariot card. The five-pointed pentagram and pentagon illustrate the fecundity occupied here as well. The four fives of the tarot cards depict hostile, antagonistic forces in action. These elements are of no use unless a high order of discipline is in effect to control their energy to proper ends. Whether through competition in the sports-minded person or through the temper of a stern disciplinary the elements should be in a recognized balance for a harmonious inner journey.

The five of wands represent a personality in Strife and refers to being prepared to face the situation. The five cups illustrates disappointment and expectations that are too high or concerns of failure. The swords for this sphere reflect defeat through fear. If we accept that our control is illusory then we can comprehend our position for what it is and be set free from limitations. The Pentacles indicate worry due to not living in the present but concern for future or holding on to the past.

Netzach, the seventh Sephirah houses instincts that are particular to each person. They are not concrete but fluidic in nature just as ideas are not of a particular Intelligence but an embodiment of formative influences arising in the mind. It is therefore wise to realize that in these lower areas of the Tree, and thus the mind, we may witness many thought-forms, which can be quite deceiving. The images of the ancient mythology gods represented to these Sephiroth are clothed as certain personages for mental convenience but their forces are real. Contact of the Netzach forces is done through feeling and expression such as in dance and art whereby the artist brings color and life into the form that is created. The evolved forces in this sphere are experienced through the movement and accentuation of the influences they represent through the astral light. They are an interplay of polarization, positive and negative forces, male and female or yin and yang on a level that strives to be higher than it is since it is a lower form of the nature of Binah or Understanding.

To digress, these spheres are attainable objective states from the forces they exemplify as we traverse subjective experiences to realize them. The arousal that they cause has bearing to us by filtering through our etheric web and into our physical body as sensations, physical energy for healing, uplifting and the changing of our appearance. This is done by conscious effort of learning the inner circuitry of our house and awakening to objective realizations with our soul being the medium for a guiding light. Essentially we become stronger and fortified by making these efforts and learn to channel energies so that positive influences pervade the house of our soul. It is not sufficient to illuminate only the central pillar of consciousness for advancement because the left and right pillars are of equal importance with life functions and are part of the whole. The strength that we receive from learning the positive and negative interplay of forces is of great assistance for progression.

To connect with the fundamental force of any particular thing through Netzach, think of its material aspect as being a crystallized form of it's true identity, just as ice is the solid form of water. In one respect we can conceive of the whole tree in this context, that from the uppermost section it flowed downwards and collected impressions and influences each step towards materialization as force became form and form became more solidified. Everything in the physical world is therefore a result of mixed impressions through the planes to end with a mixture of elements combined in such a way to become exactly what it is here on earth. It is partially for this reason that everything on lower levels is considered illusion less one can see through it and all elements of it's constitution, history and ordinance.

The Netzach is sphere is associated with Venus and illustrates the fundamental dynamism of an individual through their sexual instincts and expression. It is the life force of nature for the lower spheres. Its virtue is unselfishness and the vices are lust and impure pleasures. Through the virtue of unselfishness we can aspire from higher impressions just as an artist may create beyond preconceived capability by being unselfishly inspired. This principle is implicit in the four sevens of the tarot. The seven of wands is the only truly positive of the four, meaning Valor and is assigned to the spiritual aspect of love with purity and dynamic factors coming from the higher planes. The other three cards of pentacles, swords and cups warn against unfulfilled success, instability and illusory success.

From the viewpoint of where our personality meets our individuality in Tiphareth, the sun-center, we look upon the eighth sphere called Hod, which is the form countenance of the astral plane. Hod is reason and logic as the concrete form of the personality. It is also the magical powers in operation through the rationale that is employed in us from the scribe of the Egyptian Thoth, Roman Mercury and Greek Hermes. Hod means Glory and it is the glory of the force of God manifested into form through consciousness that has contacted that force. Hod becomes our ability of representing our thoughts in certain logical terms and the forces of nature that have been clothed and become form on the astral plane.

The Archangel for this sphere is Michael who is a protector of humanity and gives strength to overcome situations and ordeals. The power that is represented in this sphere channels the forces of the astral light into equilibrium through the virtues of science and knowledge from writings to represent something of magnificent beauty. Superstition aside, a sound basis of terminology and magical principles is the minimum requirement to avoid the pitfalls of wrongdoing and misinterpretation when associating one thing with another in qabalistic lore and is the turning point in this sphere of utilizing higher logic and the reasoning faculty.

In Hod we are laboring with formal principles in an organized way opposed to haphazard thoughts straying through the mind. The powers employed are within the Sons of God, the Beni Elohim, and are forces in balance between extremities. The four eight's of the tarot portray the nature of Hod on a personal level. The wands show swiftness as in clear communication, whereas the cups illustrate indolence in a lethargic and drained emotional capacity, without anticipation or hope, basically abandoned potential. The eight of swords displays conflicting natures with too many mixed ideas resulting in interference for peace of mind. The eight pentacles represent prudence by taking care of our body and financial concerns. These daily obstacles may stem from inhibitory or paranoiac roots, which is when higher logic steps in the room and works to dispense with them by having the Understanding of Binah thunder through the Love and Mercy of Chesed. From that point it issues through Tiphareth, the super-conscious and delivers via the path of Ayin, the eye, to Hod, where the experience is uplifted into a refreshing, enlightened atmosphere. The Vision of Splendour is experienced here through the glory of the manifested emanations of God.

Looking back from the Sun sphere we see the etheric stratum of the earth, called the Moon. This Sephirah contains the machinery as a receptacle to filter all the other Sephiroth into material existence. It is therefore required that any dealings from the spiritual plane must go through all levels and spheres and end on earth by essentially filtering through Yesod. Original subtle essence comes into life through final transactions with ethereal representations in the sphere of the Moon enabling us to realize that there are divine forces beyond this physical world.

The moon is the partner of the earth and each shares the same etheric body even though they receive their subtle life force from the Sun. The Sun (son) appears to be self-sustaining but it is the image of the great father, Kether and is the only way we can come to know the life of God and still survive the experience. The subtle life of the Sun may receive its vitality from a higher source outside of our system through Kether. This map of the Qabalah is a conscious route towards spirituality and is what we have to work with in tangible form to express a safe self-initiatory progression.

The cycle of the moon provides us with information about why we have low or high energy at different times. The effect of cosmic tides flowing through the web of etheric matter in Yesod changes according to the phase and location of the moon and therefore in its interplay of our emotional-fluidic nature. The goddesses Selene, Hecate and Diana preside over this sphere and their influences are principles that we live with in the astral level. Our magnetic nature is enhanced when we have these influences balanced and under control with the higher mind.

The four nines of the tarot illustrate parts of the personality upon this level. Wands bring the unity of the Sun and Moon together as masculine and feminine qualities providing strength through integration. Cups bring joy and happiness through love and completion. Swords become cruel natured through criticism and aggressive hostility by not recognizing achievements for their potential. Pentacles are a positive gesture here by advancing towards goals, gain and achievement.

Through meditation and yoga our consciousness can ascend beyond the physical, emotional and mental levels that are quite familiar in everyday life. Mystical experiences are achievable when we leave the world where it is and allow ourselves to go beyond the set parameters that we have constructed to encase the soul. Mystical life is experienced through the sphere of Tiphareth and it is the sacred magic employed by truly spiritual souls that are liberated from material bondage and ego consciousness. It is here where we converse with our Holy Guardian Angel to obtain the knowledge for competent and rapid evolutionary experience.

Spiritual principles liberate us from false perceptions and allow us to make steps up the ladder of enlightenment to activate causal thought and develop higher instincts. There are many functional methods to achieve nearly the same objective. Learning the principles and laws that affect nature is the same as learning what affects us. The rewards of such freedom are incalculable and the creativity and originality that comes from it are based upon understanding. The tools and signs that surround us in every day life are there whether we recognize them or not. The only thing that changes are the efforts made and the harmony achieved from the radiance of simplicity that transcends reason. Emotions may be as addictive as the thoughts we carry and both may be illusive as lies. Both of these substances are in constant change. Reality is what we make it in this world and can be a fulfilling experience. Don't carry too much baggage for such a long journey. Mistakes are inevitable in a big house but progress is assured in a clean one. ★

GLOSSARY of DEFINITIONS

"The man is wisest who, like Socrates, realizes that his wisdom is worthless."

Apologia of Socrates - Plato

The following words and their definitions are subject to variant views and subsequent study. They are given here as a guide for terminology that often appear in esoteric philosophy and magical progression. Most of these terms have been employed throughout this book. These definitions should assist in comprehending the basis whereupon the reader may further such spiritual appropriation.

Abba Amona:

THE two higher spheres of the Tree of Life, comprising Chokmah (Father) and Binah (Mother) upon the higher triad.

Abracadabra and Abrahadabra:

IN the Middle Ages the word abracadabra was used to cure fevers and from the idea that evil spirits caused plagues. It became associated with warding off those entities which brought maladies. By writing the name down and dropping a letter off of each end it was thought that the fever would subsequently diminish as well. The paper it is written on was to be tied around the patients neck with flax and left there for nine days followed by throwing it over the shoulder such that it falls into a stream that is flowing towards the east.

Crowley used the form of Abrahadabra, which replaces Abracadabra, as a NEW magical formula in the Great Work of the New Aeon of Horus.

AbracadabrA	AhrahadabrA
BracadabR	BrahadabR
RacadaB	RahadaB
AcadaA	AhadA
CaD	HaD
A	A

Abrasax:
ALSO Abraxas and is a word for Divinity having 365 virtues also called the Supreme of the Seven.

Adam:
THE "only-begotten" one, also interpreted as the "red earth".

Adam Kadmon:
ARCHETYPAL Man and represents Humanity in origin before falling into sin. The Heavenly Man represented by the ten Sephiroth of the Tree of Life.

Aethyrs:
THE aethryic dimensions of the astral plane stand beyond the elemental watchtowers and have been a practice of Dr. Dee as the thirty outer world dimensions of consciousness. The aethyrs are with the element of air, but with achieving workings in the other elements of fire, water and earth, a substantial magical knowledge may be accrued. To reach those levels, the practitioner uses the 19 Keys or Calls. The first 18 Calls are to summon the Angels of the magic squares and the 19th raises the consciousness to the aethyrs to summon the aires. The four watchtowers contain 192 Angels, 128 demons, 24 Seniors and 4 Kings.

Agni:
MOST revered of the Hindu Gods, and God of Fire in the Veda. He is the triple concept of Fire in the sky as the Sun, in the atmosphere as Lightening and on the Earth as Fire.

Ain:
The Void, Nothingness, Most Passive and Negative Existence, Unity in Repose.

Ain Soph:
BOUNDLESS or limitless abstract principle that is without form or being.

Ain Soph Aur:
BOUNDLESS Light that concentrates into Kether, the first Sephirah.

AL:
DEITY name for God in the singular also called EL, and in the plural form it is Elohim.

Amenta:
SIMILAR to the Dream State (REM); it has been associated with the dual nature through the hiding place of the midnight sun (Khephra) which is governed by Set. The son hiding behind the Sun, or Sothis (Sirius), the dog star is the complex that governs the planets which influence our Being and has been associated with the True Will referred to as the "Hidden Sun".

Ankh:
THE crux ansata or ankh is the Egyptian symbol of Life. The oval represents the great womb and the T as the male force penetrating to create the life force into form. It is also on another level the fire rising from the void and the continuity of life. The sandal strap is in the shape of an ankh going around the large toe and represents going, movement and direction.

Augoeides:
A term used by Imablichus to represent the Higher Self, Divine Being and comes from the Greek meaning "bright shape" or "Light vision". It is connected with the Holy Guardian Angel of the individual as Crowley associated it with Aiwass.

Astral Light:
SUBTLE essence surrounding the world and visible to clairvoyant vision. It is fed by the moral and physical qualities as emotions emanating from the Earth. Astral comes from Astra or Star and may be considered as star stuff or originally the essence from the star or Sun in the creation of mankind. Reacts like a crucible by giving out what has been put into it. Also relates to the Sidereal Light of which Paracelsus writes.

Atlantis:
All of the anomalies that are within Plato's (~427-348 BC) story about the existence of Atlantis can be reconciled if geology is connected with anthropology, archeology and history. He stated that it was a great sea power and launched attacks on Egypt and Greece. Atlantis is said to have been in the vicinity of Crete and to have sunk into the sea around 1500 BC The greatest known volcanic eruption took place on the island of Santorin, about 70 miles north of Crete. It now consists of three islands in a large body of water that has two volcanic inlets within the center. The area of water is about 7 miles (N-S) by 5 miles (E-W) large and about 300 to 400 meters deep and is in fact a giant crater. All similarities found between archeologists and geophysicists relate to much of what Plato described as Atlantis

Baal:
A phallic god also called Adon (Adonai). Associated with Ammon (Baal-Hammon) as the "hidden god" of Egypt.

Baphomet:

A God form that was used in the Sabbath of sorcery, and connected with Gnosticism since the rise of the Knights Templars (1118-1300). Crowley used it as a symbol of phallic transmutation, having the third eye upon the brow. Elphas Levi associated it, through the Templars, with the personification of Hermanubis and the secret of the Stone of the Qabalists. He noted it could be spelt backwards as: TEM OPH AB ("Templi Ominum Hominis Pacis Abbas").

In the sense of evil it is used as a form of the devil by inferior magicians as Crowley points out that the devil is a creation of the Black Brothers "to imply a unity in their ignorant muddle of dispersions. A devil who had unity would be a God." This makes sense in the strictest terms as unity is achieved by aspiration to the divine within, without which the sense of duality, diabolis (diabolic) or devil exists. It has also been called the witches god, and god of Mendes.

Basileus:

DURING the Eleusian Mysteries was the Archon or Chief who had the supervision and represents the staff of the Hierophant with the inner mysteries.

Bes:

PHALLIC god of concupiscence and pleasure upon the lotus prepared to devour his Abydos.

Black Sun:

A name given to the reverse side of Daath and the reverse of Beauty or Tiphereth, Apollo and Osiris. Baphomet was also considered the Black Sun or Black Snake and has been employed along with Black Moon in some secret societies.

Boaz:

A Pillar of King Solomon's Temple and he was the great grandfather of David. B refers to "in" and oz refers to "strength".

Caduceus:

AN emblem of the healer and wand of healing powers which represents the Sushumna power of kundalini with its intertwining serpent powers of Ida and Pingala. It is the Middle Pillar with the serpents curving around it like the left and right hand paths. It has been used as the symbol in medicine with the serpents signifying death and disease. It's symbol changes according to its usage as the head and tail may represent the points of the ecliptic that the planets and Sun meet in their close proximity. Also represents the currents of Life within the physical body and a symbol of restoration.

Causal Body:

THE Spiritual Soul that leads to the Turya state or highest level of Samadhi. It is the "basis of the Cause" and the incarnating principle for the Ego to incorporate the mind into existence.

Chariot:

HISTORICALLY it represents a vehicle of triumph and as Crowley points out the Charioteer is the controller and the balancer of opposing forces, opposed to the forces in the Tower card which signify forces that are going away.

Chela:

A pupil or disciple who follows a Guru or Sage in a school of inner development.

Choronzon:

THE demon of Dispersion whose name adds to 333. It is the lord of Confusion and Chaos who abides in the Abyss and can assume any character or shape in attempting to fool the magician. Crowley said it is "the first and deadliest of all the powers of Evil". Choronzon is the Tempter and force that is most harmful in spiritual aspiration if one is not prepared to handle its duping and strong enough to focus forward.

Chiim:

PLURAL meaning "lives" and is found in words as Ruach Chiim, the Spirit of lives, or life; and Elohim Chiim, the Gods of Lives.

Clairaudience:

ABILITY to hear without distance being a factor attributed to psychic ability of hearing in the astral state.

Clairvoyance:

ABILITY of seeing through the densest matter without regard to distance and time using the inner eye, or sight from the spiritual eye; having inner vision.

Daath:

THE 'non-existent' 11th Sephirah which is placed in the center of the Abyss. The Abyss or the desolate desert crossing from Chesed to Binah houses the sphere of Daath. Its name means Knowledge in Hebrew and has been called the "Gateway to the Other World" into the 22 Qlipothic pathways on the reverse side of the Tree of Life. It is a conjunction or result from Wisdom and Understanding having emanated through the Abyss to the lower Sephiroth.

Daemon:

NOTHING to do with the Christian orthodox theology of demon or Hell but refers to the rational divine Ego, or real inner person and is synonymous in meaning with angels and gods. The 'Daemon' of Socrates is the part of man that cannot be broken or thwarted.

Demon:

Dwellers of the lower world of Assiah that personify the vices of the "Seven Hells".

Deosil:

THE direction to the right, or clockwise as is the direction of the Sun. It is associated with positive powers and the direction of God forces, opposed to Widdershins. Widdershins, moving in the direction of left is said to gather negative, evil or perhaps satanic forces.

Deva:

"RESPLENDENT" deity or celestial being which inhabits the three worlds or planes above the physical. There exists 330 million Devas in these planes comprising 33 groups.

Devil:

AN illusory path that is wrought with deception and delusions. The source of duality in the material kingdom and problem in divination as the tempter towards materialism. Crowley signified the Devil as the physical or gross procreation, strictly on the material plane.

Divination:

READING the meaning of connections from one thing to another in divining the present, past or future events. Various forms of divination such as Geomancy, Tarot, and Scrying in the spirit vision are abilities to contact forces that reveal answers about life.

Druid:

CELTIC priest who believes that the soul, matter and energy can not be destroyed and practice the ancient pagan traditions. Their belief in the three circles of being are that there is an inner circle which is the central source, a middle one housing the bliss of ordinary life and an outer one or divine realm. They also have specific names for 12 months of the year.

Dwellers:

MALEFICENT astral doubles of defunct personas residing on the astral plane as has been termed by students of occult orders in the past.

Ectoplasm:

AN etheric matter projected from the mouth or body of a medium to make apparitions and entities visible. The medium goes through pain in using the gluey substance and conditions of low light have to be made, otherwise the medium incurs more problems. The substance should not be touched and it dries up to disappear after its use.

Ego:

CONSCIOUSNESS that may be considered on a lower mortal level as personality that is distinct from the Impersonal Higher Ego, which is Individuality.

Eight Bodies of the Egyptians:

THE Egyptians held the belief that there exists eight bodies to each person. AB-Consciousness; KHAT-Unconsciousness; REN-Collective Unconscious; KA-Astral Body; KHAIBIT-Etheric Double; SEKHET-The elan vital; KU-Omniscience; and BA-Atman.

Elementals:

THE spirits of the elements that are on their way to materialization and reside in the elements of Air as Sylphs, Fire as Salamanders, Water as Undines and Earth as Gnomes. Their nature should be reversed towards spirit and they require the direction from the practicing magician to steer them there in turn for doing deeds as the magician requests. Their particular natures are important in the work that the magician is to accomplish. With Sylphs one must be actively quick to avoid their quick displacements in frivolous activities. With the fiery Salamanders one must disregard irrational and belligerent energies as they have their own volatility to deal with. With Undines one must be flexible and flowing, as they can be idle and constantly changeable. With Gnomes bring happiness and cheer to them and avoid sluggishness and greed.

On the 5th to 7th sub-planes there exists several invisible beings as elementals and they are Fairies, Satyrs, Elves, Dwarfs, Trolls, Banshees, Pinkies, Goblins, Nixies, Peris, Devs, White Ladies, Moss People, Sylvans, Djins and so forth.

Elements:

THE four elements of Air, Water, Fire, and Earth have the qualities of Dispersion, Condensation (and Transition), Expansion, and Contraction. Their natures have been associated with the phases of the Moon during the times of Waxing, Full, Waning and Disappearing. The elements have many principles about them and their mixture can be used to describe someone's personality, character, and emotions.

Elohim:

A plural term for the divine names of God. The seven Hebrew names were given as: Jehovah, Ialdabaoth, Sabaoth, Adonai, Eloeus, Astanpaeus, and Oreus. Elohim has been called the sevenfold power of godhead and as attributed to Binah with Elohim Jehovah (IHVH ALHIM), SHE leads on to the following seven Sephiroth.

Enoch:

THE father of Methuselah and the son of Cain. It was the pre-Babel language and Dr. Dee used it as an Angelic Language to work in the aethyrs, which subsequently became a form of magic, called Enochian Magic.

Esoteric:

FROM the heart doctrine and refers to concealed or hidden secrets from the inner. Greek esotericos is "inner".

Evocation:

CALLING forth an entity that is within our subconscious realm. It is from the spirits that dwell within us that we use this form of operation to bring them out.

Four Animals:

ORIGINALLY from the vision of Ezekiel, the four animals of eagle (cosmic spirit), lion (energy and courage), bull (strength) and human figure (angel as combining other three animals in the higher mental capacity) are regarded as representing the elements and four lower subdivisions of the plane of manifestation. As George Orwell said, "All animals are equal, but some animals are more equal than others."

Gabriel:

"THE mighty one of God" linked with the "messenger of life" and connected with the Higher Ego or Divine Self.

Gematria:

INTERPRETATION of words using a numerical system to add them and finding the significance between relationships from addition to convey relationships and meanings. Not only from adding, but also multiplying, subtracting and dividing can Understanding be delivered in the association of words.

Genii:

LEGIONS of angels in the Gnostics for the hierarchies.

Geomancy:

A form of divination expounded in The Complete Golden Dawn System of Magic. There are different styles utilized, but one most prominent is that of tapping a pencil on a grid made of 16 squares each having a certain pattern of dots and representing names and meanings.

Gnosis:

KNOWLEDGE generated from the ages before and during the first centuries of Christianity obtained through initiation into the sacred mysteries.

God:

THE highest point, the Creator, Ancient of Ancients that began the process of Life as we know it. Humans have been called the image of god, and as such we also are creators on a lower scale, in less realization. Zeus was attributed as father of the Gods, which are superior entities that comprise the totality behind Being. Our life mission from all that can be divined is to evolve, and the purest manner of doing so is to be one with The Father, through the knowledge given by our own Higher Self and Holy Guardian Angel. Deus est Homo, Man is God. In Crowley's Liber 77, it states: "There is no god but man." The meaning of this is beyond the physical interpretation and shows a sublime respect for mankind and humanity. The only route for mankind to take is towards the Higher Genius, True Self, so that humanity is not trapped into the materialistic world of illusion and unattached to True Being. Saying that there is no god, is not what the statement signifies. It measures the spirit of man as being one with god. Einstein defined God as "the ultimate natural order" which is scientifically significant and suggests a magical unity with the ALL. Through holy inspiration is aspiration achieved.

Great White Lodge:

THE 'Secret Chiefs' is a Theosophical term and represents those higher order of Beings dwelling on the spiritual plane and forming the spiritual governing bodies for the world through their Great White Lodge. Adepts residing on the higher planes may do work for the Secret Chiefs in the order of life. Contacting those Beings has been accomplished in the physical world through magical orders such as The Hermetic Order of the Golden Dawn, the Rosicrucians and the inner order of the Astrum Argentum (Silver Star).

Halloween:
A night traditionally celebrated as the masquerading of evil souls taking grotesque forms to perform acts of horror as an antidote for Pachad (fear).

Hallucination:
RELAXATION of the nervous system producing abnormal magnetic attraction to waves of the astral light. It may be experienced uncontrollably through disorders, or else seeing through the astral light may be a controlled experience by trained Seers. Has an ability to see through the outer layers of a vision to clearly discern what the image represents.

Hatha Yoga:
OPPOSITE of Raja Yoga in that physical means are employed for spiritual results opposed to means of a non-physical nature for spiritual development.

Hawk:
TRANSITION symbol of the soul if it is lying without movement or else resurrection. If the wings are spread it may illustrate the conscious motion from one state or level to another.

Heart:
PUREST feelings emanating from the heart center evolved beyond physical attributions and are associated with a divine nature. When we speak from the heart we are stipulating about the truth of a subject being revealed more than if we speak from the head which is associated with reasoning and has many associations, memories, and imaginative conjectures attached.

Hecate:
GODDESS of the New Moon, the moon in darkness, opposed to Diana who is Goddess of the Full Moon or that of Light.

Hell:
DERIVED from the goddess Hela and from Hades of Greek origin and being either cold or hot in nature depending on the conception of the temperature at the center of the Earth. The conception of souls being tormented in a hot place comes from Egyptian antiquity with Ra as the Sun god and Lord of the Furnace torturing the sinner "in the heat of infernal flames".

Hermes:
A God of communication and language and an inspiration for writers and linguistics. Also associated with the other mythology gods of Thoth, Mercury and Odin for similar attributes. Hermes Trigmegistus is the "thrice great Hermes" which has been allotted to many great Greek writers and is the human aspect of the great Hermes or Thoth with the "elixir of Hermes" or the creative essence while being the messenger of the gods.

Heru:
ALSO spelt HRU and is the Angel of the Tarot who oversees the guidance of the cards for a tarot reading and is equivalent to Horus.

Hexagram:
ALSO known as the Star of David, the six-pointed star has two interlaced triangles. One triangle is ascending to the divine and one descending to the physical plane and their joining together is a symbol of the Great Work accomplished, uniting the lower with the higher (lower self with Higher Self, conscious with subconscious). The points have also been associated with opposing and balancing forces such as Will and Passive, Choice and Rejecting, Lightness and Darkness.

Hierophant:
FROM the Greek Hierophantes meaning "One who explains sacred things".

Holy Guardian Angel:
THROUGH initiation and the aspiration of spirituality a transformation occurs with the awareness of the psyche and elements within our Being. Directed towards obtaining the Knowledge and Conversation of the True Self and H∴G∴A∴ brings about the ability to transform into a higher, deeper, purposeful and realized destiny.

Hypatia:
TEACHER of many famous men and was a female philosopher in the fifth century living in Alexandria. Her father was Theon, a great mathematician.

Iamblichus:
MAGUS of Neoplatonic times (250-325) who practiced sacred magical arts and taught mantrams and incantations as a method for enlightening the soul and becoming one with the Divine. He was born in Chalcis, Coele-Syria. His original work of Theurgy as a benevolent practice of magic has also been abused in later years with selfish motives as many magical practices have. He wrote Egyptian Mysteries, and was also a biographer of Pythagoras and adept in the Chaldean Mysteries. Some of his writings deal with "daemons" as elementals and to be wary of close association with them.

Iao:
LIGHT that is discernable from the higher intellect and called the "male Essence of Wisdom". Also, as I.A.O.-Isis, Apophis and Osiris (Beginning, Middle and End).

I Ching:
THIRTY-TWO pairs of opposites of the Chinese Hexagrams that can be attributed to the 32 Atus in the Tarot. A method of divination.

Incubus:
MALE Elemental whereas Succubus is a Female Elemental called up from lower forms of passion and lust gratification being soulless and without sense they fester as "subjective protoplasms" in the lower astral plane.

Initiate:
ONE who realizes that there is everything to know about life and nature and works towards the spiritual Understanding and Wisdom of that sacred knowledge. Great magicians are initiates on the Path of the Wise if they become adepts of mystic lore, directing that knowledge-power to the proper ends. Initiate comes from the Latin word Initiatus.

I.N.R.I. :
TRANSLATED as Iesus Nazareth Rex Iudorum (Jesus of Nazareth, King of the Jews), or Igni Natura Renovatur Integrat (All of nature is renewed by Fire), or Id Numquam Rogat Iterem (He will never ask again) and many other contrivances are given to those original initials, said to be once upon the cross.

Jachin And Boaz:
STRENGTH and Beauty as the white and black Pillars to the Temple of Solomon. Jachin is Yod, the will, phallic masculine symbol and in Hebrew is IKIN derived from the root KUN meaning, "to establish". Boaz is strength (see Boaz) and a representative God. They are the Pillars distinguishing man from God, the rise and fall, opposites in a sense as Light and Darkness or Higher and Lower Ego, or Self.

Jagrata:
STATE of consciousness during the awakened period or condition.

Jhana:
OCCULT wisdom and knowledge.

Kama:
IDENTIFIED with "the tempter" or Mara with lustful and evil desires.

Karma:
ETHICAL retribution from causes or the law of action and reaction in or through time being indifferent to the results as it is the Universal Law just as the Egyptian Maat keeps the scales balanced.

Kundalini:
The enlightening energy from the chakras is awakened from the serpent power called kundalini at the base of the spine. It is a threadlike subtle substance and is dangerous if aroused prematurely, as moral and spiritual developments are prerequisites to its influx of potent power. Kundalini Shakti is the power of life that comes through concentration in yoga practices generating a Light within and resulting in an increased clairvoyant ability.

Lama:
PRIESTS of high grades that become Gurus in eastern monasteries.

Lamen:
A breastplate used to signify the secret keys used in the work of initiates.

Lotus:
CONSCIOUS immortality and manifestation are depicted from this eastern flower as well as symbolic of the microcosmic forces within the macrocosmic influences. All elements are contained within it, as it is a water plant rising into the air to receive the element of heat or fire from the Sun. Also used in titles of creative gods representing powers of the Universe.

Lucifer:
ASSOCIATED with Venus but only with the devil after usage of such by Milton. During the 3rd Century a Christian sect was titled the Luciferians and in Revelations (xvi, 22) is used in terms of Light and Venus as: "I am…the bright morning star…"

Maat:
GODDESS of Truth and Adjustment/Justice in Egyptian mythology. Maat weighs the heart against the feather in the afterlife. Without Maat evil becomes deeper in ignorance as She represents Truth.

Magic:
"The art of divine Magic consists in the ability to perceive the essence of things in the light of nature (astral light),

and- by using the soul-powers of the Spirit- to produce material things from the unseen universe, and in such operations the Above and the Below must be brought together and made to act harmoniously." -Madame H.P. Blavatsky.

"All Art is Magick." -Aleister Crowley.

"Magic consists of, and is acquired by the worship of the gods…" -Plato.

"Magic is the Science and Art of causing Change to occur in conformity with the Will."- Aleister Crowley.

"The Goal of Magick is the knowledge and conversation of the Holy Guardian Angel."- Aleister Crowley.

"Magic is the art of changing consciousness at will." - Dion Fortune.

Magnum Opus:
PRODUCTION of the Philosopher's Stone or the "Elixir of Life" in the completion of alchemical symbolism.

Mandala:
A circle or wheel that represents the divinity of God one wishes to invoke, with the center being God and all that is within the circumference being the magical universe within Oneself.

Mantra:
VIBRATIONAL words that are voiced for training the mind to be directed and focused.

Maya:
THE illusion of the world typically related to the material plane according to Madame Blavatsky's esoteric doctrines. Also potentially it can be the mask of the personality, which can be changed and altered. Hindu philosophy basically states that things, which can be changed, are illusory (Maya) and that which is eternal and non-changing is reality.

Meditation:
PRACTICING becoming in tune with the inner self through relaxation and revealing insight.

Mithra:
THE connection between man and the divine represented by a man hauled in a Chariot by four white horses symbolizing the elements. Originally of Chaldean in origin it uprooted in Persia as Mithraism.

Moon:
THE Archetypal anima and ruling element of emotions, desires and feelings on the astral plane. Its cycle affects moods and things containing the element of water with its' gravitation forces. Also long considered to have 28 mansions divided into parts of the zodiac.

Neophyte:
NOVICE of the Mysteries who studies and assimilates the four elements Air, Fire, Water and Earth to emerge into the fifth of Spirit. Neophytes were marked with the sign of the cross in older traditions, CROSS of LVX, light extending through the awareness of the clear-seeing composition of the elements of the lower self.

New Aeon:
DISTINCT from the New Age which is associated to astrological changes. Present "new age" is that of Aquarius with the Sun being in that zodiacal sign and its influence affecting great technological achievements and advancement in mankind. Moreover, the New Aeon is a period lasting approximately 2000 years per Aeon. The present Aeon is that of Horus, the previous 2000 years was of Osiris and the prior one to that was the Aeon of Isis. Within this Aeon the duty mankind is to realize is the Crowned and Conquering Child within him/her Self as a time of awakening and Illumination. Combined with the "new age" of Aquarius, changes are multiplying daily in the evolution of our place in the cosmos.

Nirvana:
RELEASING from the bondage of existence and entering the highest spiritual state, according to Buddhism. Also being released from karmic debt and entering a state of true spiritual unity and divinity. The complete removal of Dualism within the Self occurs in this state.

Nuit:
INFINITE space and the stars thereof, is this Goddess of the Universe and universality.

Ob:
SPIRIT of Ob considered by Jewish as an evil current and residing in the astral light near physical plane and can be possessive to anyone delving into necromancy or working with such spirit entities.

Omen:
SIGNS of future occurrences sometimes of good or evil nature but good is more usually associated with auspices.

Pan:
GOD of the shepherds being illustrated as goat-footed and a symbol in Pantheism. Great potency representing the ALL as the name implies and can never die as nature itself lives on.

Pantacle:

SYMBOL of the All of a magician, in the microcosmic sense. "Every fact and every falsehood must enter into the Pentacle; it is the great storehouse from which the magician draws."-Crowley. It is a sometimes made of beeswax and used to harness the cosmic forces. Also used as a protective force holding evil away and represented by the five points of the pentagram star. The five wounds of Jesus upon the cross can also represent the microcosm with the Spirit descending into man. Can also be the symbol of the Higher Ego, as the elements comprise to ascend to the Spirit.

Paracelsus:

A great alchemist and physician of the 16th Century who was born in Zurich, Switzerland in 1493. He taught the art of alchemy as an inner process and that disease was caused by the separation of three vital elements within man being salt, sulphur and mercury. His principles were based on the microcosm and macrocosm with the famous maxim "As Above, So Below". He was renowned for curing illnesses with the use of talismans. One of his great discoveries in physics was nitrogen gas. His original name was Philip Bombastes Aureolus Theophrastus von Hohenheim and he also possessed great clairvoyant abilities.

Philosopher's Stone:

CONTRADICTORY in terms, the philosopher's stone is an inner conception of the human mind being abstract as philosophy or concrete as stone. Mercury represents the intellect or functioning mind and as the alchemists taught in metallurgy: Metallurgy becomes meditation and meditation becomes metallurgy but if you have one without the other you end up with either philosophy or stone but not the realization of the philosopher's stone. IN a subtle sense it is transmuting the lower nature of man into the greatest divine nature possible and is also sometimes called the "Powder of Projection".

Qabalah:

ESOTERIC interpretations of Jewish scriptures and methods of biblical interpretations through the keys of Chaldean Secret Doctrines, Hebrew letters, certain holy names, sounds, numbers and assimilation of philosophies. Also the use of Gematria, Notaricon and Temura with these means.

Ra:

PERSONIFICATION of the Sun in Egyptian religion and representing the divine Universal Soul in manifestation.

Raja Yoga:

CONCENTRATION in the practice of yoga and developing spiritual and psychic powers. Raja is attributed to the King and the powers are self-assertive.

Ruach:

HEBREW meaning Air, and represents the higher Intellect.

Ro:

ALSO Ru and is the gateway into the cosmic womb where the primeval light comes or was born.

Samadhi:

YOGA state before Nirvana by uniting the Self with the Not-Self. In Samadhi (Sam-adhi "self-possession" is one translation and "together with god" is another), one has control over all faculties of the mind and body.

Scrying:

IMAGES that appear in vision by the method of crystal gazing that have particular meaning. Usually the images are recorded for later examination using intuition and other faculties.

Seven Levels of Consciousness:

ELEMENTAL (Moon); Mineral (Saturn); Vegetable (Venus); Animal (Mars); Human (Mercury); Demi-God (Jupiter); and God (Sun).

Shells:

PHANTOMS of the dead as illusive forms and void of any higher principles usually associated with forces from the Qlipoth. Generally the word "spirit" is misused in many writings, whereas the term "shells" would be more appropriate.

Siddhis:

POWERS that are supernatural in nature and are attributed to yoga practitioners who achieve particular levels or attainments. They are allotted to the abilities of Anima (ability to shrink in size); Mahima (ability to increase in size); Laghima (ability to levitate); Garima (ability to increase weight or heaviness); Prapti (great knowledge); Prakamya (an irresistibility in the will); Isitwa (hypnotic ability); and Vasitwa (ability to make other people do your will). These powers are not cultivated by the true yogi, but are a mere result of attainment.

Sirius:

THE Dog Star (See Robert Temple- The Sirius Mystery), named as such after the Dogon tribe in Mali, Africa who had super astronomical knowledge about the star. Their knowledge is claimed to be received by Sirian explorers who visited Earth ages ago teaching them of the dual star system, elliptical orbit and sacred knowledge. Also referred to as Sothis.

Six Six Six:
A numeral that has been associated with Satan and the Devil out of ignorance from lack of proper investigation. Is associated as the Anti-Christ which may be interpreted as "other than Christ", and not pertaining to an evil force in itself. The Devil and Satan are completely different terms and not associated with the Anti-Christ or 666 in any direct way. Revelations ascribes it to the number of a man, signifying that a man will identify his self with this number. The name Aleister E. Crowley adds up to 666, and he identified his mission of changing the world thought from the old aeonic conceptions to a new order for mankind. He taught that every man and every woman is a star and we all have our particular orbits or destinies and should develop the abilities to contact the Higher or True Self. This is anti to Osirian and Christian thought, which formed religions and offspring Sects of "Following" opposed to "Being".

Soul:
NEPHESH as used in the Bible refers to the soul and also refers to the infusion or breath of life that is within everyone and is to be nourished and raised to enlightenment.

Spirit:
USED in many contexts but primarily the changeless, formless Being composed of the highest spiritual substance. There is no potential for hurt, pain and suffering of "spirit" as it is beyond any such form conception of "feeling" and thus possibility.

Swastika:
FOUR armed cross representing the forms of Brahma in Hinduism and represents the universe flowing outwards as in evolution when drawn clockwise. It represents involution when the arms are counterclockwise, (as in the usage from Germany in the 1940's). When the left arm is pointed up and the right arm down it represents receptivity and blessings, which is the Persian version and signifies the Holy Spirit. It was the mystic cross in Masonic teachings and as "the originator of fire by friction, and of the 'Forty-nine Fires'" in eastern esoteric philosophies.

Talisman:
AMULETS or objects made and endowed with power that is transmitted into them from the magician. They are used for protection, attraction, gain or fixating the mind in a certain direction as well as other purposes. It is derived from the Arabic talism meaning "magic image" and relies upon the faith of the maker for creative powers to be projected into it.

Tantra:
TIBETAN in origin and relating to practices that cultivates energies directed towards particular gods or devas. The word is Sanskrit and its chief concern is in the worship of the female power that is represented in Sakti

Tattwa:
FOUR elements of the Hindu system called Vayu (Air), Tejas (Fire), Apas (Water), and Prithivi (Earth).

Tetragrammaton:
FOUR-LETTERED name of God written in English as YHVH, which is considered very sacred and was later used in the form of Adonai, meaning "Lord".

Thaumaturgy:
DIVINE, "wonder" and "miracle" work through the assistance of the gods.

Theosophy:
THEOSOPHICAL Society was founded in 1875 in New York by Madame Helena Protrovna Blavatsky. She established it with Colonel H.S. Olcott and several devoted and spiritually oriented people such as W.Q. Judge who became involved and wrote many books on the nature of the Higher and Inner Worlds. It was the Universal Brotherhood with well over 250 Branches across the world having the Headquarters in India.

Third Eye:
POINT in the center of the forehead between the physical eyes and is associated with the pineal gland and the source for acquiring inner visions as well as intuition.

Typhon:
LOWER cosmic principles of the body of Osiris or as the materialization of Osiris in the manifestation of an Ideal personified Universe. Also associated as Set as a former aspect of Thoth. Typhon is the "terrestrial and material envelop of Osiris, who is the indwelling spirit thereof". Typhon was used in the fourth Dynasty as a later name of Set and is similar in myth to Shiva, the destroyer, and Saturn as the "dark god". The goat was sacred to Typhon and over its head, Egyptians once confessed their sins and then the animal was sent into the desert. Typhon was of the

lower quaternary, wherein exists the differentiated chaotic matter, a lower aspect or shadow of Osiris who dwelled in the spiritual triad.

Upanishad:
ESOTERIC doctrines that are said to be dated about 600 BC producing hidden truths about the origin of the universe, connection between spirit and matter, essence of the manifested gods and a range of other spiritual topics that assists in the liberation from material constraints.

Vedas:
MOST ancient and sacred of the Sanskrit works being "revelations" of "divine knowledge".

V.V.V.V.V.:
VI Veri Vniversum Vivus Vici ("While still living, I have conquered the universe by dint of truth.") This was the motto that Crowley had as a Magister Templi in the sphere if Binah. They are also attributed as footprints of the camel and the Abyss as a great desert, shows that camel in motion with the fifth V in the desert crossing. Crowley also had the magical motto of Perdurabo, "I shall endure until the end", which is fitting for the great conquest of annihilating the ego in the becoming a Master of the Temple when the Abyss is successfully crossed.

Will:
THE essence of abstract eternal motion that becomes awareness when one is free from the bondage of materialism. It is the force of the Spirit and the beginning of all power that comes through the planes and manifests as mind, feelings and physical results in the lower level of Life. However, with aspiration, one ascends towards inner harmony and sanctity and develops the Will by not misdirecting the potential powers emanating through the soul.

Yetzirah:
WORLD of Formation and of the angels wherein all Genii or Angels govern and take control over the planets.

Yod:
TENTH letter of the Hebrew alphabet and a symbol of the WILL and creative force. The path it is attributed to has the Hermit tarot card which remarks that the will is inherent in the Self, pure and alone and that all else can be illusion when the consciousness is not focused with the Will and projections are muddled in the lower planes. It is the creative fiery energy in YHVH and the symbol for Yod is the hand, or hands, which have 10 fingers and are the "material" directing energy of ones will into the material world. The English equivalent is Y, J or I. It is also a symbol of the lingam or male organ in its triple form.

Yoni:
THE female principle which is also associated with the womb.

Zohar:
DOCTRINES of Chaldean thought which were impressed upon the Jewish during the Babylonian era. Many teachings of the Qabalah originate from these doctrines which include "The Secret of Secrets"; "The Mysteries of Pentateuch"; "The Mansions and Abodes of Paradise and Gaihinnom"; "The Faithful Shepherd"; "Discourse of the aged in Mishpatim" (punishment of souls); "The Hidden Midrash" and others.

S.L.MacGregor Mathers had published some of these works into English as the *Book of Concealed Mystery* and the Greater and the *Lesser Holy Assembly.*

The subject of all these definitions touches a personal nerve within each and every aspirant unto the mysteries of progression. It also bears upon that concept called Intent. Similarly as the workings of magical practice are directed towards neither non-selfish nor lower desires for their outcome, spiritual enlightenment unfolds when we are directing our course and approaching the objective sphere of inspiration. Within this unfolding process, the way is made clear and a greater Understanding is achieved. This is the purpose of intent such that the dry state is passed and one becomes engulfed and saturated with the knowledge and symbolic representation according to the conscious uplifting that is achieved.

This again brings us to the clear importance of intent along the path of magical attainment. The direction is to ascend and the method is by means of giving up the lower nature so that the higher nature will unfold the ability to SEE, HEAR, FEEL and DISCERN what is correct for the course of actions and what is incorrect. If we wish to balance ourselves standing on one leg upon a six-foot board, we would not go out and drink alcohol or engage in activities that are not concerned with balance. It is therefore incumbent that the use and acquisition of mystical experience be further directed towards the supreme and the most Holy of tasks we strive to realize. The awakening unto the destiny and accomplishment of the enlightened Will is that task by way of assimilation towards Understanding and Wisdom in their true spiritual capacity. ★

Part Two

Poetic Verse

Mystical Arousal

Pure Innocence from the First Swirling it Arose,
Enwrapped in Wisdom ushering Glory into Residence;
Metatron awoke in formative world and challenges ancient Prose,
With Primal life, beseeched ten angels from his Presence.

Holy Living Creatures amidst the Crown of God,
Vanishing across the spheres by Wing;
Through gray mists they wander, dressed in silken Shod,
Angels are sent from Higher by the Ancient King.

Most Admirable and Hidden is He that Speaks,
Without neither Beginning nor Ending from the Divine Spark;
Results emanate as He Seeks,
Root of Powers fluctuating into the World from the Dark.
- Lux Interna -

Ever inspired, yet division Occurred,
Lighting mercurial fires Within;
Echoes of life are subtly Heard,
Beyond restrictions and beyond all Sin.

The Magus' House is Supreme,
Sanctity lighting the corners of the Soul;
Orderly is everything it would Seem,
When aspiration is unto the Whole.

Explicit Truth, He converses Light,
In touch with One, Magnificent and True Will;
Flowing colors sublime, beyond Sight,
Most wicked and fantastic comes the Skill.

Upon the Camel crossing the Fires,
Crescent Moon brings on the Night;
Within her heart she deeply Desires,
Khonsu! Artemis! Hecate! What Might!

O! Priestess of the Silver Star,
Sliding into Consciousness Anew;
Wanderer of Wastelands not Afar,
Arousing passion as e-motions Grew.

No-thing
and
Everything

The swift messenger delivers by Intuition,
As the magus balances above and adjusts Below;
With flexibility opened to communication and Saturation,
Sprouting seeds from Naught, daring them to Grow.

Everything Matters and Creates some Change,
Stability rectifies duality in the prodigy of Nature;
Juggled mixed elements, extended out of Range,
No-thing is lost in Serene and Silent Rapture.

Each question is given Light,
Upon the Path as it magically Shines;
With certainty, Truth reveals clear Sight,
Ideality surpasses the Extension of Lines.

Soaring eagle, hears not disinfected Cries,
As it catches the lift beyond Imagination;
Cosmic connection attaches Everything without Lies,
Surpassing dryness, parched with mere Infatuation.

CREATION

Healing has filtered through the Moon,
As Priestess brings down the Light from In;
Energy, Equilibrium shall arrive Soon,
Creations of astral designs will Heighten.

Life is filling through the Sun,
From this point She Draws Upon;
Every action accomplished so Done,
Awakening to an early Dawn.

Access opens doors of Power,
Reservoir fills with purest Liquid;
Uplifted to a enlightening Shower,
Eternal discomfort we will forbid.

Guard is up, Chalice is Cleansed,
Opening Sight of Silver Star;
The Great Mother so often Sensed,
Unity bridges gaps Afar.

Path of Eternity

Absolute, Indefinable, Basis of Possible Vibration,
Positive, most distinguished sense of Creation,
Matter and Motion, dwindles through Time Immemorial,
With Sensual Rapture through arduous Testimonial.

Kings dine while the Empress Unites,
As spectacles are achieved by the Knights;
Consciousness tackles Knowledge with Bliss,
Permeating Reality with a Kiss.

Life fulfills complements with Abode,
Travelling the path across the Road;
Boundaries are sought with a Guiding Light,
Steadfast Inspiration provokes Immensity just Right.

Together maidens danced in their Apparel,
With illustrious melodies brightening each Carol;
Paladins enthused, watching from Aside,
Revealing their ALL, amidst nothing to Hide.

The Pure Fool walks eternal Path,
With sparkling jewels, he does the Math;
Majestic Empress at his side in Vision,
Sublimed within some Angels Mission.

INITIATION

Entering the Sanctuary, the Pillars are Ahead,

Carrying Orb and Scepter the initiate has Said:

"Unto Infinite Space, Blessed Light and Love art Thee;

Sustainer of mine Soul, Most Holy Radiant Powers, So Mote It Be."

Sacrificing his ALL, great dynamic power Raised,

Allegiance of the Provider; Seeds are sown and holy Praised.

Initiator delivers the Organized One,

Unto the next level, as Illustrious as the Sun.

Amongst the Himalayan rams, submissive to Cosmic Doctrines There,

With humility at his Side, and perfect Balance he did Dare.

Strong desires and discipline leads the future Race,

The Emperor has Created, with authority upon his Face.

The Arian wisdom shines through the Martian Power,

Exalting change throughout his Nocturnal Living Tower.

He is the sulphur in a natural Myriad,

With the Empress and Priestess, becoming the Alchemical Triad.

All things to consider, he resists not the Tao,

Recollecting the teachings of the historical great Lao.

Then the initiate has become The Enlightened Pioneer,

As fatherhood begins, all is renewed from the visionary Seer.

Inner Guide

In Higher Life the Inner Guide may at the moment Await,
As a Supreme Pontiff with vestments beyond our causal living Fate;
Mysteries may appear sinister from a Lower View,
But always are revealed to the Sacred Chosen Few.
The Hierophantic Task bridges god with mortal Man,
Through five petals of pure love its' transformation surely Can.
Wearing nine thorns as nails they bond and join Together,
It occurs with trust, receptive sensitivity and utmost sincere Surrender.
Scarlet Woman stands, with Wisdom, Love and Serpent Power,
Holding sacred sword through the Eucharistic Shower.
She Bestows benediction upon the ordained Brow,
Delivering Divine Light unto the Here and Now.
Be ready and ever open as the teacher may Arrive,
Earnest to evolve, integrate and be Alive.
Yin and yang are united in the Holy Being,
While four cherubim guard the altar as the opened Eye is Seeing.
The bull steers physical matter, with the lions' power of Desire,
Little feet upon the earth arousing intuition torching Fire.
Humans upon the mental level strive to Spiritual Plane,
The Eagle is emotion and thine work is not in Vain.
Transforming through the pain of desolation is a perfect Choice,
If in contact with the Hierophant, our heart becomes the Voice.

Lovers Unite

Lovers brighten the Astral Plane,
Providing sustenance like the Rain;
Energized Communication and Enthusiastic Revelation are righteous Both,
And are treasures given from the Almighty Thoth.

The field is shared from two that Care,
Giving their Self as ONE so Rare;
Living against the greater Odds,
While fully trusting in all the Gods.

Everything entwined becomes better Still,
Living with love, under Will;
As Children under the Stars of Light,
Crowned and Victorious, yet ready to Fight.

They reach a mutual Understanding in Peace,
Then all the chaos begins to Cease;
Harmony has been Restored,
As love flows through their Silver Cord.

They dance merrily and live life Free,
As it was surely meant to Be;
Within they begin to make a Child,
Magical it is and ever so Wild.

It leaps like Pan across the Rocks,
And dives off from the water Docks;
Then up it came to grant their Wish,
Like a Genii from a Dish.

She looked at her lover and held his Hip,
Gently kissing him on the Lip;
He caressed her body soft and Sweet,
Penetrating her emotions engulfed with Heat.

United Lovers creating Passion,
Under the Stars in Nuit's Fashion;
Score with channeled energy Alive,
As playful mortals always Strive.

CHARGING THE ELEMENTS

Mind and Matter is divided by four elements of Life,
Poor mixture of them is what causes Strife;
Knowing each in turn will Give,
Harmony in nature as we Live.

First there is the element Earth,
It has hardness and material Worth;
But if we use it calm and Still,
It will nourish and strengthen Will.

Then there is that of Air,
It is there for all to Share;
It means motion and Adaptability,
Another virtue of increasing Capability.

Next we have the element Water,
It is attributed to the Daughter;
It flows and causes things to Grow,
In order to reap, we must Sow.

Last there is the famous Fire,
It is flaming with Desire;
Use it to increase our deepest Needs,
Procuring always, noble Deeds.

Combine them now and Adjust,
Remember Fire is what gives us Lust;
Fantasy is an air Acclaim,
But can create and give us Fame.

All these elements steer our Being,
Mutable and changing as we are Seeing;
Sternly motion them to Earth,
Providing desires with a Birth.

Opening the gates of Intuition,
Realizing what causes pangs of Derision;
Motions balance so needs are Met,
While mastering the elements derived from Spirit.

Balance

Bitter may be Truth, when it is Revealed,
Ravished like a broth, of personality disorders Concealed.
Harlequin romancing, entangled with her Mate,
Upon the Scales of Balance, She awaits to Insatiate.
Adjusting every cause, with the final Effect,
With action creating change that only Nature will Select.

Daughter seated upon the throne, the Mother shall Subside,
Filled with spheres and pyramids, through Understanding she will Ride.
Lord of Life and Death, with limitation and the Law,
The woman satisfied moves and talks without Flaw.
With her witnesses called to portray the virtue of each Act,
Assessing every deed for satisfaction to be Fact.

Directing each integral and form of Energy,
To compliment and fulfill it's rightful Destiny.
Without prejudice the logic is soundly Impassive,
Holding neither conscience burden that is dire and so Massive.
Adjustment is learning through ordeals in life to Handle,
But the key to do it is not to stir the subtle secret Candle.

LOVE AND LIGHT

Will conceived pure love poured within the virginal Chalice,

The Sacred One enters the nine gates to the Great Palace.

The Secret Fire that burns in the Heart of Devotees,

Flames in the hermit's Lamp and holds the hidden Wisdom Keys.

This is the hand with healing powers to manifest the method's holy Vow,

Extended through the wand and staff, the fluidic essence pours into Now.

Courage brings Trust gives Attitude provides Growth,

Through this love and light, they are shared Both.

Then the sigil of the Sun, shines brightly through our Face,

With visions of clarity, serenity, and peaceful, tranquil Grace.

While meeting other seekers of the Light upon the Path,

Nothing of the past remains to haunt us in its' Wrath.

With this inward journey, surpassing shadows of Illusion,

Pain and sorrow are transcended, as is all Confusion.

The deceptive light is external with transitory Fears,

When Perfection is met, nothing ever Interferes.

This is what experience is, for the Hermit and the Sage,

Beyond comprehension, for the average mind Enraged.

When thou meet upon thine way a Seeker of the Light,

Smile accordingly and pass to them a Secret of the Night.

Upon the Wheel of Life

Great Wheel of Life we ride Upon,
Harvests the outcome Dusk till Dawn.
It brings perspective from the Celestial,
Down to reality and into Terrestrial.

Listen amongst the noisy Crowd,
The thoughts we hear are sent Aloud.
Sent amidst many Things,
That rides upon Dusty Wings.

Through them something else is Spoken,
With emotions that are Broken.
Following them, they have a Trail,
Why did they falter and why did they Fail?

Through a person, into their Eyes,
We may count many Lies.
If they speak from their Heart,
They have achieved and mastered an Art.

Why say we this, that is it So?
We all know that people Grow.
Within which is the greatest Key,
To unlock our personal Mystery.

An Endless Night

The heavy Night blankets us All,
Into the darkness we all shall Fall,
Through the depth of midnight to Morning,
There came to my door some strange Warning.
I arose to answer the noise out There,
Opening the door was my greatest Dare.
I stood there staring at some great Vastness,
Feeling it's Strength, my presence was Restless.
As the image appeared with such Angelic Love,
My voice stuttered as I looked Above.

My eyes blinked then I saw nothing More,
So in I went and closed the Door.
There was a message She gave to Me,
Which was, "Teach Us how to be Truly Free".
Ghastly grim I felt Inside,
Walking the room and increasing my Stride.
The Angel that night outside my Door,
Made me leave to walk the nightly Shore.
What to think of the Presence that Night,
The appearance was there and ever so Bright.
I wandered and thought of how it made me Feel,
No longer did it matter whether it was Real.

Its' appearance was there and not for the Worse,
Giving me a clue to this mysterious Universe.
On I went realizing the Reason,
Of Her visit that particular Season.
To live with Love under Will I Thought,
Is to open the Veil of Destiny Sought.
Quietly I sat and accepted a Silence,
Becoming in tune with every Sense.
Did She represent the Holy Ghost,
Or was She a glittering dove from the Coast?
Maybe a reflection from a bright Moon,
Regardless, the communication dropped me in majestic Swoon.

Realizing Love Energy, something dear to Caress
As it brings Truth and Ultimate Happiness.
Divinity is behind this trail of Holy Grail,
The powers of which shall never Fail.

Breaking Through

A card of old was placed upon the wooden table,
It didn't look so good nor was it notably Stable.
Breaking through old patterns of behavior and letting Go,
When they are mired with falsity, dogma and Ego.
If it all seems of burden and nothing goes so Well,
Subjected with endless sorrows delivered from personal Hell.
Manic and depressive, whatever states they Are,
Patience then Victory, remembering each is a vibrant Star.
Hang-ups and viewpoints are always an Extreme,
From a little ego that has grasp, it would Seem.
Falsity is everywhere but Truth always Brings,
Guilt is not an answer and pity rarely Sings.
As the mystic reveals the nocturnal sleep of Shiloam,
Iacchus arises through the mists and begins to romp and Roam.
Karmic cleansing is required at the lower End,
Never give up nor stop, as the Will can never Bend.
Then into the deep sea, selflessness Awaits,
The corridors of time have opened all the Gates.
Replace the insolence of faith with certainty you Took,
Knowing all the answers are not in any Book.
And chastity must go then Ecstasy will Come,
Into the age of glory, realized by precious Some.
Joy beyond Joy, Arise and Awake,
Splendour breaks through for you to Make.
The pillars of life will always make Sense,
To the student of Qabalah who climbs over the Fence.
And seeks to know Paths and Spheres and Attributions,
Rising above such Vengeance that causes dreadful Persecutions.

Dispersing Evil Advocates

Entities live on lower Planes,
Hunched back they are with walking Canes.
They wander and they always Lurk,
Mischievous creatures, with sinister Work.

If in these levels you will Traverse,
Be prepared to handle Curse.
They may steer you from the Way,
And turn you into hardened Clay.

Protect the Soul with a Shield,
To this, they will always Yield.
And behold the essence within is Pure,
It may be the only Cure.

Should there ever be doubt with This,
Seek Holy Names, and shout in Bliss.
Call their Names all in Tune,
They will answer very Soon.

They come when there is need and Worth,
Working in heavens and on Earth.
So if you encounter a viscous Troll,
Send him back into to his Hole.

Transformation

It is the Art of an Archer that is truly Divine,
Like in the life of Diana, when the Greeks drank deep red Wine.
When the arrow focused will and pierced a Rainbow Serene,
Sagittarius grew fonder combining forces that weren't Seen.

Creativity developed, from exalted Energies,
Temperance touched Jupiter, without Allergies.
It was internal process, through a lofty Visionary,
Elaborate and combined yet the fusion was Elementary.

Contradictions in the cauldron with water and fire in the Urn,
The sulphur, mercury and salt then had their lustrous Turn.
Nurtured universal solvent to feed the True Will,
As transformation occurred, consuming the holy Pill.

Unifying opposites, integrated synthesis, elastic yet Rigid,
The philosopher's stone was anything but Frigid.
White Lion, red eagle, the Royal Marriage soon Begun,
Life into the orphic egg, originated through the Sun.

The highest art of Transformation,
Is without Substantiation.
As Revelation of this higher Order,
Releases vitriol as an astral Border.

Dinner With Baphomet

Set within an ancient castle, guests arrived one by One,
They came from every land, all worshipping the Sun.
Each from a different Order, they Came,
Sharing vaulted secrets without judicial Shame.
They wined and dined with great Feasts,
To discuss the mysteries of ancient Beasts.
Baphomet was on the slate Tonight,
Where, did he come from, that devilish Sight?
The Bell rang, the butler open the Door,
Someone walked in with magical Lore.
Then in came a magnificent Breeze,
A man dressed in regalia, down to his Knees.
The host stood up at the table that Night,
As guests toasted to the riddled Plight.
Could he be the goat of Mendes,
And the lotus flowers, who sent These?
Why are you wicked, you little old Man?
Are we not all from the mystical Clan?
Indeed we are, so on with the Query,
Let us move on, without casting such Fiery!
Equating Him with Mohammed is Silly!
Please close the window, it's mighty Chilly.
Could Baphomet be from the Knights Templar?
Or did he arise from something Similar?
Some say he is the Greek god Pan,
A gentleman noted as he took a Stand.
But all have made him a martyr, in Time,
Whose head is a Relic and acts as a Mime.
With horns that reach into the Sky,
Evolving the Spirit without a Lie.
One chap was a Sufi, a Builder of Change,
To him, this creation was rather Strange.
And Masons were there, suggesting ceremonial Reasons,
That Baphomet was worshipped throughout the Seasons.
A Brother said Arabic has it, that abufihamet is the Origin,
As the Father of Understanding, Baphomet is no Sin.
Another voice called him the Baptism of Wisdom,
To that they toasted again and again.
So if Devil is diabolis and duality is Wrong,
Why has Lucifer been around so Long?
He is the light bearer, the Morning Star,
Not related to the devil, in fact very Far.
You see, a Pope was once named Lucifer in Rome,
He wasn't evil, but Christian, just as the Luciferian's Home.
And to equate this with the Devil you See,
You must look at physical Reality.
Wherein there are seven living Hells,
Roaming with demons, all Samuel's.
These are all vices in Assiah, the world of dense Matter,
The Klippoth of Shells, whose retributions will Shatter.
Let's now, gentlemen, indulge in the Meal,
We have made this a big enough Deal.

The Hidden Intelligence

Every word has a meaning, and one that we generally do not Know,
Only through etymology will it honestly Show;
That the word 'occult' means something that's deep and usually just Hidden,
The study of which helps, all confusion to be Ridden.

Believing in popular and common Notions,
Programs our mind with poisonous Potions;
Reality is Truth and simple to Seek,
Apparently not, for the mentally Weak.

It's not as simple as 'belief', you See,
Unless connected upon the Tree;
Kaballah magic, science and Art,
Is a foundation upon where we may Start.

Probationer to Adept, Aspirant to Master,
Don't be sucked into dwindling Disaster;
Keep a record of what you Do,
While planning the future with Ideals True.

Now you know a bit of Success,
Don't give up and don't settle for Less.
Find out for your Self, what is Real,
The seeking of which will Reveal.

Intelligence provides transcendental Powers,
Growing in the mind like beautiful Flowers;
Nourished with the reverie of an honest Mind
Seeking the Hidden and Absolute will always be a Find.

AQUARIUS ARISEN

Roses blossom from the Great Sea,
Emotional unfolding soon comforts Thee;
As the Water Bearer accepts supernal, spiral Forces,
From the mystical Lord, of all superior Sources.

Seeping down a universal medicine Divine,
From the alchemists, of historic ancient Time;
Like ambrosia of the Greeks, it will change our View,
As butterflies transform, in the morning Dew.

Magical memory, like twinkles in the Sky,
The oracle reveals, and would never actually Lie;
So disperse the limited illusions, of the lower Plane,
The parallel postulate is for the healthy and the Sane.

Water of Air brings great emotions, from the Sirius Star,
Progressing forward, creating beauty and virtuous by Far;
Having trust and being tested, we should not Oppose,
Then this love-chant, with perfect certainty, forever Grows.

Lastly carry inspiration, with great Perception,
Not to mention purity, as a transcendental Conception.
So alluring is this formula, Victory will surely Come,
But the seven-pointed star of Venus, is only recognized by Some.

Beyond the Door

Life is shattered beyond deaths Door,
Travelling along the path no Vain;
Illusion is nothing, 'tis nothing More
Calling upon Sandalphon, relinquishing false Gain.

Behold ! Destiny is Ours to Build!
Of this our deed through Love in the dearest Sense.
Penetrating through all, as it is Willed;
To know a puissant will, and dare with Silence.

Seek where balance is and Love it Passionately!
Wherein these kisses cluster and Overflow;
Gliding through ethers ever Tenderly,
With brimming ardor as new incantations Grow.

Around us all the Forces blossom as our love Entwines,
With thoughts, emotions, and breath rhythm Slow;
Omens appear, everywhere there are Signs,
Consecrated ring of Amethyst, As Above, So Below.

Then all things, cruel as hideous forms upon Earth
Sent to their place to be left for Eternity.
As rapturous love bliss flowers with every Breath;
Through Love, Life and Light creating Trinity.

Seeding with nourishment fantasies for the Soul,
Illusions dispersed with enchanted brow of Sublimation;
Uplifting thine inmost passions as a Whole,
Objective reality is pronounced by exalted Creation.

Make Light of the Soul

All things have another side of View,
Life isn't as though as imagined by You.
Things could be worse in other Ways,
Look within and forward to future Days.
Don't dwell on Sorrow or linger so Low,
Take a Deep Breath then let them Go.
Live for the Night and through the break of Dawn,
Pick your Self up and carry On.

When too many things are on your Mind;
Slow down your Ways and seek to Find.
What remnants or problems from past Remain;
Call and channel them and don't be Insane.
Reminiscence is good to keep from Forgetting,
A Life you enjoy without real Regretting.
Revive enthusiasm for Life in all Ways,
Enjoy the Present Reality for future Days.
Recall a feeling, a time or Event;
Relive a new day of what it Meant.
Train your Memory as an exercise of Soul,
Use it to uplift your mind with Control.

From the center of our Space,
Brightness and Glory shines on our Face.
It's a balance of Beauty and Rays,
Of Force and Strength as Light through the Days;
And behind the Night, shadows fall and Glimmer,
The Sun is always there albeit Dimmer.
In Billions of Years its' Life will End,
So Express its' energy in Feelings you Send.
Golden Streams of Life and Light,
Unifies our Path increasing Insight.

OMNISCIENCE

Infinite Space bends and kisses the eyes at Night,
Then it's swallowed up at the first Light.
Winged serpent, Ohyros, Wisdom free in Ecstasy,
Adores anew, conscious life filled with Majesty.
Of that which is true and totally Revealing,
All is new with rebirth, never to be Concealing.

Discriminate, analyze see the future through this Myth,
Using Body, Spirit and Soul it's easy to soar With.
Eternal, solar energy Hadit,
Joined in ecstasy with Nuit.

They gave birth to Horus,
Which answers reality as clarity through Us.
Who became the Hierophant, Heru-ra-ha, that double-god of Power to Be,
His extrovert side is Ra-Hoor Khuit, and can deeply See.
Whose reflection is passive on the other Hand,
That is Hoor-pa-Kraat's almighty Land.

Limitations will no longer Judge,
Surpassed with the Eye of Horus, says Professor Budge.
Whose Eye could see, what fell of Harmony,
With Deeper Insight, Greater Wisdom beyond all normal Sensory.
What life needs now, is a bright Torchbearer,
None other than in mystical pursuit will omniscience be any Fairer.

Inspiration in Aspiration

Shining the Light of the Spiritual Realm is never such a Plight
When beams of aspiration on an enigma makes it Right

With Wisdom seeking Realization in the course of Destiny
Life becomes a fabric scent joined in passionate Array

Through Understanding, accepting Purity is achieved Within
To move no shadow to curse no thought and to have no wandering Whim

Securing future and finance, all so directly Focused
Gedulah glorifies the Hosts with secrets of the Locust

Fighting only inner turmoil, expressing Control in Energy
Sentiments of symmetry exchanged with wondrous Synergy

In Harmony, Radiating the arts six-fold as the center always Does
Stars in orbits, never ending without the reason 'Because'

Victoriously aligned, colorful as Art
Venus is the morning star and touches our Heart

Rhyme of Logic, Reason of Knowledge grips on the eighth Sphere
Lending past experience to a listening Ear

Swimming in Mysterious Powers through the Gates of Soul
Moon reflects energy of inspiration, given from the Whole

Reality as Destiny, Earth Awareness in Liberty with Now
Landing healing energy, we sometimes question How

THE WHIM OF ANY MOMENT

It becomes a perplexity
In the mind of subtle parity
Given from justice a simple charity
Through a heart so close to rarity

And the mind lingers in places forlorn
Without hesitation as babes are born
Sentiments shrivel with daring drivel, all the life that gives
Incessantly breaking through and once again it lives

Vengeance strikes back and always twice
The second time is never nice
Laid back a fool so shaken it trod
Each moment draws closer to the God

Free from choice no matter given
Escapes the action once was driven
By a force no one can see
Smiles onlookers at liberty.

Entranced with visions now and then
Laughter shouts out unjustified
What whim has lost the peace and when
Shall it return more clarified?

Rose it is but white or red
Pure or passion necessitates
What ever reason it is said
That generally shrills and agitates

Lost in depths no longer seen
Stood carelessly the lie
Of thoughtless actions that had been
Meant to only die

Surely there is something more
More to all of this
Transcend the state, open door
And enter all the Bliss

~EPILOGUE~

When the chill of earth black-breasted is uplifted at the glance
Of the red sun million-crested, and the forest blossoms dance
With the light that stirs and lustres of the dawn, and with the bloom
Of the wind's cheek as it clusters from the hidden valley's gloom:
Then I walk in woodland spaces, musing on the solemn ways;
Of the immemorial spaces shut behind the starry rays;
Of the East and all its splendour, of the West and all its peace;
And the stubborn lights grow tender, and the hard sounds hush and cease.
In the wheel of heaven revolving, mysteries of death and birth,
In the womb of time dissolving, shape anew a heaven and earth.
Ever changing, ever growing, ever dwindling, ever dear,
Ever worth the passion glowing to distill a doubtful tear.
These are with me, these are of me, these approve me, these obey,
Choose me, move me, fear me, love me, master of the night and day.
These are real, these illusion: I am of them false or frail,
True or lasting, all is fusion in the spirit's shadow-veil,
Till the Knowledge-Lotus flowering hides the world beneath its stem;
Neither I, nor God life-showering, find a counterpart in them.
As a spirit in a vision shows a countenance of fear,
Laughs the looker to derision, only comes to disappear,
Gods and mortals, mind and matter, in the glowing bud dissever:
Vein from vein they rend and shatter, and are nothingness forever.
In the blessed, the enlightened, perfect eyes these visions pass,
Pass and cease, poor shadows frightened, leave no stain upon the glass.
One last stroke, O heart-free master, one last certain calm of will,
And the maker of disaster shall be stricken and grow still.
Burn thou to the core of matter, to the spirits utmost flame,
Consciousness and sense to shatter, ruin sight and form and name!
Shatter lake reflected spectre; lake rise up in mist of sun;
Sun dissolve in showers of nectar, and the Master's work is done.
Nectar perfume gently stealing, masterful and sweet and strong,
Cleanse the world in light of healing in the ancient House of Wrong!
Free a million million mortals on the wheel of being tossed!
Open wide the mystic portals, and be altogether lost!

Aleister Crowley (Collected Works, Vol. 2)

THE HIGHEST PEAK

"This is the sublime and refined point of felicity, called, the possession of being well deceived; the serene peaceful state of being a fool among knaves."

Jonathan Swift (1667-1745)

(This story is fondly dedicated to Allan Bennett and Oscar Eckenstein - two souls who gave significantly to the spiritual state of humanity.)

The five peaks of Kangchenjunga are, above all else, revered as sacred in the heart of the Sikkimese people who reside in the Himalayas. The Sikkimese people have deep respect for the peril of threat, which is housed throughout the mountain's 28,169 feet of horrific magnitude for adventurous fortitude. Allan had been a Lake District climber from the east shores of England for several years. He also scaled Beachy Head with known reputable Alpine members as well as diverse cliffs in the Alps and once on Chogo Ri but now the time to test his daring ability was going to be put to challenge. To climb over the revered five sacred peaks of the legendary prominence would be a conquest of a lifetime.

There are many vicious pinnacles that rise from the mountain's narrow icy ridges, making it a gripping challenge of endurance for the best of athletes to withstand. Kangchenjunga is located on the border of Nepal and Sikkim, roughly forty miles from Darjeeling. It is the most easterly of the highest peaks in the Himalayas and was thought to be the highest mountain in the world until 1849. First attempted in 1905 with an international party, four people lost their life in an avalanche. Mudslides and avalanches are omnipresent due to the heavy precipitation it receives throughout the year. Allan boarded the railway train and was elevated over six thousand feet of curving track to meet with the expedition team in Darjeeling.

He was the first to arrive and found the locale to be most unsavory. The rain, for one, was an utter nightmare. Most places would have rain fall from the sky, but not in Darjeeling. Since it was highly elevated, the rain flew up from below and it washed through the streets in an upright fashion making an umbrella rather useless lest it be wrapped around one's waist. Nonetheless, he made the best of it and prepared accordingly while paying tribute through daily adoration of the Sun; the life giving force of all time. Two days later his long time friend and climbing companion, Oscar, arrived on the trinket train.

"Well, if it isn't the ol' ruffian from Wales. How was the journey?" Allan asked as Oscar walked up to the front of the hotel.

"It likely wasn't much better than yours, Al," Oscar lamented and shook his friend's hand. "Good to see you again."

"Nobody else is here yet. They should be here on tomorrow's train. Get yourself settled in and we can go eat some of their petrified lunch that they overrate," Allan chuckled.

The following day the remainder of the team arrived on the tattered locomotive and prepared to escalate through the foothills towards what would be soon established as Base Camp.

Doctor Jacot Traverny, a graduate of Oxford and a surgeon was meticulous in several of his finer interests. He delighted in the intricacies of detail. He tasked himself to map out the route and established the camps to be ten in number. The porters or coolies, as the local hired help is called, were to be Sixty-one. His fascination of heights brought him to this area for the second time as he traversed the lower altitudes of the towering K-2 with an American expedition two years previous.

Alexis, a thirty-one year old engineer from Switzerland, was an ambitious climber and champion Olympic skier for her country. She was also a student in the study of naturopathy at the University of Geneva. Her mixture of herbs in a cup of boiling water could drive a devotee of religious scripture to an insane asylum, and vice-versa. She had spent several years training on the Alps and in particular on the Eiger.

Oscar grew up in Wales and developed several mountain climbing tools, hooks, crampons and instruments useful in scaling high altitudes. He had the remarkable talent of effortlessly lifting himself above his body height with only one hand. As remarkable a man of strength as he was, he conserved it entirely for each move he made, not unlike how elephants behave.

Markus, an expert marksman, was from Frankfurt, Germany and was boisterously athletic. He was along for the prestige of the mission and afforded the excursion through his inherited wealth. He trained at a gymnasium to prepare for the arduous journey and brought a video camera to capture his triumph. He knew Alexis from occasional correspondence after they met on the Matterhorn in Switzerland a few years previous and it was through her that he learned of this splendid opportunity.

The final member of the team was Angeline, who was an avid health and fitness instructor from Iowa in the United States. Since childhood she had been reveling in extensive climbing experience with her father. Her father had always trained with her until she was old enough to do it alone and began climbing with other mountaineers in Mexico and through the ravishing Rocky Mountains. The climbs were always challenges for her but with the great dexterity and muscular strength under her belt, she overcame the obstacles with fortitude every time.

On early morning of April 2nd, the team departed for the village of Hille. It was pre-monsoon season and so weather catastrophes would less likely occur. They crossed over a bridge and made their tracks up the dirt road to the foothills. In the distance was the magnificent mountain of Kangchenjunga that the enthused climbers would soon humbly touch. The mountain shone with diverse colors in the sun; faint roses, nebulous blues, and striking whites could be seen above it's base darkness from miles away. Mules carried baggage of food and supplies sufficient enough for seventy people lasting thirty days.

Allan was fluent in Hindu and could translate the discussions to and from the porters. The government sent a military officer to oversee the expedition. His name was Major Black. The Major didn't seem at all thrilled about the expedition. At base camp he was rather grouchy about the whole episode of being there, but his true colors showed through his character; he simply missed the world of waiters and luxuries.

The porters were each offered four pounds a day plus food for their work. Compared to the rupees that they seldom had to spend, they felt like kings of the earth for this given opportunity. A contract was prepared for them stating they would be paid upon completion of the excursion.

At the main camp the base station was established as a communications link to the outside world and the higher elevations. Several porters remained there on alert with tents and supplies. They also provided communications by relaying messages to Signal Hill and to render any requests demanded from the higher camps. The trip took eleven hours to make from the village. Medical supplies, food and equipment were to be strategically placed at each camp so that any emergencies could be sufficiently handled.

The first set-up was land-marked as camp number ten. Allan found it coincidental that there were ten camps and similarly ten spheres on the kabalistic tree of life. He therefore became inclined to think of the initial camp ten as Malkuth and ascend appropriately until the god-sphere of Kether, or the summit would become achieved one day in the near future.

Camp nine required the majority of a day to reach with favorable weather permitting. In the magical hierarchy it was like reaching Yesod, or the sphere of the moon. One may also associate it as the world of

Assiah or the Nepesh.

Angeline felt invigorated and enjoyed the taking of photographs, as Markus made video footage of the splendid view and of the team with whom he was so excited to affiliate.

"Hello Angeline, tell everybody how much you are enjoying this trip," Markus said while pointing the camera at her.

Angeline smirked. "Oh, it is not as wonderful as it looks. I wouldn't call it a trip really! Although the experience is magnificent, let me tell you it is bone chilling up here. The air is thinning also. Talk to me tomorrow and I might feel better."

At camp nine, several porters remained with supplies and communications. Allan was impressed with the strength that the porters displayed and believed the story one told him about a lady porter having carried by herself an upright piano from Siliguri to Darjeeling through the plains. The one thing he was not impressed with was the environment back at Darjeeling. Everything smelled of mildew - the hotel, the land and to some extent the maidens that would seek a husband through their less than convincing talents as pianists. The food was overly expensive, as were the hotels that attempted to flaunt their menus with an illiterate attempt in French. Passing beyond the stench of dawdling recollections, and noting that everything seemed to be in order, Allan settled in for the night.

The wind picked up on the following day but the skies were clear with permanence and the tundra crisp with flaked ice crystals. The crew wandered across the icy path onwards to make camp eight. Traverny didn't look too thrilled, having coughed for most of the night. Oscar held back and provided him with a hand from time to time. The comfort of reaching a destination cannot be over emphsized. Everyone looked completely thrilled at arriving and pitching tents.

Allan suggested to Traverny that they traverse the west-side coulier (which he termed Jacob's Rake) for the ease of making their way towards the final reach up the highest peak. It was agreed and mapped accordingly to take the route from the snow basin before Yalung glacier to reach Jacob's Rake. Everybody cheerfully settled in for the night while prattling away about the adventurous hike. With good reason, this camp was attributed to Hod, the eight sphere of the tree of life. Many of Hod's associated elements of logic, reasoning and knowledge lingered in their minds, exciting enthusiasm. Four porters remained at camp eight and unloaded some supplies, which would leave their associates prepared to traverse the deeper mountainside up to camp seven on the following day.

The elevation of the hike steadily increased. Allan was at the front followed by Alexis, then Markus with Angeline not far behind. Allan gazed into the heavy mountain that beckoned him onward like a familiar voice calling from a distance. An inner voice of encouragement assured him that safety was always the foremost concern on the journey. Camp seven was reached with eagerness that same afternoon.

Night settled in as northerly winds blew a blinding snow squall from the corner precipice. Drifts grew around the tents as the members nestled beside their portable stoves to keep their hands warm. Oscar looked to Allan as the expedition director and suggested they remain at camp seven for an additional day lest the storm subsided. Allan agreed to discuss it in the morning after assessing the daybreak conditions.

The relentless chilling winds whirled around the tents during the bitter evening as Allan pulled some Yi-King sticks from a small purple pouch in his rucksack. He concentrated on a question and dropped the sticks from his hand onto his journal. The Yi Ching or King dates back to Yi using the Kwi or Trigrams of Fu-Hsi around 3322 BC and were used throughout history by people as a form of divination to obtain answers about any particular dilemma. The pattern that the sticks fall into reveals a riddled answer to the question. The Kien Hexagram fell upon Allan's journal. He contemplated the meaning of it as the Moon of Earth. It basically meant 'incompleteness and lameness; time for the great man to aid thee in the climb.' Allan's memory of the mnemonic paraphrases of Ko Yuen was impeccable. Immediately he recited to himself the interpretation of the Hexagram.

"Advance adds trouble, stillness aids thee now.
Keep struggling with no self to mar thy vow.
Advance not! Seek again thine ancient clan;
Advance not! Friends come to prosecute thy plan.
Advance not! Wait for aid from great man."

The following morning frigid winds continued to blow across the camp. Breakfast was prepared and steaming coffee was an invitation into everyone's frigid hands. It would be a full day's climb to camp six if the weather fully co-operated. Everyone knew instinctively that they would remain there until it significantly improved.

That afternoon Doctor Traverny was summoned to the porters' tent through the squall of blowing snow. He grabbed his medical bag and rushed over. One of the porters was very ill with influenza. The doctor situated him into a lone tent with someone to serve him hot herbal drinks, which Alexis was adept at preparing. They would have him transported back to base camp when the weather subsided.

The setting sun glittered over the icy tundra as it slowly disappeared across the horizon, soon to retreat behind the distant mountain ranges. The winds subsided and a clear night commenced with twinkles shimmering from above. Allan looked up as the evening stars began to appear. Reaching the summit was like reaching for the stars. It was something beyond normal achievement and something you could not take for granted in earthly existence. It could cost a life in a split second of time by making one uncertain judgement. He went into the tent and began to read a book containing the writings of Baudelaire; one of his favorite writers of past eras:

"Oh Night, Oh refreshing shadows! You are for me the signal of an internal festival, you are deliverance of anguish. In the solitude of plains, in the stony labyrinths of a great city, twinkling of stars, or out-bursting of lamps, you are the fireworks of the Goddess Liberty. Twilight, how sweet thou art and tender! The rosy lights which linger still on the horizon like the death-spasm of Day trampled by the victorious car of Night; the torch-like flames which stain with their dull red the expiring glories of the setting sun; the heavy curtains which some invisible hand draws from the depths of the East- these are but imitations of all the complex feelings which struggle within the heart of man in the solemn hours of his life."

Alan closed the book and returned it to his backpack. He reflected on the other climbers and about the person that may appear to prosecute the plan, as the Yi Ching insinuated. Calculated reason was not something he could admit to. Allan was always willing to take the plunge or leap into fate and allow instinct to land him back on his feet. If he would be a fool for this, he would surely be an innocent and pure one. The only calculations he invited regarded safety on the edge. He was not such an amateur as to bring jeopardy into the life of another person.

As for himself, he performed the spiral dance, living each minute as a new one with trust in the Universe to keep his wild card afloat. This distinct attribute of his character resembled what one may associate to the precarious nature of the mountain. The cold and harsh abstract principles of the self-contained mountain where all phenomena are governed according to radical predicaments were not unlike the strength of character that Allan exuded.

He heard some boisterous noises in the next tent, but didn't pay them much heed, as the next day would require his full attention. It sounded like a tad of flirting was on and was something that Allan would not have unsuspected at camp seven. Camp seven identified with Netzach and Venus, the Love Goddess that plays through the night of one's emotions. Although Allan was more than capable and fully responsible for his decisions, he was not at all interested in the provocation of the other team members lest it would threaten the safety of lives or the mission.

Alexis was talking with Angeline in the neighboring tent when Markus entered and wished to stay and talk with them for a while.

"It's sort of lonely in the next tent with that doctor always reading a book. How about a little company?" Markus suggested playfully.

"It's getting late and I am sure we will be moving on early in the morning. Perhaps another time," Angeline declined.

"How old are you, Angeline?" Markus asked, unfazed.

Angeline giggled, "My climbing comrade, a woman never reveals that. A woman that tells you her real age would tell you anything."

"Let's play for a while, we are in a remote part of the world and should celebrate!" Markus chirped.

"Nein, Markus, wir sind müde, geh´in Dein eigenes Zelt!" Alexis requested him to return to his tent.

"You girls are no fun at all. We are on an epic adventure and you are going to sleep your life away?"

"Sleep makes a person beautiful," Alexis laughed as she patted the cool air off her sleeping bag.

"Fine then, another night. See you in the morning," the disappointed member replied as he crawled back outside.

A scant light peered across the top of the tents as everyone rolled back into awakened consciousness.

The shiny escapade of glimmering sunlight on the surrounding glacier drew them back to life as they prepared for the early hike onwards. Dr. Traverny suggested leaving at eleven but Allan thought that to be rather absurd. The doctor complained that the coolies were suffering from an unknown illness, so Allan went to check on them. They were in distress from abdomen pains, headache, dizziness and exhaustion. Allan dropped a small quantity of eye atropine solution into their eyes and in half an hour they felt normal again. It was entirely due to the glare from the snow and perhaps a little intensity from the air pressure. Allan thought it rather absurd that the doctor didn't realize this, but perhaps it was just that he was over concerned about health and didn't conceive the obvious.

Before breakfast, Alexis made a concoction consisting of piptopporus betulinus, which was to prevent trichuris trichiura or whipworm (as the volatile oils acted as a strong laxative and vermifuge, with the action of dispelling the worms and their eggs). She offered it to her comrades, and although it wasn't the tropical flavor of the month, they humbly obliged to test it.

The strangest of phenomena affects the body and mind at higher altitudes. The combinations of temperature and pressure variations happen to incite how one behaves in the open air of such lofty heights. One such instance with the Doctor is worthy of note.

Allan went onwards to scout the site for camp six, which from binoculars looked quite favorable from his perspective. His friend and most reliable companion, Oscar, and six coolies accompanied them with amiable supplies on the trek as he left Doctor Traverny behind and in command. It was a formidable climb. Upon scaling a large buff, the final route became smooth hiking towards what could be summed as certain success. As expected, the site was a broad level plateau, perfect in every way to set the next camp for those who would later follow. It was the ultimate Tiphareth of a camp. Allan also associated it with the Ruach, faculty of the mind and the world of Yetzirah, as the Son within the Sun. It was approximately two thousand feet about the glacier and altogether safe to set up the final comforts before the ultimate climb.

There was enough time for Allan to return and lead the team to the plateau, so he remarked to the coolies to stay put and not to leave for any reason. Oscar agreed to remain as well since there was no reason for him to accompany and besides Allan was more then adept to the minor challenge of returning. When he arrived to the lower camp, everyone was gone. He followed the tracks, which began where his led up the side of the glacier but then veered off to the elevated portion of the massive ice sheet. He finally caught up with the team who had already pitched tents and were prepared to settle in for the night. When confronting the doctor, whom he left in charge, the Doctor replied that he heard from a coolie that Allan had broken a leg on a moraine and so he made the sullied decision to move further and finally set up camp on bare ice. Perhaps it was one of Alexis's potions or perhaps something more serious, but the Doctor made decisions that lacked simple common sense. First of all, it was antecedently improbable that Allan broke a leg on the route he took and secondly, if he had, why didn't the Doctor send anyone in aid? It was too late in the day to pack up and leave. Oscar and the coolies would have to wait the night out on the higher plateau. Allan shook his head in contempt of the moronic imbecility of Traverny's poor judgement and settled in with the team.

Silence befell the dark frozen mountain as the particles of human flesh tinctured to begin refurbishing their wearied souls for the following day. Everyone was quietly asleep as the howling of winds rampantly pivoted around the shriek corners of precipice overhanging on the rocky mass above the glacier. The scant light of the moon bellowed atop their tents as Allan opened his eyes with a growing alarm projecting from his brow. A thunderous roar escalated from above. Quickly he got up and threw on some clothing while bellowing aloud to alert the others. There may have been no concern for alarm, but one learns to trust the jarring sensation that swirls spirally up the spine with utter impressions of being unsettled.

The noise of everybody getting up and putting on clothing increased as Allan stepped outside of the tent. Suddenly a gush of snow fell over the precipice that hung above them. Mystified with a tinge of terror, everyone stuck their faces outside and saw Allan pulling the tent out of the ice while demanding in a low voice for them to hurry up.

"Don't make any sudden loud noises. Grab everything you need quickly and get over against the wall immediately," Allan admonished.

Everybody except for Markus headed abruptly to the wall, hugging to it devoutly for protection. Allan ran back to Markus and assisted in bringing his hoard of proclaimed necessities to shelter. The team maintained supreme quietness under the ledge. A burst of snow flowed rampantly down past them as Allan hauled Markus over it and ran incessantly to a final leap in the air, hurling towards the others in the nick of time. All of his things remained to the rear as an avalanche ploughed down behind the initial burst. Tons of icy snow swept across the area where their tents had been comfortably resting five minutes previous. Thankful for the wall to provide sudden refuge, the team began digging through the top portions of snow to make their way out into the open night.

"My things! What I am going to do now?" Markus said with a distraught tone.

"You should have been a lot faster, Markus. It's a good thing Allan saved your butt!" Angeline replied while digging.

"Will everyone help me dig in and retrieve my belongings?" he asked.

"Through thirty feet of ice and packed snow? You must be kidding, lad!" The doctor rebutted with a displaced simper.

"The porters can help. I will pay them extra. They got nothing better to do anyway," Markus blighted in frustration.

Allan shook his head. "I must administer that the coolies have to carry equipment to the next few camps. Markus, I firmly doubt that a few days digging through the snow here will be sufficient to retrieve your belongings. Unfortunate things do happen and we have enough supplies to provide you with the requirements of making the summit. Now, if you would not be so oblivious as to not realize that, we shall press on."

"Fine, I will just leave everything there. You're the boss," Markus wailed while digging through the hindmost crest of snow.

Finally they were all out and atop the avalanche that previously fell before them. Allan scratched his head momentarily and looked through Markus, trying to figure out his innate sense of proclaiming to be the "all-important" one. Although he had a moot point about his belongings, he obviously suffered from a common illness of subconscious irritation. The Hindus call it Ahamkara, which may best be described as a basic disorder of the ego-making faculty.

Some of the tent loops were ripped apart in the frenzy, but otherwise quite functional. Everyone pitched the tents once again, this time further away from the disastrous area and nearer to the wall. Four hours sleep was still better than nothing, and the warmth of rest was dearly welcomed.

The shiny escapade of glimmering sunlight against the tent walls drew everyone out of their sleeping comforts at nine in the morning. Once again Alexis made a special breakfast drink consisting of psyllium, black walnut hulls, hibiscus flowers, licorice root and other herbs that helped to develop stamina and cleared all the internal organs of parasites living off the limited vitamins they had for consumption. She offered a hot cup of the mixture to Allan, who gratefully accepted with a squint of his eyes to illustrate a comical uncertainty of consuming her antidote. He admitted it was rather tasteful after which the others attempted it and spat the first portion out.

"Tasteful?" yipped Traverny, "I thought you said it was tasteful?"

"That is what I said. I didn't say it was a good taste but rather that it was full of some taste," Allan answered with a short laugh.

Allan provided Markus with a spare backpack and everyone pitched in from their clothing and gave him some items. Angeline offered him a vest and sweater, Traverny gave some pants and flannel underclothing, and Alexis surprisingly gave him a poshtin, or coat lined with sheep skin, that she purchased on her way up to Darjeeling. "This is not exactly my style, but it will do for now," Markus ungratefully accepted.

After breakfast they hiked across the glacier edge and upwards towards the snow platform that provided better footholds. Each member hauled firmly on the rope spaced well apart with their handholds as it guided them to the apex of the crest that was solidified into the mountain.

Several hours later they had reached the bottom of a pinnacle, which they would have to climb with ropes and crampons. The ropes were already in place from the previous day when Oscar and Allan scaled the two hundred feet of ascent and hooked them into place.

Allan was the first to scale upwards, followed by Angeline. On the adjacent rope Traverny began to haul himself up while Markus was not far behind. The scarcity of oxygen required tremendous effort to pull weight and dig in with ice picks. Fortunately the crampons dug snuggly into the icy side allowing them to additionally maneuver gradually to the top.

Allan hoisted baggage from below after the porters secured it piece by piece on the rope. Alexis and Traverny assisted in the pulling up of each rope as Markus took off his backpack and placed it on the ground, allowing himself to rest while the others worked through the adverse conditions.

"Alexis, I was thinking of going back to Switzerland in a few months. Maybe we can meet up and do some mountaineering there, what do you say?" Markus asked while stretching his body into the air.

"One thing at a time Markus, that is all I can think about right now." Alexis huffed.

"Du siehst erschöpft aus, kann ich Dir helfen?" Markus finally realized she was over-exerting.

"How about taking over here for me and pulling up this crate?" Alexis requested with a look of anguish.

"I can manage that," he avowed while pushing her lightly aside and taking control of the rope.

"Easy, Markus, don't ram the crate into the ice as you pull it. There are breakables in there," Angeline scorned.

"Yeah, yeah, it is ok now," Markus moaned back to her as his hand slipped on the rope causing the crate to fling against the wall. It startled him with a sudden jolt as the rope then tugged him to the ground, causing him to slacken and finally release it through the sudden shock. The crate plunged quickly down on top of the coolie that had no chance to move from its devastating velocity. His partner yelled vehemently as he quickly pulled the broken crate off of his crushed relative.

"Bright move, Mr. Confidence!" Angeline yelled in disgust.

Allan and the doctor quickly scaled down to the unconscious coolie. They could not get a pulse from the man. The doctor tried everything in his power to revive him but to no success. Allan looked up to the others and shook his head.

Alexis fell to the ground in mournful sorrow. "Das hast Du nun davon!"

"What's the problem? It was just a porter!" Markus fussed in her face.

"How can anybody be such an idiot as yourself? How in hell did you get on this journey anyway?" Angeline snarled back into his face, standing right in front of him.

"Nobody calls me an idiot! That was just an accident. Do you think I meant to kill the poor bugger?" Markus scorned back at her.

"I'm sure you don't mean to do a lot of things, Markus. By now I bet your parents didn't either." Angeline fretted in adamant disgust.

"If that is some kind of American humor, it doesn't sound very comical!" Markus yelled back in her face.

"Both of you please shut up. It sounds like a migraine wanting to burst when I listen to both of you yap like that," Alexis said with her hands darting up and pointing at their faces.

"We are going to have a ceremony for Habib. Everybody must come down. His cousin says that it will be fine if we bury him with respect in the snow over there," The doctor yelled up to the disgruntled team.

Packed in several feet of snow, Allan made a commemorative cairn for the unfortunate and tragic death of Habib. He was put to rest fifty yards from where he met with his untimely end. Angeline wished to express her sentiments in the form of a poem, which she had written the night previous before the sudden avalanche almost took everyone's life. Allan translated the message to Habib's cousin who appreciated the sincere consideration. Everyone bowed heads in memoriam before Angeline began with a pliant voice that echoed softly across the precipice.

> "High on the mountains they lurk
> Forsaken in the midst of danger
> Gods and Angels who watch over
> The sacred moves of everyone
> Sending rays of healing energy
> For motions made and conceived
> Swiftly through their silence
> They move without notice
> Around ever pinnacle
> And are seen by the seeing
> In the slightest light streams to harvest continued existence."

"That was very beautiful Angeline. I wondered what you were writing last night," Alexis whispered as she was touched by the words.

"May your soul rest safely and peacefully and may the Almighty find you," Traverny voiced while looking down at the ice and snow covered burial. Markus stood off to the side, not wanting to be noticed as he slowly suffocated in shameless self-centeredness.

The group packed what little they could salvage from the broken crate into large duffel bags.

"Markus, you are going to help the coolie carry this to the next location. If I see so much as the quiver of your lip for the rest of this mission it will be the last time you will ever move it. Is that clear?" Allan said sternly at the babbling fool.

"Just get me to the top of this mountain. That is all I am here for," Markus said as he kicked the duffel close to the rope.

"Let us make it back up, this time without accidents," Allan said as they once again hooked on for the climb.

Two hours later they safely arrived to the location of tents established as camp six on the plateau. The camp elevation was approximately eighteen thousand feet. The coolies came out of the tents as they heard the others huffing their way closer. Allan dropped his baggage and went back to assist the others. They finally all arrived and fell to the snow in exhaustion to regain some strength. Allan asked the coolie that came out from a tent where Oscar had disappeared. The coolie remarked that he had found an estuary behind the cliff to which they pointed and hooked a rope traverse to swing over to it. Allan thought it sounded splendid and grabbed a small bag and some rope and headed towards the indicated direction.

"Remarkable! Did you have a nose for that old man?" Allan yelled to his friend who was delightfully bathing in hot springs that emanated from a crevice within the mountain.

"There was a subtle calling. What took you so long?" Oscar shouted back.

"Long is correct. That describes the story of bringing inept slumber jocks into the territory of the gods. Be right there," Allan voiced as he began to swing across the ropes that Oscar had hooked and gouged into the mountainside.

"This must be the cleanest water I have ever seen and felt," Allan remarked as he stepped foot into the welcoming treat.

"It won't be after you wash in it. Good Lord man, have you been digging igloos all day?" Oscar asked as the unpleasant odor soiled its way through the air.

"We lost Habib today. It was an unfortunate accident of a crate falling upon him at the ledge we knotted into yesterday."

"Damn, that is rightfully sad. He was a splendid man and gifted with true spirit," Oscar grieved.

"For some illogical reason, Traverny moved the last camp over to an ice sheet yesterday. What happens overnight but an avalanche tumbles down over the site, minutes before everyone was alerted to move out," Allan summarized.

"Next time I would leave Alexis in charge, or even Angeline. Both seem to keep their faculties in order," Oscar remarked to his friend.

"Regret is a strange thing. But the lesson has been learnt and I've come to the exact conclusion." Allan determined as they bathed beyond the joys of comfort high on a pinnacle of Kangchenjunga.

A late meal ended with entertainment of song as the mysterious appearance of several small birds flew into the area and chirped while they scoured for leftovers. Alexis was all too pleased to provide them with crumpled crackers and bits of biscuits for the joyous entourage of frolicking melody.

Angeline was in positive spirit as she sat on a large boulder conversing with Oscar about an intrepid incident that he underwent on the Boltoro glacier during the foregoing year. A massive ice sheath slid off a snow jutty and pushed him and his companion over a ridge. Luckily they were tied by rope which was anchored in the mountainside above them otherwise they would have both fell to a final peril. The incident culminated when another ice sheet broke loose and Oscar was forced to cut himself from the rope and plunge in order to save the life of his friend. The fortunate episode of it all was that he landed a grasp on the side of a ledge on his way down. It bulked out three feet and was only a twenty foot drop but due to his incessant mountaineering formula he saved not only one life but his own as well. He purposefully always insinuated that proper measures invariably reduce the risk of accident to nothing.

Markus appeared rather terminal and scurried towards Traverny asking if he had anything to relieve shin splints then added that he felt woozy from the long day. Fortunately the doctor carried liniment oil and was able to assist in nursing the invalid back into comfort.

Early on the following morning, Allan led part of the team through a passage towards another pinnacle.

Traverny, Markus and five porters remained behind. The clear sky held excellent prospects to make another few thousand feet of ascent. Camp five became easily accessible and Allan decided it to be the last and highest camp that the coolies would ascend. He sent two of them back to notify Traverny to come up on the following morning and not before.

Some hours had passed and the blaring of people yelling was heard over the distant range. Oscar shrieked that the fools had made the dreadful mistake of coming onwards that same day. The clamoring soon followed by the reverberating sound of a driving snowcap tumbling down the mound. The coolies went outside to see if they could sight anything resembling danger.

"It sounds like the mutinous violation of orders once again," Allan remarked to Oscar.

"When a man loses his mind on a mountain, he savagely loses it completely," Oscar interjected as they stepped outside.

The two men gathered some gear and began to hike back in aid of what they feared may have happened. An hour later over a hanging cliff they spotted a body in physical distress, which was waving arms in the air and half-stuck in the snow. They scaled down the rocky vertical that had several icy patches and made their way to the screaming soul. It was Markus, bearing frantic cries in a plea for help. Quickly they dug him out from the jetting ice while he pointed to parts in the snow where he believed others to be buried. Oscar went to dig quickly and to great fortune recovered two coolies that were still breathing. Markus suffered bruised ribs and some minor cuts and gave his account of the incident.

"We were securely roped together using handholds to overcome the embankment. Suddenly the Doctor turned and began yelling at the coolie on the end. He wanted him to hurry up and stay close with the team. The next thing that happened was a noise in the snow from above. The Doctor yelled to unleash from the rope and head for cover but it was too late. The snow cavorted over the ledge followed by an avalanche. We were tied like worms on a hook, no place to go," Markus cried in terror of almost losing his life.

"Did he not receive word that he was to remain at camp five until tomorrow?" Allan asked.

"Yes, I was there when the porters came and told him. An hour after that he decided that it was a great day to move ahead and surprise you by being early," Markus replied.

"Yeah, surprise, ok. There are two reasons not to climb on snow peaks in the afternoon. One is that the intense glare of the sun can cause human error and fatal mistakes. The other is that the heat from that great sun can weaken holds, cause snow to flow and an avalanche to suddenly occur," Allan concluded as he went to help in the digging to locate other people. They soon found two coolies and finally Doctor Traverny, but it was too late. They were likely knocked unconscious from the pressure that buried them. Oscar went up to camp five to retrieve the others so that they could pay last respects to the three men that lost their lives.

Later in the evening Alexis asked Allan if there was any way that the incident could have been prevented. He believed that the inexplicable imbecility of disobeying safety orders was the direct cause but furthermore added that the men clung together too close on the rope and didn't allow for proper spacing. This likely resulted in one tumbling after another, bringing them all under the pressure of loosing control in the slide. A similar case was reported, he added, from an Everest expedition in the previous year. Having the freedom of space however, one can run, plunge, and dart over a reasonable amount of moving snow but being hooked like popcorn on a thread for a Yule tree didn't provide much hope.

That evening the harsh mountainous wind gave a wicked howl as if to say thank you for sacrificing life upon its sacred peak. Not surprisingly, Allan attributed camp five to slight disaster with it being attributed to Geburah on the tree of life. Associated with that sphere are severity, power and war. Disobeying lawful orders and refuting with disdain struggle were some of the key factors in the day's hapless results.

Camp four was established the following day at twenty-one thousand and afforded an excellent natural shelter with overhanging rock. Pauhunri Peak at 23,180 feet was a treacherous climb but had been reached with vigilant indemnity. The fourth sphere on the tree of life is Chesed and belongs to Jupiter. It is a higher ideality of love, containing mercy as a grace and with that the day ended in an exhausting acceptance of accomplishment.

With the exception of a few frivolities from Markus, the Jongsong Peak at 24,518 feet was reached on the following noon, marking camp three. The sphere of Binah is the third ideality of the tree of life. It represents the Supernal Mother of all Understanding in the most austere spiritual sense. With understanding inevitably comes sorrow, which is also akin to that all-encompassing and eminent virtue.

Although everybody, with the exception of one, felt ease and comfort in the presence of Allan and Oscar, there was always an edge of alertness taking hold with the summit climb soon to arrive. Markus felt as though his confidence had been betrayed. He deemed himself as scorned upon and that the others did not understand him for the respected person he was considered back in his neighborhood. Eagerly he wanted to regain the confidence and the only way he conjectured to achieve it was to save someone's life that held esteem in the eyes of others. Everybody was in a state of rest and otherwise asleep as he slipped outside of the tent and began meddling with some of the rigging, pretending to be checking it for damage. He slouched down on his knees and took hold of Angeline's climbing rope. He dug through to the center with his knife and began disseminating some of the interior strands of cord. Surely he would keep an eye on her during the next climb and when the rope would let go, he would be there to save her, perhaps.

Camp two would be a dream achievement for the early risers. They were so close to the top of the world with breath-taking anticipation as they fervently hiked along the ridge. The opulent view of lower mountain crests was an acknowledgement of their prosperity. The sensation of having opened the gates of a spiritual sanctuary and stepped inside to have the essence circumnavigate throughout girders that wove the soul together would not be unlike how the climbers began to feel. It is a sensation beyond words, touched beyond feelings and breathless beyond imagination. The experience of near attainment is something truly to behold. Just over 26,000 feet a dire decision had to be rendered. They could climb across an ice wall and then up a hundred and eighty feet of slippery frozen rock impediment that jetted off the edge or else slowly maneuver around it to the left on the skimpiest of imaginable ledges, with uncertainty of what lay beyond it. Clearly the climb was the safer of the two, for although either would be a thousand feet of a fall, the climb held some assurance of what to deal with to prevent tragedy. Alexis was eager to be the first and wanted to provide some step cutting so the others would have a virtual staircase to ease their footing. Oscar scaled upwards, twenty feet to the right of her and clinched in some grappling hooks for an extra measure. The morning sunlight gave glory to the inspired hearts of the active team, as though they appeared to be miniature gods zestfully indulging in the finer art of willed accomplishment. They all made it safely! One phase closer and significantly higher.

Every turn in life seems to carry a blind spot, unknown until it unexpectedly arrives. Such was the case upon reaching the next ledge. The only feasible way to the top was from the side since a heap of fragile ice overhung the upper mantle making it unreliable to ascend. The downfall was simply that the traverse would be a disastrous drop at such a lofty height. The only safe way up was to go across, frightfully challenging as it appeared.

Regardless of the abhorrent challenge, Allan and Oscar took it upon themselves to begin the procedure and placed ice hooks securely along the way. Angeline provided them with her rope to use as an extra measure of security. To Alexis, it looked like clockwork, professionally and skillfully manipulated to the last step. Three ropes were in place, Allan and Oscar were near the top, and Alexis had stepped out to begin the dangerous traverse. It may only have been eleven hundred feet to the rocky surface below from their ropes, but it would not take that much of a fall to slip out of the world for a lifetime. Alexis made it across and then grabbed Angeline's rope that was tied in place to maneuver to the next line and then upwards. Superb to the last clench, she skillfully arrived at the top with apparent ease. Angeline proceeded next as Markus stood back feeling a little unnerved. Out on less than a limb, she breathlessly carried her weight across the jagged ice wall, kicking in her boot crampons for greater grip and reaching precariously for the next rope to provide meager protection. She grabbed onto her rope, kicked the wall and swung briefly to the subsequent clasp where she was able to make the final reach. Finally, she was scaling with aid of the final rope up to meet with the gallant crew.

Markus breathed deeply with self-assurance. Angeline's rope certainly held her weight, but with the available footings already in place, he may even be able to avoid using it. Everyone watched with determination to see him make the climb and transform into a growing gentleman. With impunity he met with each clasp and was on his way. The dazzling light flickered off his crampons as they snuggled into the available crannies with which the others had obliged him. He reached for the first rope and wailed over to the next position. Smooth as chalk on a frozen hand, he nestled into the ice, fashioning his next foothold. His over-exertion of force on the next clasp dislodged a fraction of the ice, weakening its holding power into the wall. Totally unwarranted, a clasp expunged from the wall, leaving him awed in momentary suspension.

"Grab the rope, Markus! It's right there!" Alexis yelled with instilling confidence.

He looked up for a moment, and then at Angeline's rope which was three feet to his right. Options were voided and the chance was split-second, otherwise he would fall. Ardently he reached for it and used it to swing across as the others had done. The last strand of cord snapped as his feet touched the wall, two inches from a grappling hook. All heads bluntly flashed forward as Markus yelled to the mountain god on his way down. Shocked with dismay, they watched his last minute of life dash through the chilling air plummeting to the rock edge below. It thumped with a transitory bounce and hurled over the next ridge, disappearing out of sight.

The others were outrageously shocked. Angeline pulled up the top portion of her rope, which was still intact.

"How did my rope break in two? It wasn't scratching against the ice at any point!" She exclaimed to her comrades.

Allan looked at it carefully and then passed it to Oscar.

"See these finely cut, outer edges? They are all neatly cut as though trimmed off with a knife. How would one best explain that?" Oscar vented.

"We all used it, without hesitation." Alexis said as she looked into everybody's face.

"Markus seemed hesitant down there," Angeline acknowledged to her trusted partners.

Alexis fumed as she realized the truth, the relentless disorder that had gripped Markus into doing such a foul and undermining scheme. "Das geschieht Dir recht! Du Verrückter...wir wollten Dir helfen!" She said with her eyes staring thousands of feet down the slope, insinuating that they all attempted to help him but in the end he got what he deserved.

In a rather bizarre way, it seemed as if Markus had reached the threshold of Binah, or Understanding in a very limited sense for a moment, and then abominably drowned by plummeting into the abyss of dissolution though an incident of fate. It was as though he had an opportunity for Understanding but deluded his ego and abandoned his spirit.

Camp two was a heavenly send. Allan conjointly connected it, on the path to the top, with the second sphere of the tree of life, being Chokmah or wisdom. Undisturbed by the outside world, it was a freak of nature as one might hypothesize, burrowed in a rock shelter, free from harm and providing a spectacular view of the world below. It was like being an eagle, complacently suspended in the sky and able to see for hundreds of miles, mountain ranges, spectacles of distant territory beyond the whims of human conception. Everything was just fine.

Night shadowed the valleys below as Oscar, Allan, Alexis and Angeline conversed expressions of intoxicated grandeur, having overcome the formidable components of the climbing ordeal. The expedition had cost the lives of five individuals. Some good, perhaps some not so good, but nonetheless five lives were sacrificed to the five sacred peaks of Kangchenjunga that spring. Fathoming the hardships and pitfalls of life can be a devastating experience when there is nothing to fulfill the empty spaces of desire. That is partial to true understanding, that without the pain of having known suffering, the experience was otherwise only imagined. Suffering is not something ordinarily invited into life or welcomed but through reality it exists as a balance to utter joy. Having attained to the camp of wisdom, only a fool wouldn't press onwards to reach the summit and be that much closer to god. Then again, four fools awoke in the primordial morning hours of darkness and packed appropriately to ravage the final two thousand feet of potential terror.

The rugged hike was totally exasperating. Angeline was over fatigued from the altitude and slipped on a ridge.

She began tumbling down with increasing speed but was halted as Allan jumped from a rock when she passed him and hurled his body desperately upon hers. She only fell twenty feet and fortunately only sprained her ankle on the way down. They could see the top; the summit reached out to them and solicited them onwards. After ice picking his way to the top of an incline, Oscar let down a rope for the others to grab onto and be hauled up.

Beyond joy, beyond anticipation, beyond anything describable, every ounce of will was sanctioned into hauling their bodies up a treacherous ice formation. Pick axe driven in, hand over hand, scantly receiving any oxygen, pressure banging against their temples; incessantly they squeezed every morsel of energy through their bodies; driven by a force higher than any recognized in normal living conditions. Hearts were pounding to exit their chests as they gripped their axes persistently step after step. Eight hundred feet to go.

Surging group power united them as the team expanded their mediocre energies into unlimited kinetic flowing dynamism. When one runs a certain distance a second wind is achieved and suddenly distance and speed are dramatically increased. They surpassed that stage several days previous. They unleashed a combined burst of mystical exploit and were driven glissading like madmen out of control yet beyond the explanation of control into a consciousness of having already achieved that which was less than a hundred feet away. There was no telling how quickly they scaled the final approach or if they actually did, as they were simply there.

What words can possibly describe there, here, now, all, everywhere, simultaneous and it? What pray tell could feelings reveal of encompassing the soul in the hands of God? What in any sense can reflect the incidence of perfection beyond human apprehension? It wasn't a mountain that they had defeated but the ten sacred peaks within their consciousness; the ten spheres of realization that awaken the perpetual inclination of existence.

It was neither cold nor warm. There was no wind but a subtle whisper from beyond. Eight eyes looked around at the vastness of the horizon. Angeline fell to her knees and embraced the rapture she witnessed from the sky. Oscar stared deeply into the end, which was the beginning. Alexis opened her arms and held the all that fell quietly and serenely into her palms. Allan, for some strange reason undressed and ran quickly along the summit and hurled himself into the air, somersaulting as he flew, and landed at the edge of an ice pack with his hands outstretched into the sky. A foot further and he would've descended thousands of feet into the depths. Nobody said a word. They all knew that he did it by the sheer virtue that he could do it. That's why they all do it and that is what they took back with them. Returning to a familiar world, taking the experience of experiences, the knowledge of attainment that would live with them for the rest of their lives. Knowing that there is good and  there is evil, knowing that there is sacredness in all, and living for the purpose of living, holding always in a precious corner of their heart, that beyond all else, there is the bliss of the Divine.

Hail Kether! ★

ISLAND MAGICIAN

"A real Magical Oath cannot be broken: you may think it can, but it can't.
This is the advantage of a real Magical Oath."

Aleister Crowley- Magick

The alarm clock went off at exactly six am, as it did every morning. It was not a normal alarm clock however. It was a German shepherd named Hero, who sniveled every morning at the same time to let his master know it was time to begin another day. Samuel felt well rested as he sat up in his bed and stretched; then turning to his loyal pet he asserted in casual German language,

"Guten morgan Hero! Noch einen Tag voll Sonnenschein, mein Freund!" he said as his feet touched the floor, "Another day of sunshine my friend!"

Samuel leapt out of the bedroom and headed straight for his backpack. He stuffed some fruit for breakfast (and some snacks for Hero), and then scrounged around for some clothes. After filling the water bag, Samuel was ready for a little hike along his revered path. "Let's go, Hero!" Samuel said as they left their cabin, which was nestled near the coast on Grand Canaria Island amongst beautiful palm trees.

Samuel was 38 years old and had lived in America until he turned 35. By then he had saved and invested enough money to retreat on the most revered of Spain's vacation islands. The only person he knew there was a relative named Blake. That was one of the reasons why he chose to move to the Canary Islands. Samuel was a youthful man with thick curly black hair that touched down to his upper back and had deep penetrating blue eyes. He sported a naturally lush beard, which he trimmed on Sundays. He favoured a life of simplicity; without ownership of a vehicle or any other items of luxury. He primarily ate the vegetables and fruit that grew on the land behind his home. He was also well respected by the people in the area for being friendly and helpful to everyone that socialized with him.

As he did every morning, Samuel stopped along his route to visit the Spectrum Café. He smiled to the waitress as he entered, heading straight for his usual table. The waitress returned the smile as she approached Samuel with a jug of orange juice in her hands. As she prepared to pour, Samuel remarked, "Stars twinkle in everyone's eyes, Sharon; it is the light of the soul."

"I suppose they do," Sharon sighed, "but sometimes all we see are clouds." She filled Samuel's glass, then walked near the window to look down at the seashore. "It's another sunshiny day, and not much to complain about. What are your big plans, Sam?"

"Well dear, Hero and I have to juggle a few things around. First, we are going up to High Ridge for a hike, and since I am going out on the seas fishing with Blake at noon, meeting Juanita will have to wait until tomorrow. She wants a card reading done." Sam paused to sip his juice. "She said it was some urgent thing happening in her life and wanted it done this afternoon but sent Michael over last night to tell me that she can't make it and will be around tomorrow for one. That tree fort for Michael will be made this evening and finally to top it all off, my garden needs some attention. People have the gall to say that this is a boring island," Samuel snickered. "Are you sorry you asked about my schedule, dear?"

"Oh, I've never complained of boredom here," Sharon responded, "In fact, things always happen when people least expect them to. That's what makes Grand Canaria so unique, so flourishing and attracts tourists like it does."

"Yes and I am glad it is quieter on this end of the Island, Sharon. Most of the tourists that come up from Playa Del Inglis just stop for a snack and move on, taking pictures as they go."

Sharon nodded. "Hey, here comes Mrs. Robinson," she smiled while gesturing towards the open window.

"Here's to you Mrs. Robinson, and here's to the world for another day," Samuel declared as he lifted his orange juice and drained it. Grabbing his walking stick, he stood up and said, "Let's be on our way Hero, the day is ahead. Have a pleasant day, Sharon!"

"Same to you, Sam!" Sharon waved as Sam left the café.

Samuel greeted Mrs. Robinson as she meandered up the path. "Good morning to you, Ma'am," he politely remarked.

Mrs. Robinson's face broke into a warm grin. "Hello, Sam. Good news! My chest pains are gone away now. Those breathing and stretching exercises you showed me have done miracles. They give me more life and have made me feel a lot healthier lately. Thank you so much again," she praised while patting his shoulder.

"That is just great. Glad to be of assistance there Mrs. Robinson," he rejoiced while moving onwards with his canine companion.

The path up to High Ridge was winding and dry. Part of Samuel's trek involved walking up a road that was frequented by tourists going on safaris into the island's badlands. Samuel often encountered jeeps on the hill, packed with European tourists taking photos and video of their excursions. He seldom said a word when he encountered the tourists, except to exchange smiles as they drove by the narrow, dusty road.

"Hero, ist Dir heiß? Willst Du etwas wasser haben?" Samuel spoke in his limited German vocabulary to his panting shepherd on the trail. Slowing down, he pulled a plastic bowl and a bag of water from his backpack. He then opened the bag and poured water for Hero to drink. The dog quickly licked up the liquid as Samuel looked around solemnly in the humid air. The reflecting silvery particles in the air brought vitality into his etheric body and rejuvenated his inner energies. He sensed a peaceful feeling in the atmosphere but as he turned north he felt something rather drawl in the air. It was like a hue of smoke deep within the air particles expressing an abysmal sorrow. Hero looked up in the same direction simultaneously as Samuel's eyes widened in complete understanding. Suddenly, he stooped to grab the bowl and yelled, "Hero komm!"

The master and his dog ran to the top of the hill and gazed over the edge. Tire markings and dismembered soil ranged down the slope towards an overturned jeep that lay crashed against a large tree. Sure as a mountain goat, Samuel scurried down the 200-meter ridge to the accident. Hero passed him midway and made it to the scene first.

Samuel surveyed the victims. He counted seven prone bodies, all of which appeared to be severely injured. As Samuel knelt down to closely examine the wounded, a voice wheezed for help from under the crash bar. Samuel looked around for a large branch and found a broken tree lying nearby. He hauled it over and wedged it under the crash bar. With tremendous effort, he managed to pry the jeep up enough to haul the casualty out. "You're safe now," Samuel told the wounded man, "But we're going to need some more help." Samuel quickly pulled off his waist pouch and wrote a note explaining the accident, which he closed with a remark 'send medical help immediately'. Samuel then wrapped the pouch and note around Hero's neck. "Hero, hol Sharon und lauft zum Café ! Schnell !" he yelled as the attentive dog took off up the ridge as quickly as it soared down.

Samuel placed all of the patients in a more comforting position and began administering first aid. Only four of the seven were conscious, but he managed to get a pulse from the others. Samuel broke some branches from a nearby tree to splint a girl's leg. The bone was protruding a few inches below her knee and he knew that she could not be moved unless most of her body was made immobilized. He then tended to the less serious, conscious casualties and began cleaning their wounds with his bag of drinking water.

"We just fell." An agonized voice whispered from his side. "Just went off the cliff, ground was weak, jeep went down." The suffering tourist voiced.

"It is okay," Samuel responded, "Try to relax." Samuel placed a comforting hand on the young man's shoulder. "Everyone seems fine and we'll be out of here soon."

Hero arrived at the Café and barked at the door. Sharon walked to the door after setting a coffee down to a regular customer. "Hey, Hero, what are you doing here?" she said while opening the door. She saw the pouch strapped to Hero's neck and opened it. She took the note from the pouch and gasped audibly after reading it. In shock, she rushed to the telephone after explaining to the customer, Mr. Jacobs what had happened. He abruptly agreed to accompany her as extra assistance.

The scene was a disaster, but fortunately the jeep hadn't crushed anyone when it rolled down the embankment. Samuel could see the distress and suffering in the victim's faces, from their multiple injuries. He gently waved his hands across everyone's body slowly, sending radiant energy through them. Currents of power shimmered from his hands as he slowly passed them over inflicted areas in concentrated efforts to sooth the casualties.

A Land Rover pulled up at the top of the ridge. Samuel paused to look up and breathed a sigh of relief as Sharon got out with Mr. Jacobs and Hero. They brought a stretcher down the hill with a first aid kit, some sheets and jugs of water.

"Never seen anything like this before," Sharon whispered.

"It happens every few minutes somewhere in the world." Samuel replied grimly. Gesturing to one of the unconscious people, he added, "Try to dress her arm and leg wounds, and I will bandage this young man over here."

Mr. Jacobs looked at the young girl, outstretched in abstruse agony. Placing a hand on Sharon's shoulder, he said, "I will tend to her, my dear. I was a doctor's assistant years ago, and I can tell that this lady needs special attention. You go check on the young man over by that tree."

"Alright, that sounds good," she said in panic as she rushed over to another agonized and bleeding casualty.

Samuel was bandaging up a young man from the other side of the jeep and glanced around quickly. He noticed Mr. Jacobs whispering some words to the young girl but couldn't figure out what they were. He was more concerned with saving the young man's life in front of him.

Within half an hour the sound of a helicopter could be heard approaching. It circled the ridge above them and landed on the road near Sharon's jeep. It was quickly followed by another one, which landed beside the first. Medics from each helicopter made their way to the scene, all carrying pharmaceutical supplies. Samuel explained the extent of injuries which he treated and stood back while four medical assistants prepared the injured for transportation.

After what seemed like an eternity, one of the medics voiced, "We're ready down here" on a handheld radio to the pilot. The helicopter started up and lifted over the edge of the ridge, then lowered to a height where it could release a stretcher to the accident area. One by one, casualties were hoisted to the Medevac chopper. It raised four victims and two medical workers, and then proceeded across the valley. The other helicopter appeared next and lifted the remaining casualties.

As the helicopters whipped over the distant canyon and vanished behind distant trees, Sharon walked up the ridge with Samuel and Mr. Jacobs. "That young guy looked very roughed up, do you think he will make it?" Sharon asked.

"I believe so, they will all make it." Samuel anticipated in relief.

Mr. Jacobs nodded to himself. Wiping his brow, he asked. "Do you want a drive back to the café, Sam?"

"Yes, please." Hero jumped up on Samuel excitedly. Samuel patted Hero and told him what a good dog he was. "We're to meet Blake at the boat in half an hour."

Walking down the pier, Samuel waved to the old skipper who was stacking boxes on the fishing vessel.

"Hey, Sam! Should be a good day out there!" Blake yelled.

"Aye, that it should be!" responded the magician as he boarded with Hero to assist his twenty-five year old lifetime friend.

The vessel eased its way from the dock and towards the open sea. Sun shined across its side and glimmered off the name printed at the bow: 'Titanic's Widow'. The long dark hair and beard on Blake waved in the wind as Samuel looked out at the shimmering sea and whistling winds.

"The sounds of those winds are really something else. It's like they have a voice." Blake said.

"They do have a voice, the voice of nature." Samuel replied.

"I suppose that is correct, but what are they saying?" Blake queried.

"They carry vibrations in the air," Samuel explained. "Sounds that are made from everything in existence travel in the air, and are carried with the winds. On the land the winds are filled with more of those vibrations since they are always bombarded from one object to another, one person to the next, and contain a multiple of vibration levels. On the seas they are free to roam, free of most obstacles and thoughts." Breathing deeply, he added, "The sea winds are more peaceful."

"That actually makes some sense." Blake shut off the motor and dropped anchor. "So besides just having a good time on the water, people experience a sense of peace in the air?"

"Maybe that's why people want to be near water as well, whether to live or relax near beaches. The air isn't contaminated with pollution of every imaginable variety. The vibrations in the air are less to contend with and peace is more abundant."

"Interesting concept. Why do you think people carry a lot of problems with them these days?"

"Exactly Blake, they carry problems with them. Even though they do not realize it, they have a most difficult time to relax and to make decisions that affect each step in life. Some people cling onto old conceptions that bother them and strain their muscles with stress. You know a little bit about Egyptology, right?" Sam said as Hero raised an eyebrow while sprawled out on the deck.

Blake pulled up a deck chair and plopped onto it. "Yes, I have read a few books on the ancient culture. What's it got to do with anything?" Blake gestured for Samuel to join him.

"Well, in the first period of mankind's life cycle, it was the age of Isis, the female, and they worshipped basically for the ability to generate life, and many goddesses were renowned for their qualities that represented much of the continued life cycle, love and worshipping of the heavens. Then came an equinox of the gods, which is a change in the evolutionary process of mankind through a shift in the planetary consciousness. You see Blake, the earth has a combined consciousness, and it is alive. There has been proof and experiments done about this so basically again the combined forces around the planet come to make up a super force that sums up our civilization and the consciousness of humanity." Samuel paused to sniff the air, enjoying its wondrous scent. "Over two thousand years ago the equinox occurred and the age of Osiris transpired for a period of two thousand years. During that time man dominated the scene as worshippers of male deities and gods. Woman were shoved backwards as second rate citizens and the dawning of Christianity and Judaism came into existence along with numerous religious offspring that had sacrificial gods spawning their inspirations. Years of persecution have taken place. Each religion seems to have something negative to say about the next religion down the street. What tics my butt are the thought-forms on the mental plane that the end of the world will arrive before the second coming of Christ. What a lot of negative nonsense that amounts to. Granted, the original teachings of Jesus have their place, time and value, but have unfortunately been ever so thwarted with misconceptions. We create destiny to a certain extent and to feed negative thought forms such as the end of the world ideas and heaven being in the sky and hell in the ground just muddles peoples mental apparatus into pudding after a while."

"So what do you consider the present time to be, with all the perplexity and sociopath symptoms increasing and the burdens of stress and emotional baggage that people carry around with them?"

"Yes, I grant it there are those and many more problems out there. People cling onto old concepts because the mass media and thought form belief systems has made them almost lethargic and incapable of thinking and acting in a totally free manner. They may feel locked up in a confused state, always seeking something but never truly satiated. They may fear to venture into new ideas that involve work and self-discipline to become realized. Many people want a ready made system, something that everyone has conformed to and is a social circle to fit right in without question. There are those however who can channel at liberty in this new phase of mankind's evolution. An equinox occurred in the early 1900's in Egypt that brought about the age of Horus, the child of Isis and Osiris. He is the crowned and conquering child and thus you see through today's world people are always trying to portray some kind of statement and conquest. Wanting to be realized with the newest in fashion and futuristic glamour are part of the change for stability and partial to a conquest of material expression."

"I cannot really refute that my friend. It sounds rational and the theory is as good as any other. So this age of Horus, is there any advantage?"

"Naturally, it is a part of the planetary evolution as a whole. Women are now getting their freedom back in every sense of the word; an equality that should be worked to be realized as a balance and a focal point in relationships and in the workforce. Individual rights are considered more these days than ever before. The whole idea of personal rights however is a paradox and joke."

"Why is that?"

"Nobody in their right mind, provided there is such a concept, wants to be poisoned. Yet, in the food processing industry, in the air, water and through media there is an ongoing war regarding poisoning people in every conceivable way. Life is essentially a pure mixture of elements and vitality. Vitality is the life-force substance we obtain from good foods, however most purchased foods are filled with chemicals, pesticides and produced in such a way that over eighty percent of their vitality value has been removed. Fruits and some vegetables are the exception. Television and video games can become not only a learning tool but also a hypnotic mechanism that lures people away from being active and using time to strengthen their inner life. As long as we accept our identity inside and what we are capable of achieving it is fine. Personally, I had to work long and hard to accept myself simply for the fact that we all make mistakes and there comes a point where we learn to think twice before making them. Stepping back and being able to see the delusions and false pride that easily fester from emotional build-up can saturate the purity of vibrations and then weaken abilities. It becomes a struggle to sort out all the confusions and problems that burden us in life. To understand truth we have to peel off the layers that were trolled on like masks, which have created karma. Unfortunately, wrongdoing activates stigma into the lower ego, which is basically saying that it strengthens the false self and is what causes more chaos in an otherwise pure being. This is of course an extreme example, but in many ways it holds true for the average created problems through life."

Blake laughed. "I can relate that to many people that I know with problems. What can you do about it though, when they are so stuck on not doing anything significant to sort out their life problems, past and present?"

"We cannot directly change another persons destiny, nor should we shake them up. You have only to do your will and to become an otherwise busy body about another person is to not do your will but perhaps interfere with their gradual progression. Marcus Aurelius once said: 'No longer talk about what a good man aught to be but be one.' There is more than meets the eye in that statement."

"Then why are you telling me all these secrets today? Not that I haven't pried a bit about them." Blake grinned.

"I have not told you any secrets. This is just a simple conversation in the clean, fresh air my fisherman friend." The magician replied.

"Cast your line and best of luck trooper!" Blake replied.

"May the winds be with you." Samuel smiled, and settled back in his own chair.

Half an hour passed, and neither fisherman had caught a thing. Blake was about to comment on his luck to Samuel when he noticed that Samuel appeared to be asleep.

"Hey, your eyes are closed!" Blake said, nudging his friend.

"I'm awake, you know, " Samuel remarked, "It seems more so now than ever before. Close your eyes, Blake and tell me if you have a clear picture of the thing you last saw."

Blake blinked twice, then shrugged and closed his eyes. "OK, well I have a basic picture of it but am thinking other things as well."

"You write poetry, correct Blake?"

"Yes, and some stories from time to time."

"So you have a vivid imagination. What do you see when you close your eyes?"

"I see the ocean in front of us."

"Can you feel the breeze, taste the air, and see the water ripple for miles and miles?"

"In a small way, yes. What does this awareness of the senses have to do with anything?"

"By becoming sensitive to all within sight, hearing, tasting, smelling and touching your mind begins to balance your psychic centers and then have control over your mind and ultimately your passions that either excite you or infringe on your abilities to attain more out of life."

"I've done that before and it is kind of scary when I was at the verge of being over sensitive about everything."

"That is a fear that can be overcome. It can inhibit you from doing more and attaining further. Fear is a condition that is useful to prevent injury and to make an awareness occur about something. People have tons of fears, whether they recognize them or not. Fear is also a major limitation however and can block progress. To be fearless sounds wonderful huh?" Samuel chuckled.

"I've done a meditation once at home. I simply meditated upon a clock on the kitchen wall at my house. I closed my eyes and tried to realize where the second hand was and each minute I opened my eyes I was eight out of ten times correct at its rightful position. That was pretty exciting!" Blake smiled.

"Meditation can bring interesting results. Have you ever transferred your consciousness into an object?"

"Do you mean to become one with the object?"

"Say for instance you have a small cardboard box with a hole in it. You sit beside it and stare at it for a long time and nothing else exists but it. To you it is the universe. Then you transfer your whole consciousness to within that box."

"I see. That is a projection. Yes, I have tried that with a ball once during a meditation." Blake answered.

"Archimedes said to 'show me a point in the universe and I shall lift the world out from its hinges'. What do you suppose he meant by that?"

"Sounds like the secret into the fourth dimension."

"It sure does. To enter an objective state proportionally is to be at equilibrium. There is no subjective interference when we enter the nucleus of the matter, from the point of origin and departure at the same time, entering a timeless, and beyond space dimension."

"We are like a miniature expression of the universe," Blake grinned.

"That is correct, in a manner of speaking. Our body, mind and soul have the capability of expanding or shrinking at our will, as we focus. Also, we can become one with the greater consciousness so that we have greater ability, greater potential at work for us and can direct such powers to accomplish anything, if we are free to do so." Samuel's face became serious. "Let me ask you something. Do you know Mr. Jacobs very well?" Blake scratched his head. "He's a strange cat, keeps to himself a lot. He is kind of like a hermit but has a more sinister mystery about him. I don't know anybody that knows him very well, why do you ask?"

"This morning there was a jeep accident off of High Ridge. Jacobs was there and so were Sharon and I. He seemed rather peculiarly interested in a girl that was perhaps in her early twenties, and was tending to her wounds but leaning over her in such a way and talking into her face but I didn't hear what he was saying. It seemed rather out of the ordinary, in a sinister kind of way. Do you catch my meaning?"

"Aha! I wouldn't be surprised if he was putting some kind of spell into her, just the way he seems."

"I'm going to have Sharon drive me to the hospital tomorrow, to check on those unfortunate young folk."

"Not a bad idea," Blake began, when suddenly his fishing line began to dip and sway. "Hey! I got a bite!" Samuel's own line was bobbing as well. "Ah, and so do I!" he commented as the pair hoisted in their first catch of the day.

Samuel and Blake returned to port early that evening. Together, they had caught over a dozen fish, which they took back to Blake's place to prepare for a meal and then storage the remainder. Hero gratefully licked his chops after devouring a good portion. The friends ate well and celebrated their fine luck and fishing skills with a bottle of wine. It was nearly ten by the time Samuel excused himself to head home.

Shortly after he arrived, however, there was a knock at his door. It was Juanita.

"Good evening Juanita," Samuel smiled as he invited her in, "How are you tonight?"

Juanita shivered. "I have been feeling plagued about something. I wanted a card reading yesterday because of something happening in my life Samuel. I met a man on the mainland, near Loret de Mar, while I was visiting my dad. Anyway, he came to visit me for two days." She flung herself on the couch and curled up like a cat, continuing her lengthy gab. "He is a nice man, but something about his character is so peculiar. We begun a relationship, and I want to know if this is something that I should pursue or not. Normally I'd know inside but there's this uneasy feeling that I have. Can you tell?" she smirked.

Samuel smiled and sat down beside her. "It's fairly obvious, Juanita. Tell me, have you dreamed of this man much?"

"In fact, yes I do, every night. Ever since I returned home with some photographs of him and before he visited me. They are sometimes erotic dreams but sometimes they move me in a way that is uncomfortable. What does this mean?"

"Sometimes certain things in life have an affect on us when we are sensitive to them. Let me begin by saying that phantoms, for example, are animated forms of a departed person. There exists what are known as elementals that become consciously created through willpower. There is also what is termed larvae or larva which forms in the mental sphere around a person due to psychic or emotional excitement. The larva feed off the mental atmosphere of a person and become more condensed as the excitement is repeated. This happens with most people, whether they realize it or not."

Juanita scrunched her nose. "How does a person get rid of these larvae?"

"They disintegrate when the person pays no attention to them and eventually dissolve and vanish. I do not think this is what is plaguing you however. It seems more like a schema that is your problem. If the image of your friend looked rather sinister or struck you in a way that excited some vibrations within you then a schema could have begun, perhaps unbeknownst to him. Sometimes people are not so called evil but their physical features strike a sensitive person in a way that develops the sensations regarding their particular demeanor. This makes a person develop such schema about somebody. Also in this case, the face, the eyes and the person will usually follow the victim in their thoughts and to their dreams."

"That sounds like it Sam! My mind has picked up something about him and is bothered by it. How did you know that is my problem?"

"I can see his features around you Juanita. People that are receptive to these images can see them when they become condensed and it seems to have consumed you so much lately that his image is carried with your mental atmosphere."

"What does he look like then?" She asked.

"Dark, black hair down to his shoulders and dark piercing eyes and a very tanned body. He has a rather large roman style nose and likes to show his teeth a lot."

Juanita blanched. "Oh my god! I am getting a bit scared about this."

"The schema is playing a game with you. You must be careful to maintain your inner balance before it takes control over your actions. The other more common kind of schema is of an erotic nature that generates excitement into a person towards masturbation from imagining another person naked that they deeply desire to be with. Through this excitement the schema develops further and is also condensed and becomes part of their atmosphere. It takes power over the decisions a person makes in life and to some extent it can confuse a person. It can make them stop eating properly or regularly and develop various nervous energies. It has some potential dangers through the non-fulfillment of the sensual passions wanting to be shared. So, the feeding of incubi or succubi that act in a way not unlike a psychic vampire may take on form, around the victim."

"Sounds a bit sickening, but there is nothing wrong with a little bit of personal arousal is there?"

Samuel grinned. "Of course not. I am just letting you know the extension of it with an extreme case. People unconsciously create schema to work for them in peculiar and personal ways but it is when they are brought away from their inner and outer harmony from their desires being out of control that harm may befall them."

"Point taken into consideration. I already begin to feel better you know. I am going to focus on my work and interests for a while and see where this takes me. You are always a wealth of information and so much appreciated. You remind me of a young version of my father. I should have listened to him a lot more when I grew up." Juanita arose from the couch and proceeded to the door.

"That is quite a compliment, Juanita. Where is your father now?"

"He still lives in Barcelona. I visited him before going to Lloret de Mar, where I met Brad.

"You take care and see you again." Sam smiled as she left.

The following day Sharon and Samuel drove into the hospital parking lot to visit with each of the jeep casualties. As they pulled into a parking space, Samuel's eyes narrowed. "Sharon, see that car leaving at the other end of the parking lot? Does it look like Mr. Jacob's car to you?"

Sharon snapped her head around. "What? Oh, that car. Yes, I guess it does look like his car. Maybe he came to visit them also."

Sharon turned off the ignition and they got out. Hastily, they went to the third floor to check on everyone's condition. Samuel walked in to visit one of the girls to see how she was recovering.

"Good morning, I see your name is Crystal. Do you remember us yesterday at the accident?" he asked.

"Not really," she said sadly, "I don't remember that. Thank you for whatever you have done for us."

"Has anybody been in to visit you Crystal?"

"Nobody at all, just the doctor. I should be leaving later today." She smiled without concern.

"That is good to hear. Where are you from?"

"I am from Austria, here on vacation. I thought my vacation was over, but I am okay now!" she replied with delight.

"Alright, well it is good to see you have recovered so well and quickly. Look after yourself Crystal, and it was nice to meet you." Samuel waved and walked out of the room looking at her in a subtly suspicious manner. He met with Sharon in the hall. "How are the others doing?" he asked.

"Two had surgery and are stable. The doctor isn't certain about the condition of one guy yet. He is still quite severe. Apparently the rest of them should be leaving within a few days." Sharon shrugged. "That is what the nurse told me."

"Great, well, almost great," Samuel remarked casually.

"What about the one you visited, how is she doing?" Sharon inquired.

"She seems to have miraculously recovered and believes she will be out today as well."

"That sounds pretty good. I guess there is nothing further we can do."

"Not at this time," Samuel said darkly as they walked back to the elevator.

During the following week everything was as normal as could be amongst the village. Samuel decided to walk up to Darcy Road to see how things were around Mr. Jacob's little home. He was a little surprised to see a figure of a lady in the window, washing some dishes. He bent over on the side of the road to pick up a stick for Hero as he focused closer with astonishment, realizing that it was Crystal who was in the kitchen of Mr. Jacob's house. He went down the driveway to knock on the door and she answered.

"Crystal, what a surprise to see you. What brings you back to the Canary Islands?" He questioned.

"Excuse me, I am in the middle of some work. Have we met before?" she asked.

"Didn't you return home to Austria?"

"Like I said, I am quite busy now. Please go on with your business," she answered curtly.

"How is everything going? Is Mr. Jacobs home today?" Samuel continued insistently.

"He is out doing some errands. I shall let him know you were by to visit." Crystal stepped back and closed the door.

Samuel frowned, having his suspicions confirmed. He bent down to scratch Hero's ear and whispered,

"Well, Hero, some people just go right out of their mind. Somehow I do not think it is Crystal's mind in there any longer, my friend."

That evening, Blake stopped in to visit the part time mystic and full time magician.

"Have you run out of fish yet, my friend?" Blake asked.

Samuel paused to think, then nodded. "In fact, it is almost time for another catch. Will that be Friday's agenda?"

"It could be. It is one of the healthiest foods we can obtain these days. Remember you were asking about Mr. Jacobs last week? Well today I saw him at the store purchasing some items that a lady would use. Do you think that sixty-four year old hermit has a mysterious lover?"

"I am quite certain of it, Blake. In fact, it appears that he is into a little bit of hocus pocus."

"What exactly do you mean, my friend?"

"Have you ever heard of undines?"

"You mean elementals, like mermaids?"

"Precisely. Well, I believe it is possible that he has come into contact with an undine and used the girl who was on the brink of death to have the undine inhabit her body so that he has her carnally trapped for some purpose. It may be useful if you could let me know anything you observe out of the ordinary. We should keep an eye on this situation to see exactly what the old man is up to with this practice of detestable sorcery."

Blake nodded grimly. "Don't worry, I will let you know anything I find out. This Island has all the adventure. Whippie! Oh, so Friday at the dock, as usual?"

"As usual. See you there, mariner of the open seas!" Samuel smiled.

The following afternoon, Samuel went to town for a light lunch at the Spectrum Café.

"How is everything today, Sharon?" He asked as he entered and sat at his usual table that he called the stamtische.

"This morning a girl came in with some of her tourist friends and told me a gruesome story," she replied as she poured a glass of juice.

"What kind of story would that be?"

"She went to Morocco on a vacation last year from Holland, where she is from. Another girl accompanied her; it was one of her best friends. Well, they were walking through the market and went into separate shops and then somehow they lost one another. She said that she ran into every shop and asked around but nobody seen her friend. Then she went to the hotel and later that day to the police. They never did find her friend but the police told her that there are many cases of missing people in the area. It happens sporadically and what she found out is that there is some underground activity going on where people are drugged and they are brought to some little clinic and parts of their internal organs are removed and sold to hospitals in Europe for big money. I don't know if it is true but she was still quite shook up about loosing her best friend and not getting any answers. It lead to a lot of confusion and the family is devastated from the lack of assistance in getting answers."

"That is quite a sad story. Maybe America wasn't so bad for me to stay after all. I've heard of such things and they probably brought her body to the desert and buried it in sand or something after they removed her organs. That poor, young girl was victim to such a planned tragedy. Why do people have such a fixation on money? Money doesn't bring happiness or balance in life, but rather what is done with the money and how it was obtained." Samuel sipped angrily at his juice.

"I know what you mean. Juanita was here this morning and all in tears. Something is bothering that girl," Sharon shook her head sympathetically.

"Did she say anything?"

"Just that some girl was over to her house last night and talked about her father. She sounded very upset."

"Thank you Sharon for that information. I will talk with you later, there is somewhere I must go." Samuel replied as he left and headed to Juanita's house.

"A pleasant surprise Samuel; I do not think you ever came to visit me before. What brings you this way?" Juanita said as she welcomed him in.

"Curiosity, and a bit more my dear friend. Could you tell me if anything peculiar has happened lately?"

"Sometimes I think you are truly gifted in an inspirational way; with psychic abilities too! Last night a girl came over to ask about my father."

"What did she look like?"

"Well, she was in her early twenties perhaps, with short blonde hair and blue eyes and seemed to be quite a nice girl."

"I see. What did she talk about?"

"She said she knew my father from a long time ago. Apparently he dated her mother and her mother was going through a difficult time. Somewhere they lost contact and now she wants to write him an apology letter. She wanted his address so I gave it to her. She also said many sad things that put me in tears and I hope that her mother can meet my father once again. Ever since my mother left, my father has been distraught about a lot of things and it may do him good to meet with an old acquaintance."

Samuel's eyes widened. "Do you have your father's telephone number?"

"Yes, but she wanted to make it a reunion surprise so I didn't telephone him to say anything about it."

"I suggest you do telephone him and let him know. I do not believe her story."

"Why do you say that?"

"She is not who she appears to be. I will let you know more soon. I must go now but please warn your father that there is something going on and ask him to confide in you why something of suspicious nature would wish to haunt him. There is definitely something fishy about that girl and Mr. Jacob's. That is all I will say now and will return soon, but should you have any information, please let me know. Somebody's safety may be at stake here."

"How you come to know these realizations is really beyond me. You must be greatly gifted."

Samuel shrugged. "Rumor has it. Talk with you soon, Juanita. Blessed be."

Samuel went to visit his friend of the seas, Blake, to ask of a favor.

"This doesn't look good. It's not Friday yet!" Blake chuckled as he opened the door.

"How about a little drive up to Sarnia, my friend?" Samuel pleaded.

"Oh, sounds like a nice date," Blake grinned and batted his eyelashes. "Shall I bring some fishing gear?"

"No, just bring a fish. I want you to go to Mr. Jacobs and stay out of sight. When you see him leave, wait a while, then go to the house and tell the young lady that Mr. Jacob's is in trouble and requests her assistance immediately. Drive her to this address I am writing for you. A reliable associate of mine lives there and will take care of the situation. I will brief him as soon as I leave here. It will be an exercise in exorcism. The girl has to return to her natural environment, in the astral seas. I have to get to the bottom of why she is being used to plague Juanita and her father in Barcelona. It looks like a case of revenge, but for whatever reason is still unclear. I will telephone you tomorrow."

"Your associate, is he going to be some freaky guy or what?"

"His name is Aour, and he is a Buddhist Monk. You will find him most accompanying and pleasant. Make this work, Blake!"

"It sounds like an enjoyable mission to me. Talk with you tomorrow, uncle."

Samuel laughed. "You only call me 'uncle' when it is near your birthday and Yule time. Safe journeys."

Samuel returned to his humble abode and fed his littlest Hero. He then washed up and took a seat at his table to do a tarot reading on the matter at hand. At each corner of the room was a column, which represented the four elements and tetragrammaton as Yod Heh Vau Heh, or knowledge, courage, will and silence. Before an altar there was inscribed a pentagram on the floor, representing to Samuel, the microcosm or little universe, as man.

Upon the wall, a metal etching of the hexagram brilliantly reflected the room light, and represents the macrocosm. On each side of it framed paintings of the Goddesses Isis and Nephthys lit up the mystical mood. The altar rested upon a structured deck that has two long stairs leading up to it. These steps represent the physical, astral and finally the mental plane ascending to the altar. Samuel invoked the Egyptian god Hru, as the sacred god to all tarot operations. To him the cards were like living beings that had particular relationships with their neighbors or the other cards that rested next to them.

Somehow, there was an association between Mr. Jacobs and the father of Juanita and that the result could be catastrophic was illustrated in the relationship of the card spread. Consequently the danger was not only in this lifetime but involved the next one as well. The sound of thunder roared across the sky from above the house.

There was s mythic connection between the two men through a Secret Society but it was unclear as to why a feud resulted through the association. Samuel closed the reading and prepared his evening meal. A knock came upon his door. It was Juanita; standing outside in the rain.

"Maybe we should move in together," she giggled, "We are seeing one another enough, you know."

"You have some news," he answered with a smile.

"My father wants to talk with me about this perplexity in person. He is coming over in the morning so I will be picking him up at the airport. Would you like to come along?"

"That sounds nice, and I will be pleased to meet him, however I should stay around here. Bring him by when you arrive back to town."

"Alright, I have to get back home. Anything else I should know?" she asked.

"Be safe and don't give Mr. Jacobs much trust, if you know what I mean." Sam stared to her.

Juanita smiled and winked then ran back to her vehicle, covering her head with her hands as she scurried.

The roads were drenched with slippery mud as her vehicle curved around the corners, returning towards her home. She came upon a stop sign and slowed down. A car drove through the adjoining road and halted in the middle, directly in front of her car. Through her partly fogged windshield she could see a set of eyes glaring at her from the other vehicle. It was Mr. Jacobs. She lost her breath for a moment until Mr. Jacobs stepped on the gas and continued up the road. With great relief she abruptly skidded off and turned right, continuing to her house.

The following morning Samuel greeted the uprising of the Sun and proceeded to the Spectrum Café. Sharon welcomed him, with her usual charming fashion. Samuel ordered some juice then went to the back to use the telephone. Someone picked up on the first ring. "93 my brother," Samuel greeted, "How is the state of life on your end?"

Aour laughed. "93's Samuel. It is good to hear from you, almost expected. It's been an austerity working with this water elemental that you sent along; but all is accomplished. It would have been easier if that Mister had simply cheated on her, as you know how undines disperse when their master is not fully faithful."

"Yes, but that is not the situation. He was working with the idea of revenge, and inflicting it towards a friend under my care."

"Understood. It was an adjustment and welcomed change after working with the earth element so ardently lately."

"Are you sleeping on beds of nails again?" Samuel sneered in jest.

"I've condensed the elemental power of earth into physical energy. Yesterday a six inch nail was put through my arm which left not a scar after the tribulation," Aour noted with enthusiasm.

"Something to write home about. What is next, condensing the water element and locking yourself in a burning box?"

"I know a Tibetan lama that dries his washed clothes on his body in the midst of winter by accumulating the fire element within himself. But it's not a challenge in the Canary Islands. Instead I am working on the invisibility art."

"I know you were here three nights ago, checking my journal. You didn't use astral or mental invisibility then."

"Of course not, not with you my brother. Astral or mental invisibility is a simple art of filling the particular body with the Akasha as you well know. I am presently developing the filling of the physical body with light, corresponding to the appropriate lighting of any particular time of day; and to maintain such physical invisibility for extended periods. Before you ask me, Blake has just left and is heading back to your place. He was quite jovial about the operation through the night and I am sure the little undine has better things to function with than the manipulation of that particular sorcerer."

"I am digging up the roots. Will you come astrally at ten three O?"

"I will be there with the toys from the big boys." Auor hinted.

"Do what thou wilt." Samuel said.

"Love under will." Aour replied as they hung up simultaneously.

When Samuel arrived home, Juanita was there, sitting on a lawn chair and basking in the sun. A stately gentleman sat across from her, who Samuel believed to be her father.

"Good afternoon Mr. Tanguay," Samuel greeted, extending a hand as he approached, "It is a pleasure to meet with you."

"The pleasure shall be mine, Samuel. Please call me Bernard. I have talked with Juanita about the situation and it was not much to figure out the reasoning for this little mess up."

"I would be most interested to hear," Samuel replied.

"Five years ago I was initiated into a secret order in Madrid. It had appealing significance to some work I was involved with previously. Once in the order I found that it was for life; although they stipulated it beforehand I never knew the strictness of what they meant, until I decided to go on my way. Several incidents followed that nearly lead to my demise so I escaped and fled to Barcelona; suspecting they would never find me." Bernard paused to rub his temples. "When I heard the name Jacobs I knew they were going through Juanita to locate me and would likely captivate her to punish me as well. They are rather overtly concerned about their secrets being released to anyone outside the order. Now I must confront this situation, rather than be hexed by it for eternity." Bernard lowered his head in disappointment.

"What do you suspect would happen if you went to Jacobs and talked directly with him?" Samuel asked.

"Their oaths are their life, Samuel. There is no way they will bend or make any exception to the rule."

Samuel grinned slyly. "Then we require an ultimate stratagem. Some things in life require extra juggling in order to make the appropriate adjustment perform accordingly."

"I sense that we are going to dabble in a projection of sorts," Bernard chuckled.

"Is your ability to consciously project and perform a venture of deceit adequately prepared, Mr. Tanguay?"

"I've made friends who were fast asleep get up and write the prose of Baudelaire without even knowing the poet ever existed," Bernard replied smugly.

Juanita looked at both of them with an estranged glare. "What have I been missing out on all these years?" she asked in disbelief.

"Tonight there will be a visitation from a comrade of mine. He will mold his astral body into the form of the undine that Jacob's is mysteriously questioning the whereabouts of. We, my friend, shall accompany him on the journey and make the revenging sorcerer believe that tossing his sigils into the deep ocean will set him free from eternal retribution," Samuel remarked with a glowing eye of certainty.

"This could be the end of their charade and allow me to get on with my life." Bernard said with praise.

"It will at least be the end of that phase." Samuel assured him.

As evening rolled around, the men prepared for the spectacle in the magician's chamber of righteousness. At ten thirty Aour paid a visit in astral form. Everything was suffused accordingly as the magical habitants whirled their astral counterparts through time and space, reentering at Jacobs abode.

Aour summoned denizens from the lower planes as they broke the pentagram barrier around the temple of the sorcerer and entered one by one. Jacobs was preparing a talisman at his desk as he heard a faint, shrill sound coming from the basement. He walked down and flicked on the light, looking around to see where the noise was coming from. In the corner he saw his undine, in the astral form of Crystal locked in chains to the wall. She was weeping in apparent agony.

"What happened to you my little darling; where have you fled to?" Jacobs asked with a perplexed look upon his aging face.

A concerned feminine voice bellowed through the entity, "The Great Ones have taken me onwards and will not permit me to return. I am being tortured as part of what you have done wrong all these years. They are coming for you soon. You must relinquish your entire grievance. They have taken Tanguay already and he has become part of them."

"How is any of this possible? To what Great Ones do you refer?" Jacobs demanded to know.

At that instant Samuel appeared with Bernard at his side. Their astral bodies gave off a flaring light as though they were extended from a greater invisible Being. In an area to the east of the room a figure began to appear. It wore a large crown and its face was aged with experience and its ears were enormously long and pointed. The gruesome figure has tentacle legs like a tarantula spider and stood in silence with overwhelming power coming from its projection of energy.

Jacob looked over to it in astonishment. Perplexed with fear by the situation, he recognized the image and through his lips he chanted its name with concern:

"Bael!"

The entity bellowed with raw power. "I, ruler of sixty-six legions of the Infernal Spirits, Demon King of Tzalemoth and the seventh hell charge you to destroy all vengeance and disperse your talismans of revenge into the seas upon this hour or shall Azrael and all demons summoned torment your soul eternally in wrath." It shrilled with a deep, remorseless voice.

Jacobs felt a tugging sensation through his heart and upon his arms as a shrill of panic swelled through his veins. Something entered inside him and he wanted it out. He shook his body vehemently with his eyes closed then reopened them to find the undine appear to melt into the floor and the two beings do a swirling motion towards the stairs and elevate to the top. He looked over to Bael who spun in a circle, gathering energy into a violently swirling vortex.

Jacobs ran up the stairs, rushing to his closet where he held magic talismans of revenge against Tanguay and grabbed them all. He rushed to his car and drove to the edge of the cliff at the sea. When more than imaginable combined forces works together to tell a person a message, sometimes the person takes heed and comes to realize that it may be for the best.

Gentle winds bellowed across the water as he quickly pulled out all talismans and set them ablaze, then dropping them over the cliff to be engulfed by the relentless waves of the sea. A haze appeared in the distance, as he was ready to depart and it became brighter and larger as it hastily approached. Jacobs looked up at it, as it split into two forms; appearing as an image of Tanguay.

"Leave me alone, I have destroyed all and everything. You are dismissed from the order and are forever forgotten. Leave me go and let me return in peace!" Jacobs yelled at the image as he jumped into his car and rushed off.

Samuel and Bernard returned to the magician's temple and back into their physical bodies. They awoke and went to the living room where Juanita was curled up asleep on the couch. Her eyes opened as she slowly stretched upwards.

"Are you finished? Did it work?" she asked in a semi-conscious state.

Her father looked at her with a pleasant smile and remarked, "I do not think we will have any more problems with Jacobs, my dear. We helped him a certain way along the path; to let him realize the effect of creating diseases in his karma."

"You taught him a spiritual lesson? You should charge him for that; it must have been a big lesson." she giggled.

The two men looked at one another and then spoke simultaneously the same words "Spirituality is the only thing that is free." They answered with a grin and walked to the kitchen to prepare some tea. ★

ASTRAL ENTITY

"Life has done its work for us when it brings realisation, even if we are unable to achieve our realisations,
for in the next life these will be within our grasp."

Through the Gates of Death- Dion Fortune

Throughout the day loads of paperwork continually piled onto her desk but Sandra was not overly concerned about it. She was accustomed to working on several projects at one time. Today's agenda, like most other days, included translating Spanish to English, Portuguese to Spanish, and Dutch to Spanish along with designing and creating specialty calendars that her employer distributed throughout the country. A deliveryman abruptly walked in and placed a dazzling bouquet of a dozen roses upon her desk. There were eleven blooming red roses with one white rose in the center. Her jaw dropped in wonderment, as she looked at them and then at the deliveryman. He smiled and turned to exit her office. "Lucky lady, you are," He said as he walked through the glass archway with an envious grin.

Sandra looked within the lavish assortment and a hauled out a small envelope packet that was inside. She opened it and found a note upon which was written: "I feel something very special about you, but will we ever know?" The card was rather heavy, and upon turning it over, she found a red heart necklace taped to the back of it. She gazed at it, rather perplexed.

Sandra left her desk and walked down to the end of the office room to her co-worker, Teresa, and asked for assistance in attaching the lovely heart pendant around her neck.

"Who is the thoughtful man?" Teresa asked as she closed the clasp.

"You know something, Teresa… I have no idea where this sweet gift originated; it's a complete mystery. I haven't dated anybody in months," She sighed, both curious and frustrated.

She knew there was a Mr. Right somewhere, but was content in waiting for him to find her. She began doodling on paper back at her desk. Mystified, she began writing out the alphabet and attaching names of people she knew to each letter, attempting to unravel the mystery. A…Alan…B…Bruce…C…no one came to mind… D…Dave… and so on but none seemed to fit the affectionate concept of sending her this sudden surprise. The names were mostly friends of her family and no one she had any romantic involvement with. Nonetheless she continued her day until five o'clock after which she left to drive to her favorite restaurant where she was to meet her cousin, Lexi-Dawn.

Turning on the radio in her little car, she began to hum along with the song, 'Life Will Play a Rhapsody'. It helped to ease her nerves while driving through the busy city traffic. While driving over a city bridge she glanced down the side rail at the sparkling water below and was alit at what she saw. The clouds reflected in the Bay and gave off an image of a large Being with a halo over its head. 'This is too weird!' she thought but that is what she saw. The apparition startled her into considering that someone was watching over her every move. Sandra shook her head, thinking she was over-worked along with a tired imagination and gleamed while staring at the passenger seat, seeing the flowers.

Turning her Toyota Celica into the parking area of Grannans' Restaurant, she quickly brushed her hair and replenished the rouge upon her voluptuous lips. When she entered the restaurant, Lexi-Dawn was already seated at their regular table. "Hi, Sandra!" Lexi waved.

"Lexi, wow," Sandra sighed, plopping into an adjacent chair, "I thought Friday would never come this week."

Lexi grinned. "I know the feeling. The customers we got this week at the store were always rushed to get somewhere!" Noticing the red heart pendant around her cousin's neck, she added, "Where did you get that charming little glowing heart, Sandra?"

Looking down, Sandra replied, "Oh, I wish I knew. It came to me this morning at work with a dozen flowers and a note that said 'I feel something very special about you, but will we ever know?'... But I cannot for the life of me figure out who sent it." Smirking, she started to twirl the pendant between her fingers. "Maybe time will show this mystery person to me," Sandra giggled.

"Oh, it will," Lexi smiled suggestively, "I wish that happened to me, but Bob stopped buying flowers after our second year of being together."

After eating their supper salads and sharing casual conversation over a few 'white satin' drinks they agreed to meet on Sunday for brunch.

Sandra drove slowly back home and thought about whether she wanted to go out this weekend or not. She was approaching a green light when some red flash seemed to run into her window and draw her head back to the headrest as she pressed harshly on the breaks. Instantaneously, a large station wagon ran the opposing red light and continued at a high speed nearly scraping the front of her vehicle. She gasped with widened eyes as shock from the near-fatal crash ran through her mind. Once the light changed, she pulled the car over to the side of the road to calm her nerves. A few minutes passed then she felt calm enough to drive, so she cautiously continued to her apartment on the south east of Boston.

It was nearly eight o'clock when she arrived at the comforts of home. She decided to set her roses in a vase and watch some television to settle down after a tiresome workweek. The evening was cool as mist from the nearby river swept across the face of the apartment. Lighting a fire-log, Sandra felt a sudden chill as the flame gushed upwards in the fireplace. She felt nervy and wanted to pamper herself tonight.

Walking back to the couch she picked up the newspaper and sank comfortably with all her energy releasing into the fluffy large pillows on the sofa. She clicked on a television music channel. A chimney draft swept down and blew sparks from the fire log into the room with a crackling jitter. She abruptly jumped to her feet and ran to close the glass fireplace doors to redirect the fire upwards. Her nervous quirk was more than she cared to handle this evening.

Still feeling a bit nerved, Sandra began a hot bubble bath and slithered around in the tub after lighting three large candles around her. "What a week! What a day!" she whispered to herself as she soaked in the relaxing sensation of soothing water covering her wearied body. She began singing along to a song from the music channel, not caring what it was but just relieving herself from the last morsel of tension.

Sandra fell into a deeply relaxed state and sank heavily into the bath with refreshing reverberation. She had a sensation that a presence was drawing her into a dream, unlike the driven ambition to dream on her own accord. It was a strange feeling, like nothing that she could describe or recall happening before. Her eyes faintly opened as she bent her head down to see the heart pendant reflecting in the water. She slowly blinked as her head returned to rest upon the back ledge. The water gently swathed around and across her relaxed body. She was drawn into another world; dreamy and welcoming as an invitation to escape the one she was tired of. An image, which was not fully discernable but had distinct serenity around it, met with her. The entity was standing between two very large rock structures, one of which had the word Yachin written vertically upon it and the other had Boaz written similarly upon it. She fell into a trance-like state flowing with the sensations, and found herself floating in mid-air between the massive rocks.

The entity summoned her onwards as though she had an affiliation with it and it had purpose for her future. She caught the scented fragrance of perfumes through the warm wind. It was a lingering aroma of camphor mixed with aloe that was instigating the atmosphere. The astral entity brought her to meet an angel who lifted her from the depths she was trapped in and guided her through what appeared to be numerous available openings into another world. Sandra suddenly felt a thump and was brought into a maze that integrated as a picture of what she could recognize as a scenic place. It was somewhere in the south and a place that held a pleasant ambience.

A small village rested beyond a retreat area. She seemed to soar effortlessly as flashes of images went past her. Sandra saw a crescent moon overhead and then what appeared to be statues of ancient moon goddesses that were set upon pedestals. They were particular deities associated to where she was brought. Chomse, Chandra, Hecate and Artemis, were the names of the statues, which appeared lifelike and extravagant in every detail. Suddenly, they began to move their limbs and commenced walking a few steps, then all of them simultaneously fled into the air. Sandra's eyes widened at the multifarious sight.

The angel transported her to an early nineteenth century house set amidst a farm, which had a fishing dock and sandy beach nearby. Sandra could hear the faint barking of a dog somewhere around the old farmhouse. The angel held her hand as Sandra glided effortlessly through the streaming air particles. Together they hovered near a window of the old house. She looked in the window and seen a hunting bow above an assortment of arrows hung on the wall. Her attention was then focused over a mantle to a lavish oval mirror. Within it she could see a man and woman embracing one another.

The couple had a young boy who ran into the room with a ball. They laughed at him as the man took the ball and bounced it on the floor, sending it back into the child's hands. They continued playing and laughing as the angel beckoned Sandra onwards and through a wall into another room.

The same man and woman were passionately cuddling in their bed and kissing one another. He stepped away and took a small packet from his back pocket. The woman smiled gratefully while accepting it and upon opening she looked at him with the most beautiful radiant eyes he had ever seen. She held up a red heart pendant as he took it and latched it around her neck. Her arms rapturously embraced his shoulders in exaltation as their mouths met.

Sandra was in emotional awe while viewing the vision of the past, delivered through an angelic reincarnation adept. She did not associate the pendent with the one she was wearing nor recognize the fact that she had one. She was simply amazed at the feeling she held as though she was the lady receiving the lovely gift. The man in the vision leant over and kissed the jewel he had previously placed around his wife's neck. The telephone rang and Sandra abruptly shook out of the pleasant astral journey. It seemed like a lifetime, but only forty minutes had passed while she was in the bath. She quickly pulled herself out and dried her regenerated body but was too late to reach the telephone caller. She creamed her cleansed body with a soothing lotion, dressed in her sleeping gown and prepared for an early retirement into bed.

Lying in her comfortable, large bed she handled the heart pendant and took it off to set it on her night table. She clicked on the television and began watching a movie that was set in the early nineteen hundreds. It wasn't long before she fell into a comforting sleep while still wondering who sent the roses and pendant. She tossed back and forth under her satin sheets while falling deeper into a somnambulistic dream state. Curtains swayed with the evening breeze from her jarred bedroom window. Her head moved slightly. She twitched as her hands moved to her neck, unaware of her actions. Her hands grasped softly around her neck as a presence within her room touched her. She knew in it was there and felt it but could not see or discern what it was. It felt like it was touching her neck softly then going away only to return and repeat the action. She wondered what was happening in her half-dazed state of awareness. An entity was touching her neck then it left and returned to replicate the process. Sandra released her hands and stretched over to snatch the pendant and held it firmly in her hand, while turning to resume sleeping on her side. She was deeply content in her semi-subconscious cognizance and not wanting to awaken.

Her body quickly jolted as though something left it. Something did leave. It was her consciousness. Her soul was guided by an astral entity through a warm inviting mist as if she entered into another dimension or world. The entity sprayed jolts of light from its body as it fluttered around her. The emissions sparkled as they left and whisked into the air. There was a bond between Sandra and the entity. Their mingled beings cascaded into a lucent unity as they soared over high mountainous peeks into higher elevations. The world beneath them appeared serene, graceful and supervised by nature's harmony. She spoke to the entity through her emotions of being touched by it. "I sense that I know you".

It had a subtle response: "I am part of your prodigy. You are in search of your Love."

Through it she had the recollection of the small house by the beach in days of old, with the two lovers, the heart pendant, the child, the peace and tranquility that she lived as a previous lifetime.

"That is it!" Sandra acknowledged, while reminiscing, "My previous life was there!"

The entity fluttered faster as she witnessed its wings made of effulgent feathers. It brought her between a myriad of leaf-filled branches into an immense open field. She looked around and noticed a gigantic tree overshadowing her. When her eyes came down the trunk she looked over and saw a youthful man. Their immediate embrace was something for which she could not honestly account. It simply happened as they mingled in one another's soul as an exchange of pure ecstasy. It was a joyous sensation beyond description and physical capability. They whirled in extreme delight as their bodies lifted off the ground and whirled tenaciously above the Earth. They were indulged in a sensual embrace that met each other with astonishment. Sandra felt intense pleasure, as if it were the two people she saw in the old farmhouse enjoying one another in every way. It was long since she ever had physical sex, but this was something beyond any feeling she ever treasured. It was so captivating, so penetrating, and entirely fulfilling with a miraculous beauty enshrouding her and the partner. She couldn't describe the passion of the unity occurring. It was a timeless event. She felt everything within her soul go out to him. Throughout the experience she had visions that transferred from him into her. She seen some locations they once visited and some adventures which developed their evolution, and the last day of their physical life together back in 1923. How she knew, was a complete mystery, as the answers and insight simply came of their own accord.

Their house was at Riviera Beach in Baffin Bay along the Gulf of Mexico, in southern Texas. It was a hot sunny April 10th. He was commemorating a special event during the course of the evening with her. Throughout the day he laboriously toiled in the fields and while they celebrated in the night his heart enflamed and he suffered a heart attack at the table. She tried to revive him but it was unsuccessful. He fell into unconsciousness yet held a state of bliss while clenching her hand tightly. She cried deeply and pressed her lips firmly upon his. This vision was beyond any feeling Sandra had ever known. It was through the astral light that she could re-experience the spectacular bond of love that somehow remained with her.

Sandra rolled on her stomach in bed, continuing to clench onto the red heart pendant. The night bellowed on in rushing ecstatic events, one after another that consumed her with vigorous emotional dreams. Before she knew it, morning sunshine poured into her face. She awoke and twisted within her sheets, stretching happily with satisfied comfort. It was like she experienced a love revival, although she had no vivid recollection of the night's events.

After breakfast she had a shower and tried to recall the apparent dreams but her memory only faded further. She could only recall the incident of meeting someone in a dream. It felt to her like she made love with someone in a timeless way and experienced an array of events and destinies tied into great significance. Saturday was her favorite day to walk through the marketplace. It was always enjoyable to observe other people around her and sense their emotional fields while wondering what they've done throughout their life. It was somewhat of a little game she elaborated in while allowing her thoughts to randomly accept images of the lifestyles led by those around her. The sun sparkled across the fresh fruit and vegetable stands as she picked from both to fill her basket.

A tour bus pulled up and passengers disembarked. One gleeful gentleman wandered around a table vendor selling crystal. He picked up a heart pendant made of clear crystal and held it up to the sunlight as refraction's glittered from it upon Sandra's face. She stared fixatedly upon the crystal that glimmered in her eye. His head turned solemnly as her eyes caught his. He sent her an innocent deep smile while she looked into his eyes with bewilderment. In his left hand he held a small red book.

Sandra looked at the crystal heart while briefly touching her red heart pendant. She walked to him and glanced down at the book. The title was 'The Mysteries of Love', written in golden letters. She blinked as her head moved back and forth in awe. Her hand lowered with the crystal heart as the man turned and asked, "Are you alright?" Sandra nodded and smiled sheepishly. Hardly skipping a beat, the man continued, "Boston is a beautiful city. There is much traffic these days and the streets seem to go in big circles everywhere."

Sandra quickly shook her head and responded, "Ah yes, I am fine, I think. Well, I am not so used to all the traffic yet either. I moved to Boston, from down south, for business. Where are you from?"

"I am from far away. I fly often and most conventionally I must add," He said with a peaceful glow.

"Well, I am sure you will like it here, there are many things to see and do," She noted, feeling a bit congested.

"May I ask why you looked so strangely at this crystal heart I held up and then at the book I am holding?"

"Oh," She hesitated then added, "I was just so curious about something. I am not even sure myself actually," She laughed nervously.

Sandra sensed something peculiar about the gentleman but couldn't figure out what it was; only that it was something of good disposition. His voice held an extraordinarily soothing tone in it, a promising of sorts but she had no idea. Her hand reached out to his as they instantly shook and smiled with connecting eyes.

"You may call me Pete. It is a pleasure to meet your acquaintance," He gleefully added.

"Nice to meet you Pete, I am Sandra." She replied, widening her eyebrows with complacency.

"Would you like to rest at the café over there and have a soft drink?" He asked while directing his stare.

"Ummmm..." she pondered, "Sure, ok, I could use a break from these shoes."

The pair made their way to the small café, where they took a seat on the sun-lit deck and ordered drinks.

"What made you lose your eyes in that crystal heart I held up?" He asked.

"That sounds true, my eyes did leave me back there for a moment. Well, as you can see," she pulled out her pendant from her blouse, "I have one also and there is a bit of a mystery behind where it came from."

"This is fine," Pete chuckled, a sparkle in his eye, "Mysteries are sometimes good. There are many in this world and the fun in knowing answers is always in finding them."

"Tell me about it," Sandra remarked, "I had a strange dream last night but I cannot really remember it. I know someone made me quite happy and some interesting events transpired. I wish I could remember my dreams better. Yesterday I received this pendant at work with some beautiful flowers from an anonymous person. I held the red pendant through the night and the dreams...oh I wish I could recall them but they are so vague now and I cannot or don't know how to even describe what they were about."

Peter looked into her eyes with fervor and interest while stating, "Dreams can tell us a lot about future or past dealings. In that state our subconscious opens the door of timelessness and we have only to enter and be guided to some stored record or accept the vision of things to come. I only suggest that you begin to write them down and try to translate them to what they mean to you over time. As the day progresses it becomes more difficult to remember dreams and our measures regarding them. Writing them down will help to eventually solve them." Peter lifted his glass of lemonade and took a sip, making a face at its sourness.

"You seem like an enlightened person. Why do you have an interest in dreams?" She asked

"It's a long story, Sandra. Principally it is a result of being around for a long time. Having an interest in what connects everything is like bending space. Life is flat until you put a force into it, then it creates dimension. The planets and stars have all impressed space into a tangible fabric that we can skip in and out of. Relating your dreams to your understanding of life is like opening the fabric and looking at the coatings. It is truly remarkable. Nobody has to run from anything you see, not from dreams and not from life. Everything that happens provides an in route and an out route, through the fabric. If we adjust ourselves according to living a future moment while entertaining the Reality of Now, we can change happenings. That is what happens in our dreams sometimes, when we catch on. Life has multiple signs around us and everything relates to something we are connected with. We either accept or reject it, avoiding harm or being unconcerned." He glanced with a vibrant smile into her pendant as he spoke.

"I see, but do you always remember your dreams and figure them out?" Sandra questioned.

"Life is a dream, my dear one, an awakened one, an illusory one, a fun one or a tragic one. It is always part of one and the other. When we awaken from what we call dreams, we live in another dream within a dream. Everyone dreams because the mind never sleeps. Thought processing is continuously occurring, whether our body is at rest or superficially believing to be awake. Do you usually recall having good dreams when you awaken in the mornings?" He inquired.

"Yes because I don't remember anything bad in dreams, or at least I haven't in a long time. For the past year at least, my dreams have been either boringly unimportant to me or basically pleasant."

"What bothers you, Sandra?" Pete asked out of the blue.

"What, what do you mean by that?" Sandra stammered in response.

"Something bothers you inside. You may not be able to put it into words but it is in there, isn't it?" he asked softly.

"Everyone has some concerns that they ponder over all the time. Some concerns may bother me a little bit inside by I don't generally realize or pay attention to it. I am not sure if I know what you are really asking me, Peter," she answered defensively.

"I am asking you something that you are not fully aware of at all times. You are looking for something in this life. Inside of you there is something that bothers you, something that should not be there and is building up and preventing you from being fulfilled. It adds a certain tension to your body." He added.

"Well, I have a gut feeling sometimes and everything doesn't always go right for me. There are certain things I need in my life but they are not there, and perhaps they would help in fulfillment because then they wouldn't be on my mind," Sandra said while turning her head sideways, wondering why he was getting deeply personal.

"There is a reason why you do not have that fulfillment. Something holds you back from your true dreams. If you want something you only have to ask, to dig inside deeply, and you will have it," Peter asserted.

"Who do I ask to obtain my most personal desires and deep dreams?" She importuned with a questionable smile.

"Ask yourself, Sandra. We are all part of the one great divine by whatever name we wish to give it. Our chord reaches to the spirit cord and it is connected subtly with the divine cord by an endless amount of fine strands. When we focus on our desires within our authentic dreams, they are sent up that cord and begin to appear in a deeper section of life to attach to reality and eventually occur. You just have to be ready to accept it."

"Sounds like positive thinking to me," Sandra acknowledged with a pleasant tone while sipping her drink.

"Positive creation, but yes a positive attitude is a definite plus in strengthening our desires and focusing the mind energy to send the desires up the cord. All things are connected, so I use the term cord to signify they are related within other levels or parts of a great life system," Pete said as he quickly toasted his glass to hers.

"I can understand that, I think," She gulped, "Actually, you know there is something that bothers me and I think it prevents me from seeking my dreams in life and accomplishing more than I do."

"Can you realize what it is, Sandra?"

"It's not self-esteem really. Once that was my problem but for a long time it has been something else. It has been distraction. I am not focussed on my dreams as I once was. My mind is scattered about daily life, work, cleaning, cooking, meeting friends, junk on television and other social duties, I guess," She hesitated then let out a sigh.

"They are built up inside you like an ongoing program that runs everyday. If you miss them, then what happens?" He asked with a wry smile.

"Well, then I feel alone somehow, like I need one or other of them somewhat like a craving. It sounds pathetic, no doubt, although I enjoy a quiet time when I can get it. If it is too quiet I lose interest and need some kind of entertainment before long," Sandra admitted while shaking her head in disappointment.

"Nothing to worry about, Sandra. All people have a certain amount of time and duties to contend with. The problem is that cravings have been allowed to run life and so determine downfalls and personality programming and disorders. The mind is a creature and led by habitual training. Once something is put into it then it works with that as data and works from what it was programmed to do. That's why humans can be programmed and deprogrammed into faith, into social stimulus and into purchasing an item they don't really need. That is why greedy people become greedier and hungry people continue to starve. Their minds are controlled and working only in small corridors of what potential they can otherwise be fulfilling their dreams with. Dreams that exist as part of their true needs, that are always there, ALWAYS." he asserted then asked,

"What do you feel at this moment?"

"Splendor, I think," Sandra smirked.

"Don't think, Sandra. Just feel and describe it and go with it."

"I feel you have told me a key about being free somehow, even if temporarily. I just had glimpses of my dreams and what they mean for me. I seen a beautiful man who showed me so much about my life, so much about what is important to feel and to learn and I was set free by being with him. If I keep going with these feelings they could get vivid, Pete." Sandra pompously admitted.

"As long as you see them that is good. If you do not loose sight of them they will help carry you closer to your fulfillment," Peter suggested seriously.

"What do you know of reincarnation, Peter?" she asked candidly.

"I know it is a long process. When your physical body is gone, your ghost body is severed from it and wanders seeking what it must fulfill without much effort unless you prepare it beforehand while your consciousness is capable of evolving it. Your ghost carries a partial memory with it of the most spectacular importance that brings you to the next step in life after life, before it begins to dissolve. That is why all people should learn about it and do some work with it. Each moment in life is an eternity within time. Once you think of a passing moment it is already gone however. We can slow down to the point of living it and using it and therefore not wasting it. Thoughts can be devastatingly misleading and time consuming when we mentally wander. It's not that we should make life more complicated, but that we should be free, and not blindly so. We should live, but not in a staggering dream. This is what makes some people accomplish so much in life while others suffer daily routine and loose sight or interest of their developing passions. They become content in the non-evolving stage, somewhat like a person just wanting to stay in bed all day or watch television their whole life. They get to see what other people accomplish and become content with not accomplishing more than they have to." Chuckling at himself, he inquired, "What do you feel about reincarnation, Sandra?"

"I feel it is an important part of destiny to look into it and one realized partly by our interests in life. I want to ride a camel in Egypt one day. I also want to find a partner who will worship with me and through me a love of divine passion as two people united in constant blissful joy. With that special person I shall express myself as a great priestess and share deep longings and nurture our love with sustenance from the world energy, from the infinite life forces. I want to practice things and grow, to share something new each moment spontaneously and have great fun doing it. That to me is happiness and what reincarnation brings until one time we no longer have to return to grow in this world." She concluded, and then shook her head to wake up again, "Was I just dreaming?" she laughed in jest.

"A great priestess? You said you want to be one. Sandra, this is the age of the Goddess. Do you know the Stella Maris?" He asked.

"That means the 'star upon the sea', I know because my mother went to that church. So what do you mean, do I know it?" she grinned.

"That is the name that Saint Jerome called the Virgin Mary. All sacred concepts have sacred meanings and become a path to some greater interpretation. Stella Maris is the star that guides those upon the seas and oceans. That star is the North Star called Polaris. It has been the most faithful and constant star known in history and all have relied upon it to find their way. It is the alpha star of Ursa Minor and connected to Mary as well as the Priestess and Goddess and you stated you would express yourself as a great priestess. One of the great things about a High Priestess is that she can do many things and be a great guide, just like the star. She can unlock the mysteries of ancient myths, connect the days of the year to special events, like a calendar of unlimited revelations, and associate the alphabets of many languages to special interpretations as journeys with the meanings of life," Peter winked.

"That is strange. I make calendars at work for many office corporations. I also do translations from four languages. The word 'priestess' has stuck in my mind for many years, to me it means something special but I am not quite sure how to express its meaning." She admitted.

"Many myths about the Ursa Minor contain the topic of a divine flame and sacred fire, an inner guiding light that brings you to a high realization about life. That is part of the Priestess aspect within you," Peter said, nodding emphatically.

"That really touches me. I love to stare at a candle at home every night and light a fire in the fireplace. It's not for the warmth that it brings but the guidance that I feel from it. You have such a way of connecting things together Peter. Sometimes I wish I was in another time, a time where things magically happen," Sandra replied, staring into the distance.

"When you seek deeply and experience what you feel inside, things do happen magically. Then you can make that special time occur throughout life, a time that becomes perfect," He smiled with apparent ease.

"The time is likely always perfect, is it not?"

"Not always. Many things affect a person because a person is personality and is masquerade of affected materials. They change, develop, and eventually refine as a character of self-expression. Recall last night in your sleep, the Being that brought you to the old house through your dream state, was not a person. It was Haniel who brought you to meet your past. You were looking into the past through a recorded imprint of history with an entity that assisted you in the scrying journey. You were lead through a corridor of your subconscious mind that enabled you to enter a doorway and witness a part of history that you were connected and influenced by. The people in that house were you and your husband in your last lifetime. You were not ready to part and for the rest of your life living there in Texas, you held onto him, not wanting to believe he departed. Inside you are still bothered by not being with him, but you do not realize this consciously," Pete noted while observing her attentive reaction and widening eyes.

"How do you know so much, Pete? How on earth could you know my dreams last night? Furthermore, who are you really, and if you know all the answers then tell me who sent the flowers and pendant to my work office?" She urged, feeling edgy about this bizarre encounter.

"It was him, your previous lifetime husband, your soul mate, who sent the flowers and is alive again, but he did not know what he was doing. A force came upon him to send flowers but he meant to send them to a girl he met accidentally as he couldn't conceive of why he should send them to you since he doesn't yet know you in this life. The flowers went to your office in the building you work at by accident, as it were. It was a delivery mistake, Sandra, but one with purpose. He wants to meet you but he doesn't know it yet. He is not really aware of any of this and there will be an instant perpetual attraction between both of you." Pete smiled with positive affirmation.

"I almost believe you Pete. It sounds like you are either an angel or saint or else that was the longest pick-up line I ever heard in my entire life," She huffed, while giving him an evil eye.

"The attraction is mutual," he chuckled, "And it is not between you and I, but between you and the man walking his bicycle right over there." Pete slowly nodded his head towards a middle-aged, good-looking man beaming with enthusiasm while he walked his bicycle and browsed everywhere as he passed by the market.

Sandra looked over and her eyes were caught in acute examination. "This is just slightly remarkable, who is that cute guy? His presence gives me a tingle, I admit, and besides he is more than cute, he's very attractive! What should I do, Pete?" she asked nervously and almost convinced.

"Everything has occurred for a purpose, and you were given opportunity. Don't let it go until you know for sure the truth that is within you. Go with your feelings, your true intuitive ones beyond the mundane senses." He smiled as she stood up and looked at him feeling full of dare and then walked slowly to the gentleman approaching with his bicycle. She looked back still trying to figure this odd situation out and wondered who Pete really was.

As her head turned back towards the man pushing the bicycle, a water bottle fell off his bicycle as the tire hit the curb. Sandra quickly bent over to pick it up. "You don't want to lose this," She smiled nonchalantly.

"Oh, thank you so much. Not many people will stop and pick something up for a person these days," He said soberly.

Sandra extended her hand; as she had to know what it was like to feel his hand in hers. "I am Sandra, a pleasure to meet you Mr...?" She hesitated.

"The pleasure is as well mine, and I am John," He replied holding her hand in his as though it was neither the first time nor the last. The warmth Sandra felt was deeply attracting her closer to him as she sensed something within his friendly glow and energetic sparkle. She looked back to the outdoor café table where she and Pete were inspiringly conversing at, but he was gone. She looked around quickly but she couldn't see him anywhere. Peter the saint had simply vanished. Her eyes turned and looked into John's as he asked confidently, "Are you hungry? I could sure use some company while I sit and eat a little something."

"That, that would be fine, if you answer me one question," She said.

"Well, I shall try to. What is the question?" He asked dubiously.

"Did you send something to a girl yesterday, like a gift of affection perhaps?"

John's eyes dropped with his jaw and then he lifted his head admittedly. "Yes, I did in fact. A girl in an office that I thought was pretty. I met her in an elevator and I just did something crazy out of the blue. You know how guys can be," He laughed with a nudge.

"What was it you sent her, if I may ask?" Sandra said with a little growing smile.

"Well, it was a dozen roses, eleven red and one white and also a little pendant that I didn't buy for her specifically but had for two years and bought it at a market in Italy, strangely enough, because I was attracted to it when I seen it. Why do you ask this?" John said, staring at her with a comical jump.

Sandra put her hand in the top of her blouse and held the pendant between her fingers then brushed it back and forth slowly. Her eyes captivated John as he stared deeply into hers with wonder and anticipation.

"Let's have dinner." Sandra giggled and walked over to the café with him. "Lunch is on me today, is that alright?" she asked.

"She picks up my water bottle, she is awesomely beautiful and she buys my lunch. I have to say this has never happened before," He laughed whole-heartedly.

"Maybe it's about time it did. I want to ask you some things; things I am very curious about and just want to see how you feel about them John, is that all right with you?" She grinned with a smile that stole his heart.

"I love answering your questions, and boy, I am hungry," He laughed as he scraped up the menu and took a seat.

"What made you just happen by and occur from out of nowhere?" He asked, trying to remain collective.

"I believe it was caused by a Saint," Sandra smiled away a frown while thinking about Peter.

She sensed something about John that was familiar to her. It was like it wasn't the first time they were together. Something was ageless and timeless between them. Looking into his eyes her heart began to beat faster with some sensual passion intertwined. He looked straight into her eyes and saw life to be so beautiful it would take him some time to gratefully express it. She looked at the sky then met his glance once again.

"Do you feel something different about this, about yourself perhaps?" She asked.

"I have some strange feeling inside. I cannot explain it really. It seems like a dream to sit here and be near you." John exclaimed, clamoring around for a stick of gum in his pocket.

"A dream huh? What do you really feel, without thinking about it?" she asked glaring at him gently and peacefully, awaiting an answer from someplace deeper within.

"I feel," he paused for two full minutes in silence, " I feel you." He answered unbelievably as he made a small circle with his head and swallowed dryness within his mouth as a tear slowly passed down his face.

Sandra breathed in slowly with her eyes closed and placed her hand over his. "That's what I wanted to know; I am seeking the truth." She broadly smiled as the waiter came by. ★

THE SPIRITUAL DOOR

"…esoteric science holds that matter is built up on a framework of spirit; that spirit emanates matter, not matter spirit…it seeks to discover what spiritual factor has emanated the particular material object under consideration…it seeks to find the relationship that, ex hypothesi, exists between the seen and the unseen."
The Training And Work Of An Initiate- Dion Fortune

"**Y**ou must be getting really excited about leaving," Mona said as she looked at her friend in admiration. Debbie held up her drink and turned her head, looking at children running along the sidewalk beside her. She was seated at an outdoor Café in downtown Winnipeg, having a final discussion with her life long companion, Mona.

"Actually, there is not that much excitement involved with it, Mona. It will be an adventure for sure, but one likely filled with great horror. I hope that I can provide some help to good people while I'm there and make a difference that counts," She responded while looking out through her soft blue eyes.

"Well, make sure you send a letter when you get a chance. I want to know that everything is going well for you and what is happening with you while in India," Mona said with a concerned look on her face.

Debbie lifted her fork with salad in it and looked at it at intensely. "You know, for the past few years, every time I put some food in my mouth I think of where it came from and what caused it to be produced. All of the things that went into making it enter my mind and how it came possible for me to eat it. It is sad to embrace the idea that every year between 13 and 18 million people die of starvation and each day at least 35,000 people drop dead on the ground because they lack nutrition. That amounts to nearly 24 people dying each minute, and 18 of those deaths are children under the age of 5 years old. The problem is world-wide, but if hunger was eliminated in India then one-third of world hunger would end." Debbie finished her tirade with a long sigh.

"That is staggering," Mona replied, "But it is people like you who care do make a difference by showing the rest of humanity that life is precious. I am so proud of you, Deb. You are such a good person!" Mona leaned over to give her friend a hug.

Debbie returned the hug, and then resumed eating her salad. "Thinking about the future population is mind staggering. Around the year 1800 the world population was up to 1 billion mainly due to the industrial revolution, then by 1930 it was at 2 billion. In 1960 it rose to 3 billion, and that was only 30 years later from 2 billion people in the world. Then, just 15 years later, in 1975 it reached 4 billion. Now we are well over 6 billion and as the world population grows so to does the multiplicity of problems. Everyone has a job and destiny, but for the love of humanity we should each do one thing to make life on earth a better place." Putting her salad slowly into her mouth, she added, "There is always time to do that."

"What about population control and more food for the world?" Mona asked.

"It sure sounds nice but it is a lot of work and a world wide effort. Poverty and hunger are simply encouraged by the tremendous increase in population. Food development can't keep up with this and besides that, it is a threat to world survival in the future, as are other catastrophes. Education should teach about these issues and demand the birth rate to be slowed down, especially in under-developed countries. Without realizing it, the growth rate is changing economics right under our nose. Most countries have to double their economic output to keep up with the demand. I mean, in India they need over a thousand new school classrooms a day, as well as over a thousand hospital wards, ten thousand homes and shelters and just about everything else you can imagine," She replied, stabbing into the salad with hyped determination.

"This is going to be some major experience for you," Mona smiled, a tinge of envy in her tone. "Remember you can always phone me if you need anything. Whatever I can do, I will do it. Are you pretty much packed and ready?"

"Yes, for the most part, but I have a few hours of work to do at home tonight. We better get going soon. I have to phone some people also you know, family and relatives."

"Of course Deb. I will drop you off at your place then pick you up at 7am to bring you to the airport. When is your sister moving into your apartment?"

"She has prepared everything and said she will be bringing her things over this weekend, so she will start living there then."

Nodding, Mona left money for the bill. "Okay then, let's go!" she said excitedly. The pair then stood up to walk down the street to Mona's car.

Debbie looked over her three packed suitcases when she arrived home. Plenty of light clothing, rain-suit, camera, jogging shoes, writing materials, books and many other miscellaneous items. Everything that was required appeared to be there. She then put on her nightshirt while looking at her arm where she received several vaccines to prevent disease. After she made phone calls to some friends and family she packed some additional items then went to lie down on her bed. A cool breeze swept through her room from the window and quickly brought her into a tranquil sleep.

She felt relaxed yet remained collective about the journey ahead. She imagined already being in India and beginning the hunger project, envisioning the aid that she was capable of providing. Her visions revealed many deeply sick people scattered about in tents through a field. She was walking by a long line of people, watching them waiting for food that was dished out of a pot into small bowels, which they held up while walking through the line. Her hands pressed against her heart as she looked up and seen an image of a mother and father holding hands. She was deeply asleep and dreamt of being in a large room. Her hand reached for a door handle to open it but the radio alarm clock rang aloud with chatter from the radio station and woke her up.

It was 5:30 am and she stretched her body along the bed, wondering momentarily about the dreams she had just experienced. Debbie looked around in a daze as the curtains swayed from the open window. She sat up and stretched in her bed then placed her feet on the floor, anxious to ensure that everything was packed. She got into the shower and began to wake up feeling refreshed but subtly anxious.

An hour later Mona arrived and took her to the airport.

"This is it! The big day has arrived. Did you sleep well?" Mona said while driving down the freeway.

"Yes, it was comfortable, and probably the best rest I had all month," Debbie remarked, her mind still spinning about her final dream of entering a door or some kind of magnificent archway.

"That's a good sign. I hope they give you a decent bed over there."

"Oh, that doesn't matter to me. As long as I can do the job I want to do, I will be fine."

They cordially arrived at the busy airport. Numerous planes sat motionless on the tarmac and were being loaded for journeys. Debbie made her way to the front desk, where a stewardess smiled inanely. The stewardess informed Debbie that her flight was delayed ten minutes but she could go to the boarding gate.

She asked Debbie a series of questions about the time she was planning at her destination and her belongings.

"I'm definitely going to miss you," Mona said, her voice cracking, "You be sure to have a good time, and save the world while you're at it."

Debbie reached over and gave Mona a big hug. "I'm going to miss you, too. Don't worry, I'll send a postcard once in a while to let you know that everything is fine."

The pair cried and cackled for a few more minutes, then Debbie waved an emotional goodbye as she left the terminal to the departure section. She looked a little nervous as the security guard waved his metal detection wand over her body. For some reason, it made her self-conscious. Mona giggled as she watched Debbie fidget. The guard then smiled, tipped his hat to Debbie, and waved her through the security gate. Finally the moment of leaving the airport and boarding her flight to India had arrived. It was a long flight, but a few movies later and seven magazines thereafter the captain made a final announcement.

"Ladies and gentlemen, in ten minutes we will be landing in Calcutta. The present weather there is 38 degrees Celsius and sunny. On behalf of Air Canada we thank you for flying with us and wish you a pleasant day," The captain's voice sounded like it had a professional smile sent with it over the speakers.

Debbie stretched in her seat and looked out the window as the plane descended. She was relieved to finally arrive, just to get off the plane and once again feel her feet firmly on the ground. She picked up her luggage and proceeded to the passport section.

"Welcome to my country. Do you have anything to declare, Madam?" queried an East Indian customs officer.

"Nothing at all. Just coming for employment purposes, here are my papers." The exhausted lady replied.

"Very well, have a wonderful stay and thank you very much," The bearded turban-man said after briefly scanning her employment visa and then quickly gesturing her onwards.

Three children rushed up to her and asked to push her luggage cart.

"I am fine, I am ok, no thank you," Debbie said to them as she made her way to a man and woman flagging her to them.

"Hello Deborah, we are glad to see you," The youthful man said as he helped her with the cart, "It must have felt like the longest journey you've ever made. How are you feeling?"

"Oh, I would have to say a bit tired, but no problem," She replied, shaking his hand and then the hand of the accompanying lady.

"Hi! Great to meet you! My name is Pamela and I also work for the hunger project here," A middle-aged lady interjected, "We are parked just outside the airport, and have about an hour drive from here to reach the shelter."

"That's not too bad of a drive. I can handle it since I am finally on the ground," Debbie laughed.

Exiting the airport, an old man came up to Debbie who seemed to be seeking money. "Please Madame, I must show you something," He said with a serious glare.

"What is it that you must show me?" Debbie asked.

The old man grabbed her hand and opened it saying, "I knew this. You are going to have an unforgettable journey. For three dollars I will tell you many remarkable things. Please, this is most important." The man seemed almost in tears.

"I don't believe this. A trip to India would surely be unforgettable, what is it that you could possibly say to make the journey any more remarkable?" She laughed.

"It is your personal line Madame. Please I must tell you, this is very different," He implored.

The onlookers smiled while thinking to themselves that this display was a very typical encounter for tourists.

"All right, here is the money," Debbie gave in. Handing him three dollars, she added, "Now please tell me."

The man's eyes narrowed as though he were in deep concentration. Slowly, he intoned, "You are going to meet a great part of your destiny. This line on your hand stops here, which means a great change of life comes soon for you. It can happen anytime now at your age," He sniffled as he looked into her eyes and back to her palm.

"What kind of destiny, and what can you tell me of the great change?" She asked, not entirely convinced.

"You will be taken away, Madame, away to somewhere special. There will you meet with your personal guide to find the legend of your life. It will make very big changes for all time to you. Many changes from what you know. Your life will be on a new road. It will not be the same, not at all," The old man whispered, and gently released her hand.

"Can you, like, be specific about any of this? Is there anything particular you can see?" She asked inquisitively.

"You will be here for a very long time. Be very careful on the way and in the end you will see what I mean. I must go now," The old man offered as he touched her shoulder, then quickly departed into the crowds.

"Is six months a long time to these people?" She asked Pamela.

"To some of them a minute is a long time. That all sounded pretty positive though. What did you think, Stephen?" Pamela asked her companion.

"Sure, it was cool, but sounded more like a two dollar reading to me," He smirked.

The drive was very humid as the ladies fanned their faces in the car.

"We have been in touch with the India Development Group and they are doing everything possible to alleviate the poverty in the rural areas where eighty percent of the people live. One of their main institutions is the ATDA or Appropriate Technology Development Association, which develops small machinery for plants and industries in the rural villages. The other institution, which they have established, is the SIAT or Schumacher Institute of Appropriate Technology that trains youths to develop in technologies to create employment and income potential. These are some of the solutions that have helped to generate a better life in a fast growing society like this one," Stephen explained while driving down the old winding pothole-road.

"What about the mission to feed all the impoverished people?" Debbie asked.

"The numbers continuously increase. There is just not enough of everything for the amount of people that require care. Many of them help to grow, cook, clean, and feed others, which are more unfortunate. They also instruct their fellow citizens to do the same and it does make a great difference, but to reach out to everyone in need is something only a very great power can accomplish," Pamela remarked.

Along the way Debbie noticed so many sick people trudging along the roadside; people carrying baskets on top of their heads, filled with vegetables or wheat and others pulling carts that contained the same with little children seated on top. There was only one in every hundred people that looked remotely healthy.

"We are almost there. Tonight you will sleep in the main warehouse and tomorrow we will take a train to the village where we work," Stephen smiled.

The dusty car pulled into a dirt parking area near an old dwelling where the group got out and went inside.

"This is a shelter but we mainly use it for storage of anything that we can obtain which may be eventually useful. You can wash up in there and this cubicle has a cot in it, where you can rest until morning when we shall leave to catch the train at 9am," Pamela declared

Debbie went into a small shower stall and washed before retiring for the night. She curled up in the cot and before falling asleep she wondered about what the palmist at the airport said regarding her legend and destiny friend. It was a sultry night with a stale air lingering around. She turned carefully on the small cot to regain comfort throughout the night and before long sensed the lights go on. It was 7:30am and Pamela came to let her know that they will go for breakfast.

During the train ride down to the camp, many people hopped on the train for a free ride while it was in motion. Several sat upon the rooftop with their knees bent and rested during the journey. It was as if they were used to jumping the train, climbing aboard effortlessly for routine trips.

When they arrived, it was something of a shock to Debbie. She knew of the sick and famished people but to actually see them in such masses was a heart-breaking experience. There must have been thousands of people lingering around with lifeless energy hoping to get some food and attention for survival. One line-up had hundreds of people moving ever so slowly. Each person held a bowl, waiting to have it filled by a large soupspoon from a wearied lady dishing out from a giant pot. Another line-up was for medical attention. At the end of it people were forked off separately for either vaccinations or physical examinations. Some famished folks were regulars and were given pills for their ailments.

Pamela brought Debbie into a large tent to meet an administrator, who asked her several questions and filled out some papers. She was instructed on the policies and pertinent information about care and being careful. She was given a nursing uniform and began working as an assistant in another tent area.

"This will be your area for the week, Debbie. You will work with Dr. Hartman in General Care," the nurse gestured as the doctor smiled with acknowledgment, shaking Debbie's hand, "If you have any questions you can ask him or just come to see me. Every day at 6pm you will be bused to the sleeping quarters and there you will wash up and eat and have leisure time until you decide to sleep. The bus returns from there in the mornings at 8am. Every second weekend we provide a trip to a nearby town where you can get away from the stressful situations and relax while enjoying some sight seeing. Again, feel free to talk with us about any questions or concerns you may have. Talk with you later," The nurse said as she lifted the side of the tent and walked out.

"Good morning, you may call me Frank, it is wonderful to see you." The doctor said to her.

"It is good to finally be here, a dream I have had for a long time," Debbie replied.

"We try to reassure these people that life will continue although for many of them it is inevitable that it will not. It is fortunate that most of them believe life does not end but only changes. Some of them feel it is a blessing to die, especially if misery has taken over. To begin a new life, better destined for survival, is seen as a positive in their eyes. They are very strong-willed and determined. That is one saving factor in their survival. All these people on the left side are critically ill with malaria and diseases such as tuberculosis. The ones on the right are mildly ill and are overcoming a sickness. Most of them on the right should be able to leave soon as they regain strength. If you could change their wound dressings and feed them as required, add some reassurance and smiles, they may be able to leave sooner than later. I will provide you with a list of medications they individually require and show you where to get them from the cabinets in back," The doctor explained.

"Great, it will be my privilege, and I will do my best" She nodded with determination.

During the next few weeks Debbie became accustomed to handling most situations that she was confronted with and gradually acclimatized to the heat as her blood thinned from the drastic climate change of India compared to 'Winterpeg'. She managed to communicate fairly well with the patients and came to understanding their needs. Her performance was greatly applauded by Dr. Hartman. He filed a request to retain her assistance with him for the rest of the month. One gentleman in his forties thrilled in telling her about the Hindu customs and beliefs. His name was Raja and everyday she sat beside him when she was not busy and listened to his philosophies.

"Good morning Raja, are you feeling alright today?" Debbie asked.

"Another day and one towards being free. Winning isn't everything, it's the only thing," He said with a pleasant smile.

"We should get you up and try walking today. Are you ready for that?" She asked.

"Always ready for something. Right now, if you wish," He agreed.

She took him by the arm and lifted him from the bed carefully. "I was thinking what you told me about the chieftain Krishna, from the holy book, the Bhagavad Gita yesterday, and why he was in favor of war against the tribes," She mentioned.

"Yes, but he was also the incarnation of the great god Vishnu, and it was his will that war takes place despite Arjuna arguing against it knowing that Krishna had no foundation for it to occur. He explains to Arjuna the nature of the universe and that you must put aside sorrow to do duty as it is meant. The important mission is that the soul must be freed from the mortal body to accomplish greater things, but it continues to come back until its duty is done on earth," Raja remarked.

"I see, so the belief is that there is no such thing as death as we know it?" She asked while walking slowly with him down the aisle of the medical tent.

"Birth follows death as death follows birth. It is a cycle like everything in life, in one form or another," He replied, "Pure contemplation is wisdom, it is not action. When we find our self we realize that the soul is part of the vessel of our holy life. What you in the west have called the soul as being part of the intelligence linked with the right and wrong decision making factors is only part of it. It is, in its vastness, connected with much of your human nature but reducible to your totality in the end."

"What do you mean by that, Raja?" She asked, obviously confused.

"Your realization of personal existence is not confined to self but expands to the world and all of life existence. Your ideal self is not confined to merely personal actions. Action is karma and it has effect and stirs things up to make complications. Your spirit touches all of life by encompassing the totality of everything without being restricted with time and space. Death cannot affect it, but is only an experience like going on holiday. What I am saying is that you are immortal and when you can realize that you will be closer to the greatest freedom," He muttered, struggling to keep pace as she turned around and headed back to his bed station.

"There is nothing wrong with that, but how can a person be closer to realizing it?" She asked.

"Detachment is a method. When you can detach yourself from the outside world and the subjective calling, then you can see clearly. I hold pleasure and pain to be the same; they are both feelings. They are different only in the grip of compassion. I have been ill for two years and unable to walk for most of that time and now I am walking. I am doing this now not just for the desire to walk but for the purpose that I must. I prepare myself for action, not because of it. Embracing the all allows me to flow freely. It is the same in victory and loss. Krishna advocated war, as he was the creator and destroyer in the universe. He is the God in the Gita. He is also that steady, unchanging state called Nirvana, which is bliss beyond the phenomenal world and it is timeless. We are all part of him and cannot separate ourselves from the whole and at the same time cannot ignore functioning. Survival is required to pursue destiny and live as we are meant to live. At the same time we must, if at war or using action, be able to detach ourselves from it otherwise we become enslaved," Raja smiled as his arm left hers and he walked in front of her a bit faster.

"This sounds familiar to what you said about the state of Brahman yesterday. Hey! Slow down! You are not going into the Olympics tomorrow!" She laughed.

"In the manner of love, yes it is Debbie. Absorbing personality into the immortal center you become integrated by the process of disintegration, and through the element of complete love you can become Brahman and reach Nirvana. Loving and fearing the Greatness is unavoidable. Dreams can be shattered and fury can arise even when peace is a thought. Life can change so quickly, and we must always be ready. Karma can be a wicked thing from a personal perspective. Through divine grace you can defeat karma and speed it up to dissolve it. Love and devotion can make miracles, but at the same time there has to be the detachment from pride, desire, anger and possessiveness as the Gita tells us," Raja concluded as he paused to take Debbie's arm once again.

"Everything sounds easy and wonderful when you hear it, but to experience it is a different story. Life is not easy with ups and downs," Debbie remarked.

"Yoga changes that. Practice is everything you know. Bhakti yoga for example is yoga of devotion to God and is one way of achieving union with the divine. The less problems we entice and invite in life, the easier it becomes," Raja grinned, trying to step up his pace again.

"If you don't slow down, marathon man..." She warned with a wry giggle, "How did you come about all this sudden energy today, Raja? Yesterday I wouldn't have attempted to get you walking and today you are a new man!"

"It is kind of wonderful. Sometimes that healing just clicks right in and when it does, oh goodness glory!" He praised and added, "I am ready to go back to work."

"What kind of work do you do?"

"I am a professional traveler. I go by train and by foot from village to town and work where there is a job for how long it might be. I have worked from the north to the south of India and let me tell you, it has been such an experience."

"For sure. Well I shall check with Dr Hartman about giving you some inoculations before releasing you. He would probably agree to let you go tomorrow. I am going to miss all of these discussions you know," She lamented.

"There is somebody you should meet Debbie. He is a good friend from me and lives only two hours by train from here. Do you not have a free weekend coming tomorrow?" Raja inquired.

"Yes, it is Friday tomorrow and I am free from noon until Monday. Why should I meet this friend of yours, Raja?"

"His name is Mahatma Shivaji Sabalini and he is a very special person. You will see," Raja smiled.

Their journey was like a dream, travelling amidst the masses of people that were of another world. The rickety steam locomotive whirled down the tracks with a hot air flowing through its opened windows. Raja leaned outside of the train happily, letting the wind stir his dark, matted hair. Debbie giggled like a schoolgirl, thinking the man foolish in his antics yet excited that he felt like he did.

"Do people still follow the philosophies of the great leader Gandhi?" Debbie asked, once Raja withdrew from the window and reseated.

"Yes," Raja smiled, brushing his hand through his hair, "In different parts of India there are many people who remember him and hold praise for him. He was a remarkable man during his 79 years, and when he passed in 1948 he was sorely missed. Back in 1891 he met a great theologian named Madame Blavatsky just before her death and became an associate member of her theosophical society, which was set up in Madras. He was influenced by their remarkable work on the inner planes and their remarkable scientific research in occultism. It is very intriguing to investigate such matters."

"I believe that Raja. I've read books about Guardian Angels and Spirit Guides and they really fascinate me. I believe that what you do inside will have a great affect outside. The inner world and the outer world are always at some kind of play together, don't you agree?" Debbie offered.

"Naturally, they cause an influence upon each other and that becomes the laws of karma. To have a spiritual marriage goes beyond that, to the bliss of enlightenment. It is not simply enough to accept the woes of social life and what happens in your life, but to master them and be above them is a key to not allowing them to play with you. Nirvana is a step and Brahman is another step that is immortal and knows no change."

" Is it right to want to change somebody, to help them to become better?" Debbie asked.

"Only if they are at the stage and willing to be helped. It would be a natural event in any case. To look upon a poor soul and try to change them can be either a disaster or a mistake. Everybody is what he or she is and where he or she is for some particular purpose."

"Well, we discipline children so that they learn and appreciate life more. I think it is all right to do the same with adults because some people do not learn so quickly and to help them is possibly a good thing, wouldn't you agree?"

"Every situation is different, and you can help people most by being yourself and living the example. Going out of your way is one thing, but changing the course of life can be detrimental. Look at all the people who think they know truth and salvation, and the havoc they cause. Life is really strange in your country! Self progress is important but many western people are blindly pretending to be something they are not."

"Do you think we can change destiny, Raja?"

"We have a path in life that relates to our individuality and ideal nature. Being in balance allows us to have the vision of our destiny and to perform it without creating more obstacles. It is detrimental to our "would be" destiny by not working towards realizing it. Being firm yet flexible provides us with understanding and a brighter light to experience and cause change to work with our destiny," He smiled.

"That kind of makes sense. When I look around at all these people, they do not appear to be striving towards any great material success in life. In fact they seem content in what little they have. Do you think they have goals with their destiny?"

"They have few desires for anything material. Many just want to help their family to stay alive. Survival is not easy when disasters take everything away. When the people of Lutur in Maharashtra went through severe earthquakes and the people in Andhra Pradesh suffered floods from the rainfalls they lost everything. It is hard enough to get by but when nature comes with havoc, all is worsened and destiny is lived by the moment," Raja concluded.

"That is so true, and it happens in many places across the world. Tell me about the Mahatma we will visit," Debbie asked enthusiastically.

"Well, he does not prefer that name but it has been bestowed upon him. There is a clear radiance around him that projects the peace he holds within. Nothing is too complex in his answers. He likes to clarify life in a simple manner. Life is complex but when we can concentrate we can solve any mystery. He is a fascinating man, you will soon see," He smiled gracefully.

The train slowed down to a gradual halt at the station. People climbed down from the rooftop and out from the cabins. Debbie and Raja walked up the road with conventional backpacks slung over their shoulder. Old bicycles rode past them and mule drawn carts hovered down the dirt road as they casually paced along.

"This is definitely a different atmosphere than what I am used to. It is like stepping into an old world and not knowing another exists," She said while looking at people working in the fields.

"Each to their own Debbie. You may find this a slow pace, but if you lived it long enough it would be quite normal. You see, we change with our surroundings, with the people and atmosphere, and we become accustomed to what we perceive. We are very much like machines that work on routines, you understand," Raja replied with a sweep of his arm.

"Aha, I agree with that. How far is the walk?" She asked.

"It is over this next hill, then up a path. Not really that far," He smiled as they walked along, casually chatting about the poverty of the villagers and drought in the area.

"You step on the ground and dust flies up to your knees. Look at those dusty twigs on the branches of the trees. When has it rained here last?" Debbie questioned.

"A long time ago. In two months it will begin to rain very much. It will rain heavy then," Raja replied.

"I see. Well, my blood better thin out soon, this heat is overwhelming!" She laughed.

"Here is the path, Sabalini is not far from here," He said, his face growing serious.

"Oh, look at that carving in the tree stump. It is a goddess, is it not?" She asked.

"Yes, he has made many carvings. That one is of the creative deity named Kali. She is the universal provider, a Great Mother aspect of life. Sometimes she is regarded as a divine harlot giving illicit love and other times as a pure virgin. She has many different forms to her nature. The primordial mysteries in our mind come from her nature as feelings of terror, war, and avenging cosmic energies."

"Does her name mean something?" Debbie inquired.

"Kali means black. Many stories have what is called a black goddess in them. Egypt had Black Isis, Rome had Black Venus and Greece had Black Demeter. She is regarded as the personification of blackness because she may rule over all the dark elements in life."

"That is interesting. I guess we cannot ignore the dark side of life. It is inevitable what exists," Debbie remarked while pushing some branches from her view. As they walked around a bend, her face widened with delight. "Wow, is that where he lives? It looks like a miniature temple. He has a garden and a walkway around his little place. It looks really adorable," She crooned.

"This is his humble little hermitage. He knows we are here without us coming in his doorway," Raja noted with a sly smile.

"How does he know that?" She asked.

"I talked with him while at the medical station with you. At night he communicated with me. He helped me to heal faster. I could see him with me at times and we communicated about many things. He has the ability to do things without using his body and he has done much I am sure, Raja said as they entered the threshold of the respectful sanctuary.

Sabalini was sitting on the floor upon a pillow, under a window. His eyes were closed as his lips moved to greet them. "Good afternoon and welcome, Raja and Debbie. So good of you to come," He said as his eyes slowly opened.

"He knows my name?" Debbie whispered in awe.

"You must look like a Debbie," Raja chuckled.

There was an unmistakable radiance around the great Guru. His appearance was of great calming serenity like a vast placid sea of tranquility. His head was shaved and his skin of soft golden purity as he rose to his feet and bowed his head gently while gesturing for them to enter.

"You have a lovely, clean and intricate home. It looks very comfortable," Debbie said in a reverent manner.

"Home is where the heart is," He replied with a magnetic attraction that she felt throughout her body and mind.

"There are different forms of meditation. Do you practice a certain kind of meditation?" she asked.

"We can practice transcendental, penetrative, and reparative meditations by tapping into the unlimited source. It enlightens our insight and strengthens us to focus on goals. There is no specific style that I practice. I use each of several styles as they are required." The Guru smiled.

"You must have experienced states of mind that are very deep," She said in a relaxed tone.

"Do you truly desire to experience deeper states?" Sabalini asked with a solemn majestic look.

"I would love to know a secret of life and what it means. It must be a very rewarding experience," She answered excitedly.

"It comes with a price, dear one. It is a search, training and a responsibility to know the divine duty it involves. It becomes devotion," He said as she looked deeply into his peaceful eyes and then to Raja while adding, "Everything requires some amount of devotion. The more important the experience then the greater is the devotion."

His affect upon her was incredible. Her ability to open up and communicate was broadened with enthusiasm. The train journey had been long and it was unbearably hot. Raja recommended that they wash up. The great Mahatma brought a beautiful robe to the door and told her it was a gift he had made. She accepted it.

"This is beautiful," Debbie whispered, " It is so soft cotton and the embroidery is magnificent. Thank you so much."

"You will look like a little Empress with this," He smiled.

After washing they drank a special tea that was prepared and sat on floor cushions prepared for relaxation and a special meditation exercise.

"This feels so exciting in a unusual way. I feel guided and have not even begun," She quietly noted.

"You have begun and you have prepared long in advance," A voice whispered back across from her as their eyes closed. Almost immediately, they drifted into another place. To Debbie, it felt almost as if her body was jerked clean from her bones and hung in mid-air above the devotees.

She felt his presence guiding above her body as her consciousness opened and experienced the most incredible sensation. She could see clearly through another dimension. There were Chatur Maharajas angels at the four cardinal points, which extended into another realm. These Angels were named Dhritarashtra, Virudhaka, Virupaksha and Vaishravana. From them emanated elemental hosts that were directed towards her to bring her in touch with boundless space. It was like they rushed inside of her and up her spine as a specific energy from each quadrant summed together and delivered her to another sphere. Debbie felt fully receptive to the experience and flowed with it in ease, like a river to the sea, being in acceptance of a spirit guide that overlooked her venture.

She was raised to a level of realizing great sorrow through the giver of life and death as represented by the timeless Saturn. A tall, dark archangel wearing a crimson robe under a cloak of black met her and wrapped his shawl around her in utter darkness. His name was Tzaphkiel and he unleashed her in an ageless temple of silence. It was pitch black for a moment then light began to trickle through like a fountain being turned on before the measurement of time. She cried with the vision of sorrow and The Great Mother principle, which to her became a yearning to accept the ALL. Her devotion prevented any interference from what otherwise may have been a wasted effort by all accounts. The experience held out a hand to her and she followed the line it displayed. All of her feelings, every morsel of her soul were aloft normal description. She had awareness of all worldly sorrows but a shield protected her, which had a doubled-headed white eagle upon it and blocked any impacts of energy that protruded from the vastness. She could in no way put into words what was occurring. The palmist back at the airport had majestically seen this coming.

A sparrow flew by and turned into a dove. It was like the past became the future. It was beyond any meditation experience she ever conceived of. Debbie was gripped into a tight spot that she tried hard to be free from. Every muscle and organ in her body, not her actual physical body but her emotional one, tensed and squeezed through the corridor of time as her arms outreached to haul her through a deep tunnel.

A force propelled her forward and caused her to tumble as though her body fell from a cliff and turned in all directions as it spun through space. Her eyes twitched as her hand reached to grab onto tall grass from a field that suddenly appeared from nowhere. She plunged upwards and landed on a path, amidst a field of corn. Before her was an aged pregnant woman, who strangely appeared out of the Stone Age and was connected to agriculture. Looking up to see the morning star shining upon her, she was relieved once again.

The feeling that Venus and Saturn represented all the goddesses of nature and life, the feminine principles of mankind throughout the pantheon, became one supreme goddess quality in her cognizance. The seed of inspirational love was injected into her. She had glimpses of many goddesses from Aphrodite to Hathor, the cow-goddess to Kali and of Frejja, the Norse Goddess of Love. She held a lotus flower in front of her heart as these goddesses infused her with radiance. The brilliance emitted from their brows and into Debbie's aura, filling her heart chakra. The Mahatmas presence was there but not in any personal sense. It was as if he was a director to a story behind the scene, in constant contact with some other Great Masters.

She was engulfed in realizing each minute of her existence for an eternal moment. There was a doorway resembling a giant archway ahead, which she entered. She seemed to glide effortlessly over cobblestones embroidered with emeralds and up a heavy stone stairway. There were signs and meanings and everything imaginable through the entrance. Reaching through it she experienced a connection with everything in life. She turned to look back and could see all directions as the same. Unexplainable in ordinary terms but the oneness that she became was nothing less than abandoning illusions and entering the reality of the inner worlds. It was a connection that holds all life together as a universe. Her hands reached above her head and clasped together as she seen and became one with the image of the full moon and an equal armed Greek Astrological cross below it. It was just like the scepter she was suddenly holding in her hand, the symbol of Venus, a circle with a cross under it. Through the moon she felt the radiance of the sun and the life energy that is given beyond it from all stars in the heavens. Beauty was in everything, everywhere, at all time and beyond imaginative description.

Each moment was a lifetime experience, a connection to another part of the Universe and a significant association with the Whole. The completion of sorrow and silence, of life and death, of mother and father swept her soul to a distant plane. The Empress within her whispered a word of luminosity and of immeasurable worth. It was about her Destiny. It was a word that she carried with her but could not utter. It was a word within silence and was not of any known language. She entered the door of the inner mysteries of creation and the vault of love, in the womb of time dissolving, unlocked for her to see the great Egyptian Goddess, Isis, standing through the brilliance with a silver crescent moon upon her brow. "Goddess above me, shine for me the way," Debbie silently transported.

She felt her soul on many levels, specifically the four worlds of spiritual, mental, emotional and physical in a simultaneous manner. Upon Assiah and Briah she felt her negative, feminine form and upon Yetzirah and Atziluth she experienced the positive form of her manifestation. The physical and mental feminine forms of her character were receptive whereas the emotional and spiritual forms were actively masculine allowing her to use the creative forces through her being as an Aphrodite and to manipulate them upon each level into existence. The Great Goddess opened Debbie's inner eye so that she could see the Divine Spark that fused her positive and negative polarities as a single nucleus. Her soul began to radiate a magnificent hue of bright colors, which invigorated her inner senses as extensions of her physical ones.

Her physical body rested on the pillow in such a peaceful manner with her back straight into the air. Her left and right nostrils breathed the incense in slowly and deeply. It was the forces of nature, Ida and Pingala. Chokmah was the positive force of Wisdom and Binah was the receptive, negative of Understanding. They worked in unison to balance her to the core of her being, as an omnipresent experience. A mist seemed to flow from the air above her into her entire body and then leave again. It brought some potent energy within her body and left its influence inside of her as a reward.

Her eyes opened slowly as she regained normal consciousness. She turned her head slightly to see the Mahatma sitting in a cross-legged yoga posture as her eyes lit up. His body was elevated over a foot from the ground and he was still in trance. She had just witnessed actual levitation by a great yogi. Her hands left their resting position upon her knees and she clasped them together in front of her heart. The Guru Sabalini slowly returned to the pillow beneath him, as his physical body lowered in an eased and controlled manner.

His eyes opened to look at her, delivering a smile through their souls from within their eyes.

"Did you receive what you came here for?" he asked.

"More. Much more," She whispered in a clear and soft voice.

"Now that you see yourself and love your Self, you are at one. You may do anything during this lifetime," He whispered back to her.

Debbie looked around and could not see Raja. The great master stood up as though the air hauled him to his feet. He walked to the door as she followed him out into the garden. Raja was sitting at the bank of a stream, looking into the water. The Master Sabalini took some vegetables from the garden and passed them to Raja. He then walked to a tree and from a branch took off a necklace that he had made some time ago. He placed it around Debbie's neck and looked into her eyes saying, "You will help many people. You have helped yourself. Keep upon the path and never defy your positive Destiny."

"You are a wonderful man. You can teach so much and even without the use of words," She returned the smile with a soft embrace around his shoulders. She held on to the necklace, looking at it. It was a small wooden Sun with a crescent Moon within it, and a seven-pointed star carved within the center, connected by a fine gold chain. She pulled it to her lips and touched it softly with a kiss.

Raja and Debbie got changed and she humbly put the lovely robe into her backpack. Debbie held up her palm to the master as they began walking down the path, away from the holy abode.

"Master Sabalini is a great man. Does his name mean something special?" She asked.

"I think of him as Super Aba Kundalini Man. That's Sabalini!" Raja laughed.

"How long were we here, Raja?"

"It was roughly seventeen hours."

"What? Are you joking?" She asked incredulously.

"We arrived on Friday, early evening and it is now about 3 p.m. Saturday afternoon. You had a transcendent experience. You went beyond space and time, and what is more, you did not age during that earthly time you missed," He smiled.

"I feel something within me Raja. It is all through me," She remarked.

"You should talk not of this. You should use your powers silently. Take the experience with you to help others in the way you must. It is vital not to loose what you have achieved."

They continued up the dusty road towards the village where they would meet the train. There was a young girl sitting in a ditch and looking very ill.

"She needs some help, Raja," Debbie uttered.

"Most certainly she does," Raja voiced.

Debbie walked down into the ditch to speak with the girl. "Hello there little one." She smiled to the saddened young face that was about to vomit from an illness.

Debbie held her left hand in back and her right hand in front of the child's stomach. A radiant energy flowed from her into the youngster. It flowed from her right hand into the front of the child and a negative stream of energy emanated from the back of the child into Debbie's left hand. Debbie turned her head and vomited on the ground. She took the sickness from the child and into herself and dissipated it through her system. She then shook her hands abruptly to rid herself of the accumulated energy. The little girl stood up and held her hands on Debbie's cheeks. She looked into her eyes and slowly a beautiful smile came upon her face. They exchanged a love of life through their souls. The child was beyond being esteemed at the ability and her feeling of wellness.

Raja stood at the top of the embankment looking down, knowing Debbie had found her talent. She was performing natural healing through the acute channeling of energy and concentrated efforts. It was the gift, and she was in touch with it through the secret word, the one that lived in silence. The little girl's hands left Debbie's cheeks and slid down her arms to touch the elder's hands softly. Debbie could see through the young girl and feel her other affliction. She reached down to the child's stomach and moved her hand around then seemingly reached inside the child and pulled out a mass of negative energy that was stored within the vital organs of the child. Debbie fainted to the ground. Raja began to walk sideways down the slope to check his friend but she arose suddenly and sluggishly. She shook her hands, hitting her hands upon the ground to rid herself of the pain that she felt from the encounter. The little girl looked normally healthy although a bit frightened. She ran up the hill, looking back at Debbie who was beginning to stand up. The girl smiled widely and then turned to run home.

Raja began to laugh. Debbie looked up at the clear blue sky and then peered down to her necklace. She held it and gave it a little kiss once again. "The Sun, the Moon and the Stars, we are all of that!" She laughed with deep inspiration. All emotions were dormant within her, as she could summon their powers and convert them into focused healing energies. She smiled radiantly like a Gypsy Queen of Healing Powers, an Empress of Energy. She realized that she could grab an illness and dismember it from any person. Raja took her hand as they walked up the embankment and then headed into the village, ready to live with what has been given to her as a duty. ★

The Holistic Boarder

"...the white light which descends upon him indicates the position of this card in the Tree of Life. His authority is derived from Chokmah, the creative wisdom, the Word, and is exerted upon Tiphareth, the organized man."

(The Emperor) The Book of Thoth- The Master Therion

"**Y**ou have a great friend, it may seem as a brother or father figure, someone close akin to your deepest dreams, that communicates with you. It is neither male nor female, but encompasses qualities of both in the most sublime sense of the word. It is a guide and an angel of sorts that may have once lived a human life but is far removed from any human conceptions that you are aware of. When you pass through the portals of the inner sanctuary it converses with you and teaches you the secrets of your hidden dreams."

I put down my diary on the table and thought for a moment about those words that Kenneth Gardner told me a year ago, as I hastily scribbled them out as he spoke. I remember well the period of six months when Kenneth was a boarder at our house. He taught me something dearly important about the path of life. Kenneth was a traveler, adventurer and prudent salesman. He had a company that pretty much ran itself as he went from one place to another, setting up the foundations for his company to expand.

I was just sixteen years old when my mother accepted Kenneth into our house for a six-month period. My inquisitive mind wanted to know about the strange man and how he attained his success and freedom. Through the harmony of Kenneth's strength, I saw a man that had accomplished much, not only in this world, but also in another. From the first day I saw the boarder, there became an intuitive realization that we would share knowledge about subjects that I was yearning to learn about. Our relationship developed so that before long neither of us had to say a lot of words to get our message across. Kenneth was there for only a week by the time I began waiting in anticipation for the evenings when we'd sit in the den or out on the porch, questioning all sorts of topics that arose from our conversations. One night, I walked outside to start talking with him while both of us stared into the starry night.

"Do you have a formula for success or a number of special methods you use to achieve what you want?" I asked.

"Anybody can create a formula that proves to work for their desires," Kenneth smiled, "It depends on what kind of success you are after. It is fine to want something, but the desire should be strong in order to make it come to you. To want something you should have a great need for it otherwise it may be a burden to you after you receive it. If you combine the devotion of focusing with the energy of emotion in a desire to have something, it develops in your mind and may come to you sooner or later. The power of being able to focus on something is the main key in the formula, which I use."

"I suppose you are right," I responded, "There is a big difference between needing something and wanting something. There has to be a balance otherwise a person can get lost with too many desires and wanting things that creates problems sooner or later."

"Desires are like fire, they expand and grow when you feed them. That is where maturity comes in, so that you are capable of making wise decisions. If you desire something so much and all the time, when you do not have it, your mind may make you feel left out, weakened or sad because the desires are not fulfilled and the cravings take over. I consider this principle for my business success and other matters so that they do not end up ruling my mind. Emotions can certainly rule the way a person thinks, so it is best to be inspired by them and not ruled by not having one thing or another fulfilled at any particular time."

"That makes sense," Was all I could say.

I remember another night where I was curious about something I had seen on television, where writers take pen names for themselves and how actors always make up names that look good on the big screen. I decided to ask Kenneth about it after our evening meal.

Kenneth grinned, "Many people take a name that conceals their true identity or to establish a connection to an identity that they wish to portray to the world."

"Is it for some mystical reason that they would use a name to associate their identity with so that other people recognize them as something different?" Danny asked.

"Sometimes and in a way, yes. It may be to keep them focused on a particular path or desire that enhances their aspirations. Choosing a name to be associated with should reflect something sacred to yourself as well as something you aspire towards. When people grow through time with their given name, they become some of the qualities that the name is attributed to. It is the same when they choose to use a different name for a certain time. Then they may have attained the level they desired, associated with that name, and choose another name to go further with more realized aspirations."

"Can it not become confusing in their mind, after choosing different names?"

"Sure it can, but it shouldn't. A name is kind of like a set of clothing. It distinguishes a personality. There is nothing wrong with changing the personality as long as it is done under will or control of the inner flame. It should be done for the right reasons and not to gain recognition under false pretense."

"What if I wanted to have a secret name, to associate towards my ideals in life?"

"That would be fine, an interesting exercise actually. If you meditated upon your ideals, to seek your true identity, then an inspiration will arise within you and let you know that secret name to use."

"What about who you were before, like in a past life using some other name? Do you believe in reincarnation?"

"Many people do and their beliefs may differ from one to the next. Buddhists, Celts, Druids, Britons, Gallics, Gnostic Christians and a host of other teachings talk about the subject. Poets of the Roman era like Horatio, Lucretius, and Vergil talked about reincarnation. It has been an intriguing subject for ages."

"If people remember a past life, do they become more aware to live the present one?"

"Everything depends on a number of things, Danny. Some people are quite aware in the present life that their mind is not focused on previous ones and the one they live encompasses so much experience from previous ones. In such a case, they have a good insight of their soul and do not recreate problems that they've previously made. Sometimes parents live a rather dull life and it seems their purpose was to bring their child into the world. Being born is from the desire to incarnate into human form to accomplish something, and this something may be to create a child in the future that has a specific desire or purpose to fulfill. That is not to say that the parents did not have their own purpose to fulfill, but after the child is gone on it's own, the parents may lighten up and realize more about their purpose."

"So when a child is born and the parents give it a name, it begins a new identity?"

"Awareness changes just like the body changes over time. At first the infant is given a name to identify its spirit with its human form. During puberty the child then takes on a new awareness as their chakras or inner wheels of light-vibrations become activated. The solar-plexus chakra brings an ego-identity to the person. They begin to realize their distinguished identity and begin questioning their connections with the world. They open their sexual energies and self-expression through the Hara chakra and base chakra and life progresses from there."

"So people go through transformations while they are alive. That is interesting. What if I wanted to know who I was in my past life, is there a way I can find out for myself?"

"There are many ways, Danny. You can develop your memory into the past. Begin by thinking of major events over the past year, then two years and so forth until you were very young. Then try to imagine the feeling you had before being born. Most people remark that while they were in the womb they felt such bliss and love. Sometimes birth is a painful experience. It usually is for a baby. They felt great love when they were attached and alive within the mother. Now they begin a series of transformations into the human form, all of which include some form of pain. Other ways to begin a past life regression are through hypnosis or simply looking at the things in your life that have become a part of you and your surroundings. If you think about the family that surrounds you, the feelings you have, the things you truly hate, the language you speak and so on you can begin to get a grand picture of who you are and open another sense of who you were. You should not judge the thoughts that come into your mind since that may cover the previous identity even more. Sometimes an event will trigger a feeling inside of you. Like if you are visiting somebody or gone on a trip somewhere. A sense of deja vu may occur where you have a feeling that the incident occurred before. If you flow into this feeling and seek visions with acceptance, then they may come to you. Also, if you perform some particularly repeated pattern and are not usually aware of doing it, then it may have a connection with your previous life. Like for instance, if a person always seems to play with a gun, perhaps a gun was a big part of incidents in the past life. You must remember however, that if you died in a tragic way and you find the circumstances out in your present life, you may fall into depressions and live with fears hanging over you. You don't want this to hamper your daily life and progression, so be very careful as to what you believe and how you handle it. Life is not perfect, and the previous ones were likely less perfect so be prepared to handle what you may be tempted to feel, and do so in a mature and spiritually understanding way."

"That is wonderful advice Kenneth. How long would a person be on the inner world before they inhabit another physical life?"

"It could be months, a year, ten years or hundreds of years. When many people die, like during the wars, many of them return to fulfill some appetite that they didn't have the opportunity to. During this day and age, population is soaring because there are so many people creating more life forms for souls to inhabit. Life is more intriguing these days and draws souls from the astral plane, with desires to return to partake in the rapid changing society of advanced technology, entertainment, and spiritual progress that are now far more abundant. Their main concerns, attachments, insights and connections to the physical world play a role in determining how long before they return to this physical sphere again to continue their physical world learning, exploration and experiences. Some people that seem to have many personalities such as in the case of schizophrenia may be harboring entities within. That is to say that there are lost or bounded entities that need a connection to the physical world and end up projecting their cravings into the minds of schizophrenic or drug abused people that may welcome them. Being possessed by entities is also possible for those whose mind and soul are not fully intact."

"I just became curious about something. What if a person commits suicide? What do they go through afterwards?"

"The trauma of suicide results in depression and confusion afterwards. The soul, after suicide, resides in a dense, dark area of the astral plane and comes in contact with other distressed souls that live in confusion of what they did to end their life. Sooner or later the distressed soul will inhabit another body, but the reasoning and result of the previous suicide comes back to haunt them in many forms. It comes down to this, that there is no escape from handling any situation in life. All situations appear for a purpose, to overcome, to learn from, to move on, to adapt, and to master. It is a simple fact of life, it is basic common sense no matter how complex the predicament is that arises. So, escaping it in any form, such as causing intentional death, is a very stupid idea that they will simply pay for and deeply regret."

"How many times has the average person reincarnated, Kenneth?" Danny asked.

"Well, that is a relative question. It could be five or ten times, or perhaps twenty. I would say no more than that. The reason that there are more souls now, more population than before is that more souls are being created as it were, from the source, by whatever name you would give it. Just like there are more houses in the world, and pets, there are more people as well, or more expressions of the 'one'. One of the interesting properties of the physical world is expansion, however we have to be careful with that as we are working with limitations of air, water, fire or energy for consumption and earth or habitable living space. You may think that you will or will not return in the next life, but regardless, we are all connected to the 'one' as a proportional realization of consciousness that changes expression in varying forms with constant transformations. So basically, we may have stupid thoughts and foolish words at one time and later they seem to change into wiser thoughts and words. It is a part of growing, so that nothing remains concrete. Ego aside, Danny, we are expressions of God, working towards self-realization."

"What about all the obstacles a person goes through in life, things they have to cope with, the place they are born, disasters and restricting environmental or social problems and all of that?"

"A soul realizes some of that prior to its physical birth. The problems that enter our life are there to pay off certain debts from the perspective of karma. Everything that encompasses a person is there for a purpose, to expand spiritual awareness. If it appears to be a problem or perplexity, it is there to learn how to master and overcome it in order to find a balance and regain harmony to be aware of something even greater. This is part of realizing the connection that everything has to everything else. Problems occur to promote facets of ourselves so we may become aware of unlimited potency and broaden our vision as a lifelong guidance. The unfortunate thing is that there are more distractions these days, and that causes us to focus less."

Kenneth always had what seemed to be the right words for any question. Over the coming months he taught me a great deal about life, past life, destiny and becoming aware of each moment during life and not to waste it. He once said that, 'In the moment, you have all the power in the world.' I didn't know what he really meant then, but now I have a better understanding of Kenneth's point. If a person lives only in the moment, then they are not worried and are devoid of fear. We become unconcerned about the past or future and we can accomplish much more. If we connect one moment to the next, we live a simultaneous, kinetic, all-encompassing and realizing existence. A person has to be really focused to experience that, and there was a time where I thought I was.

It was at the beginning of summer when my family and I went to visit my relatives for a few weeks. It was along the East Coast, and was always a pleasure to be near the ocean. Dad was cooking lobster with my uncles in the backyard and I went to make a beach campfire with my cousins. It was a beautiful night and one I shall always remember. Rob played guitar and sang French songs as Stephan skipped rocks on the water, next to us. Linda and Carol came down and brought a friend along. Her name was Monique. They started giggling about silly things and finally sat around the fire with us. We all talked about little things that didn't seem to matter and then I looked away and into the sky.

Stephan threw a rock into the fire and some ash burst up and landed on Monique's shirt. I didn't see it but an instinct drove my hand over to grab it before it starting burning her. How I knew there was a fire on her shirt is still beyond me. As I grabbed the ash and threw it to the ground I fell over onto her knee and she looked down into my eyes. At that moment I was captivated by her glare into me. It was like I saved her life the way she looked at me. That feeling surpassed the time barriers and lasted an eternity. We were locked in the moment for probably twenty seconds but had to return and resume normal conversation. She called me the fire catcher and joked with me for the remainder of the evening. A bit later we found a solitary rock to sit on to express intimate emotions on many levels to recapture the earlier experience.

Every day became more wondrous and beautiful than the previous one as we swam together in the ocean, went on walks and collected seashore paraphernalia. When it was time to leave with my family, she waved as our car drove away. I still remember the tears that softly made their way down her cheek while the car was pulling away. We kept in contact through my cousins but her family moved away and I never saw her again. It is such moments that become another language through the heart, on other levels, that so much becomes possible, when captured and lived.

When we returned home, Kenneth was in his room writing something in a book. I knocked on the door and went in. I asked him what it is with time that makes you feel like you have lost something important and dear to yourself.

"Time is an illusion," he began, "a limitation in linear terms that is always collapsing and something we use to file our experiences in. We have been trapped by the concept of time imposed through society and the ages. Your thoughts are creating energy or the raw material of creation through your continual active consciousness. When you have a thought it is imprinted on this energy and develops a vibration. This vibration is something that you feel with your emotions and in turn stored inside and later to be reacted upon as an experience from memory. So, young man, if you feel that you have lost something, perhaps a love, always remember that it can be there forever, if the moment imprinted the vibration in your memory. Memories are subtle imprints so let's hope that for the rest of your life you have wonderful ones." He smiled.

"What if they happen to be bad memories?" I asked.

"In that case, they become warnings. If they bother you, then you have to learn to tap into the rhythmic patterns of their vibration. This is what everyone does every day, to some degree, with the images in their mind. People tap into the vibrations around them and expand on that pattern. Healers do it, scientists do it, and organizations do it, all in an effort to expand on the vibrations. People that are in deep meditative states may affect situations on the other side of the world, simply by tapping into the patterns of vibrations surrounding the characteristics."

"That is amazing, Kenneth. It means that life is so much more than a physical mass, that it is subject to change by the powers of the mind and forces that are used." That thought triggered another in my chaotic mind. "I've always wondered if there is a secret in being able to distinguish a holy person from a person that may have ulterior motives, yet pretends to be someone with great and good powers."

Kenneth never skipped a beat. "When you are around someone that seems to radiate light, and they are devoid of fear and express love, the chances are good that they are a good person. Everyone is essentially good, but their methods and practices may have caused them to perform sufferings unto others. Either way, it can be seen and felt through the vibrations they emit. People may make fear and time a desperate conspiracy against their hidden dreams. They may feel inferior or superior to another person, but the fact is that we are all stars, some are more or less aware of certain abilities than others. Some people plunge into the opportunities available, whereas others may see it as not required for their course in life or are confused and have fear hanging over their head. Life is really simple in its apparent complexity. People are the same way. Some may wish to be seen and noticed and they thrive on the glamour whereas others may simply wish to express qualities that are meaningful and sincere. It is becoming easier to see through people as society advances simply for the fact that when a person is soul searching their instincts tell them the truth about everything. Instincts work with love, so the deeper the love you have the greater the instincts and the better the qualities you bring out from other people."

"You can express things so easily. How is it that you do this Kenneth?"

"How is it that you do not, Danny?"

That caused me to pause. Unsure of how to answer, I changed the subject.

"Were you ever married Kenneth?"

"No, but one day perhaps. I've shared my dreams with some special people but they went on towards another path in life. That is the way it is, better to have loved and lost than to have not experienced it at all. Now that I am aware of what I must accomplish in life and how much work it involves, I am not on a search to be with anyone. If it happens that I meet someone and the attraction is felt as something deeply shared, then that would become part of the journey through the search that I am on."

"I know what you mean. Relationships come and go and they don't necessarily have to be forever with one person, although if it is a life experience with one person it should be a great one. What is it that makes a person realize their destiny, their importance in life?"

"The initiative of searching inwards to answer your questions begins to make changes in your outer world. You may be swept up with creative energy that touches upon inspiration and wisdom and this is exerted into the organized mind. Leadership of any form requires the ability to direct power, and when you have become aware of your every move and motion through life you will have a subtle dominance over your environment. This is the unique power of an emperor or empress, one who commands and becomes the paternal authority for those around him or her. They know their destiny, their purpose and what has to be done. They have a vision, a dream that they are creatively divining through the world. Your importance in life is no less than that. Everyone goes through experiences before realizing their importance. It may be refined from one year to the next, but eventually, Danny, the essence of it is realized and accomplished to perfection."

"This is something I want to go to bed and think about. I wish you a good night and great day tomorrow Kenneth, and thank you for sharing this with me tonight." I always felt light-headed after speaking with Kenneth. He would always give me so much to think about, and I'd like to believe that not a lot of sixteen-year-olds thought about the same stuff I did. I was truly blessed to have Kenneth's company, and I appreciated that he always took me seriously.

A few months after Kenneth stayed with my family, I had grown into realizing much about many different subjects. He would come and go at different times and sometimes be gone for two or three days. He was clearly a good man, one who has cleansed his past and became free to move in ways through the future with delicate ease and forethought. Whenever we were not talking, he always seemed busy with something. I have never seen him once watch television yet he knew about everything in the news. One day I saw him in the park during my lunch hour from school. He didn't see me and I never mentioned it but what I saw was absolutely stunning. He was touching a tree and looking up at it, kind of like feeling for some energy. After a few minutes of that he went down a walkway and began to talk to a lady. She had a young daughter, so I presumed, who was in a wheelchair. I stood behind a tree and watched inconspicuously. The little girl looked rather pitiful crunched up and confined, yet she smiled. Kenneth then touched her on the head and was talking with her. He held her hand and she stood up. Her mother began to laugh with excitement and was overwhelmed with joy. Kenneth then talked with both of them and touched them on the face then slowly turned to walk away. The last thing I saw was the mother hugging her daughter and then I went back to school totally amazed.

A few evenings later I was able to catch him outside our house and talk about the subject of healing. "Are there some mysterious forces that people can tap into and use to help other people in distress and to heal them?"

"There are many people involved in the study of this and it is a large field. Some may refer to the force as a power of chi, or ki. Some may call it manna, the life force, prana, or even cosmic breath. A person that requires healing may need certain energies directed to particular areas. Sometimes it is physical healing that is required, sometimes it is emotional or mental or a combination of all. Each level and sub-level of the physical, emotional and mental affects one another and so a particular area has to be focused upon. A healer, for example, may call down the subtle matter energy from the seven flames or seven spirits of God or of the seven Mighty Archangels. So, in basic terms, this energy comes from the collective Holy Spirit; the seven inner worlds as some may define it. It streams through the healer and is focused to the illness, and seems to have a consciousness of its own to do the required work. The seven chakras within the etheric body, or body next to your physical body have seven corresponding pranas that are attributed to them from the crown chakra to the root chakra. In order these pranas are called, vyana, prana, udana, prana, samana, apana and apana. Even though some of these energies are called by the same name, they are on different levels. They determine the state of health or disease that your body is constantly dealing with. That is why there are so many things in life that are important for balance on the inner levels. Things such as proper eating and exercise, care of mind and emotions, purity of air and water are all important in reaching balance."

"What is it about light that is so mystifying, is it something that comes from the spirit world?" I asked.

"Not exactly, and it may be deceiving to hear about the topic of light as it can be used in so many contexts without regard to accuracy. Many people using the term light in spiritual discussions may call it light of the soul but in actuality having psychic connection to the astral plane, they may be talking about the astral light. They may be referring to the medium that you travel through while on the astral plane. The light of the soul nurtures our development and transforms us into a revised, greater identity. It is an enriching and inspirational light, emitting from higher octaves as it were, with various orders of experiences and realizations. You may think of it as different intensities. For one thing, when a person is in touch with a higher intensity, it does not evaporate as readily and has longer, lasting effects. One flame can ignite and create more flames, but when the light is of an intense spiritual nature, its significance is undoubted and abilities seemingly unlimited. Everyone has an imprint or signature in the akashic or space realm. The physical body has an etheric counterpart and by being deeply stimulated through the higher light you can feel some other person of your choice through the akashic level. The solar plexus is the heart of your inner system, it corresponds to the sun and you can emit the prana that flows through your solar plexus to their etheric counterpart and begin to help them heal in special ways, no matter the distance. The healer projects subtle laser rays of energy connected with the intelligence of the cells through the prana to the person they connect with. It becomes a resonance of frequencies aligned from the sender and fused with the receiver."

"It seems like a complex subject Kenneth, and one that may take years to comprehend. Can people that are aware of and use these energies and light mediums enter higher states of consciousness from the effect of the sender?"

"Definitely, Danny, and in fact some masters do initiation from great distances in the astral and mental planes and utilize the patterns of vibration of their students to help develop and initiate them. It becomes an incredible subject of possibilities," Kenneth added.

"No doubt. Anything seems possible, even changing reality." I laughed, thinking myself foolish the moment I said it. Still, I truly believed that Kenneth could do anything.

"Reality is unchanging. We live in a world of illusions, Danny, and it becomes the task of the spiritual person to rise above those illusive levels and to become face to face with reality; one with their higher self living in supreme awareness."

"That is a great thing for me to remember. I must do some homework now so I wish you a good night."

One night, I was out late playing Dungeons and Dragons with my friends. I really enjoyed the fantasy worlds that my game master made. I was playing the role of a wizard who specialized in conjuring and summoning spells. I loved making something out of apparently nothing. In fact, that's pretty much what I was like outside the game as well. Any little thing that came to my mind would turn into some long-winded conversation. It drove my friends nuts, because they always had other things on their mind, like sports, or girls, or girls in sports. My wizard got me thinking about the conversation I had with Kenneth the other night, which piqued my curiosity about something else. I got home from the game around midnight, and the full moon had risen to its pinnacle. I found Kenneth outside, eyes closed and head raised as he mouthed silently to himself, or perhaps to the Moon. I watched quietly, not wanting to disturb him. He looked so tranquil and at peace. I hoped to find such peace in my lifetime. He soon came out of his trance and looked over to me. "Ah, back home from your gaming." He grinned, "Did you win?"

I couldn't help but smile stupidly. "It's not the goal, but the adventure that matters."

Kenneth laughed. "Spoken like a true aspirant"

We walked into the house, where Kenneth cooked up a delicious veggie stir-fry for a midnight snack. After the meal, I couldn't contain my curiosity any longer. "Do you know anything about conjuring spirits?" I blurted.

Kenneth blinked once. "Spirits, as many term them, are always waiting to be called. Many of them are bored; holding a sense of loneliness just as humans often appear to be, and live with a craving to perform, to substantiate their existence. Having a good purpose in calling upon spirits is important, as they are not the best of guests to have around. Many of them may appear to be rather dumb, without imparting knowledge of much value, and sometimes make it a chore to be rid of them. Is it something you are planning on performing Danny?"

"Not quite, I was simply curious to know. Where will you go once you are finished setting up your business here? Do you have a plan?"

"I am going to help a friend in California with some unfinished business. After that, I will be going to Mexico for a few months," Kenneth replied, starting the dishes.

"I've never seen anybody so busy and yet so free. You sure keep yourself organized, Kenneth."

"Someone has to, and so I've taken it upon myself."

My recollections of the times with Kenneth left an imprint inside, a subtle imprint to advance myself in the teachings of the holistic boarder. I stood beside my bedroom window and looked out over the city. I put my hand over my forehead as I reveled in the final great memory I had of the man who taught me that the price of freedom was to be consumed upon the spiritual journey.

I remember the last evening that Kenneth was at our house, I went upstairs to my room to read a book. After reading a few pages I heard some noises. The weird thing about them was that I could discern that they were not from the physical world. It was completely bizarre, like I had tuned into some frequencies somehow that my mind could now pick up. It was a very strange sensation. Within the low-pitched noises I could hear the sound of bells. I got up and walked slowly to the door of my bedroom and held my ear towards the hall. I stepped into the hall and tiptoed towards Kenneth's door, listening in for any sounds. The door was open a crack and I put my hand on the handle and cautiously opened it further and looked in. At the corner of the room I could see Kenneth staring into a mirror. There was a haze surrounding him. My eyes must have widened as the haze formed into several figures of human beings. Kenneth stood in some trance as I looked on with astonishment. Suddenly, I realized something about the figures surrounding Kenneth. They were not alienated beings but images brought from the past that were connected to Kenneth. They were the lives that he once lived. Kenneth was holding a comb but stood motionless. There was an image of an Indian man, a Spanish man, an African, Egyptian and someone of possible further ancient decent. I was intensely intrigued but something within me told me not to interfere with the operation. A sudden heat entered my body and I quietly closed the door and returned to my room. I walked over to the mirror on my cabinet and looked closely into my own eyes. I began to breathe very slowly and feel every breath go deep within my body as though it was performing something incredible within. Through my eyes I could see who I really was. I had great enthusiasm to practice the teachings that I learnt from Kenneth and to keep a record of my advancement.

I felt invigorated breathing in the clean oxygen, as I became aware of the presence of another body outlining my physical body. It was my etheric body and within it I envisioned my chakras. I had a new awareness of life energy and could continually see prana circulating around my chest and flowing outwards. I looked at myself and vowed to make each step into the future count towards aspiring up the spiral ladder of lights. My desire was to become the emperor of my inner world and master of my temple, just like Kenneth. ★

THE ORACLE OF OSIRIS

"The gods are not persons to be seen or spoken to, their utterances are delivered in oracles, and these are normally cryptic and difficult to understand. There is a Pythoness in every one of us, and a Delphic cavern, namely our imagination, into which we must retire if we are to accomplish anything of worth."

General J.F.C.Fuller

"**M**erry Meet, Druid. Have you heard any news about CrimsonFyre?" Tanya typed in her frequented chat room on the Internet.

"Merry Meet, Coventry. She is still in the hospital. Tonight everyone agreed to meet here at the regular time to send prayers for her well-being and recovery," Druid responded.

"I shall be here."

At that instant Shawn barged into Tanya's bedroom as she was typing. "Don't you know how to knock?" she yelled.

"Yeah, but I need a ruler," Shawn replied without concern, "Don't you have one on your bookshelf?"

"Take it and leave. Next time make sure you knock on the door before you come in!" Tanya scolded.

"Okie-dokie, Sis. By the way, Mom wants you to help with the dishes," Shawn grinned as he walked out.

"Did the police find the guy who assaulted her?" Tanya continued typing.

"Nothing yet, Coventry. Last night SilverElf told me she was going to meet someone she met in another chat room. Don't know if there is any connection, we will talk about it this eve. Have to go to work now. Blessed be," Druid typed.

"Merry part Druid, have to go help Mom." Tanya signed off from her chat room and grudgingly went downstairs. The sink was already full of hot water when Tanya got to the kitchen. Tanya's mom flashed her a smile as she entered, gesturing silently to the pile of dishes.

As she began her chore her father, Troy, came into the kitchen with his usual cup of coffee. He sat down at his regular seat, and let out a sigh as he relaxed. "Tanya," he began, a smug smile on his face, "tomorrow we are going down to the mall. I'm going to buy a little gift for you and Mom."

Tanya's eyes lit up. "What's that, Dad? Is it the phone?" she asked excitedly as she washed a frying pan. Troy nodded. "Yes, we are getting a cell phone. You and Mom are going to share it, so don't make a bunch of unnecessary calls on it, alright?"

"Thanks Dad! I promise not to call everyone I know," she giggled as he set his cup on the counter. Troy kissed his wife, Andrea, then saluted and headed off to work.

"I hope he gets home for supper tonight," Andrea commented, "Your Dad is overworking himself lately."

Tanya smiled reassuringly. "He will probably be late again Mom. You know how he is fixated on the business now."

"I have another migraine coming on," Andrea sighed, rubbing her temples, "I need to go lay down in my room."

"Mom, I read that a lot of people get migraines from drinking too much coffee. A study showed that some people get a headache after six hours of caffeine withdrawal. MSG and artificial sweeteners can also give headaches. They say the best things for relieving it are exercise, proper dieting and relaxation."

"Maybe I should take some vitamins."

"If you get withdrawal symptoms you can take vitamin B and B6 and also niacin. They will help. Do you want me to give you a temple massage, Mom?"

"Thank you sweetheart, but I will be fine. Just going to lay down for a while."

"Ok, I will clean the house a bit. Just go relax, Mom."

"Good morning, Mr. Johnson," The receptionist smiled as Troy walked into his office.

"Good morning, Silvia. Is the Madison report ready to deliver today? "

"Yes, it is completed and ready. Would you like a briefing on it beforehand?"

"I haven't the time right now. Just bring it in on my desk and I will review it while I prepare the afternoon speech," Troy replied as he rushed into his office.

"Certainly, Mr. Johnson." Silvia cordially responded.

At 2pm Troy began the seminar. Hosts of people gathered in the lobby of the Inn and then were seated in the conference room.

"Competition is what we are all involved in through our businesses," Troy began, "Existing firms have established such a large clientele that they are capable of producing lower per-unit costs. Of course the government is interested in seeing new industries grow and create more jobs, which increases the gross domestic product. They impose trade tariffs and trade barriers so that growing businesses may become competitive to the world markets."

Confident that he had the audience's attention, he continued, "Innovative marketing strategies that substantiates its worth in expanding a business is what our firm is all about. Our research and development team will provide a portfolio for your company to work with. If your goals are to reach a national market, we will systematically provide the strategy to do so. Let's face it, there are companies out there that will dupe you for every penny they can. What is the world coming to if we are going to let this be a common practice? People will eventually be fed up with purchasing luxuries, if they are going to be nickel-and-dimed to death. The paradox of thrift comes into play here. If enough people decide to not spend and rather save their income, then the total income earned in any country would decline, there would be a loss of jobs, and so forth. As a result, there would be less money distributed and in turn savings will be reduced. We talk of prosperity, but there has to be some truth in that statement. We have to reach people in a way that is required and honest if we want a steady stream of return.

"The circular flow of money means that it flows from businesses to households and then back to businesses through repeat purchasing. The consumer is the demand and the business is the supply. Here we have expenditures and incomes at work together. Through speeding this process up, profits will increase. We have successfully doubled and tripled the expansion of over one hundred companies this year utilizing the principles that we have strategically placed within each one.

"Every business has short and long term goals. If you look in the brochures that you were offered on your way in, you would see just how we operate in the examples given. Before we commence with the projection presentation, I offer you to take a five-minute recess for some of the refreshments."

The rest of the presentation went flawless, as Troy had designed the presentation himself and knew exactly how the company's goal oriented projections were best delivered. At the conclusion of the seminar a man walked up to Troy with a look of concern on his face.

"That was a very well done consultation, Mr. Johnson. I would like to take a few minutes of your time to ask some questions about a company I am developing," he voiced.

"Certainly, what is it that you care to discuss?" Troy replied.

"My name is Darren, and it is great to meet you. I am in the construction business but am setting up a business to distribute artifacts throughout the country."

"What particular types of artifacts are you distributing, Darren?" Troy asked inquisitively.

"I have collected several from South America and Africa and have much from Egypt as well. I was wondering how I could reach out to the public and create an awareness and need for them."

"There could definitely be potential in marketing them. We would have to make an appointment for a consultation for your business plan. When would be convenient for you to drop into the office?"

"How about next Monday?" Darren replied.

"That sounds fine. Say, about 11am?"

"I will be there with some of the ideas I have, on paper," Darren responded with excitement.

During the evening, Tanya entered her usual chat room on the Internet and met with several of her online friends.

"Merry meet, Coventry," A warm welcome came to her from another chat name, Amen-Re.

"Amen-Re! Greetings, it's been a long time!" she replied.

"Everyone's been discussing CrimsonFyre's condition for over an hour now," Amen-Re commented.

"What is her condition?" Coventry asked the room.

"She is in a coma. Nobody knows exactly what happened. Some kids found her off the side of a highway and she was unconscious. Her family is at the hospital still but tomorrow I will know more. I shall telephone them in the morning," Druid replied.

"Goddess Bless. I want to go visit her on the weekend. I saw her last month at her home in Galveston when Morgan and I visited," Coventry wrote.

"She is such a wonderful person. Who could do such a horrible thing? Angel-Dawn wrote.

"You know the infamous history of Interstate 45. There are really sick people out there and because the highway is frequented by a multitude of travelers, the worst of them can show up at any time," Druid explained.

"Why do they let people that are like that continue to live in this world? I mean, the victim doesn't have a second chance, so why should the criminal?" WiccanRite expressed.

"All life is sacred, even that life belonging to the twisted mind of one who causes harm to another. Human rights try to restore the appreciation of life into such people, but it doesn't work in all cases," Amen-Re noted.

"Their wrong-doings will come back to them threefold, even if they wish to not believe it, it will happen!" Angel-Dawn exclaimed.

"Nobody is without fault, but a line has to be drawn somewhere, otherwise chaos will destroy all those who are in the basic preparation stages of learning their spirituality," Druid remarked.

"The law needs to be tuned! Why spend time and money and lawyers on a person that is so messed up as to seriously harm another?" Angel-Dawn questioned.

"Perhaps because time is money and lawyers are both? It is the fallacy of the judicial system. Everyone has equal rights, but let's face it, the line should drawn when one person removes the rights of another," Coventry wrote.

"I agree! Why should prisoners have nice meals and televisions and free room and board? Why should we pay for their wrongful decisions?" WiccanRite intervened.

"These are all legitimate concerns and opinions, however I am sure there are people who have taken them into consideration. Remember, not all prisoners are lifetime bad people. Some crimes are minor compared to others, but I agree in the instance that those who commit serious crimes shouldn't get bargains and special treatment. Bribery may be an offence, but the police use it ever day to obtain information," Amen-Re interjected.

Suddenly, Shawn burst into her room. "Mom wants you downstairs, Tanya!"

"See the hard surface on the other side of that door, Shawn? Smack it with your hand next time before coming in, will you!" Tanya snarled. "Tell her I'll be down in a minute. Now get out!"

Shawn bowed deeply, "Yes, your Highness," he quipped as he left. Tanya turned back to read her screen.

"WiccanRite, are you coming to Houston this weekend?" Coventry wrote.

"Will call you if I can come, Coventry," her friend replied.

"Have to go help downstairs. Merry part everybody," Tanya concluded. Sighing, she pushed herself away from the keyboard and trudged downstairs. Her mom was waiting for her at the foot of the stairs.

"Did you finish your homework, Tanya?" Her mother asked.

"Of course I did, Mom. Finished it an hour ago in fact. Just 'cause you are a teacher at the school, you don't have to check up on me every day, you know," Tanya replied with an earnest attempt of being pleasant.

"I will consider that in the future. I know you are responsible enough to make sure you do everything you are supposed to," Her mother smiled back. Just then, the front door opened and Troy entered. He flipped his hat onto one of the empty hooks and kicked the door shut. He smiled at his two favorite women. "Good evening, ladies," he grinned.

"How was work today, Dad?" Tanya asked.

"Oh, just wonderful dear. Got another twelve clients for business plans," He replied while heading to the kitchen.

"Hey, that's great Dad. Can I get some accessories with the cell phone tomorrow?" Tanya grinned.

"I suppose you want a car to go with a car antenna and adapter?" Troy called from the kitchen.

"I never thought of that. See dad, that's why you are the prudent business man in the house," Tanya called back, smiling at her Mom all the while.

The following Monday, Darren entered the Business Market Wealth Corporation, which Troy administered.

"Good morning, my name is Darren Haseling and I have an appointment with Mr. Johnson," He voiced to the receptionist.

"Mr. Johnson is expecting you," She courteously replied as she telephoned into Troy's office.

"Hello Darren, please come in." Troy announced at the doorway.

As he took a seat in the office, he opened his briefcase and set some folders and a notebook on the desk.

"These are some photographs of several artifacts I've received from various countries and on the back of each is a full description of their history," Darren explained.

"These look very interesting," Troy remarked, clearly impressed. "I am sure there are many people who would delight in such treasures."

"I believe so, but I do not want to give them all to some business that will just double the price. I want to begin a business through them. Here also is my prospectus and business plan. I would like to develop a large client base across the country and abroad if possible. I am always receiving new pieces from my contacts, and believe it will be an ongoing business for several years."

"I see," Troy nodded, "Well, I am sure it will be successful. I've never seen so many wonderful looking ancient art pieces in my life. We will review your business plan and prepare a statement of strategy and provide numerous connections for the growth of your business. We can contact you in about two weeks with the completed statement," Troy suggested

"That would be great Mr. Johnson. I brought one piece in to show you. In fact, I would like to give it to you as a gift. It is from Egypt, and I've had it sitting on my mantle for about a year," Darren replied as he took a foot long dark blue glass rarity from his briefcase.

"That is very beautiful. It is shaped somewhat like an Egyptian god figure actually."

"This is a curio that I do not have much information on, but want to give it to you as a token of my appreciation for what you will do for me. I am not sure of the kind of glass it is made out of, but it appears to resemble the Egyptian god of Osiris."

"Well, I certainly thank you for this crafty little present, it is very nice of you," Troy applauded.

"No problem, so I will definitely hear from you in a few weeks Mr. Johnson?" Darren responded.

"Most certainly. Looking forward to seeing your business flourish for you, Mr. Haseling." Troy concluded as they shook hands.

Tanya stopped at the mall on her way home from school to meet with some friends. She walked in to the food court with her friend Jill and together they sat and had a soft drink.

"What has been bothering you lately, Tanya?" Jill asked.

"A friend got hurt by somebody and she is in a coma in the Galveston Hospital. It really bothers me to think that at any time an innocent person can have their life and freedom taken away by some thoughtless and cruel person. I want to do something for her but there isn't much I can do really."

"There is always something we can do for someone we care about. Even if it is to send them a kind thought or to show appreciation," Jill answered.

"Yes, I know. It is never too busy a world to just show someone you care," Tanya replied.

"They say it is the little things that count the most, and I believe that. A guy that I went on a date with a few weeks ago wanted to promise me the world. You know the type. Well he said he would buy this and that for me, but what is the use of having things when they don't mean anything of real value? There wasn't a true connection between us but he was determined to make one," Jill frowned.

"The best connection with someone I can think of is with a person that shares the value of life. Money is secondary to everything else that is important and of course only good to get the things you need. Besides that it can trap a person into its addictive illusions," Tanya gracefully added.

"Are you still a teenager? I mean, come on girl, we all want things in life, don't we?" Jill questioned with a feeling of perplexity.

"World peace, harmony, giving to others in need for survival. What can be more important than that, Jill? Money is a big circle and should be used to help others. Greed is a disease and it takes a person away from the values in life, the true treasures that live inside," Tanya responded.

"Ok, I see your point. Hey, there is Steven and Allan. Let's ask if they are going over to Karen's tonight."

"Sure, then I have to go pick something up and go home, there is something I have to do right after supper."

That night, Troy presented the Egyptian artifact gift at the supper table to his family.

"This was given to us from a client today. It is from Egypt and is a rare glass slate with the image of an ancient god named Osiris. We will keep it in the china cabinet so whatever you do, don't drop it. It's made of some precious glass and I don't want it to get cracked," Troy warned.

"Wow Dad, that was nice of someone to give it to you," Tanya commented in awe.

"How much is it worth, Dad?" Shawn asked with glaring eyes.

"Not sure, but it is an antique and we are not going to sell it or lose it, so don't get any ideas," Troy remarked.

After supper Tanya telephoned 'Druid' to find out more about the condition of their Wiccan comrade, CrimsonFyre.

"She is still on life support," Druid sighed, with anguish stemming in his voice, "Her family is devastated and doesn't know much, and the police haven't any clues from the crime area to follow. It doesn't look good at all, Coventry."

"We should take up a collection from the friends in the chat room so we can send her something special. I wish there were something more we could do. This bothers me so much. I've never met anyone as caring as she," Tanya began to cry.

"I wish there was something more we can do also. Let's meet tonight in the chat room so we can all discuss it. Maybe somebody will come up with an idea," Druid replied.

"That sounds good to me. I have to help with some chores then get some homework done. I will see you there, old friend."

"Be in the Light," Druid said as they hung up.

During the evening as Tanya was finishing a math assignment, Shawn walked into her room, carrying the Egyptian glass gift.

"Ah, sorry I couldn't knock, my hands are full," He blurted while holding the ancient relic. "Do you think we could make a frame for this and surprise Dad with it this weekend?" Shawn asked.

"A frame? Why would it need that?" Tanya asked, annoyed at the interruption.

"Oh, it is just an idea. It looks pretty weird, huh?" Shawn noted as he tried to look at Tanya through it.

"It is only weird cause you are seeing an image of yourself, little brother. Let me see that," she retorted.

"Fine, but you put it back. I'm going out to play basketball," Shawn replied as he set it on the floor beside her and walked away.

Tanya continued her assignment but looked over at the dark blue relic from time to time. It constantly caught her attention and she found herself wanting to hold it. She picked it up and looked into it. The glass was nearly two inches thick and obviously the image of an ancient Egyptian god. It was rather heavy and cumbersome.

"They should have at least drawn a face on this thing to give it a bit of character," She thought as she tapped her pencil on the side of her head, trying to solve an equation. A sudden noise outside made her drop the pencil, which landed on the ancient relic. Her eyes glared as she seen the dark blue color change to an iridescent glow on the spot where the pencil touched it. She picked up the relic and looked at it closer, examining for the reason why it would turn color. Tanya pressed her fingers around it but the color remained the same dark blue as it always was. She grabbed her pencil and touched the glass with the eraser and nothing happened. Then she thought for a moment and turned the pencil around and rubbed it along the front of the relic. Several colors appeared prismatic and opalescent as though light came from within it and glittered throughout some internal cavity. She was stunned with the appearance. Somehow the lead of the pencil caused a chemical reaction to the glass that made colors appear through the ancient object.

Was it playing tricks on her mind or was it real? She was amazed either way. She wrote the word LIGHT on the magical stone and suddenly a golden ray of sparkles rained within it.

"What could this be? Is it from an ancient King or mystical lord of archaic times?" Tonya thought, both bewildered and astonished at the object's magnificence. Her head rested upon her chest momentarily then she thought of CrimsonFyre. With anxiety she wrote the chosen name of her friend on the slate to see what would happen. A haze formed within the object and slowly formed into a picture. It was an image of a dwarf figure entangled in chains and covered with blood. "Was there a link between a magical name and the fate of a person who chose that name?" She abruptly questioned many things that entered her mind. Somehow this magical object could communicate with her but she needed to know exactly how to ask the questions. Furthermore she needed to know something about the god figure it was representing. She recalled her father said it represented the god Osiris. She looked up the telephone number of her online chum, Amen-Re, in her little black book of friends' numbers and telephoned him.

"Greetings good friend, this is Coventry," she said as the other line picked up.

"Haven't talked with you in months little angel," Amen-Re greeted, using his pet name for her, "I was going to go into the chat room this evening to see who would show up. How are you doing?"

"I am fine Amen-Re. Bright Blessings to you. I have called to ask you of what you know about the ancient god Osiris. I know you study Egyptian gods, and I would like to know what you can tell me."

Amen-Re laughed. "I know a bunch, so get comfortable. Osiris Asar, my friend, is the god of the underworld, king of the dead and ruler of inundation and vegetation. He originally represented the male productive forces and was equated with the setting sun, which thereafter enters the underworld. The realm of the dead was considered to be below the western horizon and that is the corner of the world that he has been linked to, as the ruler of the dead. He is the brother and husband of the earth and moon goddess, Isis, but through their son Horus he was regarded as the source of renewed life. Does that help you any Coventry?"

"Not really. What are some of the other holy aspects of Osiris?" She asked, unsure of what she was looking for but certain that Amen-Re would blurt out hints.

"The great Osiris has been called the Lord of Eternity, King of the Gods, whose names are manifold, and whose forms are most holy. His hidden form in the temples, whose Ka is holy is revered and praised as the Lord, the Prince of divine food, the Hidden Soul, and the Ruler supreme in White Wall or Memphis. Osiris is also considered as the beneficent one, and allows the souls to be raised up in the afterlife. He has many titles and is also the Governor of Abydos, and the substance of the Two Lands of Egypt. In late times he was called Un-nefer which may be roughly translated as meaning manifesting, bringing to appearance or opening good things. He was a beneficent spirit amongst spirits, and at one time he lived on earth. When he died, a very special ceremony was done and through some magnificent powers, he became the ruler of the region in the afterlife. It was then believed that distinguished ceremonies and reciting of words of power and divinity were required for important people when they died, along with presenting special amulets to them. Amulets and talismans were important to bring them into the afterlife. Osiris had very powerful magical objects made in his reverence. You see, Coventry, Ra and Ra Tem are the important gods in the world of the living but in the Underworld, Osiris is supreme. He was the Governor of the Companies of the gods and held such an important role in the religion that he was not termed as one of the gods but as The God."

"Osiris held great importance to the Egyptians, then. Is there a way to communicate with the gods that you know of?" Tanya asked.

"It is a spiritual search within that brings you in contact through their influence. As a person masters different tests in life, they communicate with inner guides through the medium of the voice that resides within the heart. It is a process of trust, surrender, sensitivity and being receptive to the vibrations that exist in the subtle levels of love and wisdom. Communication with the gods is not like communicating with another person. It is far removed from such simple patterns that we subconsciously take for granted. When gods deliver messages it is believed to be coded from our normal way of deciphering information. This is all that I can tell you now, Coventry. It may sound complex, but once you develop on the path of your desires a light unfolds and you become aware of what is before you and how to achieve it."

"I understand and thank you very much for the insight. I will talk with you soon again. Be in the Light." Tanya remarked.

"Blessed Be my friend." Amen-Re ended as they closed the conversation.

Tanya picked up the mysterious object and stared at it once again. "You are an oracle of history, I know you are. You have some answers and I shall seek to ask the proper questions to you so that you will bring light into them," She whispered into the object as she held it close to her face. She closed her eyes and thought deeply about how to ask the question of who assaulted CrimsonFyre. She held the image of her friend vividly in her mind and began to slowly write her friend's real name on the surface with her pencil while whispering it through her heart. "Kristal Clark", she wrote and concentrated upon the image of her dear friend. She opened her eyes and looked closely within the oracle and saw Kristal lying in the hospital bed. Again, she slowly began to write: "How did this happen?" Then closed her eyes and became receptive to any images that were forced within her mind. She opened her eyes again and looked into the oracle with intense interest. There was an image of a man standing beside Kristal in a ditch along a road.

The elucidation was like a vague black and white photograph several decades old. She could faintly see Kristal's face but knew it was her friend lying in the dirt for dead. The image of the man was quite clear, she could make out the facial features and body outline. She grabbed a piece of paper and began quickly scribbling the likeness down the best that she could. The image slowly vanished as the intensity of her concentration wavered. She began to refine the drawing slowly, illustrating the clothing and facial outline that she distinctly recalled. Tanya held the sketch up to the light and looked ardently at it for a few minutes. Could this be the guy that assaulted her friend? Could this oracle of Osiris answer any questions that it was presented with? This was really too much for her to take in at once. She went to lay on her bed and rest awhile, thinking of what to do next. She drifted off slowly then felt a jolt in her leg muscles. Tanya became anxious to test the oracle with another question. She got up and went into the chat room, on her computer to meet with her pagan and Wiccan friends.

"Pleasant Greetings everyone," She typed as she recognized several familiar friends online and some she had not seen before.

"Merry meet Coventry. How fare thee?" DaughterOfTheLake, an unfamiliar name to her asked.

"Well as well can be. Nice to meet you Daughter," She replied then continued, "Morgan, what is new with you?"

"Trying to decide about going to San Antonio this weekend or to Dallas. Have either option to meet some friends. What is new with you?" Morgan replied.

Tanya held the Osirian Oracle in her hands and wrote Morgan's name on it as she felt herself going into a trance to connect the name with a vision while writing them. She closed her eyes for a minute then opened them and looked into the oracle. She saw a blue car crashed into a small pick-up truck. She shook her head in disbelief. "Morgan, do you own a blue car?" She asked.

"Yes, how did you know?" Morgan replied. Tanya wrote back in private to her.

"I just know. Do not go to San Antonio. I am in touch with something very strange and know if you go to San Antonio this weekend, something terrible will happen, most likely a bad car accident."

"I wanted to go to Dallas anyway, there is a cousin's wedding I am suppose to go to. Thanks for the advice, Coventry," Morgan replied, a little bit astonished.

"Druid, Merry meet, I was hoping to see you," Coventry wrote.

"What's up, Coventry?" He asked. In private message, she responded to him.

"I have an image of the man who assaulted CrimsonFyre. I want to bring it to the police, but how can I explain it to them without them thinking I am insane?" She asked.

"You could copy it and mail it to them or you can try to explain how you got the image. Whatever you think is best. How are you sure the image is a positive identification?" Druid replied.

"I just know it is. It is from something remarkable that I cannot explain now. Keep this secret for now, I do not want people to be imagining all kinds of weird things."

"That's not a problem with me. You should give it to the police soon before the person harms another. You may be saving a life by doing that, an important and innocent life." Druid wrote back to her.

"That I shall. Do you plan on visiting CrimsonFyre soon?" Asked Tanya.

"I want to drive down on Saturday morning to check on her. Would you like to come?" Druid said.

"Yes! Call me Friday night and we will plan to go together," Tanya requested.

"That sounds good. I must go and do some work, so I bid you a pleasant night," Druid wrote, and signed off.

"Same with me, good night everyone and Blessed Be," Tanya wrote as she decided to take in some sleep. The following morning Tanya took the drawing to school with her. During lunch she went a few blocks away to the police station to talk with someone that may listen to her. When she entered, she went to an administration office and told them she had to talk with a detective about a special matter. They told her to go to the fifth floor and she would find that department. In the elevator she was nervous but gradually contained herself to explain what she had to. She walked into the investigation bureau and was greeted with friendly faces.

"Excuse me, I would like to talk with a detective about something," She congenially requested.

"Certainly you may, just one minute please," A secretary replied. "Simon, this young lady would like to speak with you, do you have a few minutes?"

"Yes, send her in," A stern voice summoned from the background.

Tanya walked over to his office as he stood up and invited her in.

"Sir, I have some news and am not sure how to tell it to you," Tanya said shakily.

"Just say whatever is on your mind. Don't be nervous or shy. If you want it kept secret or confidential that is no problem," Simon replied in a gentle and confirming manner.

"Well, it is like this. I have a... a special ability at certain times," She thought and composed herself, as she did not want to reveal the identity of the Egyptian oracle. "There was a good friend of mine in Galveston who was abducted and terribly assaulted. She is still in the hospital, lying in a coma. I had a vision of the person who abducted her and was able to draw this picture of him," She continued while pulling out the paper and showing the detective.

"That is a pretty good drawing young lady. There is a lot of detail. Would you be willing to fill out a form and leave the drawing with us? We will need some information and if possible we'll need to be able to contact you," He assured with confidence.

"Yes, that would be no problem. I just want you to be able to locate the man before he hurts someone else. I am very certain the vision was true, although I cannot explain to you exactly how it happened. I am sure you know some things about psychic visions in such cases," She proudly exhorted.

"We will do everything we can and thank you for coming in. Here is the form, take your time and make all available information that you possibly can. Everything helps us, no matter what details you include, they are all pieces of a puzzle you understand," He replied with praise for her assistance.

"This isn't as difficult as I thought it would be. I was worried that I would be laughed at or at least not taken seriously," She retorted while filling out the paperwork.

"Crimes are serious, and whenever the public helps the law enforcement, it should be appreciated. We are here to serve and protect. That is why we are paid and why we take the job. I would never laugh at anybody trying to help me with my job. I will give you my card and please feel free to telephone me at anytime if you have any more information," Simon responded to her in a comforting tone as she continued to fill out the report.

That night while she was trying to sleep, Tanya awoke from tossing in her bed. She was deeply agitated from some dream. She sat up and looked out her window, not knowing what to do. She could not fall asleep again, but didn't have any reason to get out of bed either. She grabbed the original rough sketch of the assailant she had drawn the night before and went down to the living room. She took the oracle out of the china cabinet and sat on the armchair with it. Deep in the caverns of her imagination she tried to envision the man, to see what he looked like, to connect with him and to feel his energy. At first she was apprehensive but decided that she had an obligation to perform beyond the comfort of her otherwise desires. She pictured him exactly as she remembered, as though it was moments ago. She held on to the oracle tightly with one hand as she wrote the first thing that came to her mind on it with her pencil in the other hand. "Killer" was what came into her mind as her hand took over her liberated emotions. She opened her eyes and saw the man in the oracle. He was standing outside of his large car beside a service station and there was a girl beside him. It was a still picture, as were the others but she could see the vague image of the girl as though she appeared innocent and unaware. Her mind grabbed a sense of fright and horror at what was about to occur. She studied the picture quickly as it began to vanish then drew the scene from memory. She then redrew the picture of the man again. She felt nervously agitated and deeply shook from the experience. Tanya did not know if the incident related to the image already occurred or if it was about to occur. There was nothing apparent that she could do. Shaken and distraught, Tanya went to the fridge to pour a glass of milk, hoping to settle her stomach. She felt overly tired and walked aimlessly back to her room to fall asleep.

In the morning her alarm clock startled her from deep dreams. Slowly she got showered and ready for school. She went downstairs to the kitchen to have some cereal and fruit. Her father was standing in the living room and walked in looking at her. He was holding a piece of paper towards her. Tanya recognized it as the original composite of the alleged killer that she gave to Simon the previous day.

"Tanya, did you draw this picture?" He inquired in an apparent state of confusion.

"What? Oh, that picture, yes I drew it dad, why do you ask?"

"That looks like the man who gave us the Egyptian artifact. Have you ever seen this man before?"

"Dad, are you sure that is him?" She froze up in stupefaction.

"Well, I tell you, I saw him twice and it looks identical to him. Why did you draw this picture?" He asked most curiously.

"What is his name, Dad?"

"His name? It is Darren. Why do you ask?" retorted Troy, quickly growing more upset.

"Darren who? What is his last name?" Tanya was also growing more frantic.

"I think it is Hastey. No, it is Haseling. Yes, Darren Haseling. What is this all about, Tanya?" Troy demanded to know.

"Dad, this is crazy. How much does this sketch look like the Darren Haseling that you know?" Tanya asked in a frightened yet sincere tone.

"I would say that my little daughter is an artist and that Mr. Haseling stood beside you for an hour for you to get those details onto paper. Did you ever see him before, Tanya?"

Tanya got up and walked into the living room pulling her father's hand behind her. She took the oracle out of the case and sat in the chair with it on her lap. Her father looked over her shoulder as she drew the name "Darren Haseling" onto the oracle while concentrating on his features. Troy's eyes blazoned with concern as his head fell closer to the oracle and peered within it. He saw Darren's face impregnated with a maddening expression with eyes closed, as though it was a hazy black and white photograph. "What is this?

How did it do that?" Troy asked as he put his hand softly on her shoulder.

Tanya explained the complete story to her father and told him it would be best not to let anyone know about the oracle less it fall into the wrong hands for purposes that would harm others. He was very proud of her and knew in his heart that she was the expression of his lifelong dreams. Together they went to the police department to talk with Simon, the detective she had met the day prior. Tanya told the detective about the vision of the night previous with the girl, Mr. Haseling and the gasoline station. The detective agreed to put surveillance on Mr. Haseling and to watch his every move as a prime suspect.

Saturday morning Druid showed up at her house to pick Tanya up for the trip to Galveston.

"This is a nice truck you have, Druid," Tanya commented, as she tossed her backpack into the cab. "My Dad wants to trade in the car for a truck soon."

"It gets me around comfortably. I owe a lot of money on it still, but sometimes you have to say one thing is worth another," Druid chuckled as they got in and started their journey. They drove on in silence for a good distance, each lost in their own thoughts. Tanya had a lot on her mind, with the oracle and the man in the images, and poor CrimsonFyre. Druid looked thoughtfully at her, almost as if he could read her mind. Taken off-guard, she blurted, "It will be pretty sad to see CrimsonFyre today, I mean in the condition that she is in."

"I know, but hopefully she will recognize some presence of us being there. What do you think will happen with the report you filed at the police station with your Dad a few days ago?" He questioned.

"They are keeping a close watch on the man and I hope that they find him to be the guilty one. I don't want him to be able to harm anyone else."

"Do you think they met on the Internet or in some way before it happened?"

"No, I don't think so. She was on her way to the store when it occurred, and that is usually when things like that happen, when you least expect them to."

The drive was pleasant, other than the uncomfortable topic they discussed. When they arrived near their destination and drove down a side street, Druid remarked on how busy the traffic was for the time of day. Tanya looked up at the buildings passing by them as the little truck swiftly drove on. She noticed the street sign of the street they were driving on. It was 'Morgan Blvd.' Tanya shook her head and suddenly yelled out to her driver, "Pull over, pull the truck over right now!"

"Ok, take it easy. What's the problem?" Druid questioned.

As they pulled to the side of the road to a stop Tanya caught her breath as Druid looked over to her, feeling rather bewildered. Her eyes caught the last part of a vehicle crash ahead of them at the lights as the smashing noise rampaged through the street. They both looked forward to see a blue car and a pick-up truck demolished in a collision.

"That could have been us," Tanya whimpered in disbelief as she grabbed onto her hair and clenched her fist. She realized the vision in the oracle was not meant for Morgan in the chat room but meant as an incident to occur with herself on Morgan Blvd.

"We just missed that light, and you might have saved us from that accident, Coventry," Druid acknowledged while he wrapped his arm across her shoulder in comfort.

When they arrived at the hospital and entered into CrimsonFyre's room, a sense of concern and sadness shadowed over them. Life is always grand and wonderful when everything seems to be going well, but when someone suffers in agony and experienced great pain the joy ride slows down considerably and reflection occurs. They stood on the side of her bed as Tanya reached to hold her hand. A tear came from her left eye as she looked into the bruised face of her dear friend. She wrapped both hands around the motionless girls' hand and directed healing energies into it. Tanya envisioned her friend coming out of the coma and regaining all of her previous abilities. Druid closed his eyes and culminated similar sensations and channeled them towards the girl. Several minutes later the nurse came in to check on the patient.

"Good afternoon," she said, with fatigue evident in her voice. "My name is Laura. I've been tending to Kristal Clark for the past week."

"How is she doing? We are friends that came from Houston to visit her," Druid said.

"There is no improvement on her condition as of yet. She had a serious concussion and was unconscious for a long time before being found and transported to the hospital," the nurse informed the pair, a tinge of sadness in her weary voice.

"She will come back. She will, I know she will," Tanya softly echoed through the room.

"We are all hoping that. Her parents just left a short while ago but will be back later," Laura mentioned.

"We will stop by to see them today. Thank you, Laura, for taking good care of her. She knows you are helping and knows that we are here to help as well," Tanya said as she looked compassionately at Laura.

"I am sure she does know in a special way," Laura commented as she walked out of the room.

Kristal's parents welcomed the friends to stay at their place that night. After discussing the affliction that came upon their daughter, Druid and Coventry were left alone for a while in the front room.

"Do you think about the cycle of ups and downs that people go through in life?" She asked him.

"It has to do with many things I am sure. There is such a thing as bad days and good days in a month, and the pull and push forces that the moon has on the chemicals in our body probably has some effect on our moods and behavior as well." He replied.

"Of course it does. Nobody is immune to the consequences of forces and energy. We either work with them or against them and either way they will have influences on the outcome of any situation. I guess that is what changes people, to do harm to others or to their self. Some people find it hard to cope with certain issues and to make changes to their self when they are not quite right upstairs."

"This is true, Coventry. The plight of one may be the anxiety of another and together the mesh may be opposing forces creating chaotic behavior. We never know what is going to come from any situation and unless we work with it in harmony, the outcome is certainly worsened."

"Harmony is something so few comprehend; they seem to run from it, to stir more negatives rather than let be what is and to this end what comes is not creative but destructive. Why do so many thrill on the excitement of punishment and torture; the building of conflict through forces that are unclean?" Coventry questioned.

"You've answered your own question. Rejecting harmony shows that a person is not evolved enough to direct the forces that are within. To channel the forces that are ever present towards an ultimate aim evolves maturity and thereby helps other people in the long run," Druid surmised as Kristal's parents walked in and showed them to their rooms.

Before visiting Kristal once again the following morning, Druid made a stop to a local florist and picked up five white roses. He set them in a vase alongside her bed as Tanya looked on with admiration knowing it was a symbol of love in its perfect form. They stayed with her awhile then embarked on their return journey Sunday afternoon. Druid was a friend that Tanya could confide in. She trusted him completely and knew his sincerity was true and devoted. Sometimes she would see a light blue haze in his aura surrounding his chest area and knew that his devotion was blossoming stronger. There was nothing manipulative or self-gratifying about his nature qualities, which he humbly adopted. His confidence and courage matched well the attitude towards growth that he exemplified.

"What is the task that we all must face, the ordeal that delivers us to the stage of being fully awake?" Tanya asked as they drove up the interstate.

"To each it is different but yet similar in substance. Transformation involves pain and suffering. It is not easy to give up what the mind and emotions hold on to as truth and comfort. Uniting all the elements in harmony fulfills the ordeal to progress as the awakened one. To have an abundance of any particular element will cause the personality to mold into that area and limit the free flow effect."

"Are you referring to the four elements and having insight and control over their dissipation or unity?" Tanya asked.

"Yes, indeed," Druid looked over and smiled, "Just as the bull, the lion, the person and the eagle represent these elements, it becomes a formula to integrate them in a way to cause change to occur to fulfill your life realization. Look within and see the things that represent concrete matter to you; then outline what you can realize as your will power and intuition. The mental airy aspect is creative, it is imagination and fed with intuition. All can be transformed with the watery element, the fluid of emotional essence that bridges the physical plane to all others. Each element requires the other to be fulfilled and it is the lack of using insight into this formula that people become disenchanted with life and surrounding circumstances. Anything can be overcome, mountains can be moved, simply by using the proper ingredients or mixture of elements as in a recipe. That is how life works and that is why we are responsible for our actions and reactions," Druid remarked as they developed a deeper interest in the mystical conversation.

"The oracle of Osiris that my father got, we may use it to help other people, to create positive results and further progression," Tanya suggested.

"Sometimes that is good, and sometimes not. We are not to judge what is right for another person. Each person has karma to fulfill. The sad truth is that some things which occur are impersonal yet imperative for a spiritual purpose. Not all things are meant to be good from one point of view. The spiritual person sees all things as sacred from a multi-dimensional vista. God is in all people but walls of belief and disbelief limit the stage of consciousness. That differentiates a person who makes claims of being one with god and one who simply is. Being is the ultimate level of achievement."

"It is the revealer of the mysteries, he who has mastered the tests of life. It is that person who becomes the revealer of the light, the Hierophant master that is the true teacher and not the illusory one." Tanya remarked.

"True enough, Coventry. There are scores of professed teachers that are skilled in misleading the unwary. There are many that avow to have the greatest connections and powers. The truth about them becomes too obvious and revealed through a trained and opened eye. They are crooked mongers with sinister intentions that ultimately prove to be cruel, opposed to helpful. They harvest demonical deeds that pervert the personality and make mock believers out of people. All prophets contain truth when they touch the feet of understanding and wisdom but some professed teachers can be ludicrously blain and misleading," Druid remarked with a sigh of serious remorse.

Tanya thought about what Druid had told her. She realized that each step towards inspiration and awareness is crucial for understanding what life means. 'What we perceive as truth', she thought, 'is limited to the level we are attached to.' To her the journey was just beginning. When she arrived safely home her father called her into the living room where he was reading the newspaper.

"The detective phoned me this morning Tanya. They caught him yesterday trying to lure a girl into his vehicle at a service station. They arrested him and impounded his vehicle to collect evidence. Simon is writing you a thank-you letter and told me that you are a brilliant young lady," He smiled with pride and admiration for his daughter.

"That is good news, Dad. I hope he never gets to hurt another person ever again. In fact I hope this whole rat race gets cleaned up one day and people use their abilities in a profound way and not so stupidly!" She remarked with a strike of contempt towards civilization.

"I know what you mean Tanya. Just be careful wherever you go, 'cause that day is a long way from coming. How is your friend Kristal doing?"

"I feel that she will make it through, Dad. It was a sad experience. My heart connected with hers and I could feel what she went through." Tanya said in recollection.

Tanya began to walk up the stairs when her father reached out to embrace her. "I understand sweetheart. Listen, I want to say something about that antique oracle thing. I don't know how you figured it out or what it can do and frankly I don't want to know. I am not going to mention a word about it to anyone, not even Mom. I know that you have a link with it and will leave it entirely up to you as to what is done with it."

"Dad, you are absolutely wonderful. I wouldn't trade you for the world," She laughed while giving him a hug.

"That is rather nice of you to admit. Actually, it is the best compliment that I have received in ages," He smiled as she looked up at his compassionate face.

"I wish to keep the oracle in my room, if that is alright," She requested.

"Certainly, but don't let your brother catch you using it. Otherwise he'll use it to get every chick at school after him."

"Nothing to worry about, I will be most careful." She replied as she took the Oracle of Osiris upstairs with her.

Tanya sat on her bed holding it and thinking about the possibilities. Did she really want to know things that will happen before their time? Was she ready to uncover the truth behind incidents that have already occurred to people she would become overly concerned about? It was an intense instrument of responsibility for her to have control over. She embraced it as her guide and advisor, accepting to use it wisely to integrate Time and Being with the teachings of the ages. It was her mystical mechanism of veraciousness.

Her divine desire to become Priestess of the Mysteries was about to blossom. She was ready to work for her next stage of self-initiation by listening to the inner voice and become prepared for the invisible teacher to arrive. She placed the oracle upon her dresser behind two wooden elephants that she told to guard it and then she took a shower. Before going to bed she looked out of her bedroom window and saw Venus in the night sky. "Ruler of Taurus the bull, and revealing star of instruction," she thought, "there is the dove and there is the serpent, prepare me to receive guidance so that intuition follows curiosity. Prepare me for the days ahead so that the light of consciousness brightens the darkened halls of ignorance. Watch over me and guide me along the path to do righteousness and seek truth."

Tanya got into bed and closed her eyes. During her sleep, she became aware of some peculiar communication from beyond. Within her the qualities of yin and yang rapidly evolved and united. She could feel the feminine and masculine polarities through her soul becoming meshed together. The pain of transformation at first felt like nails being driven into her sense of identification. She let go of the archaic concepts long held in the recess of her mind. The serpent stage of transformation was complete. It was midnight and she had become in a sense, the daughter of midnight holding within her reach the son within the Sun. The great Egyptian mystery had been revealed into her soul awareness. It was as though she gave birth to a new innocence within, a child mightier than anything she had ever known. Each breath she inhaled while asleep fed her holy child and gave it life. The morning had just begun as Horus, the child of Isis and Osiris awakened within her astral consciousness. Through the qualities that she assimilated into being sensitive, trusting, receptive and surrendering she impregnated herself in a mysteriously initiated manner from a connection through the oracle to foster the crowned and conquering child within her Being. She became the living child of the oracle. She slept in tranquility and would awaken to begin life prepared as an intermediary between the human and the divine. ★

SHELLEY VISIONS

"Everything has its beauty but not everyone sees it."

Confucius (c. 550-c. 478 BC)

Colossal waves bolted up the sides of the Pleasant Princess cruise liner, jetting a splendor of mist along its side walkway. Shelley's hair was tousled in the breeze as she watched the distant sandy beaches along the coast of California. She was so happy to be aboard this holiday cruise and determined to get the most from this trip after writing tiresome exams and working nights to pay her way towards a University Degree. The relaxing atmosphere embraced her spirit as she casually strolled along the promenade deck of the magnificent ship. 'What a great getaway! An adventure of dreams awaiting to be lived and soon I will be visiting beautiful islands and cultures,' she pondered while taking a seat in a reclining lounge chair on the upper deck and observing the smiling vacationers diving into the refreshing swimming pool.

She recollected the last stop in San Francisco, and the visiting of Treasure Island, bussing over the hilly streets, enjoying her favorite seafood at Fisherman's Wharf, and seeing magnificent animals at the City Zoo. In particular she thought of the miniature white dog that they had on display. It was a dwarf. 'Absolutely incredible!' she recalled as she wished it were on her lap now to cuddle and adore as a companion.

"Is everything okay for you, Miss?" a tall, dark and very friendly man in a white uniform asked.

"Oh, definitely," she replied while glancing at his nametag. "I love it here. You're very fortunate to travel this beautiful route, Mr. Coady."

"Thank you. I am pleased to meet with people that enjoy their time on board. If there is anything you request or need or may be curious about regarding the Princess, just ask any of the crew and they will be glad to answer you."

"Wonderful," she replied, "If they are as pleasant as you I am sure they will answer any questions I may have."

"Take full advantage of the ships' amenities, Miss," the officer responded as he made his way through the cabin door, leaving her with a gratifying smile.

Shelley closed her eyes as the sun delivered heat and light upon her skin. All of her thoughts drifted away as she pleasantly relaxed and drifted into a nap. She was not fully asleep, but in a state where images randomly entered and left her mind. She smiled at the screening image of natives running through the forest and then her mind settled down upon a sandy beach, which had low hanging palm trees swaying amidst a warm breeze. The bright aquamarine water aroused a spoor of puissant fervor upon her face as she tilted her head and felt someone's arms wrapping around her waist. She was not startled but felt very comfortable. Together they pulled one another into the sea and swam amongst the coral reefs and into large underwater caverns.

Shelley's head turned the other way as the rays began to redden the left side of her face. Her heartbeat increased as she envisioned a stone wall in front of her. An uncomfortable irritation swept through her body and tears wanted to drop from her eyes as she sensed an unpleasant presence before her. It was a staunch, fair complexioned man with wild deformed white eyes laughing cynically in her face. Fear burrowed in her body but loosened its grip as another image quickly intervened. She was being lifted up a mountain. At the top of it was a man in a suit waiting for her. He grabbed her arm as a shrill of sinister emotions from him entered her and dribbled through her veins. She gulped in fright as an image of herself falling down the other side of the mountain to jagged rocks below entered her mind. Her body jolted as she awoke with a trembling sensation and a fearful feeble scream murmured from her lips as she tumbled within her chair and whimpered.

The thought of falling out of a tower suddenly entered her mind as an immediate translation of her lucid dream. She could not accurately recall what she had just dreamt or envisioned. Was her mind playing tricks? She could not translate to her awakened self what she just experienced. 'Thank goodness nobody actually heard me', she whispered in embarrassment to herself.

The cruise continued to be excitingly indulgent. The food was superb and the stopover in San Diego was enjoyable. She was relieved to see her sunburn turning into a luscious darkened tan. She had met, conversed and danced with a few young gentlemen aboard the ship. The thought of becoming romantically involved had amused her mind. One man that caught her attention blurted flauntingly about his worldly travels and cultural experiences. He was beyond boisterous and babbled about his sense of wealth and overall importance as a character in the business world. He was too wrapped up in meaningless drivel and himself for her to continue acceptable conversation with. Another man, on the other hand, was always reaching to touch her and was obviously a flirt that yearned for constant physical contact, which turned her away from him rather quickly. If at all, she desired to be with someone that flared enthusiasm with a delicate taste of romantic sensuality. She decided to put the idea of romance to rest with other propositions that fed her mind and began to simply enjoy the tranquil scenery and casual swimming in the pool. She progressed to swimming three and half pool lengths under water and was excited about the achievement.

A few evenings after passing through the Panama Canal she sat near the window in the ships' nightclub and watched the setting sun. The waitress, Anne, brought her the usual drink, a Singapore sling and remarked, "Wow, Shelley, you are going back to Canada soon. Your friends are going to be overwhelmed at seeing your wonderful tan, maybe even mistake you as a Caribbean native."

"Isn't it great, Anne?" she giggled in reply, "This is the most fun I had in years, just to be away and enjoy something new."

"We are stopping at Aruba tomorrow. You should visit the island, it's magnificent!" Anne exclaimed.

"Probably will, Anne. Could you get some time off and bum around with me?"

"Sorry, I'm afraid not. I must restock from the storage departments amongst other duties. Look, I have to bring Mr. Millar his beer. Talk with you later ok?" Anne said as she wandered past the tables with a smile to her regular, good tipping customer.

Shelley returned the smile and replied, "Sure, talk with you later." She peered into the lovely sunset, sipping her sling and feeling good about everything, including going on such a venture alone.

The following morning after the ship docked, the passengers made their way to the exit, anxious to set their feet into the fine Aruba sands. Shelley grabbed her camera and shoulder bag and quickly left her room. Aruba was a quaint little village with dozens of side streets offering shops and stands, which sold artifacts and hand woven apparel. A number of people were boarding an old rickety bus, which had a sign on the back window stating- 'Visit The Soul Of Aruba with Us'. Shelley entered the bus and looked out the dusty window as children skipped around on the streets and played with one another. An admirable looking man came and sat next to her, smiling from ear to ear. He was apparently enthusiastic and happy about something.

"Hi there. Are you from the Princess, princess?" he remarked in a slick amorous way.

"Ah, yes I am, and thank you for the compliment," Shelly replied and paused before asking, "And where are you from?"

"I am from Pittsburgh," he said with a gleeful smile, shaking her hand, "and my name is Terry Knight. It's very nice to meet you."

"Oh, that's neat," she remarked, "I am an easterner myself, but from Canada. What brings you way down here?"

"Well, I was doing some work in Brazil and after I finished, the decision to enjoy a little vacation crept into my schedule," he sighed and made a show of stretching.

"What kind of work was it?" she probed with curiosity.

"It was something of an investigation actually," He replied while being captivated by her inquisitive green eyes.

"Investigation, as in police work?" she turned in disbelief.

"It is something more intense than the average crimes, actually."

"What do you mean? What could be more intense?"

"To tell you the truth, it is occult criminality. Hard cases to solve, and yet they are on an increase and requiring more occult minded cops as it were to solve them."

"Sounds frightening, but I bet you have to know a lot of criminal psychology to catch on to such motives and clues to solve them," Shelley attested, duly impressed.

"It is an everlasting study in esoteric sciences and philosophies, but it has a lot of good moments, very gratifying really. There are people out there that are corrupting others for their aggrandizement and in turn creating havoc with the fundamentals of nature. Not only physical disruption harms society, there are multiple kinds of havoc at play, most unfortunately."

"That is weird, but I suppose there is truth to it, since there are a lot of crazy people looking for something to disrupt," Shelly agreed.

"Some people are very sensitive to what they believe in, at times so much that they exhibit chaotic behavior and thrive on creating problems in other peoples' lives. They go so far as to use unseen forces and powers to overcome other people weaker than themselves and delight in the conquest. This sinister sickness may sound silly, but the fact is what happens out there is not much of a comedy to those in such distress from the embroiled menaces. Individual cases are as important as cases of mass destruction. Everyone in life is important, as far as I am concerned," He pledged in solace.

Shelley grimaced at the remark, not completely understanding it, although the element of danger purposely intrigued her. She considered his presence to be very serene and became more receptive to his calm and collective nature.

As the bus narrowed a winding bend and stretched across a plateau the driver turned and spoke. "Have your cameras ready folks, I see something very strange coming up." Everyone peered out the left side as they witnessed some native children running through the bush being chased by a huge panther. They scurried to a large tree and frantically climbed up as the menacing creature clawed its way around the trunk. The sound of clicking Kodak cameras was most irritating throughout the bus. The bus driver chuckled as he winked out the side window at Bagheera, the panther that was trained to do the same routine every day with the children.

The tour continued through the hills passing beautiful scenic sights and stopping for short panoramic views before it arrived at a small town where the driver allowed the passengers to wander about in the petite shopping area. "We'll be here for one hour folks, be back in the bus by then," he smiled and swayed the bar across to open the screeching old door.

Shelley and Terry wandered around together with amusement of seeing the trinkets offered by vendors who obviously had mastered the challenge of creating souvenirs that tourists would snatch up. They began to perspire under the dry heat of the blazing sunshine as Terry turned to her and motioned, "I'm going to use the washroom over there, be back in a few minutes, okay?"

"Of course. I won't be far", she replied. Shelley wandered across the street into an alleyway, which seemed to have colorful shops stretching to the end. She snapped a few pictures of the old buildings as they towered over her head, heralding an old fashioned style of renaissance. 'Interesting', she thought as her eyes were drawn to some workers down the side of another alley, busily loading a van with large boxes.

"Looks like hard work in this heat," she voiced as she wandered close to them and snapped their photo. The men turned and stared surprisingly at her. A heavy-set man pointed his finger at her as his two accomplices pounced sternly upon her and within seconds had her in their grips and hauled her into the back of the van. They tied her to some overhanging bars and gagged her mouth. It all happened so quickly that she couldn't resist their overpowering strength through her squirming and whimpering attempts to be freed. Terrified out of her wits, Shelley wheezed to let out a scream but their hands muzzled her mouth while gagging it.

"What are you doing, what is wrong? Let me go, please!" she exuberantly mumbled through her gag. The men ignored her and continued to load the van as she kicked around and murmured restlessly. The heavy-set man peeked inside at her and began to laugh and grimace equivocally in her face. Fear ran through her heart, as she felt some kind of recollection jumping in her head of having seen his unbinding sense of cruelty somewhere in the past. It was almost as if she was in this plight once before. Tears of helplessness ran down her reddened and bruised cheeks while moans of desperate fear uttered from behind the ragged cloth tightly covering her mouth. She thought this event occurred for a reason but shrilled at why she felt this way in the face of such danger. She could no longer think straight and was becoming weary of trying to pull herself loose. From a distance she could hear a familiar voice calling out.

"Shelley, Shelley, where are you?" Terry wandered down the alley and noticed the men loading the van across the way as he continued searching.

"What shall we do with her?" an obese, greasy looking man said to his boss, named Roscoe.

"We'll dump her somewhere no one will ever look, but we have to wait, remember!" he replied while nudging his unconcerned and inquiring accomplice named Hazen.

Terry's eyes squinted as he suddenly stopped in the alley. He picked up a large stick from the ground and began to maneuver around the van in curiosity holding it behind his back. He knew something was definitely out of place and could not waste a moment analyzing his feelings or seeking more assistance. He pulled the stick in front as Hazen was coming towards him with clenched fists. Terry stepped forward and slammed his impromptu weapon across the assailant's neck. Hazen fell to his knees as Roscoe came from behind and whisked his right arm around Terry's neck, pulling him quickly to the ground. Terry's foot flung from the ground over his head and knocked directly into Roscoe's skull, sending him backwards and incoherently to the ground.

"That won't be necessary anymore!" a convincing voice trumpeted from ahead of him as Mr. Rocha pulled a pistol from his coat and opened the rear door of the van, directing the gun to Shelley's head. Terry looked up in anguish and relinquished. His head twisted frantically to the right as Hazen and Roscoe grabbed his arms and threw him harshly into the back of the van. Roscoe grabbed some rope and feverishly tied Terry up beside Shelley, then blindfolded him. Mr. Rocha nodded to them and departed with some final words, "It's about time this got done!"

Hazen drove as Roscoe sat in the passenger seat occasionally keeping an eye on the snared victims. They drove through the back alleys and into a mountainous area of the island. The van screeched around winding bends as it hurriedly heightened into the hills. Shelley's mouth curved downwards as she felt like incessantly crying. During the drive she thought it was the end, as apparently it was. Terry heard her sniffling and bumped her a few times with his elbow to let her know she is not alone. He knew how frightened she was but did not want her to dwell on the fear. 'Fear is failure and the forerunner of failure,' He thought as a swirling energy for the challenge of doing his best in every situation coveted enactment.

Terry believed that one must not only grasp the emotional horrors of reality and life but also become a friend of the martial powers within Geburah, the warrior sphere of living vibrant energy. To give an invitation to fear is to let it overpower you and build personal doubts and restraint. The true warrior has great control within self, a control that surpasses mental meandering and emotional turmoil. 'Seize power, as you would love; in a refined, diligent, and fervent manner,' He pondered philosophically.

Terry's breathing was deep, regular and slow as the vehicle approached the top of the mountain. Hazen and Roscoe exited the van and open the rear doors, blatantly untying the hostages and then hurling them onto the ground. As they grabbed the blinded bystanders and tugged them forward Roscoe remarked, "We are going for a little walk down the path." Shelley moved her head instantly and, wild-eyed under her blindfold, sniffed the air and recalled her series of previous visions. Terry directed his attention to the location of the assailants, and noted in his mind their probable positions.

"Terry, a cliff, we are near a high cliff," Shelley blurted without hesitation.

Deducing their motives, Terry lunged forward and landed a leaping front kick, firmly planting his heel in the ribs of Hazen. The stunned brute shook violently and plunged backwards onto the dirt. Shelley screamed once again, glancing at an area behind Terry. Instinctively, Terry turned swiftly with a flying crescent kick so abrupt that Roscoe had been taken completely by surprise, losing his gun to the unexpected attack. Terry swiftly ducked and brought his tied hands under his feet to have them in front of himself. Immediately lifted off the blindfold, he was impressed at how the strikes made their way to the brutes, but did not flaunt his efforts. He saw Hazen coming towards him from the side and without hesitation ran a lunge kick into his groin. The distressed menace leant forward in scrutinizing agony as Terry spread his fingers and thrashed his middle and index fingers into Hazen's eyes. The tortured vile man fell face first into the soil grieving for his life, with one hand covering his eye sockets and the other covering his damaged groin. Roscoe wrestled fiercely towards Terry's backside, grabbing him with might and smacking his fist in the side of Terry's face. Swinging vehemently, Terry knocked him off and orchestrated a full force knee into Roscoe's jaw. He plunged backwards and fell on his rump with a somersault, landing him several feet further away. Terry swept over to Shelley and removed her blindfold. As Roscoe began to crawl back up Terry leaped four feet into the air and came harshly down upon his ribcage. Large white eyes glared up and quickly became pale, as Roscoe was rendered unconscious.

Terry hastily untied Shelley's hands and then hastened into the van, quickly glancing back to assess the surroundings, and slammed the door shut.

"It appears we can become attached to the vibrations of the people we are around. Those dudes had bad vibes, didn't like them one bit!" Terry toned in exhaustion as he clamored to turn the ignition key.

"You sure kicked their vibes out of commission. I can see how you use each minute and make it count. Took me by surprise," She huffed with a sigh of relief.

As they swerved the van around to escape, an old truck came towards them and blocked the exit. Terry veered around it and into the field, plummeting down a steep grade into some rocks and over them without hesitation. The van romped back and forth as he attempted to regain equilibrium from its top-heavy mass. The truck picked up the casualties and turned back in pursuit of the victims.

"Somebody sent reinforcements. They are on to us, Terry!" Shelley shrilled.

"I wonder! On second thought, nah, I don't," He heaved in a rejection of cynicism.

"Why are they after us? What is the big problem here?" Shelley voiced with utter regard.

"We all have a responsibility in life, my dear. I suspect they are shunning the truth of responsibility in lieu of being bad boys involved in twisted occupations. We will just have to outsmart them, somehow," Terry shrugged while attempting to get back on the road.

The truck quickly caught up with them and steered back and forth, attempting to get in front of the van. Shelley looked into the side view mirror and saw one of the brutes leaning out of the window in back of them with a revolver pointing towards her. She ducked back inside the van's protective cab.

"Gunfire coming our way!" she yelled.

The van began to torpidly slow down as the rear tire was suddenly blown. It wobbled turbulently as Terry attempted to regain speed but failed.

"How far to town, would you figure?" Shelley asked while poking her head back up.

"Not close enough," Terry despondently wagered whereupon the cargo truck slammed into the rear of the van, knocking it further into devolution. Terry's struggle to keep it mobile came to an end. A few more miles may have made the difference in reaching assistance, but the truck rammed harshly into the side of the van, the collision forcing it off the road and into the ditch. New faces appeared in the window of each side of the van as Terry and Shelley leant backwards with tarnished complexions.

"Out! Come on! We have to talk!" A voiced commanded through the window with a gun pointing at Terry.

He smiled death in the face and obliged without fret. Shelley wearily pushed her door open and complacently tagged along. Two aggressors grabbed the tourists by the hair and yanked them to the rear of the cargo truck. On the way, Terry looked up and saw the smug face of Hazen peering out for revenge. Roscoe was still unconscious with his head resting on the dashboard. They were transported to a house in the outskirts of town, set alone like it appalled invitations of nasty activities. When they arrived the victims were smacked around in the rear of the truck before the door was opened. It was their gross reminder that pain is the payment when transacting with the powers of the demented.

"Rocha wants a word with you, fellow," A languid voice breathed in Terry's ear as they were forced into the side entrance of the tauntingly lavish dwelling. They were forced every step of the way into a room and each tied to chairs, apparently awaiting their arrival.

"What would all this have to do with two indifferent tourists?" Terry breathed as Mr. Rocha entered and sneered at his presence.

"Indifferent, you say?" Mr. Rocha cocked an eyebrow. "What about your quaint trip in Brazil, Mr. Knight? What about the disks you have confiscated and given to the authorities in Sao Paulo? We have kept tabs on you for a long time and are tired of your meddling with our international business."

"It becomes my business when lives are at stake, Mr. Rocha. People matter! Life matters! Everything matters and when it is turned upside-down and perverted inside out, then it becomes my business to rectify it. Somebody has to put a little light in the dirt pile so it doesn't trap the unwary," Terry snarled with conviction.

"Your sympathetic concern is amusing and absurd. Do you have any idea of what we are really doing, why we are doing what we are?" Rocha laughed harshly.

"Allow me to guess. You cater to depraved agents that are in the spirit world to corrupt certain traditions. No, no wait," Terry blinked, "You induce chaotic behavior into people by disguising cults as an enlightenment tool to gain powers and exploit fraternities that have real values for society! Oh no, wait again!" Terry grinned evilly, "You play upon peoples fears to instigate them into your lavish cults then create slaves out of them unwittingly? Is there any truth in any of what I said, Mr. Rocha?"

"It's a matter of opinion, my little scapegoat. I was hoping to see your body sliced in pieces at the bottom of Pinnacle Ridge, but oh well, this can be more fun. Let's call it an experiment of endurance."

"What kind of freaks are you people? Don't you have any cares for other people than yourselves?" Shelley scathed.

"Cares are for the weak at heart, my little precious. You're a different breed. I'm sure we can do wonders with you, after you enjoy what we do with your precarious Knight in rusted armor," Rocha squealed with batting eyelashes. At that instant, a strangely outfitted woman jaunted into the parlor. She wore a ragged pink dress halfway to her knees and had silver nylons on with short black boots. Her face was wrought in purple and black make-up, fantastically portraying a twisted, grotesque personality.

"What, oh what have we today?" she delighted in a depraved expression of exasperation.

"What in God's name is that?" Terry mocked with equivocal laughter.

"I am the Love Goddess of the Temple, you mortal! You little foolish man! I am Relisha the Ravishing Revel!" She winced with her tongue hanging out.

Are you male or female? Actually cancel that…were you born as a male or female?" Terry blurted.

"Baby, I was born to become! I am the Apprentice of Aphrodite. I am the Transvestite of Tenacious Tender loins! You wait until I spend time with you tonight. Oh boy, I am getting so excited, are you?" she chanted unmercifully.

"Were you by chance locked up in prison for a long time?" Terry grimaced.

"Oh you, you are just so cute! Wait, wait, you just wait!" the thwarted creature crawled lasciviously around him batting its painted eye shadow up at him while drooling a mist of lustful indulgence.

"Oh, I couldn't infringe on the invested rights of Mr. Rocha. Thank you, but I decline the ravenous offer," Terry relinquished. Shelley looked at both of them as though they had severe disorders. Why Terry would further tempt these revolting individuals was beyond her.

Mr. Rocha walked up to him and slammed his fist down onto Terry's head. "Do you know that the spirit can be equally weakened and destroyed as can the human body, Mr. Knight? You will be a completely different man before long," He reverberated while ushering the others to join him in the dining room for the evening meal.

"We have to get out of here soon, Terry. How are we going to do that?" Shelley squirmed in her seat when the door was closed behind the deranged hostesses.

"They are inflicted with a variety of diseases, can you tell?" Terry snarled.

"How is that going to help us any?" She sobbed in remorse.

"By not being affected by it and being separated from their anguish we can see through it," He suggested.

"We better see through it quickly or that transvestite is going to have you for dessert," Shelley almost cried.

Terry managed to maneuver his hand into his back pocket and pulled out a pocketknife. "We have to act fast. There isn't much time. Blair, I mean bare with me for a minute," He urged while straining to cut his hands free from the tight rope. Shelley looked over in amazement.

"Why don't women carry knives in their back pocket?" She shook her head.

"Most women don't whittle wood?" he shrugged then added, "Werewolves wonder and worry why women warn weary wrestlers with warped whiney warnings when wizardry works wishes," He giggled nonchalantly.

"What the hell was that?" She rolled her eyes.

"A way out," He continued to chuckle as he slipped the ropes from his hands behind the chair and hauled his arms out to untie his feet from the chair legs. Terry unraveled himself and quickly got Shelley free then went to open the window. Abruptly they quietly climbed out and began running into the forest.

"That was incredibly easy," Shelley huffed as she struggled to keep up with the marathon marvel.

"They will likely be searching for us before long. We better not slow down. We have to get as far away as possible," He alleged while reaching back to grab her hand, gesturing her onwards.

"Which way should we go? We want to arrive at a town somewhere," Shelley maintained.

"Instinct, pure and natural. We will arrive at some place before long. The island isn't that large," Terry testified as they fleeted over the dry underbrush.

They suddenly heard the resonance of distant motors revving up. The wretched, sadistic barbarians were in pursuit as Terry listened to misplaced gunfire shot into the air. Shelley relentlessly wished for her vacation to come to an end in her struggle to keep pace with her savior. Terry slowed down for her to catch a breath as he whispered into the warm welcoming winds, "O thou Sovereign Paladin of self-vanquished knights, whose path resides through the trackless forests of unbeaten space and time, transcendental beyond despair over the mountains of ages… Lift the lightening-hoofed courtesan past the twin-cities into eternal nameless starlight. Clouds without water pass and are done," His fingertip rose to his lips as Shelley caught her breath without discerning the words whispered into nothingness.

Terry turned to the east and began running with his comrade once again. Over a hill they came upon a rushing torrent river. With a glance to one another, they hurried down and jumped into it, swimming across recklessly as the flow carried them downstream. Shelley gasped for air, trying to keep her head above the forceful current.

"Almost there, we just have a few feet, struggle, push yourself, we will make it over!" Terry avowed while pulling the shoulder of her shirt behind him. His free hand grasped onto shrubbery hanging from the bank, hauling them to shore in tiresome relief. Climbing up the embankment, they heard uproar down the river. Turning in exhaustion, they saw the conceited faces of Hazen on one four-wheeler and Relisha on another. The transvestite yelled over to his sweetie, "My little meat-pie, I am coming for you. Relisha is here baby! Don't go too far, I want to eat you, remember!"

"Mansions on the Moon! Will you look at that sight?" Terry shivered. Rocha suddenly pulled up and pointed his shotgun towards the prey. Shelley was devastated. She yanked on his arm to continue their escape. Through the woods they scurried as gunfire blasted into the trees around them.

"Nothing like a little bit of raw reality to stir up a holiday," Terry emphatically ushered as their feet engaged consistently in front of them, creating rapid tracks deeper into the greenery. Shelley incurred a vision during the egress, which chilled the haunting dismay that burdened her mind for the past hours.

"Terry, I see a car driving down the road," She stammered in their retreat.

"Shelley," he looked in perplexity, "there isn't any road in view."

"But I can see it, clear as crystal," She blurted out while slowing pace and turning her head around a large tree.

"Ah, there is beauty in everything." He recalled an ancient proverb as he twisted his body and ran with her inclination.

At the top of a barren hill they could see a car driving through curves on the distant roadway. They scurried down the rough terrain as familiar horrid revving returned into their ears. Shelley pushed Terry when they came to the road and ushered him to reside in the ditch bushes until the vehicle appeared and she gained the confidence of the driver.

"They may not stop if they see a man with me. You know how fearful people are these days," She blurted while dawdling on the side of the road awaiting the vehicles' appearance to show. The harsh noise of the all-terrain vehicles grew louder as time ticked impatiently in their veins. Majestically the vehicle came around the bend prompting Shelley to rush onto the road and flag it to a grinding halt.

"Please help, I have to find the police with my friend, right away!" she exclaimed as Terry dashed behind her and into the back seat. Shelley jumped into the front and continued, "They have guns, hurry Mister, they are dangerous!" The automobile sheered away with the four wheelers gaining on them from the rear.

"You better use more gas my friend, or all of us will become lunch in a butcher shop!" Terry warned, pivoting on the seat. The driver looked in his rear-view mirror and spun zealously onwards, gradually loosing sight of the ill-bred menaces.

"What is that all about? Why are they after you?" the courteous and timely driver asked.

"They are criminals. Ruthless, calculating and conniving criminals!" Shelley said while looking over to him in gratitude.

"So strange! We never have problems like that here. Are they tourists?" the driver questioned.

"I don't know what they are. Can you get us to the police station quickly?" Shelley asked.

"In about fifteen minutes," He estimated while sighing in relief for their safety.

The car veered around the corners of the winding down-slope with drenched and perspiring passengers reviving with vivacity. If cruelty had a place in the world it was imbed in their path. The macabre reality of three quad-runners humped over a distant hill and vaulted towards the forefront.

"Quasi-modo, delicate sounds of thunder! You have to appreciate their determination," Terry shrilled in the backseat.

"Do you have a gun, Mister?" Shelley nervously shouted.

"A gun? I don't even have a nail-file," He attested as his face dropped. Obstinate as might, the gentleman pressed on with frenzy to pass the intruders before they would hit the pavement beforehand. They entered a straight stretch of road as the car sped forward at ninety-five miles an hour, passing the antagonists by split moments. Gunfire blasted past them as the car enigmatically gained additional acceleration, leaving the atrocity once again in the periphery of diminishing view.

"Is it over?" Shelley murmured, looking back.

"Three strikes, they're OUT!" Terry laced his hand ethereally upon her shoulder. Inside of herself, Shelley had a deep urge to caress the man who saved her life and gave her a romancing adventure of a lifetime. She leant back and grabbed the rear of his neck and hauled his face into hers. Daintily she kissed him passionately and continuously.

"Did you say go to the police station or the church?" the driver squinted his eyes and leant forward. Shelley and Terry looked into one another's eyes with perpetual wonderment. Minutes later they arrived at the authorities and relayed the inadvertent encounter with accurate descriptions to the chief.

"Not surprising to me. I am sorry you got mixed with that crowd. I've been trailing them for a few weeks and knew something was foul when Rocha had daily scheduled flights for his aircraft to the mainland. We will pay a visit to his house. The warrant can now be signed and delivered while we search his residence," The obliged officer smiled as he prepared with his assistants to storm the residence.

"I've missed the boat," Shelley remarked, looking at the clock on the wall.

"Indeed you have, but we can have you flown to the next island, where you may meet up with the cruise once again, Miss," The chief offered. Shelley turned to Terry and shrugged her shoulders. "Of course, it would be better if you remained here and testified against the gang." The chief added.

"I can accommodate that request," She admitted in unison with Terry.

The fugitives were brought in with a stack of evidence and most unexpectedly the chief called the resting tourists at their hotel room to give them a special surprise.

"What? Is this for real?" Shelley awed on the telephone.

"You look rather flabbergasted," Terry grinned while Shelley dropped the telephone.

"A reward, Terry! They are giving us twenty-four thousand luscious American buckaroos! He said it is a combined award that was offered in four states for three of the gangsters. What are we going to do with the money, honey?" Shelley erupted with exhilaration.

"Such lovely clean water. Oh my, what a superlative great beginning to a tenacious ending," Terry breathed as they nestled together aboard a rented yacht.

"It is, it is," Shelley agreed as they tanned in the afternoon sunshine, then released a sudden remark. "Terry, I just had another vision. It was of a future jury that incorporated psychics to question the guilty parties. The psychics were previously tested of their abilities and paid for their service. Then a number of faces flashed before my eyes and I saw justice being served, without the red tape and waste of time and money."

"Hmmm, not a bad idea actually. Money should not buy justice. Justice means one thing and one thing only…and it is supposed to abolish crime and provide safety to the public. How long do we have before testifying to the jury?" he queried.

"We have to be back in three days. Remember, that is how long we rented the yacht for," She gleamed radiantly.

"Whale eel beefa dolphin mermaid tuna-ight," he puckered his lips like a walloped snapper.

"Hush, you silly angelfishy! Kiss me and make it count!" she stared him in the lips and batted her lashes.

They anchored the elegant cruise boat off a small deserted island, near a gigantic rock formation. Together they jumped into the inviting deep aquamarine waters and swam to the rock, then began climbing it. Immersed in a world of tranquility, she hugged her enthralling inamorato at the height and then whisked herself off gallantly into the sea with her beau following. This was the happiest exploit Shelley had ever imagined to experience in her life. From a fiasco she had found her Romeo, through an escapade she had adventure and without distilling her fears the pair may have never met. She would also have been out twelve thousand mackerels, since they harmoniously divided the reward.

The loving twins swam between coral reefs, amidst the sea world and found an underwater passage into the magnificent rock. Schools of fish sparkled by them as they entered a remarkable inner cavern. Their heads bobbed above water as they paddled to a ledge within the giant rock formation.

"Wow, this is like another world, another place unimaginable," Shelley expressed in wonderment.

"There is always another world to be discovered, somewhere, somehow, when we search for it," Terry smiled as his arms stretched and wrapped around his beauty.

"Oh!" she squirmed, "I thought that was a water snake."

"It's just Merry Terry. Ho, ho, ho," He chuckled as her hands touched his lips and through the dim light caught his eyes into the ecstasy kindling from hers.

"What do you think will happen with that group in South America now that their comrades are going to be imprisoned?"

"That is a good question Shelley. It is just the beginning. There is much work to be done but at least the surface is skimmed. You are a very beautiful person." He smiled with a radiant glow of true affection.

"Let's stay awhile," She inquisitively jittered while welcoming his warmth. ★

ALIENS ARE HERE

"Above, the gemmed azure is
The naked splendour of Nuit;
She bends in ecstasy to kiss
The secret ardours of Hadit.
The winged globe, the starry blue,
Are mine, O Ankh-af-na-khonsu!"

Liber Al vel Legis - A. Crowley

"**A**ngels are one thing, but little bald-headed fellows flying in a spaceship from some distant galaxy, coming to visit a planet that is filled with problems and counter-evolutionary… why would they even bother?" Mark scorned at Phil as they walked across the University Campus heading for a soccer game.

"Well, for one thing Mark, the whole planet is not full of problems with evolution. Everyone is at a different stage and although the masses of people are at lower evolutionary phases, there are some that transcend ordinary life and enter dimensions that we are not aware of. In our world there are a variety of people and there are many that have experienced miraculous events, which we will never hear about. It is those people who have links to life beyond our ordinary world and I plan on finding some of those people and learning what I can if the chance is made available to me," Phil replied ardently.

"How do you propose to do that, Mister astrophysicist?" Mark asked with a touch of contempt in his voice.

"There is only one way my dear friend, and that is by being ready," The diligent student remarked to his sports partner, "Now let's go win a game, since we are at least ready for that."

Phil's enthusiastic plays throughout the game proved his athletic genera and zest for assisting his team in winning. His maneuverability around people and over their hooking feet was nothing short of agility and elasticity at its best. His third goal in the game came after flipping over two players and landing in front of the moving ball, then swinging it into the opponents net. The goalie only caught Phil's feint to shoot to the right of the net but at last moment Phil struck it to the left and it zoomed in. After the game, the guys soaked themselves with drinking water in the locker room while shouting their victory. Phil laughed along with them as he peeled six oranges and gobbled them quickly into his body then prepared to retreat back to his noisy dwelling in attempt to study before morning class.

"Good morning, good morning students! I am Professor Gerald Gammon and am taking the class for the next week as Professor Bud Knight has taken leave to Ireland on a conference. "

At that moment Phil walked into the class late and scurried past the professor as the class made thumping noises on their desks while hassling him onwards with accompanying laughs. The professor looked at his rapid rush to be seated and remarked, "I notice you carry the Doppler effect with you. As you came closer to your desk the noise in the class increased."

"That is strange Sir, as I usually notice a blue shift in people when I make a presence," Phil remarked and stirred laughter though the class of twenty-two students. He then smiled as he turned to bow to everyone while opening his text to the middle of the first chapter.

Mr. Gammon smirked then began his lecture. "All right, so shall we proceed now everyone? Last week Professor Knight reviewed the theories of Newton through the comprehension of Kepler's laws with the attraction of gravitational pull between any two bodies. This, of course, led to his third law of motion with the action of one body upon another being equal and opposite to the action of the second on the first and taking place along the line joining them. This allowed him to deduce all three of Kepler's laws of planetary motion, providing thusly a perfect causal description.

"The planets move under a force towards the sun, which is in consequence with Kepler's second law. His first law stating clearly that this force varies inversely as the square of the distance such that if a planet is twice as far from the sun the force upon it is divided by four. The third law implies also that the force between any planet and the sun is proportional to both their masses. This is all elementary to our present knowledge of the solar system so we will talk today a bit about the expanding universe theories." Professor Gammon continued while spotting his laser light on the blackboard at his diagram.

"Think of the expanding universe as compared to a balloon that is being blown up and all the galaxies are like spots painted upon the balloon. As the balloon is filled with more air the spots move further apart and the spots furthest apart move faster than the ones closer together. This illustrates a model of the universe in expansion, as there are three models, according to Friedmann.

"In order to determine which model applies to us for solving the question of whether the universe will always expand, or eventually stop and begin collapsing into itself, we need to use the Doppler effect, isn't that correct?" The professor said staring down at Phil listening attentively in his seat.

"That sounds perfectly correct, Professor Gammon," Phil replied and asked, "And if the density is less than a particular critical value from the rate of expansion would the gravitational attraction be too weak to halt the expansion?"

"Yes it would, young man," Mr. Gammon nodded, "and likewise if the density is greater than that certain value then gravity will stop the expansion at some point in the distant future and re-collapse the universe. The universe expands between five and ten percent every thousand million years. The mass of all the stars in all the galaxies put together is less than one hundredth the amount required to stop the expansion of the universe. This includes all the dark matter taken into consideration that we cannot see, making it a maximum of one tenth the requirement. The universe will continue to expand for another ten thousand million years as it already has. By that time we will have colonized beyond this solar system, beyond the conceived human capabilities, and our sun would have become what is called a red giant."

The professor drew some curves on the board to illustrate the bending of time and matter to illustrate the models of the universe while combining general relativity with the uncertainty principle of quantum mechanics. The professor's diagram illustrated a theory of finite space and time without boundaries and edges. Phil looked on with great interest as his mind soared and leaped further into the discussion.

After all of his classes, Phil visited his friend, Hanns Holstein, in the Chemistry department at the other end of campus. "Hello Hanns," he greeted, "How is my Swiss friend doing lately? What are you working on today?"

Looking up from his copious notes, Hanns grinned and returned, "Hi Phil! This is a new government funded project for vaccines. How was your weekend?"

"It was quiet, except in my noisy apartment. People across the hall are always bashing things around and playing loud music. I wonder if they ever study in there. It's outrageous because it never seems to stop. Anyway, I attempted to study periodically and also played a soccer game."

"Sorry to hear about the disturbance, I hope it quiets down for you soon. Is there anything else new, my friend?" Hanns asked curiously.

"Well, I've also been tracking four moons around Jupiter with my little telescope and making some notes to compare what I know. It's so interesting to put on the shoes of our great scientific ancestors and collate what they found out with their limitations by relating past with present information. I suppose you worked in the lab most of the weekend, did you Hanns?"

"You know it, Phil. It is part of working towards a master's degree. It is also part of a thesis I am preparing to take a stand on for the vaccines I am developing. Do you have any plans on visiting Jupiter in the future?"

"Well, it would be absolutely interesting to see Jupiter up close but the journey you know, it would take most of my lifetime to travel in any space shuttle of today," Phil conjectured with a grimace.

Hanns looked at him for a second then jotted down a telephone number on a piece of paper. "I know this person, he stops by sometime to ask questions about molecular structures but he is very much interested in astronomy and life out there, so you should call him. I know he won't mind to talk with you. His name is Martin. Let me know how it goes, alright?" Hanns requested as he handed Phil the paper.

"Hey, thank you, my good friend. I will definitely call him. I better let you get back to work. You never know when those vaccines will be crucial to our existence. Have a good night, Hanns" Phil smiled as he walked away.

After supper Phil telephoned Martin to find out what the two cosmic buffs might have as common interests in astronomy to share. It seemed like Martin was a knowledgeable and sincere man as soon as Phil inquired about an interest in extra-terrestrial life forms. A meeting was set for eight o'clock on the following evening. Martin was very pleasant and willing to discuss the subject openly on the telephone and Phil felt as though they could share some astronomical knowledge and insight.

Phil did a few hours of homework before bashing and clanging noises began in the neighbors' apartment. Footsteps creaked back and forth and began to be outright irritating, distracting Phil completely from his studies. He got a glass of water and then brought his telescope out back to sight in Jupiter and once again made notes from observation for his amusement. He set it up as usual on the lower deck where light glaring from the other side of the house was non-visible. He made his routine notes and sketches while holding his miniature red lens flashlight in his teeth to see what he was writing.

It was soon after midnight and he quickly grabbed his things and headed back upstairs in pitch darkness to the house. In the middle of the climb he slipped and held onto his telescope, keeping it above him so as not to crash it on the steps. His mouth slammed into the stair in front of him and drove his teeth into his lower lip. Blood began to gush down his jaw and neck as he clamored and growled at himself whilst grabbing his apparatus and getting back up to walk inside. He rushed into the washroom to clean up and packed his distorted lower lip with an icepack.

The following morning Mark seen him in a hallway at the University and motioned to him with a laughingly sarcastic tone, "What happened to you, did you ask a girl out?"

"Ha- ha, I was playing catch with a set of stairs, you should try it Mark," Phil replied sardonically.

"Don't forget about the game tomorrow night, it's over in field three," Mark said, changing the subject.

"Yes, sure thing, I am running late so will catch you there ok?" Phil said while rushing onwards.

The classes seemed to go by quickly with his eagerness in meeting with his new acquaintance just hours ahead. After supper, at 7:30, he got into his little clunker of a car and turned the ignition. The engine turned over and got weaker as it declined to start. Phil got out and opened the hood and turned the battery posts, which seemed a bit loose. He got back in and the old beast turned over and finally the engine revved to a familiar clatter. He drove to the address that Martin had given. It was a large Victorian, burgundy house with a black metal gate surrounding the perimeter. Phil drove in the circular drive and parked near the front door. Just as he was about to knock on the door, it opened.

"Hello Phil, I am Martin. Glad you could make it over!" A sudden response came to Phil's surprise.

"It's nice to meet you, I am glad Hanns gave me your number so we can have the opportunity to have a discussion."

"Please come and make yourself comfortable," Martin gestured.

Phil noticed several paintings of planets, galaxies and other space related paraphernalia on all the walls that only a fervent astronomy enthusiast would collect.

"It appears quite obvious that we are both looking for similar information and facts about the same subject," Phil augmented.

"Life out there is what you are referring to I am sure," Martin remarked as he offered Phil a glass of orange juice.

"Thanks. Yes, that is to what I refer. More specifically however, I am interested in life out there that has come here. Since the 1940's, there has been a dramatic increase in UFO sightings around the world. This is rather bizarre and of course a large percentage of them may not be validated however I am most interested in the small number that may be valid. Our planet is filled with unknowns that seem to link to extra-terrestrial life having once been a part of civilization here or at least in communication with it," Phil asserted as he sipped from the glass.

"You allude to majestic structures like the pyramids in Egypt and how the scriptures even state that the gods concealed a great secret at Giza. Also, the Vedic texts of India and ancient Egyptian markings indicate the visitation of flying machines so many thousands of years ago."

"I am aware of that. Other ancient cultures such as the Mayans in Mexico and the nine large stone temple structures that appear to represent the planets and are all in line. That is rather strange don't you think? Back in that era, nine planets were not known to have existed. Pluto was only discovered in this century," Phil mentioned.

"I know what you mean. It's an unsolved mystery of our time. On the top of one of those structures, scientists found mica. That is rather strange, since nowhere in Mexico could mica ever be found. Why would the ancients put mica on the top of a sanctuary anyway?"

"That is the material used in space crafts because of its light weight and resistance to temperature up to 800 degrees. I agree it is a bit bizarre to find it on a temple. I doubt we will ever know where on earth they received it from back then. Another strange place that has inklings of alien visitation is in Nazca, Peru. The desert there has tapestries that extend miles in size. There are shapes in the ground that from the air resemble a spider, a hummingbird and one that outlines the figure of a monkey. It has been deduced that some of them relate to the structures of the stars. You have to wonder if the civilizations of that time were welcoming visitors that they considered as gods from the skies," Phil said with a glimmer of curiosity.

"In Turkey there are about two hundred subterranean cities that are also a mystery. Tunnels and rooms dug deep into the mountain side," Martin added.

"I know about them. It was as if they were protective chambers from something that the civilization of the time deeply feared. Perhaps asteroid showers rained the earth or perhaps even hostile forces from somewhere. Do you have any theories about the megalithic stone monuments that are in Karnak, France, near the coast?"

"There are thousands of them, I know that. Some of the stones weight up to 350 tons each. Scientists date them back to about seven thousand years ago. There are theories that they may point to some place in the sky and that they are situated as geometric formations. Strange however, since they date 4000 years before the Greeks came out with the geometry of Pythagorean triangles and so on. Anyway, yes there are numerous mystifying examples that stretch into the past but I am interested more in discussing the present with you, things that we can realize now. Let's talk a minute about the concept of light," Martin implicitly requested.

"What do you know of the laws of light?" Phil asked.

"You already know much about the principles and theories of light. In words that defy the reality of it, it is an instrument, a medium of writing principles of life upon darkness that we can compare every thing to every other thing. It is an essence or medium that transfers information. You could even say it is an intangible substance that we use in attempts to explain theories. As Einstein's formula of $E=mc2$ indicates, energy is mass times the square of light speed. Light has a relationship with mass and energy. It is a useable substance," Martin responded.

"That sounds very plausible, but then what is darkness?"

"The absence of light? Well," Martin chuckled, "it becomes a part of thought that composes blind beliefs and what shadows are made of. Just as the term 'the Devil' is not a person nor force in life but rather the creation of thoughts designated to an image of something with power. It is merely a projection and creation from darkness or ignorance entirely from creating a duality of forces. It is a result of imagination impinged with fear and illusions or to put it another way it causes a psychosis from not accepting light for what it is."

"I've come here to find out what you know about extra-terrestrial life. There are so many reports and I've found thousands of references directed at UFO sightings and abductions, and am so intrigued by it as I've been for years. Understandably most are hoaxes for attention and glorification, if not hallucinatory in nature. Have you done any investigations into this, Martin?"

"We were coming to that. You see, some people have produced projections from their subconscious and felt they have seen such alien crafts, whereas others have been fooled by fake images put in the atmosphere to mislead them. Still others have had some genuine experiences with alien visitation. We must remember that for such intelligence from other life systems to be able to travel around our planet and appear from over a hillside or from the atmosphere and to disappear again minutes later, they have an ability that most people do not comprehend."

"What ability is that? Has it something to do with light?" Phil asked, his face lit with excitement.

"They appear through the light, even in darkness, but from a light through other dimensions. That is why they can travel such great distances and perform abilities that our minds do not comprehend. When they materialize they do so for specific purposes and then they can vanish again at will. To state this in simple terms, they can pop in and out of our world quite distinctly as they traverse through other dimensions using light to manipulate their voyages. Sure it sounds far fetched Phil, most remarkable things do, but all we have to do is look around our own planet, step outside of our shells, and we will see things much more remarkable than we ever imagined.

"Life," Martin continued, "is much greater than we perceive in our little limited circles, which we create to live in, out of fear or lack of interest to research further into what we do not know. We become mentally trapped and mindset into psychological complexes. Science is catching up to explain how phenomena works beyond the physical appearance of life but it will take some time, which is the downfall of learning. Just imagine what people knew fifty years ago and what they know today. Now imagine what they will know and experience in another hundred years. Quite astonishing! Through the equilibrium of light and darkness, we can mathematically explain aspects of eternity and powers, which are a result of light. With the existence of light we have form, it is a basic principle, just like the sun is responsible for our existence here. Now, what we must do is be able to work with these principles in an order such as to solve and coagulate the mysteries of life. We can travel in the bus of light and begin realizing the intricacies of the universal puzzle," Martin added while looking at the star maps on the wall.

"I think that in order to catch on to the bus of light that you refer to we have to understand what we are doing, where we are going and what it is all about. We can't just jump into other dimensions without analyzing what we are doing. Our minds will not accept that. It is easy to be misled with so many frequencies and distractions around us that we really miss that imperative concept of what we are trying to achieve," Phil replied as he stood up and walked around in wonderment.

"Einstein caught the bus to a certain place and realized something very significant on the journey. He caught it then he was able to slow down enough to get onto a stage to realize and explain some great principles about it. Many other people caught the very same bus concept and got off at other places and did ingenious things from their personal journeys. The light bus is a means to an end," Martin noted with enthusiasm.

"I see," continued Phil, "and what kind of bus would the aliens take to come to earth and why would they appear here on our planet?"

"Sometimes they do not mean to emerge here. Other times they have a purpose when they come. If you ever got on an elevator and pressed the wrong floor and the door opened up and some stranger looked at you with a weird expression, you would know how it might be for the aliens when they suddenly appear. When they become visible to people on earth, they may decide through their inter-dimensional capabilities to do something specific while here or else simply vanish and continue their space-time voyage to their specific destination. I have to add though Phil, that some of their appearances are not physical but astral in nature. That is to say that their physical nature is still in the place where they reside and they simply send their mind controlled counterparts to our planet and use a form of ectoplasm as far as I know to materialize into visibility. Other elements in the atmosphere are also used and manipulated by them either accidentally or for a purpose so they can accomplish something while here," Martin insinuated while looking inquisitively into Phil's eyes.

"How do you know all this Martin? Have you ever met any aliens, or is this all something you read or figured out on your own?" Phil questioned.

"I will only say that it is coupled with some personal experience. They can travel in many forms. I've seen them appear in chariots. Not the kind you would normally imagine but due to lack of understanding the concept, a chariot is the best analogy to use when they manipulate a singular bus that passes through dimensions. But to make it conceivable the bus appears as a chariot just in a symbolic sense to convey the concept to you. The aliens exist on an entirely higher level that can escape a zone and enter through a warp by traversing conception. I do not know much about anything, compared to what I must learn in life." Martin hesitated, " I can say this however, that once we learn how to use the chariot or bus as a medium of light to transfer we can then learn anything we imagine and accomplish feats beyond our normal capability. This is the chariot form of travel and I am still studying the principles of it," Martin acknowledged to the appalled visitor.

"I see; so have you met with extra-terrestrial life forms yet, Martin?" Phil inquired incredulously.

"Yes, I have met with some aliens as we consider them, but hold off on locking me up in a padded room Phil. I am only telling you what I am supposed to tell you, it is not by a personal choice but by a given purpose for lack of better words. If you want to manipulate space and time, and I know you have the interest in finding out how to do that, and travel either back or forward through history, then you have to practice devotedly to catching this bus and learning where to move while you are within it. Then you can read the so-called Akashic records of mankind in the higher ethers, gather information about any subject, receive any answer to any problem or make something happen on earth that you would normally have no chance to accomplish. This will only happen if you source your destiny to make it occur. So you have to do work to get there and once there you have to be prepared for what happens, both here and there. You will learn to travel through a human section where there are many invisible human entities then into other levels where there are non-human entities. Training your mind to fathom these regions is the beginning for you to learn how to manipulate the medium of light to travel through. Once you learn to focus into doing this, you can transfer into the chariot and travel past time. That is what I have been working on," Martin explained.

"I would like to say this sounds believable but I have much to learn beforehand. Has there ever been life on Mars or Venus to your knowledge?"

"From what I know, I will answer yes. It's a very complex subject to get into, so I promise that another time we will talk about that. When we do talk about Mars, next time, remind me to mention some things about Phobos and Deimos, the moons of Mars" Martin augmented.

"I certainly shall. How do you suppose that alien crafts can go through space so abruptly?"

"Having studied physics, I am sure you are aware that anti-gravity is equivalent to gravity manipulation. So, from what I have gathered, they have a system to expand space behind the ship and shrink space in the front, and I'm positive that you can imagine the rest. Just imagine, it is 70,000 years to the nearest star as a normal space trip, so how well they must be developed in order to travel so far from other parts of the galaxy. I think they can manipulate photons as well. I believe that they use the energy of sunlight when they come into this space realm during physical visitations and somehow store it for other purposes or use it to regenerate something within their space ship. This is not the same light source we previously discussed with the light bus, it is photons that are emitted from the Sun."

"How are we sure that what you said about travelling through the human section into higher dimensions is not just imagination, Martin? How do we know the difference between reality and illusion on these levels?" Phil questioned with ebullience.

"That is a nice question and you will be able to know the difference. Imagination is something we play with, but reality is something that simply is and always will be. It is an absolute and is completely changeless. We experience it as an event that is real, which can be measured against other data in comparison to know the validity of it. Don't worry, you can pretend as much as you want and fool yourself to your heart's content but you will never get anywhere doing that and the experience will be a laughing phantasm before anything is gained from it. We change, mold and form our illusions but the principles of reality are the masters that change us."

"Well how can we come into contact with beings from other parts of the galaxy and beyond? Is there some mystical experience that we have to build up to or can it happen by a stroke of luck as it were?"

"It can be both and it can be neither. There is a certain harmonious mesh between the soul and the body, and threads of finer matter define this mesh. When our consciousness is centered through these threads we can manipulate many instances into and out of existence. Provided we have developed other particular qualities to work with that are prepared for us when we do this. That is just part of the process that enables us to contact other forms of beings. There is another method when you are alone and want to connect with alien consciousness. Remember that I have done a fair bit of research and have considered all possibilities that I've investigated. Believe it or not, through working with what the east Indians refer to as the chakras within the etheric body, a person can contact higher forms of intelligence. This method gets a bit complex to discuss, so again I will leave that one for another time. The other method is through luck as it were. That is basically the method that most people have with encounters. That is also the method that we will use tonight, for your sake," Martin ascertained.

"Well, what are we waiting for? Are we going hunting for an ET?"

"Would you like to be the hunter or the hunted?" Martin cautioned with widened eyes.

"There is a strange feeling flowing through me and I don't know if it has anything to do with what you talked about but I would give anything except my soul to see a real alien. It seems weird to me Martin, but I knew for a long time that I would have a very interesting occurrence with something far removed from ordinary life. It is not something that I can rightfully explain but something I have awaited to experience," Phil answered with uncertain trepidation.

"I know exactly what you are saying. Many people feel the same way as you do. They think something will happen to them somehow, someday, that is an important part of their life. They simply keep it inside as a vague recollection of knowing a part of their future. Anyway Phil, it's time to go. I will bring you somewhere but you cannot see where we are going. It is very important and you must trust me on that. I have to blindfold you. Is that alright with you Phil?" Martin asked.

"I do trust you, and I don't know why exactly, but I feel that you are beyond the interest of harming anyone. I'm telling myself that this isn't a practical joke Martin, so I hope it isn't. There is more honesty in your soul than I have ever seen in another, aside from my mother of course. I am ready, let's boogie," Phil admitted.

Martin took him to his truck outside and drove away after placing a dark blindfold around Phil's head.

"It is about a thirty minute drive. I will put this CD in for you to listen to. Some people I know produced the music, I think you will enjoy it."

It sounded like the music of Vangelis but had some Spanish guitar mixed in with it. It carried Phil on an inward journey of receptive relaxation. The music symphonized a story as though it was orchestrated to bring him from one level to another and then join all levels. He felt at peace and ready to open himself to an unimaginable experience.

The truck drove off the paved road as Phil began to feel the rough terrain across gravel and evidently into deep woodland. They drove another ten minutes then Martin removed the blindfold from Phil.

"Hey, this is a relief to see again. Wait a minute Martin, shouldn't you be driving with your headlights on? It is pitch dark here!" Phil cautioned.

"I just shut them off a minute ago. It is all right Phil, I have this trail memorized very well. I could drive down it blindfolded, and in fact I once had to do so," Martin replied in all seriousness.

"Well, fine then. I hope we don't end up in a tree," Phil said, a small smirk on his face.

"You will end up in a tree all right, in fact a tree within a tree. Don't be surprised to be bedazzled my friend. We are almost there," The starlit-eyed friend responded.

The truck came to a curve in the road and turned off down an apparently smaller trail and finally came to a halt at the end. Facing them were tall trees beyond which was a faint glimmer of a grand field. The stars above shined over the horizon and onto the field as Martin got out of the truck and was shortly followed by Phil. It was a large grassy area surrounded by thick trees so dark in places that you couldn't see anything through them. The grass was high around the circumference but appeared very short through the middle. There was a fence standing about three feet high out in the field that would appear to serve no apparent purpose. The two young men walked towards the edge of the tree line and looked into one another's eyes through the darkness.

"What are we doing here Martin?" Phil asked in a tone of subtle fright.

"Your deepest desire was to know and so you should. Just remember this, Phil; there is a purpose for everything. We are going to experience luck that is manipulated. Be patient and you will soon find a key to answer your deepest questions," His new friend murmured as he beckoned him to move forward.

Phil's heart began to pound faster as the thought of the unknown thrust throughout his body. He began to nervously shake subsequently as the cool night air did not help him to remain calm and collective. Over the distant trees he heard a high whistling noise that contained a fluttering sound as though something was breaking through the air. His face lit up in a deep shade of blue as a large, thick, bluish-silver saucer appeared from the distance atop the trees and spun concentric blue circles of light towards the ground. It moved slowly, yet with great force then halted in mid-air about forty feet from the ground. It did not lower or move but remained poised in a fixed position at the center of the field.

Phil wanted to run every which way but he simply grabbed on to his emotions and drowned them with enthusiasm, hoping this to be true. The magnificent machine was noiseless other than a faint hum that drummed from the center of it.

"I, I, I don't believe this. This cannot be true. I must be dreaming this. Martin, are you there?" Phil crackled against the tree with concern.

"I am right here, Phil. These beings are a related race of the so-called Pleiadians. They have no hostility and they come to teach certain people on earth things that are truly remarkable about future life. Aliens appear in different flying saucers because they are from different regions and communities of our galaxy. There are no recorded visitations from other galaxies that I am aware of but there are several from our own Milky Way. Walk closer to the ship Phil and stand about twenty feet from it, just on the edge of the fence. I promise you will be alright and end up back home safely tonight," Martin guaranteed while nodding his head slowly up and down.

"Can I take this tree with me?" he asked while hugging onto a large tree. "Just kidding. I feel a lot better than I did a minute ago. Wow, this is so intense. What if they want me to come inside?"

"They won't, don't worry. They have no desire to dissect you, as far as I know" Martin gestured while grinding his teeth.

"Nobody would ever believe this, but it doesn't matter to me. Okay, okay, I am going, don't go anywhere my friend!"

Phil walked slowly towards the fence and stepped closer as though he was at the edge of a cliff and was overly cautious not to get snagged nor falter. He edged his way about twenty feet from the large silver craft that had a bluish hue light under it and a deep blue glow emanating from its sides. Phil stood there nervously considering what could occur. Deeper within he maintained trust and faith in his life and the provider of his existence.

Without any warning a dark shade appeared around the center of the craft. It did not seem like a doorway at first however through it a hole or opening suddenly appeared. Darkness overshadowed the ground as the craft contrived an intensified humming noise like a giant transformer. Everything appeared ominously dark and then tinges of light appeared through the darkness. Phil absorbed everything that occurred as his eyes widened with a remarkable awareness, surpassing his controlled reasoning faculty. What he could ordinarily dream of and hypothesize now became a living reality. Through the darkness he could see a faint image coming into life, like a three-dimensional photograph being developed before his eyes. Chariots disembarked from the spacecraft with alien figures upon them. Then the front of a shield sparkled into formation and then next to it, another one.

Phil whispered to himself: "My mind is the embodiment of the power of the one who sent me into life. I shall not fear that which I cannot understand; so if you are listening, then please embrace me through this. My courage is through my heart and my heart emanates from yours," Never before did he utter such words, but a force generated beyond his logical comprehension issued them from his lips. If ever he had a sense of spiritual endowment through his mathematical and scientific mind of logistics, it was at this moment. He trusted the powers to be, for they would certainly not abandon him.

The shield glimmered with purple radiance and grew in stature as it came closer to the fence. Then it appeared! An alien standing behind the shield, not unlike the normal image one would have of such a creature. Its body seemed to be masked in a tight uniform although it may have been made from a kind of skin material. Phil was awed at eye witnessing an Intelligent Being from another place and time. He wondered what their planet might look like and if it is anything that people ever imagined such a place to be.

Several feet in front of him, Phil witnessed the other chariot shield image becoming brighter. He wanted to walk closer and touch the object and feel the texture but remembered what Martin had said about remaining behind the fence. In front of him were two chariots with alien beings standing up looking over to him. Phil lifted his opened hand as a gesture of human, earthly peace. The foremost alien lifted his hand simultaneously and pointed directly at Phil. An energy field surrounded the creature and a line of scarlet colored glittering fluid with a shining luster extended from the aliens' hand, directly towards Phil and entered his mouth. He felt a tingling sensation upon his lips while trying to send a thought of earthly harmony to the dynamic extraterrestrial. The sore on his lower lip from falling on the stairs, the previous night, had miraculously healed from the fluid's contact. It all occurred simultaneously and without concern or fear of harm. He yearned to experience further communication with the incredible dark-eyed life form.

The alien did not display any emotion, as it stood there steadfast, like a surgeon preparing for an operation. The aliens acted as a catalyst for what Phil was about to experience. Phil stared into the dark, ominous, slanted eyes as though looking deeply into the sky and allowed himself to be receptive by neglecting his thoughts that he might otherwise have entertained. Martin looked on from the tree line and did not make a noise as he had gone through the same tribulation several months previous.

An envelope of purple and silver subatomic matter surrounded Phil like an egg shaped orb filled with translucent fluid. The egg was not unlike the shell of a crab, used to protect his inmost self through a turbulence he would soon experience. Upon the shell were ten crystals or glittering Stars of Assiah that were assembled as dews or droplets of enlightenment from the secret masculine aspect of time through the Great Mother. His eyes closed at the same time as his mouth while he tried to breathe through the fluid that filled the egg he was enshrined within. Moments later he found himself breathing with apparent ease. His essence was submerged with his entire body as the process of time-travel began.

The alien creatures were still a short distance away but somehow kept direct contact with his mind and body. Phil looked sternly through the orb into their eyes. In one alien he could see the vague figures of a lion in one eye and a bull in the other. The creatures were sending him symbols that his subconscious mind would translate as a language. He moved his attention to the other alien and in one eye he seen the stature of an athletic man whilst in the other eye was an eagle with a golden eye. His attention did not waver, as every moment of time became time within time itself. The cherubs in the eyes of the aliens sent him in a twirling motion as though the egg was spinning through space. Suddenly he felt an onrush of energy as the primordial elements within him of earth, air, water and fire became interchanged with one another and no longer distinguished as four but sixteen elements.

He was transmuted through the egg sphere into another dimensional area that had no limit or boundary. Phil emerged from it as though he was metamorphosed into another Being. He felt complete innocence throughout his soul as though a cleansing process had occurred. His hands reached above his head and he felt his hair was gone. He was completely naked as though he became an alien himself, transformed as a vague, translucent figure of utmost purity. His arm reached forward as his hand touched the Holy Grail before him, which made his head move backwards followed by his entire body, rotating in the air within the egg until he emerged into another plane.

A vaporous substance streamed through his throat as though he was swallowing some form of Vicks balm, which inseminated into his organs and made each organ of his body seem as though it had an individual consciousness. It was as though he was put through an initiation in some other sphere of the universe. His eyes strained to open slowly as revolving purple rays of darkness darted through the strange, unfamiliar atmosphere.

Through the vastness of the place he entered, there was no light as such but an infinite distance like he could see through space for millions of miles. His vision soon took on another form. Everything began to appear in shades as though it was a deep illusion of the subconscious. He could feel each beat of his heart and what it did for the rest of his body. He was as a babe in an egg engulfed in the silence of another periphery within the universe. Emotions were absent as he stood in silence, awaiting as though he was on trial for his life.

His body felt like lead and was held down in a deep thick shield of subatomic matter. In the distance he could see strange beings constructing shelters and developing or expanding an ancient city that was set in ruin. It began to take form quicker as a goat-footed beast similar to Pan danced across the structures and played music through a flute to the concentrated workers. He knelt down and sprung himself up with every ounce of available force and came through the egg as his head appeared atop a vast sea. His head bobbed above the silent sea as he gradually awoke into a great storehouse of Influence.

His body arose and was abruptly standing on something similar to soil with his feet caressing the softness of a black weightless earth below him. In the distance he could see a pyramid shaped structure that had an incandescent current of energy emitting from its top. Phil was suddenly zapped towards the edifice as though he was in a place where the measurement of time was nonexistent. He stood motionless within the center of the pyramid as an energy current poured gold fluid over his naked body and covered it with a resplendent peaceful tranquility.

He was no longer Phil, but an apparent realized facet of true identity. He smiled surreally as his palms opened up to receive the great influence. The influence transported him to a crossroads where he was to make a decision. His head looked down one road and then another. From some inner cavity within the ether his hand touched his Intuition and he began the journey down the decided route. It was a return to his earthly existence. His body shook vehemently as it twisted with his mind reentering, back through space and time and arduously returning to the field where the aliens stood. Phil opened his eyes and saw a flash of light fluttering through the night sky then he fell heavily to the ground. He turned his head around, looking at the nothingness that surrounded him. Slowly he lifted himself up and turned around, suddenly spotting Martin, whose apparent position didn't change. Phil walked over to his friend and whispered, "Did you see anything?"

"Not this time Phil. But I know where you went and why you returned. It was for the same purpose I did when I experienced the same journey not so long ago."

"How can we put it into words Martin? What actually happened? I mean I can remember seeing it, feeling it but in no way can I ever explain it."

"Sometimes science isn't prepared for an explanation or to give one, Phil. Sometimes people are not prepared for one either. When our soul is guided beyond time and space by alien beings that are here to show us something that we cannot understand and are so unfamiliar with, it defies any logic we are capable of using. They were the Children of the Powers of the Waters and simply charmed you into realizing an avenue towards becoming the Triumphant of Light. That is how they are able to travel beyond the speed of light and never age nor lose time in their life."

"It is an overpowering feeling, Martin. Somehow, I know what I must do with my life, how to accomplish it and where to direct myself at each moment without a loss or thought or strain of muscles from unconscious jarring. I was in a world where things begin, where they simply begin to take form before they are actually realized. Do you know what I mean?" he questioned to his friend.

"I understand what you mean. Every second of time is in your favor and it is best used towards fulfilling your quest in life. That is why you chose the road to return, to fulfill that promise to your self and accomplish that which becomes a harmonious destiny."

"Why did the aliens leave as I returned?" Phil asked.

"Why would they stay? Every being in life and beyond our planet has some kind of destiny to fulfill. The aliens obviously realize their destiny and when they stop or slow down they loose time and begin to age. That is why they visit our planet abruptly and then leave through the continuum to their next destination. Something directed them to come to me one night and then someone directed you to come to me and for me to bring you to them. We can not answer all things in life but it's safe to know that all things exist for a purpose and happen from a cause," Martin said as they walked to the vehicle.

During the return drive, there was a calm, resilient silence between the friends. It was as though they could read the thoughts of one another and were busy with a conversation beyond words. Phil had a quiet determination beyond any he had ever felt during the coming days. He moved from the noisy apartment to a quieter area of town. His schoolwork excelled beyond his previous circumstances and each minute was used to the fullest in accomplishing his desires toward higher goals.

Every once in a while he would visit Martin and converse over subjects that linked their bonding friendship but the greatest feeling he would have throughout time was when he looked up at the stars each night. He did not see it as merely an endless expanding universe but the perpetual beginning of life as a multi-faceted jewel of creative forces. In the microcosmic scheme of motion on earth he could see there was precious life in everything small and yet within millions and millions of star systems in the sky, there was some form of activity on planets that was well beyond human cognizance. There were beings so advanced that they could work on planes that our spiritual plane only touched upon. They could create and manipulate different forms of matter and color through the powers of their omnipotent mind-forces and use mediums to travel through places of which we had no working knowledge. This is what Phil recalled from his experience and knew to be as a reality beyond our civilized conception of truth.

Phil nestled in his chair out in the backyard gazing at Saturn through his telescope. One day he too might become a charioteer in a distant lifetime or perhaps this one and manipulate the inner planes to ascend out of our solar system and into another one. His aspirations were more alive than ever before. There was nothing that prevented him from stepping outside of the sheath that he lived in to discover new territory and amazing realizations by fathoming the activities within the azure night sky. The lifetime encounter provided him the ability to go forward without inhibition into the vastness. ★

LADY OF THE SWORD

"Behold, there is a Pageant of Triumph as each Star, free from Confusion, sweepeth free in his right Orbit;
all Heaven acclaimeth thee as thou goest, transcendental in Joy and in Splendour; and thy Light is as a Beacon
to them that wander afar, strayed in the Night."

On the Harmony of Will and Fate- Liber Aleph, the Book of Wisdom or Folly. A. Crowley

Kelley looked attentively into her grandfather's gray eyes of wisdom as he told her another story of her youth. She listened intently as his lips moved with control and ease recalling the past as though it was a mirrored image of yesterday. His voice was soothing and most comforting to her.

"You never would believe in anything little dear. You always had to find out the truth before you would accept anything that was told to you. Your parents had such a great affect on your growth and discipline, but of course you know this. I always thought of you as the star in the family and everybody was proud of your determination," The warm hearted man said to her solemnly.

"I wasn't one to believe in things, was I grandfather? I either knew it by experience or had to prove it through setting an example somehow," Kelley chuckled and continued, "One thing however, I recall you always looking from the corners of your eyes to see how I was doing. If I was about to fail at something you still allowed me to find out for myself and then you showed up with some strong principle about the incident to show me that I had to learn something through it. Remember when I was eight and talked with you about the problems I was having with other girls at school? You told me that everything is linked together and grouped in accordance with its particular nature. You also said that if I paid any attention to them I would begin to lose sight of my own visions that would show me the way through life."

She tapped her head with her index finger and grinned, "I remember that well because I didn't have any clue what you were talking about and tried to figure it out for a long time. Then finally it hit me that you were referring to the quirk that people live on and how circumstances can become very distracting. People cling to feelings and always seek stimulus from other people and are attracted through the ability of what they consider. It's simply a psychological aspect about how things conglomerate and attract to one another. After much work to understand that concept I saw through it to the vision of my dreams and they spoke to me. It wasn't a voice, as people know it really but a communication that is much faster and contains more information. When nothing disturbed my mind and it was at perfect ease, these dreams intensified and taught me who I could be and truly am."

She warmly touched her grandfather's arm and added, "That communication guided me, grandfather, to do everything that went right through my life so far."

"You have come a long way over the past fourteen years, my little dear," the grandfather smiled pleasantly, "Nature swings perplexities into life every moment. Through the disciplines your father taught you when he was alive, you have come to master those emotions and thoughts that, in an ordinary life, control people's actions and prevent them from listening to their dreams. You have learned to focus on a single thought to the point of basically becoming that thought."

The grandfather grinned as though he was about to burst as he handed Kelley a long, rectangular box. "I think it is time to give you this birthday present. Today you become twenty-two years young and you are now ready for it. It's just a few weeks before Yule, but that's no problem, there will be something special under the tree as well," The elder man chuckled with a wink.

"Oh grandpa, thank-you so much!" She smiled as she opened the large box wrapped in blue and gold shiny paper. Beneath the paper was an old wooden box with a silver latch. Kelley's eyes lit brightly as she undid the latch and opened the box.

Within the box lay a long, slim sword placed atop a cushion of crushed velvet. Specks of light danced up and down its slender double-edged blade. Its hilt was cup-shaped, and seemed to be made of pure gold. The sword was unmistakably a rapier, like the ones she saw in "The Three Musketeers".

"Oh wow," she whispered in awe, "It is so beautiful! It is beyond magnificent, grandfather! Is this the sword I was told you had since you were a child?"

"Yes indeed," the grandfather confirmed, "this is that very one, my dear. It dates back hundreds of years. My grandfather gave it to me one day after I worked in the hay field. It was late at night and I just came towards the house when I heard him yell my name. The shouting came from the upstairs window so I went inside and up to see what he wanted. At first I was worried he was going to scorn me for something that I perhaps forgot to do that day but instead he rewarded me for the work that was done. He told me that his grandfather gave it to him and got it through a Secret Mystical Order in Spain in 1774. It has magical powers within it dear child. Real magical powers, in fact! This sword was held by powerful hands through the ages of time and never used in any slaying. The history of it is built with energies from every person who held it and directed positive powers into it for use should they ever require it. It has become a bank of stored, cleansed energy. Pick it up and close your eyes, little one," He requested with a deeply sincere smile.

Kelley reached in the ancient box lined with purple velour and wrapped her hands around the hilt of the magnificent sword. She lifted it out from its house and held it up to her chest while closing her eyes. Her body was filled with warmth that was also somehow cool and refreshing. Her mind tingled as she embraced the sensations of the energy contained within the blade.

"It has a good energy," She said breathlessly, "God, people that need a coffee in the morning could sure use one of these to perk them up. It has an awakening, rejuvenating effect! I can feel a stream of energy going through my hands and up my arms. It has such a positive stimulus, and I can feel it going down through my chest with increased intensity," She added with a glow around her body.

The elder's face grew serious. "Always keep it in the case and protected somewhere in a dark place. A closet would be fine. Do not let other people handle it and make sure you wash up before touching it, as you would with anything sacred. You should put energy into it when you have abundance and only use it when you feel depleted and need some energy. You know how to charge talismans, well now you have a highly charged one for life. Think of the energy that you store into it as the Vril force, the stored energy forces that mystics developed and stored in the 1930's, and be respectful of it, as I know you would be. I was also told always to give it to one of my children's children. I'm sorry, but I didn't make the rules, so you better find Mr. Right someday soon so you can give it to your grandchild one day."

Her eyes opened wide as she set the sword that had small rubies and sapphires inlaid around the hilt back into its resting-place. "This is really a wonderful surprise and a powerful one at that grandfather. Thank you so much!" She smiled while reaching over to hug and kiss the wise man.

"You are as full of deep love as you are a true warrior my dear. One day a fortunate man will share that with you," The grandfather said as he returned her embrace.

"Share the love or the warrior in me, grandfather?" She laughed.

"Hopefully just the love, the abundance that you hold," He returned with a sober smile upon his aging face.

Kelley checked her watch. "It is late now and I am on duty in the morning. This gift will always be cherished as you always will be, grandfather. I will come by again next Sunday. If you need anything just send a message on my Viewer," She concluded while getting up and walking with him to the door.

"Be careful and stay safe Kelley. You are my little angel. With the new law passed, people are living in fear and uncertainty and it is more dangerous than years past," He added while she hugged him and kissed his cheek once more.

"Thank you, and don't worry, I am always on duty with another officer and we are careful. It's not like it was ten years ago in the year 2000 when officers went on patrol alone."

She waved to him as she went out to unplug the charging cable from her auto. She wrapped it around the electric post and clicked the vehicle door open of her lime-colored 2009 Baytaz. With its highly charged power, the auto sped off quickly down the lane to the inter-cruise.

When she arrived home, Kelley placed her sacred sword under her bed and relaxed during a refreshing shower. Once cleansed, her body felt relieved and ready for a required rest before commencing another week of work. While lying in bed she decided to hold the sword once before falling to sleep. She knelt on the floor and hauled it out from under the bed and slowly opened the box to lift out the sword. Kelley sat on the chair and poised the sword with the blade facing downwards touching her foot and wrapped her hands around it. She breathed ever slowly as her hands lifted off the hilt to find the sword was perfectly balanced on the tip of her foot and standing up by itself. She lowered her head and grasped the hilt again, feeling as if part of her soul had entered into it. Before setting it back in the box she noticed a small inscription at the center of the blade. It read as: 'Ius Suumcuique Tribuit'. She looked into a translation lexicon and found that it meant 'Justice gives each his due'.

The following day was dismal with showers but otherwise quite welcomed by people enjoying the rain upon them. The population increase soared as more people flocked from the southern states northward, escaping the heavy drought that was estimated to diminish the world population in years to come. Food was not as plentiful as the year before and prices continued to rise, causing more theft and crime in populated areas. This drove the criminal investigation departments to make drastic decisions that were initially voted in by the public.

Escaping the harsh reality that plagued civilization was unavoidable. It was the portion of society that turned towards greed that caused increased injustice. Pollution was unnecessarily rampant and created unavoidable disasters as the climate became too much for Mother Nature to withstand. There were monthly meetings from environmentalists throughout the world but they were at a loss to change the havoc that spun out of control. There is always a price to pay for unbalance in the environment and society was beginning to pay the cost, in more ways than imagined. Hurricane season was two months longer than previous years and wiped out much of the coastal states time and again. Insurance companies closed the door to seafront properties and the military was stretched to its' maximum in assisting local police agencies with preventing looters, cleaning up disaster zones and providing aid to tornado victims across the central states.

Kelley arrived at work for the morning briefing. She sat amidst the other officers in the conference room while the Captain opened the meeting with the weekly strategy. "It's not getting any easier on the streets, people!" He shouted as the attention from all ears turned to listen. "One strike you're in and two strikes you're gone. That is what we are dealing with and it doesn't make the crooks any less likely to pop your head off if they have the slightest opportunity. Society isn't paying the bill for prisoners any longer as you well know. If they do wrong they eat bread and rice. That's what it amounts to. Nobody wants to get caught so don't turn an eye on anyone because they will not think twice about escaping. If it's their second offence they're off to the ISLAND! That goes for the whole nation! If they are caught as a murderer, then they get to choose which hand they want sliced off. If they don't make the decision, they lose both hands. Life is really pretty now isn't it? Yeah! It is, so whatever you do out there, don't spare a taxpayer's dime. Crime rate has fallen three percent since last month, so this system must be working," The Captain yelled while making the point strike home to all the attending officers.

"What about the south side Captain? Are we getting more patrollers soon?" Officer Riley asked from the back corner.

"We are still working on that. Our prescient gets four more officers next week so we may supply two of them on the south side, " The Captain replied as he gulped down his coffee.

"Isn't the Island already overcrowded with prisoners, Captain?" A female voice echoed from the side.

"Yes it is, however it's all we've got. All prisons are overcrowded and for serious offenders there is only the Island to send them to. It's out of our hands and it doesn't really matter. If people choose to do criminal actions they know what happens. Prison is not a haven for the winter months any longer. Those days are long gone. So keep your wits about you at all times. Jordan is slowly recovering from the gunshot attack Saturday night. He is now in stable condition. Other than that, I have nothing more to pass on today," The Captain concluded as he closed the conference.

Kelley got up and walked to the locker room as Mike, another officer, walked beside her. "Remember you have that school lecture at two o'clock this afternoon, Kelley," He reminded.

"Oh, that's right. Thank you, Mike, for advising me of that," She replied as she put on her blue bulletproof vest and proceeded to her patrol vehicle with her partner, Allan.

"Are you keeping yourself busy lately Kelley?" Allan asked as they entered the vehicle.

"All the time, it seems. I do a gymnastics class on Tuesday nights, a violin class on Thursday nights and in between I am studying law to finish a degree," She responded as she started the engine.

"A well-balanced bunch of activities you have going on," Allan remarked, clearly impressed.

"Well, I try to avoid extremes in daily life but this job doesn't much help to maintain that frame of mind."

"What about dating?" He wondered. "Have you taken some time off to enjoy yourself a little bit?"

"Once in a while, Allan. But there are a lot of guys around here that are in a rut. I try to avoid those kind because it's a drag to listen to their problems."

"What kind of rut do you mean, Kelley? How do you know if you like a person or not?"

"It's not an easy matter to discuss. But I will tell you. I like a guy that has something going for himself; somebody that has interests and works hard to achieve them. I mean interests that are not just physical in nature but are of a higher goal, an aim towards achieving a little bit of perfection you might say. To know if he is right for me I may ask him to drop his conscience on a little scale that I have at home. If it sinks the scale to one side I know he has a heavy conscience and holds a lot of remorse over things he has done," She giggled.

"It must be difficult to ask a guy to remove his conscience," Allan chuckled and continued, "So for something of a higher goal do you mean to say that if he is into Tai Chi or mediation you may like him?"

"It's not that simple, but in a roundabout way I suppose those qualities are good as well. As long as he has positive ambitions and shows good energy towards them, he is something to consider."

"You must be a Leo," He jested as he rolled his eyes.

"Not quite Allan, I am a Libra," She replied with a wry grin.

"What do you think of our cruel and inhumane prison system Kelley?"

"It could be much better. People make mistakes and sooner or later they are sorry that they did. I thought about prison life and I bet it can be horrid. If I were to make a suggestion, I would say that the criminal should be made to feel in some way the pain that they caused. But then, after they realize what feelings are and what it feels like to be a victim then the correctional system should implement spiritual awareness and growth to their rehabilitation. It is a proven fact, to me at least, that practicing teachings of spirituality will diminish hostile energies and therefore would drastically decrease crime. We are one world and it is time we begin to acknowledge and work towards that fact." Kelley said.

"You sound like a philosopher, but there is potential in what you said. I mean, we couldn't expect to turn a prisoner into a Guru but to get them in touch with feelings and have them seek spiritual direction may very well curb their mentality in a positive direction."

From the police radio they heard that assistance was required at the corner of Glen and Main. Kelley spun the vehicle around in the middle of the street and accelerated with the siren on.

When they arrived at the location, they could see a commotion escalating outside of a convenience store. Kelley got out of her vehicle and asked another officer that stood beside his vehicle for the status of the situation. He said that a man was holding the store clerk hostage inside, behind the counter. The lieutenant's police vehicle quickly pulled up alongside of them. He talked with the abductor through his car phone to find out what demands or concerns were involved.

"Apparently it is his ex-girlfriend in there and he is distraught about their break-up," The lieutenant stated as he shook his head in dismay.

"Let me go in there and talk with him, Lieutenant. Tell him you are sending somebody in to talk with them in person about the situation," Kelley requested.

The lieutenant knew he did not have many options. "Don't make any mistakes. It may end up costing someone's life," He affirmed and got back on the telephone. "His name is Jack Barlowe. Okay, he is going to let you go in, so be careful," The lieutenant warned while leading her forward.

Kelley slowly walked into the convenience store and looked around. She saw that the man behind the counter was armed with a pistol, held towards the girl's head.

"I am Officer Trudy, Mister Barlowe. I just want to talk with you for a few minutes," Kelley assured him with her calm voice.

"What is there to talk about?" Jack sputtered, "She has ruined my life and she goes around glorifying it. I am not taking this any longer. She has to realize I did everything I could but what did she do in return? She just walked away like nothing matters to her. She took everything I had and left me with her bills; bills that you wouldn't believe! Is there any justice in that? Would anybody listen to me then? No! Nobody listens to the man! So what is there to discuss? It's time for a little action here today." Jack waved around his pistol for emphasis.

"It happens all the time Mister Barlowe. There are ways to handle it and this isn't one of them. You have to do yourself this favor and not go to the isolated prison for the rest of your life. What you have to realize is that there is no way out with what you are thinking. If you put your gun down everyone will be much better off," Kelley reasoned with a hypnotic, relaxing tone.

"She is not getting away with this any longer, Officer! She is not walking out of here. I can guarantee you that much!" The man cried out in grief.

"I agree with you there. She will have to confront her wrongs, and we can make that happen. We are just as concerned about you as we are about her. We don't want to see you do something that you will regret for many years because someone brought some anguish into your life. Let's handle this the proper way; nobody gets injured and everything gets worked out, alright?" Kelley proclaimed with a positive and focused voice.

"It's too late for that now. I tried and I tried. She doesn't listen because she doesn't want to listen," Jack sneered, pointing the pistol back at the cashier's head.

"I didn't listen because you only have your view! You have your side to everything but what about other people, Jack?" The clerk cried out to him and continued, "Look at what I had to put up with when we were together! You drank every night and every second night you were out gambling your money away on those damn machines! What kind of life is that? Don't you think that if you really tried I would have been there? I tried Jack, but you didn't try!"

"Listen to me! You never cared about anything, Beth! You were never home when I got home, you always ran the roads and where to? I never knew! You lie and lie about everything because the only person that was ever in your life is yourself!" Jack asserted, slamming a fist on the counter.

Beth shook her head. "Do you think I have to wait home for a drunkard to come in whenever he feels like it? I put into the relationship as much as you did. I just left the bills that you didn't pay your share into! Everybody has their own justice, Jack, and mine was to leave and never talk with you again!"

Kelley could see that there was a lot of work ahead for the pair. "Listen, folks," she comforted, "we are getting somewhere can't you see? Each of you has a different view of the situation, but it's obvious there is truth in what each of you feel. You have to let loose and accept to listen to one another. You have to communicate which is something you both haven't done in a long time. It's not going to hurt to do that. It will prove better than to punish anyone, including yourself."

The man looked at her and appeared to begin confronting his emotions. Kelley walked a little closer to him. "Everything can work out and you can have a good life still. No one should be the judge to take that opportunity away from another person. We are all essentially free to think, feel and act the way we choose so please Jack, let this be a positive outcome and do what you know is the right thing. Have that courage Jack to stand up against your frustrations and know that we all make mistakes and to accept it and make changes to correct them is the only real victory."

"That sounds like a great game, but it doesn't play with me!" Jack spat, losing his patience. "I said she isn't walking out of here! She owes me something and I am here to collect! Do you think I am doing this just to show how nice I can be? I want to spend some time with her, so turn around officer and walk out of here now!" Jack snapped his head back towards Beth and narrowed his eyes. His intentions were clear to Kelley.

"Get the hell out of your rut, Jack! You are wasting my time and I am not liking it!" Kelley yelled to distract him as she flung her body over the counter and slashed his arm down with her fist, releasing the pistol to the floor.

It happened so unexpectedly and abruptly that Jack was startled enough for Kelley to have the time to fling her body across the countertop at the same time as the weapon hit the floor. She locked her arm around his neck and pulled him to the floor with the force of her weight in motion and managed to twist his arm around his back to constrain him on the floor.

Kelley nodded her head to Beth and requested her to go outside and tell the other officers to come in.

"Thank you so much! You saved my life!" Beth cried as she sighed in relief and rushed outside.

"There are issues that you have to resolve here, Jack. You will never get anywhere doing things the stupid way," Kelley voiced as she firmly pressed her knee into his back.

"I have rights, don't tell me what to do!" He oozed from his mouth as she pulled firmly on his arm to the point of almost snapping it behind his back.

"Listen, moron," she whispered into his ear, "you can save your rights for your conscience 'cause down here you just lost your rights. You're a big boy, Jack, and your decisions just cost you some serious school time. I wager that five years of eating rice and bread and having multiple brutal boyfriends will make you wish your decisions were better chosen."

"I'm not going to your stinking hell!" He voiced back as she tightened her restraint on him.

"It's not my hell, Jack. It's yours. It's unfortunate that parole was abandoned a few years ago, so time you get is time you'll do." She said as the other officers came through the door.

That afternoon Kelley made her appearance at the elementary school to deliver her lecture on being lawful and careful in society. She walked into the gymnasium of nearly two hundred children, all of which were seated around the floor.

"Good afternoon, we are most pleased to welcome you to our school," The Vice-principal said as she shook Kelley's hand.

"Thank you and it is a pleasure to be here," Kelley smiled as she walked to the podium. Her gaze fell across the student body and she seemed to take them all into her own aura of power as she began to speak.

"Hello, it is lovely to see all of you young and ambitious students today. My name is Kelley and I am here to talk with you about safety tips and being careful with the things you do. When I say safety tips, does anyone have some ideas of what I mean?"

A little boy raised his hand from the center of the crowd. "I know, I know!" He said confidently, "We should not go away from our parents when we are in a crowded place."

"That is a good safety tip. Yes, thank you for that. Are there any more that anyone can think of?"

"We should not go anywhere with a stranger or without telling our parents?" A little girl shouted from the front.

"That is a very good safety tip," Kelley confirmed, "Strangers could be bad, although not all of them are, but if there is ever a bad one, you have to know how to deal with it in a safe way. Your parents probably have told you already to go straight to them and tell them about anything that happens. They are always concerned about you because it is a responsibility that they have. If you have to run from a bad situation then do it and think inside of yourself where you are running to and don't ever give up. Always be very careful and when someone tells you to do something that you think is not right, don't be afraid to tell the person that it is wrong. The important thing is if you feel it is wrong, then don't do it. You have to listen to what you know inside of yourself to be right. Everybody knows there is a difference between doing right things and doing wrong things. Wrong things can cause harm to you and other people. Right things can bring you happiness and it is something that good people approve of or think is right to do. It is that simple you know."

Kelley paused to survey the audience. Confident that she had their full attention, she continued, "Being a police officer is a big job. I hope that one day it will not be such a busy job and that it will be safer for everybody to go where they want without being worried about what could happen to them. There are too many people living out there that do not understand or care that they are doing bad things to other people. They do not care enough to understand. I am hoping that all of you people will grow up and know this and will be good citizens, to help society in positive, good ways and to have a successful and honest life."

She continued to ask them questions and then did some demonstrations of how to handle getting out of a harmful situation. She picked volunteers to enact scenarios which she described and explained their roles to see what they would do and how they would react. At the end she concluded her lecture with telling them the barbaric and cruel life in prison for anyone that is sent there. She wanted to let them know that they have a choice in life and they should always think twice before doing anything that they may regret.

After the instructions, Kelley talked with the Vice-principal, Mrs. Anderson, about problems in the schooling system. Mrs. Anderson was concerned about the children who thrived on being bullies to others and were always getting into disrespectful mischief.

"Many parents don't have the interest to spend quality time with their children and so those children are always seeking attention which comes in a variety of patterns," Kelley observed.

"I can see that through their behavior, and on Thursday we are having a District Counselors Board meeting. I want to bring up these points to see if any changes may be added to the schooling system," Mrs. Anderson remarked.

"That is a good idea," Kelley agreed, "If children were given responsible situations to prove their capabilities, that would be a beginning. Also, their value system could be developed stronger. Without infringing on their personal freedoms and rights, they could be developed mentally and emotionally stronger and therefore likely lead a more productive life with better decision making through the future. The knowledge of right and wrong has to come through force to be most effective. People have to be blatantly told that certain things are wrong to do by illustrating the consequences of the action. When they can see, for example, that ten positive actions brings them to another, greater level of reward, then they will work harder to perform such actions. It's simple psychology really, but they have to realize that rewards become greater as the actions become greater."

"Thank you so much for coming by and I will take those suggestions to the Board and see what they can engineer with the present curriculum. In times like this, children are our hope to continue life in a positive direction and we want to give them the best possible guidance," Mrs. Anderson declared.

"It has been a pleasure. Until next time," Kelley waved as she walked out the door.

She went back on patrol until five o'clock and then returned to the precinct to finish some paperwork. When she arrived home that evening, she immersed herself in a warm bath then sat on a carpet and did some stretching exercises. She felt much better and livelier after stretching the muscles throughout her body. Kelley went to her bedroom to once again hold the mystical sword. She stood up and pointed the tip towards her toes and concentrated on the feelings she received through it. A stream of positive energy swirled through her body, down her arms and into the sword. It appeared to go through the sword and into her feet as though vibrations from a high level entered into her, through it and into her feet. It was a semblance of manifestation as higher potencies went through her and were charged and materialized on the earth level as sensations. She felt analytically sharper than she ever had before, with a clear mind and capable of handling just about any complexity that confronted her.

She looked down at the guard on the sword. Emblazoned on the cup was a pair of stylized crescent moons back to back, which simulated a waning and waxing moon. Within the hilt she could see a shimmer of light traverse through its copper core that represented an aspect of Venus, accepting the radiance and transferring it to the steel blade peculiar to the warrior energy of Mars. She was rejuvenated and could discern the power she had in dominating the thoughts that came to her mind. It was unlike the usual ability as she uplifted to a new level of realization. Kelley sat on her chair and looked once again upon the blade, close to the hilt. She saw some words very finely edged into the steel. She got a magnifying glass and read them. Upon it was written: 'Ateh Gibor Le-olahm Adonai'. She went to her book collection to seek the meaning of the words. It meant: 'To thee be the Power unto the Ages, O my Lord.'

From her practice of yoga, she knew that an ultimate state of achievement was Samadhi, which meant 'to be together or joined with the Lord'. The Hebrew word 'Adhi', from Samadhi came from the same etymological root as the Sanskrit word 'Adni', or Adonai. To her there was something obvious and simple within this connection. It was like the sword was a supreme symbol of the mind being under control and capable of channeling the greatest powers through being in unity with the Lord. At that moment she had no emotions, no imagination, no concern. Those were more like obsessions and tools in a spiritual carpenter's shop. The potential of genius seems to sit upon a fine line, and one that is undisturbed by any known or hidden vibrations. The Genius that she connected with was the Lord, her Lord and Guide.

There was much more to this realized phenomenon that she was contemplating. Thoughts and theories about life seem to be relative lies about the essence of facts when viewed from a level higher than that which they were formulated upon. Kelley realized something about justice and adjustment. Somehow there was a link between making things right, preserving the rights of individual consciousness and the path that light created through the maze of shadows that we live within. She recalled the concept that she mentioned to Mrs. Anderson about doing several so-called right things to achieve something greater, like a reward or realization. This seemed to be what people on the physical level play upon in life. To her there was something more to it. She surmised that to go through the painstaking process of balancing one incident with another, or a feminine principle with a masculine one such as in the case with the inner life yin and yang theory, that a new existence would evolve through it. The new existence seemed to be a birth of some sort. All birth begins with perceived pain into the level of which it does not comprehend. Just as a child is born into the world of uncertainty, the consciousness becomes thrilled when born into a new realization and seeks to unite with its totality. The totality in this instance is the inmost Self through the Lord of the individual's spirit.

She had conceptualized, of course, that the reason we live amongst people with created problems is basically quite simple. They play with thoughts and emotions because they are on a particular level of realization and are seeking some form of energy to unite with, to feel or express fulfillment. They are lost in shadows of surrounding illusions and are always desiring amusement and filling their cravings so they do not have to confront the supreme silence of non-action. Action is a distraction, but non-action is frightfully boring. As silly as it all appeared, there was some truth to this and why there are so many world created problems. People are afraid to confront their inner self because of uncertainty, so they pack on a big mask of influential persuasion that gives them a personality, an exterior expression of power and control. She realized that the physical world justice system was an exterior expression of what should be done on the interior world. Despite the tremendous flaws of the exterior system, the essential principle was the same. Balancing the strengths and weaknesses through the pain of seeking realization or new birth, the stillness of consciousness goes deeper to the point of touching the brink of the inner genius. Then the Adonai within, the Lord of Self can guide it, and every action has a greater meaning and purpose and therefore fulfillment. Kelley set the sword back into the box under her bed and read part of a book as she decided to lie down upon her bed.

Before falling to sleep she did an exercise with her mind. She concentrated on the left and right sides of her entire body all the way to her feet. Then she contemplated other opposites such as her emotional and her mental well being. Following that, she meditated upon her physical and spiritual qualities. Then she said to herself, "I will avoid extremes in daily life and not allow havoc to come into my mind over any matter. Good and evil, ebb and flow of any circumstances will not sway me into any course of action that will bring harm to me. All justice requires adjusting any action to create the appropriate reaction. I will sleep in peace and live in harmony."

Kelley opened her eyes to look at the mantle on the wall and seen her little statues of the Egyptian Goddess, Maat, the Hindu Deity, Yama, the Greek Gods Themis and Minos and a statue of a Tibetan elephant. All these symbols represented, to her, the Rulers of Balance and Truth. She was prepared to live in accordance with adjustment, as though she was living in a Taoist purgatory or cleansing procedure to cancel opposites that occurred in her life. Her eyes closed and she fell soundly asleep.

When she awoke for work, she felt completely renewed with vigorous energy. There was a connection established between the sacred sword and Kelley. Although some may assign tragedy and sickness to the symbology of a sword, it is only a carrier and has much greater and subtle affinities of logic assigned to it. She thought about the sacred analogy of it and concluded that it should not be used mystically without an appropriate crown upon her head to link the mental process with none other than the Supreme. True balance is the result of harmony and to have the sword as the symbol of the divine deity is wrong, since it is a representation of the piercing intellectual facet of the mind. It is a tool as it were, to penetrate into falsehood and allow light to come through. She enjoyed a large breakfast and then went to the precinct, carrying with her a faithful consciousness embracing the powers of the sword so that it would remain with her through the day as she walked in the shadows of those amongst her.

While on patrol she received a call to report to the airport for an emergency crisis. When she arrived she found out that a hijacked airplane had stopped to refuel and held four hundred and eighteen passengers hostage. She was directed to stay near the gate exit and await further orders.

The hijackers requested a person they knew to be removed from a nearby prison and to be brought to them. If there was any way of preventing them from getting back into the air, Kelley wanted to do it. Her job entailed protecting the passengers from any possible harm, and to do that she had to conjure a tactic to free as many as possible. She suggested to the lieutenant on the radio that they release two hundred passengers in exchange for the prisoner, knowing that if any, they would release far less than requested. Amazingly they agreed to release thirty if they had word that the imprisoned associate would be released and delivered to the airplane within three hours.

Kelley was given an order to deliver food into the airplane and to dress as a delivery person from the airport food services department. She was sent a summary of the hijackers on her portable VieweR that included photographs of the hijackers and brief descriptions of their history. There were six of them and they each had extensive criminal histories in Eastern Europe.

Kelley had some assistance of bringing the food on board the aircraft with a few other undercover officers. When she got on, a fanatical looking dark hair, heavy man pushed a machine gun to her face and bluntly told her to drop the food in the isle. A stewardess said to him, "We could use some help to pass out this food. These passengers haven't eaten anything since crossing the ocean!"

"If I need some help to think, I won't be calling you alright?" The man blurted at her.

Kelley noticed a dead body in the isle. "Listen, food girl," the haggard man spat at her, "You and your friends go and take that body and bring it to the authorities. Tell them we are here on a mission and not to screw around with us! Do you hear me?"

"Perfectly well," Kelley said as she walked down the isle with her assistant to haul the body forward. She looked around to get a view of the passengers and the concerns she had to deal with to control the situation.

"Look, I am a student studying nursing, and I can see there are some sick people on board. Let me help them. I promise it will end up making your job easier and everything will go smoothly," Kelley assured the brute.

The brute paused to consider her offer. Smiling lewdly, he oozed, "Okay, we can use a cute face around here, but if you make any stupid moves, you will be the next to be carried off. Understood, little nurse?"

"I'm not here to do anything stupid, don't have to worry about that Sir," Kelley assured him.

"You other guys get off this jet!" The staunch man blurted as he pointed his machine gun towards Kelley's assistants, "Remember to take this body and my message to them, and I expect to hear back with a positive answer very soon"

"Definitely, I am sure they will call you as soon as we speak with them," The undercover agent replied as he and his friend carried the bloody body down the steps to the runway.

Kelley remained on the plane and walked down the isle checking on passengers and told them to remain calm and that she would come around to everyone. The stewardesses slowly handed out food while Kelley casually assessed people and kept a watchful corner of her eye upon the assailants. She whispered to a stewardess that she would begin at the other end of the plane and work slowly forward. At the rear of the plane she saw a man with a gun around the corner, digging into a bag. She looked around then walked casually to him and placed her arm around his shoulder.

"This isn't really my kind of job," She smiled as her arm quickly went under his chin and twisted his head into a snap, breaking his neck. She walked out into the other isle with a smile to cheer the wearied folks as another hijacker walked down that isle into the back corridor. He noticed his accomplice leaning over the sink without moving.

"Come on, get out here and keep an eye on the back area!" He sternly said to the dead man.

Kelley walked behind him and pressed a point in his back that made him fall to his knees as she quickly grabbed and snapped his neck while whispering softly, "Sorry pal, the prisons are full."

She looked around and then quietly hauled both men into the rear toilet facility, shoving them in to fit and then closing the door. She looked up and imagined the sacred sword coming through her head down into her entire body, giving it a force of steel as her arms, followed by her entire body, stiffened with vigor and strength. She breathed in slowly through her nostrils and then out through her mouth as she sent a message to her invisible guide:

"Through the light of your ineffable powers, guide my every movement."

Kelley walked casually back to the isle and continued examining some of the passengers. An East Indian man wearing a turban looked up at her and asked if she could inquire about getting a vegetarian meal. Kelley replied with an obvious smile to his curiosity, "I will check for you but am not quite sure, so if there are none, just dig around the meat and eat what you can."

She could see the fear in many faces scattered throughout the airplane. One of the accomplices walked from the front to the center of the plane and held his machine gun in the air. "Listen here, everyone," he shouted, "On good faith I am letting thirty of you go free. My associates will decide who will go. When he points at you, simply stand up and be ready to leave. I will let you all go at the same time but if there is any problems I will not hesitate to shoot anyone. I hope that I am making myself perfectly clear."

He then went towards the front to talk with his conspirators. "Gunter and Herbert, I want you two to grab thirty people and prepare them to get off. They should have Gothart released from prison and here within a few hours. If not, then we will give them some extra bodies that suddenly stop breathing. I have business to take care of up front, so go choose thirty and set them free." The apparent leader groaned, then turned and walked back into the cockpit.

"You, you, and you." Gunter pointed and shouted as he walked along, pointing at hostages that he chose to be free. "Stand up and wait for my signal to move to the front!"

"Anybody want my lunch?" A teenage boy asked as he was chosen to leave. Nobody found it amusing as they groveled in their seats hoping to be picked. Kelley smiled sedately at Gunter as he walked slowly past her towards the rear of the plane. "Excuse me Miss, may I take your pillow for an elderly lady in the back?" Kelley asked.

She was given the pillow and then walked back, following Gunter quietly and as he looked around the back for his comrades Kelley pulled out her silencer revolver and shot him through the pillow which was forced to his chest.

"You're not going to fit in that puny washroom there, sir. You will just have to wait out here," She whispered as she set his corpse on the floor against the wall. She quickly walked down the other side of the plane towards Herbert.

"Get out of my way you dolt!" He groveled as he pushed her aside making his way between her and the seats.

"Excuse me, I am just looking for some more ill passengers," She said as she leaned over to grab another pillow and pressed it against his stomach while shooting twice into the pillow with her gun. His hand reached to grab her hair as he slowly fell to the floor in a deathly anguish.

"May the forces of creatures that await you swallow up your soul and digest you kindly," She whispered as she looked at his eyes closing. A large gentleman got out of his seat as Kelley motioned him to haul the bloody corpse out of view to the back of the plane.

"The thirty passengers may now move to the front of the plane and prepare to leave. Stewardess, please get the door," Kelley requested.

"You don't take any shit from anybody, do you?" The stewardess grimaced.

As the passengers slowly made their way out the exit, Kelley went to the rear of the plane and wiped some blood from Herbert's shirt onto a small dishtowel. She spotted a man near the front of the plane and requested that he play dead on the floor while she wiped the bloody towel upon his shirt.

"This looks rather sickening, but I rather play dead than be dead," He jested as she swabbed the wet blood on the back of his shirt. The thirty passengers were gone and Kelley took a revolver from one of the dead felons and pointed it outside the plane towards a small grassy knoll. She fired a shot and then jumped back awaiting the cockpit door to open with an alarmed fugitive to come through. The door opened and a tall dark man named Morris, exited and yelled, "Gunter, what was that shot?"

Suddenly the stewardess jumped down to the floor at the man who appeared dead and began to scream. Morris walked ahead three feet and looked at the man on the floor without much concern and yelled, "Throw that body off the plane! We'll tell them to hurry their asses before we send them more!"

Just then Kelley turned from the corner and shot Morris in the chest. His body toppled over as he attempted to grab onto the cabinet but his hand fell short of it and he continued to plunge into the wall. He slid down to the floor slowly as his eyes locked onto Kelley, catching his final breath. Aaron came out of the cockpit in rage, hauling with him one of the pilots. He held his revolver to the pilot's head as he stared into Kelley's eyes. "You would do best to drop your gun at this moment before this sweet man meets the end," He said with serious intent.

Kelley conjured all the powers within her as she breathed deeply and maintained a relaxed and collective stance while pointing her gun to his head.

"The past and the future are right now, scumbag. Whatever you do will meet with your end, which is not long in sight. It is coming faster and closer to you, there is no way out and you have to give in. No matter what you do you are checkmated," She intoned while attempting to weaken his thwarted interests and steadily holding her gun towards his eyes.

"Your time is over!" He sternly voiced as he pointed his gun towards her. The pilot shoved him off to the side and attempted to escape as a shot roared near him and into the terrorist's head. Kelley walked slowly towards the falling criminal as he cringed to the floor tightly holding his weapon. She stood on his forearm and removed the gun as his head slowly fell backwards.

"May your soul return with better intentions," She whispered as she stood up from him and looked back to see the passengers stand and applaud with intense exhilaration.

Never before had she encountered such a situation. It was the first time she had to kill another human being and it was not an experience she embraced no matter what their character exhumed. As she walked out of the plane down the steps she breathed a sigh of relief to be alive. Suddenly her VieweR sent an impulse so she grabbed it to see a red light flashing. She pressed a button and the screen illustrated her grandfather sending a call. She pressed the memory button and clicked to dial in her grandfather. Kelley walked towards the airport door as passengers came out of the plane in the background.

"Grandfather, it is me, what is wrong?" She clamored and stuttered with an inner anxiety of feeling something amiss.

"My love, I am leaving now. My time is here," He said in a pale soft tone.

"Grandfather you were with me, I know you were," She began to cry with relating to her fortunate outcome of the deadly situation.

"You were with your Self, my child. You were in touch with what had to be done, you saved lives and must approve yourself for the job you had to do," He whispered in a fainter voice.

"Grandfather, I will miss you so very much. You are a real part of me, you always have been. You are always there in some very meaningful way to guide me. I love you grandfather, I love you so much," Kelley whispered back in a broken voice while feeling that somehow he had given his life for hers while she was on the aircraft.

"We will meet again," Were the last words of a wise man as she could hear the faint beat of his heart touching hers. She looked into her VieweR to see him finish those words as he looked up at her. He was lying on the floor at his house, and slowly fell down in final rest as his VieweR phone fell with him onto the carpet. A tear rolled down her soft face as she entered her patrol vehicle and started the engine. She began to drive towards his house. She lifted her head looking into the sky and could see a light come through the clouds as they opened up. Kelley breathed in whimper as her feelings embraced the remainder of presence she knew her grandfather had upon this plane.

When she arrived to him, she knelt over to kiss his forehead and then covered him with a silk blanket. In the background the sound of an ambulance siren increased as it arrived closer. Kelley stood up and noticed that his Christmas tree in the corner had a small wrapped gift sitting under it. She looked at it for a moment then looked down at him before walking over to pick it up. She brought the gift over and sat down on the carpet beside his body to open it. Inside of the small box was an elegant gold chain with a set of gold BALANCE scales hanging off of it. A tear of love trickled down the side of her face as she touched it to his heart, then hers and then put it on, around her neck.

"In this crazy world I will work to balance all things that come my way," She vowed to herself and uplifted her head as she felt her spirit touch his. ★

LIGHT OF THE SAGE

"Therefore the sage concentrateth upon one Will,
and it is as a light to the whole world. Hiding himself, he
shineth; withdrawing himself, he attracteth notice;
humbling himself, he gaineth force to achieve his Will;
Because he striveth not, no man may contend against him."

Aleister Crowley

Alexander trudged through the pelting rain as vehicles drove by, splashing his clothes with wet grime from the city streets. His innocence radiated a calm aura around his body, exuding a strong determination through perseverance. Now in his mid-thirties, he was a wanderer of many roads near and far. His light brown hair dripped with rainwater down his soft skin. The purple haze of moisture rising from the slick streets reflected the city lights into his gray eyes as he looked on with a positive smile. His head followed a car driving by him that suddenly slowed down to a halt. It backed up quickly as Alexander turned and walked towards it. A young girl opened the passenger window and yelled, "Hey Mister, it's pouring outside! Do you need a lift somewhere?"

Alexander opened the door and entered. "I am most graciously pleased for the drive. Are you headed towards the south side?" he asked as he wiped the rainwater from his face.

"Yes, in fact, that is where I am going. It will give you a few minutes to dry off." She started the car in motion and, turning to face the pleasant passenger, she added, "It's been raining for three days now. The weather is sure crazy, huh?"

Alexander nodded in reply. "Everything is in a state of change, and mother earth is just following along with it." Alexander was a very observant person, always curious about his surroundings. He looked quickly around the inside of the car. The floor was dirty with small rocks and empty fast food containers. A small pair of fuzzy dice hung from the rear-view mirror. The lady's perfume smelled faintly of lilac, which filled the whole car. The radio was playing a light rock hit, probably from the 80's, but Alex couldn't place the name or the artist. Scattered upon the back seat lay several large texts. Turning to face the driver, he smiled. "Are you majoring in anything particular at school?" he asked.

"This is my third year in University," she replied with a flip of her pony-tail, "and I am working towards a teachers' degree. My major studies this year are English and History. With that and my job, I rarely have any free time to relax, unfortunately. What do you do?" Pausing, she rolled her eyes at herself and added, "Oh, my name is Jessica, what is yours?"

"My name is Alex, and thank you for stopping in this unpleasant weather. I have a small place at the end of Marigold Street but am often on the road travelling. I work as required to get by, generally doing jobs like maintenance to houses, yard work and what may be required at the moment wherever I may be."

"You look like a great guy Alexander. Quite sincere and pleasant yet intense. Strange that you are doing odd jobs," Jessica noted, "Are you originally from around here?"

"I came from Sicily, where I lived for seven years. Before that I was in Idaho for several years, but I am originally from Maine," Alex shrugged. "It's hard to keep track sometimes."

"That is so strange. I am from Italy. I moved here three years ago. Where exactly did you live there?"

"I began my stay just outside Palermo but made my way to the east near Mt Etna."

"I was born in Roma. Did you ever go there?"

"Yes, it is a spectacular city of architecture. I visited cousins there while traveling through."

"That is quite a coincidence," Jessica grinned. She paused to look seriously at Alex's face. "I almost feel like I met you before. I think they call it deja-vu. Do you know why people feel like that sometimes?"

"There could be many reasons for that, Jessica. Sometimes we dream and experience things before they occur. We are in a physical world but in order for things to occur here they have to begin somewhere in our mind beforehand, even if we do not realize they are taking form there. Our dreams, thoughts and desires account for most of what happens each day of our life," The young man replied with a smile.

"That sounds quite plausible. Some people say they don't have dreams, do you believe that?" she asked.

"Well, I have 30 to 40 dreams in an evening that I am aware of, and for me to answer that would be to pretend that I am one of those people. We may as well ask what those people are aware of and when doing so we may be at a loss. Everyone is different and some people accept to understand certain things while they reject to be open to other things. Some people have chemical reactions taking place inside them that makes them think and say what they feel and they may be insensitive to what is and what could be. Their intentions and their heart may be in two different places as well," Alex responded as his head tilted up to the windshield observing the rainfall.

"Why is such an intelligent man as yourself without a regular job and why are you doing odd jobs?" Jessica asked with a pleasant smile.

"First of all, someone has to do the job that is at hand and also it is not below me to do any job that is required. I accept the responsibility of the circumstance I am in at any particular time and enjoy to give of myself for anything minor in return of my service. It is a kind of yoga you might say. I have held some regular jobs but enjoy being on the move with life, like a stream that seeks a lake or ocean. Oh, Jessica, slow down at this corner," He abruptly shouted. Jessica stepped on the brake while sighting in her rear-view mirror just as a blue car swung around from the street in front of her. Moments later, two police cars rushed down the street and turned, chasing the car in frantic haste.

"What was that all about?" Jessica bellowed.

"It looked like a bank robbery pursuit. Why can't people earn what they need in life instead of creating problems after problems?" Alex uttered.

"Some people just hold in bad vibes I guess. They want something for free and don't mind hurting to get it. It's a pretty sad situation in the world. How could it ever change for the better?" Jessica asked.

"Education headed in a positive direction certainly proves to deter crime and assaults. There is more however, and it has to do with making the best use of time before you lose it. If troubles come in life, it is usually from desires that they interfere with. If we focus desires and are not bothered by any surrounding situations or affected by people with their mental and emotional projections we can quickly grow to know ourselves. To have balance and insight we have to continually work for it and in so doing we perpetually aspire higher and deeper."

Jessica scratched her nose, partly to break her gaze that she had been giving Alex the whole time. "That sounds very positive. I am sure looking forward to being a teacher in the future. There is only so much we can do to steer youngsters in a positive direction and to teach them the value of time. They affect one another a great deal and the attention and love they receive from their family helps mold their behavior patterns as well."

"Agreed, but there is more that can be done. The education boards have to bring a non-biased spiritual emphasis into the classroom such that the children learn there is something to achieve, to work towards and to develop within. Ancient cultures have many secrets that the western world is ignoring. The concept of success is outweighed by materialism and should be refocused to higher goals, an education of the higher life and reality of the world. Children want to learn eagerly and want to achieve something great. Sometimes a mask is put over them and it forms as a negative and problematic personality. They have a great ability to communicate and it is up to older people to furnish them with positive feedback, vital knowledge and experiences, before they become lazy."

"I would like to drive you straight to your home since the weather is getting worse," Jessica said.

"That would be much appreciated, young lady. If you turn right at the next lights it is only a few blocks from there," Alex replied.

"You are a very fascinating man and you seem incredibly stress-free. How do you manage to not worry about anything?" Jessica asked.

"How do you manage to worry about everything?" he threw back, grinning.

"You must be Jewish," She laughed, then abruptly slowed down for fear of insulting her guest.

"Why do you say that?" a chuckle came back.

"Well, when I ask a question and you answer it with a question, they say that is the sign of someone being Jewish. I think it is rather cute," She flushed.

"The only thing to worry about is not living in the present. If you don't even worry about that, then life becomes rather simple and clear. Everything occurs spontaneously and works itself out just fine as long as we do not invite problems into our sphere." He said while interlocking his hands.

"I would like to phone you and talk with you sometimes, if that is all right with you, Alex," Jessica zealously requested.

"I do not have a telephone but I am sure we will meet somewhere again," He gently replied.

Jessica drove over a small bridge as Alex pointed at the windshield towards a little house in the corner of the street. "That is my place right there," he directed, "Thank you very much for coming by and saving me all those extra wet footsteps." Alex laughed.

"I would not normally pick up anybody walking on the street, even if they were hitch-hiking but a voice within me said I really should and although I fought it, there was something of a power that made me turn to the side and stop for you. It sounds pretty weird and I normally do not hear voices but this was distinct and I have no way to explain it. I just feel like I can say anything to you and you can understand in a very deep way what I mean," She softly uttered.

"I know what you mean, Jessica. The most important person that will ever understand you is yourself. If you work long and hard at that communication skill, you will receive many great answers through life. I wish you a pleasant journey homewards and for true success to shower over you throughout life," He smiled as he opened the door and held his hand in air giving a sincere wave adieu.

"Sayonara, my friend, oh, I meant buona notte and I wish for you the same success. Until our paths meet again, I fare thee well." Jessica ushered with a gentle wave of her hand in the air as she heard him say "Ci vediamo" and then looked forward. When she turned her head to catch a last glimpse of him, Alex had disappeared. "I hope I do see you soon." She whispered back.

Thunder roared through the clouded sky as mist sprayed across her windshield during the drive home. She felt a magnetic attraction to the stranger, one that opened her to the feeling that she had long known this gentleman. She could see through his simplicity as though he was without mental restraints and was filled with clarity on every matter that came up. His poise and physical constitution enchanted her interests in him more than words could flaunt but she couldn't help but wonder if he was similarly captivated with her. When she arrived at her apartment, Jessica drank a bottle of mineral water and did eighty sit-ups, which was her habit three times a day, and then showered before slipping into bed.

The following day was not unlike any other except on her way home she had a mechanical failure with her car. While driving across the Brookdale Bridge the car began to sputter and cut out. She endeavored to press harder upon the gas pedal to keep it moving. A mile later up the road the engine had a final stammer and shut off. She pulled over to the side of the road as it rolled to a halt and she got out.

Jessica opened the hood but could not see any visual malfunctions and so proceeded to wave down a passing vehicle. Four vehicles passed without concern but the fifth pulled over several yards in front of her and began to back up near her car. A rugged, bearded man got out and walked up to her, looking at her with exaggerated interest. "Would you like me to help you?" he asked in a conspicuous manner.

She was slightly nerved by his character and felt distrust from the vibrations around him. "Could you please go to the next service station up the road and ask them to come with a tow truck, Mister?" She requested.

"I would drive you there and you could come back with them, if you come with me," He beckoned.

"Oh no, I would rather stay with my car, but if you would send the message for me I would be grateful," She replied, as she started to step away from the imposing man.

"I would drive you there and you could come back with them, if you come with me," He beckoned.

"Oh no, I would rather stay with my car, but if you would send the message for me I would be grateful," She replied, as she started to step away from the imposing man.

"It is only a short drive, just come along," He insisted as he took hold of her arm with a strong grip.

"No, no, it's ok, I will get some other help. Let me go!" She shouted.

"You are going to be just fine. Come now, let's go get some 'help'." He smiled with a grotesque grimace while hauling her to the door of his rusted old car.

Frantically she attempted to pull away and slapped his arm with her free hand as her heartbeat felt like it was going to open her chest. He grabbed her striking hand with his other hand and pulled her forcefully against the side of his vehicle while opening his driver-side door. She kicked his shin but it did not affect him as he swung down along her face and punched her into the seat. Jessica fell on the seat barely conscious as the brut pushed her over for him to get in alongside of her and drive off.

From behind him, his hair was pulled and he was forced out of the vehicle onto the ground. Jessica slowly lifted her head and attempted to pull herself up on the seat. The assailant looked up at a man holding his hair and began to swing at the man's legs to trip him to the ground but was quickly kicked in the face. The assailant was hurled backwards against the car with his head crushing powerfully against the metal fender. Jessica's bruised face looked out the door and focused in at the sight of Alex. His hand reached in and grabbed hers, pulling her out from the vehicle. Her arms wrapped around his neck as she looked into his crystal eyes.

"How did you happen to just come along?" she asked, with tears streaming down her face.

"How did you happen to break down just beside my shortcut into town as I was on my way in?" he answered with a question.

"You must be Jewish," She laughed with great relief.

"I am just myself, an envelope of the cosmic postal system, being shipped through life and being halted from one hand to the next until I reach my final destination," He said in a serene voice as his hand touched her bruised face and sent a healing energy through her.

"You are one miraculous envelope of cosmic stuff! I can't believe this all just happened. Are you some kind of angel?" She questioned.

"Every sincere deed from your heart gets paid back. Sometimes people are at the brink of being tested and sometimes in the wrong place and situation at the wrong time. There is a fluidic essence within light that causes certain things to occur and generally those things are good," He said, taking the compliment in stride.

"Is that why people have fear of the dark and the unknown, because there may be less help for them there?" she asked.

"To know yourself is to have the light around you at all times. To know yourself is to know your total surroundings," He smiled.

"Look, a police car!" she shouted as she ran to the side of her car and flagged it down. The police car pulled in front of the attacker's vehicle as Jessica ran to begin explaining the drama. As she pointed to her friend Alex, he was not there. She looked around but he had vanished. The attacker was beginning to stand up when the officer rushed over and handcuffed him then placed him in the back of the police car. He called for tow truck assistance and took a full report from her. When Jessica arrived home that evening she placed an icepack on her face to chill the injury.

While relaxing in bed that night, her thoughts wandered back to Alex. "That's twice within two days this mysterious stranger came to me when I needed somebody there. The first time, I knew right away that he was somebody I needed in my life, and today, he saved it. I wish I could call him right now and tell him how grateful I am. Maybe I should stop by his place tomorrow. Yes, that is what I'll do…" Jessica quickly drifted to sleep, exhausted from the day's events.

The next day after University classes she picked out a bouquet of flowers and made a zesty bowl of rice and vegetables with a salad and went over to Alex's house. She parked in front of his little home and knocked on the door. It opened with a gentle smile behind as he remarked, "I was just wondering what was for dinner this evening. You are very kind. Please come in, Jessica."

"All heroes need their nourishment," She smiled wryly as she entered. As she expected, his home was simplistic and cozy. It possessed almost a balancing Zen quality throughout it. The walls were decorated with fancy artwork, obviously foreign by design. The main living room had little more than a low table, some cushions and corner lamps. The kitchen area was also sparse, save for a few dishes that Alex had already laid out for himself and strangely enough, an unexpected guest.

"This is a nicely organized place you have here, Alex. Everything seems to be in a certain place for a particular reason," She observed.

"I may be a bit of a perfectionist, but not to an agonizing habit," He grinned.

"You have many beautiful Egyptian paintings on the walls. Were you actually in Egypt before?" she asked.

"Once upon a time I was," He sighed wistfully.

"Well, I hope you like rice and salad," She remarked, "I eat that a lot since I am vegetarian."

"My body will have no problem with that. Thank you for being so considerate," Alex agreed.

They sat at the little wooden table and enjoyed one another's company as the food began to disappear.

"Why are you without a girlfriend or wife?" She suddenly blurted.

Alex blinked once, then replied, "I generally resist social pleasures. One might say I listen to the beat of a different drummer. I quite accept to be alone, as I know I am not. The world is around me and the closer I am to it, the closer it is to me." Noticing her wistful gaze in his direction, he quickly changed the subject.

"Your face looks much better than it did last evening. You are healing well."

"I feel much better also, much thanks to you. I still can't believe that happened. There seems to be more and more negative, sick and violent people throughout the world. I wish something would change that. It is really so sad," Jessica lamented.

"It is, yes. There are many organized societies in the world that preach good behavior but the majority of them lack one great thing."

"What would that be?" she asked.

"They create contradiction. Many of them are not practicing comparative religious studies to find harmony with cosmic truth. They all say because this and because that, which amounts to further turmoil. They replace the cosmic scope of science with mental programming in the name of belief. They chase their tails and have Cerberus, the three-headed hound of hell, biting at their heels. To make it perfectly simple, yet not totally accurate, the world has to combine as a unit, a spiritual unit. There is much fusion and much chaotic reaction without aspiration, direction and focus," He said with a blessed understanding and sadness in his face.

"It would be like Utopia, a perfect world then, would it not?" she remarked.

"The Utopia dream is not feasibly possible with a society. We will always have chaos and changes to contend with and circumstances to overcome and conquer. But, in the expansion it would be a nice dream to have a global appreciation for spiritual awakening." Alex responded.

"I know it would be great for a gal to walk down any street and not worry about being attacked. I know it would be an overall better place if people sorted out their emotional traumas and not hurt other people because of them." Jessica said.

"Everyone has unresolved issues in life. It is a self-induced curse of cause. It results in built up tensions and prevents proper relaxation to funnel the light. Our false identifications, the ones we want other people to believe in, can be a real burden to our psyche. If you every noticed how some people change when they are around different people, you can see they wear different masks. Their energies are consumed by a dominating ego and are incapable of ascending to loftier, refined feelings, in a willed manner. What would you think is the greatest gift that anyone can achieve in life?" Alex asked as he collected the supper dishes.

"I would have to say it is love, Once we have love we are happy and content," She replied, flushing again.

"But what is love? Does not love bring everything, including strife? Does it not hurt the heart at times from its intensity or lack of fulfillment? Is it not also a distraction from something more precious at other times?" he motioned.

"That is true, then what is of greater importance than love? What is the best quality to possess?" she asked earnestly.

Alex returned from the kitchen and sat back down to the dinner table. "Does not everyone talk about freedom? Complete freedom implies love and liberty. What is the greatest sense of liberty that is attainable? If we are free of burdens then we are free to choose. If we are free to walk down a dangerous neighborhood at night or free to walk across a minefield we then possess a certain liberty. If we are free to think the greatest thoughts and feel the greatest inspirations then we are at liberty to experience bliss beyond conception. If we are free of our inhibitions and free of what anyone may say or attempt to do to us, then we have acquired a certain stage of liberty. If we are free to make each move in life for a greater benefit and purpose, then we can realize liberty. A mouse is sporadic and appears to move in constant fear whereas an elephant is slow and makes each move as is decided for his purpose. Do you ever wish to have liberty throughout the day or night and to be able to attain something that is beyond your reach?" Alex intimated to the young beautiful lady sitting across from him.

"I have desires and wishes every day, Alex. How can everybody be at liberty though? Everyone is at a different stage in life. We all live for different purposes, dreams and have particular responsibilities."

"Just about everything imaginable occurs at every minute of the day somewhere. Desires may cause greed, which causes burdens, which causes tampering with the simplicity of our answers to our questions in life. If we knew the affect of each cause that we create then we would perhaps change our decisions and create a better outcome. One of the greatest things we possess is the ability to act and react to any given situation that we are confronted with. Sometimes non-action is the key for attaining the state of peace and problem-free affairs in our perpetual sphere."

"This sounds pretty philosophical. You must read a lot of books. What becomes of a person once they are at liberty? Where do they go from there?" She asked with a smile.

"Our great spiritual source is an inspiration and will continue to be forever. If we are bored or uncertain, then we have not touched our source. When we have attained liberty we are one with the source. Each action has a significant purpose, each breath is one with the source and each thought creates positive vibrations and changes in the world. We become when we know, without belief and without the concern to prove anything. The one becomes the all without doubt even during the direst of tribulations," He remarked.

"What if a person does not believe in God, or what if they are of a different religious understanding than what the popular belief of God is?" she asked.

"It would not matter, in the sense that God is a term used and understood differently through the ages and by each person. Spirituality is one thing and religion is another. Sometimes one attempts to tie in the other but the reality of the matter is that it is a hard-earned and worked-for journey into truth beyond truth. It is a developmental progression of awareness by revealing many mysteries about life. In the end, it really does not matter what we believe but what we are confronted with. The reaction is what we must be prepared for. That is one reason why no one should harm another person. When we cause harm to another person it becomes a distraction from the course of events that would lead otherwise to something of greater value."

Jessica nearly swooned. "I could talk with you for hours, for days even. Could we meet again?"

"Yes, it is getting late and I am sure your day is going to make you busy tomorrow. We may meet again. I am going out of town soon. There is a matter that calls my attention. I am sure we will meet," Alex smiled as he walked her to the door.

"I want to give you a giant hug for being such a good person." She said while reaching behind his back and pulling him close to her.

"You are as good a person, Jessica. Your beauty radiates from your smile and you are not unlike a miniature sun, so keep on shining little star," He gestured as he softly pulled her away from him. She wanted to kiss him but inside knew that is was not welcomed, that his heart did not invite the temptation of her passion for him to be closer than a friend.

"One more thing, Jessica. Sometimes I am busy with certain projects and if you feel it is an emergency to talk with me then do a special set of knocks on the door. Knock three times then pause, then five with a short pause and then three more knocks. I will always answer the door when I hear that combination," Alex said.

"Thank you and I will remember that, arrivederci" She heeded. He was definitely a different kind of man and she felt he was very special in many ways. She walked out with a chuckle of delight as he waved while ushering "Ti salute" with a gentle voice. To know him was wonderful but held a sentiment of loss for not gaining his physical affection.

A week had passed without Jessica visiting him but yet every morning and night she would lay in bed wondering what he might be doing and where he was. She longed for his companionship and to hear his gentle voice talk about subjects that mattered most to her inquisitive mind. He was a mystical personage and could help her to find that precious liberty that he knew so much about. On Friday after school she walked by a shop and her eye caught The Daily Telegraph newspaper. On the front page there was a photo of a car accident and a rough sketch of Alex beside it. She snatched up a copy and reviewed it in her car. The headline read: **"Angel appears and saves Mother and Children!"**

Alex had emerged to save the people in the accident before the car thrashed into flames and then he disappeared just like he vanished when she almost got abducted. She was stunned and wanted to go visit him but went home instead and made dinner then settled down to study and do homework.

Jessica was exhausted and needed rest from long nights of studies and working on assignments. It was late and she finally rested in her bed. She was thinking once again of the mysterious sage she longed to know more about him. Her eyes fell shut but before long the heat from the sun came upon her face and she had awakened. She felt so hot and needed some fresh air badly. She put on her tracksuit and went to open the back door. As the door opened a wave of heat engulfed her body while her head turned as though it was forcefully punched. It felt well over a hundred degrees outside. Sweating beads, she stepped out to see the strangest of things she ever imagined. Every house was on fire in her neighborhood and trees were smoldering for as far as she could see. She ran in to turn on the kitchen facet but no water came out. She put on her runners and ran out the front door but it was no apparition, it was still occurring. The whole city seemed to be inundated with flames and smoldering ash. Jessica's face dropped in unbelievable shock as the horrific sight waved perplexity through her mind. She ran in to turn on the television but it did not work. She ran to the telephone but it had no dial tone; it was as dead as the world around her.

"What is going on? What happened?" she cried loudly as she ran back out to the street. Fire brewed everywhere and scattered throughout the streets in burning vehicles and fences along the sidewalks. There was no life in sight but streams of dark orange and yellow flared across the sky. Sweat poured from her brow while she staggered down the street in search of anyone that may be alive. Suddenly she halted when a large ferocious animal appeared from the sky in front of her. It had long slanted eyes and horns that twirled up into the clouds. She gasped at its frightening evil glare that ripped through her skin with ostentatious ardor. It's nostrils flared and let out a heavy hot vapor that shot into her stomach and knocked her backwards. Jessica gripped the smoldering grass in exhaustion from the impact and fought to stretch out her arm and then swung violently at the horn of the beast as it approached her chest. Her arm struck it and caused her to uncontrollably fall forwards. Her eyes opened abruptly and realized that she was falling out of bed while striking at the bedpost. Her wrist bent when it struck the floor but prevented her head from crashing down. Jessica shook her head and ran to look out the window. Everything was as normal as it could be but she wasn't sure why such a dream would come to her. She looked at the clock and saw that it was six-forty am. She went downstairs to have a quick glass of orange juice and then drove to Alex's place. While she drove up to cross the little bridge before his meek house she wondered if it was a good idea to bother him about the nightmare. It didn't matter, as she wanted to see him and that was final. She walked nervously and unsuspectingly up to the door and was about to knock softly but remembered the code. She did the three five three knock loud and clear and he opened the door on the last knock.

"Alex, my God, life is freaking out at me. May I come in?" she asked in panic.

"Most certainly, please do," He smiled with a pleasant gaze.

"Thank you. Look, I saw a picture in the paper of someone describing you as saving her and her children in a vehicle accident just outside town on the interstate. I don't know how or why you always appear in the wrong places at the right time but you are angelically endowed, my friend," She stated frantically at first but calming down near the end.

"Oh, well, that is life, sometimes." He smiled. "May I get you a cup of tea?" he asked.

"Sure, I need something. That sounds fine," She replied, still nervous.

He went into the kitchen to prepare it and a small black cat came out. It walked over to Jessica and began to purr around her leg. She knelt down and patted it as it stared up. Her eyes were caught in its glassy gaze as if she saw Alex's face staring up at hers. She shook her head as Alex appeared with two cups of tea. The cat ran back into the kitchen suddenly as he handed her the tea.

"How do you feel, Jessica?" he asked.

"Really, really strange. I felt I was living in a nightmare and when I woke up it was gone. But in the nightmare all of civilization was gone. In the dream, the world was consumed in fire. Perhaps it was from asteroids hitting our planet or something, I am not really sure. I had to come over to talk with you about it because I have never felt something so real in all my life. Why do you suppose I had such a bad dream?" she asked.

"It was more of a sign. The world has so long to make certain changes for the better. Many people have those visions in their dreams. You were passing through a state of subconscious affiliation with disaster and change. Perhaps a sense of duality overtook you and showed a side of life that is in torment. It was nothing to be alarmed about but to overcome so that you can prepare for a higher awareness of what may be," He explained while sipping the morning tea.

"That is so weird. You mean to say I could be ready for some great change that may be a part of my inner life?" she questioned.

"Every step is progress, Jessica, and all processes lend to personal growth. You were awakened by an element that needed to be there to show you the next level to ascend towards. In this case the element was fire, to show the great desire within you to seek answers to something that is troubling you. All avenues of the mind are roads and thought patterns upon those roads and you came into contact with one area that is trying to bring you into a particular balance. I am maintained on a particular path for the present time and you were on a path that I had to undergo to find a balance. Think of the legend of Persephone and of the guide that steers the soul through the lower regions of subconscious entanglement. It has to be accomplished to understand the secret fire that burns in your heart which will open your inner eye to the path that you must travel. How is the tea?" he chuckled.

"Just fine, just fine," She stuttered as her hands shook with inquisitive interest. "What am I to do about all of this?"

"Every once in a while there will be a special key in your life. It may be interpreted as a symbol or an omen. In either case you will be able to associate it with something important to your path. The more that you practice this, the more keys you will see and the more meanings you will interpret around you. Life is multi-dimensional and has greater and greater purpose as you become aware of it my dear. To become connected with the All, to see the connections and how everything works in nature and the cycles of life will broaden your vision to maintain adjustment and liberty. Realization of your intricate association with life forces will endow you with clearer visions of how to handle circumstances."

"This is magnificent," Jessica whispered, agog with excitement. "I feel so uplifted when you explain things, Alex. Everyone must be on a special path in life then, correct?"

"Yes, we all have an orbit that keeps us in perfect alignment. Many people prefer to be sidetracked from it and to avoid the reality of working for anything other than physical pleasures. Apparently the dumber a person acts they seem to think the more they can avoid any sense of responsibility. On the other hand, some use particular responsibilities to avoid truth or to avoid greater understanding of what their life is about. Some people just enjoy not knowing because to know means to act according to the laws of life and those laws seem SO complex but they really are not so complicated," He commented.

"I am so grateful that Fate has brought me to you. Picking you up from the wet streets that night is something totally out of what I would ever consider. There was some command within me that went beyond all I know and would ever dare. Since I met you I seem to pick up on many things and am more attentive. I have many more feelings and they are deeper than the ones I generally entertain. I have a conscious sensation of what is occurring inside of my body. It's difficult to ascertain exactly what is going on but do you know what I mean by feeling things as though they are whirling up on different levels in my body?" She asked hesitantly.

"I am glad you are not shy to say exactly what you feel, Jessica. That helps you to understand your reasons and feelings. There is a seven-fold substance within everyone that exists on the next plane from the physical level. It is through the etheric web that you will find it and there are seven in number. They are called the chakras and are wheels of petals not unlike a lotus flower blossoming in your soul. These chakras are attached through inner cords upon this inner plane and send energies that you feel beyond physical ones from one level to the next. The first chakra is called the root chakra and is the lowest one at the genital region. It is mainly concerned with self-preservation and basic instincts. The next chakra is called the sacral and controls the sexual energies that flow within you. The next chakra is the solar plexus and it runs the emotions and desires that are always going throughout your mind and body to cause changes within you. Then there is the heart chakra that paves the road to higher consciousness and sincere devotion, which is an unconditional love. As you see, these chakras are extending from the lower regions to higher areas in your body. The next one is at the throat. This one emits a clear blue light like the sky appears on a bright summer day. Through it people feel restful and confident with a strength and attachment to the divine self. In fact, when two people connect through their throat chakra, a beautiful blue emanates and conversations can become miraculous to the point of envisioning fairies and little mythical creatures of beauty. They nonetheless enjoy one another through humorous and harmonious vocal interchange. The next chakra is upon your brow. That is also the area of the third eye which when stimulated and made aware of you begin to have great psychic abilities in life. It unfolds the intuitive endowment and brings an awakening into spiritual enlightenment. The highest and seventh chakra has the most petals attached within it and is called the crown chakra. It resides just above the head and projects energy from the deepest individual source for conscious evolution. There are many books written about these chakras and how to assimilate them by meditation. They exist as much as any part of your body exists. It is up to the individual to become aware of their existence in etheric substance, and how they circulate energies throughout the body, soul and mind," Alex said while sending a positive feeling from his harmonious core.

"I shall go with that knowledge and seek what my destiny truly is," Jessica said as she clinked her cup to his, smiling with gentle ease.

"Our world is the method towards true identity. It is what we have to work with and contains endless potential everywhere around us and we can tap into that and use it for any purpose. When you cast a small stone into a lake it makes ripples that extend to all sides of the lake. It then drops to the bottom to return once again with the elements it is associated with. Our thoughts and emotions travel with as much force as we give them to extend. They exist and have effect no less than the rock with the force it is given. The logos or deepest point within us is very much a part of our truth, our particular element and spirit. To reach it we must cast a pure stone but that stone has a special name and exists deep within you. If you utter its name, you will break it," he said.

"What is the name of that stone, Alex?" she asked.

"Silence," Alex said softly.

She knew it was time to depart and left touching his hand with a stroke of hers. An essence left his hand and entered into her. She felt it and seen a soft glowing light run up her arm.

"Ti auguro una buona giornata." Alex blissfully said as she walked out.

"Have a great day yourself. I know that I will now. Ciao." Jessica gleamed.

She left his home looking back at his honest face vanishing behind the door. What happened next in her life would be a matter of decision. She held fate by the edge and could manipulate the outcome through the guidance of her higher intuitive nature.

Jessica looked up at the rising sun and seen particles of light dancing in the atmosphere. She entered her car and drove away feeling refreshed and invigorated from something she could not put into words. She felt a greater devotion to herself than she ever had before. The concept of inner truth rang through her, as an awakening grew more intense, realizing that she understood all of her schoolwork and everything that was important for her success and future. It was the only time in her life that she felt she was void of worries and problems. It had nothing to do with the feeling of being more or less serious about what life meant to her and did not take away the beauty and pleasures of having fun in everything she did, but rather enhanced it. The weekend had arrived and she was to go over to her parents to help them with some farming on their land. It was an hour drive away so she packed a bag for her overnight visit. During the drive down the highway something told her to slow down. She pressed easily on the brake as a deer ran from the side of the woods across in front of her vehicle. Her eyes widened as she wondered how the voice from within told her to use caution so abruptly. Gradually she regained speed and began singing with a song on the radio until she came upon the turn off to her parents' farm.

Her mother welcomed her with open arms before they sat and talked for a while. That night Jessica sat in her bed wondering if she would see Alex again. She imagined his boyish face and felt attached to his unconditional smile. She began to meditate upon the chakras as she recalled them and to become familiar with using the energy she felt through them. Suddenly she felt something touch her shoulder. She kept her eyes closed for another minute, as the presence intensified. Slowly she opened her eyes and behind her she could see a haze of light in the form of a human figure. She sat breathless in anticipation as the figure reached around to her front and placed its hand on her chest. She could feel a radiance pour through her as a stream of light entered above her head like a cup overflowing and creating a waterfalls of brilliance and entering the many cords that inter-linked her chakras with a variety of bright colors. She breathed in deeply to her abdomen and exhaled slowly. In the deepest sense she felt it was Alex on another level that was there in front of her. She could hear his soft voice on this other level explaining what was happening. She believed that she could open her mind and could focus it to anything in the world and see the outcome. It was as though she had no bonds or restricting mental blocks. She was at liberty.

The following day she helped her father in the fields. Everything seemed so beautiful and bright. She gazed up at the afternoon sun and it turned into another shape. She could see it radiating like a six-pointed star. It was like an interlaced set of triangles, one pointing up and the other down, yet all sides connected with one another. She realized her connection with the cosmos. Destiny was a path and travelling it was the search for understanding and wisdom. An overwhelming sensation continuously poured through her body as though she consumed an elixir.

That next evening on her way back to the city she stopped at a shop to pick up a white rose. She wanted to present it to Alex and let him know how very important he was to her. She drove over the little bridge near his place. Jessica was filled with happiness and respect. She looked towards his home and in awe turned to the side of the road and stopped abruptly. Jessica got out of her car and stared at where his home was. It was gone. A little brick building that housed a barbershop stood in its place. She walked up to it as a tear rolled down her face. It was beyond comprehension and any dream she could fathom. She knelt down in front of the barbershop and placed the rose on the small stretch of grass as the last bit of sunlight rode down her back.

"Alex," she whispered, "you have guided me to where I am and where I will go from here. You are a radiant sage Alex. I know you exist and live with and beyond this world and I will forever treasure the love and liberty you have shown me. I will leave now but know that someday our path shall meet again and our souls align to travel part of the course of destiny. I will hold your touch in my heart unconditionally," She whispered as her voice echoed through the ground while a tear dropped and fell on an inner petal of the white rose. ★

A DATE WITH FORTUNA

"Without contraries is no progression. Attraction and Repulsion, Reason and Energy, Love and Hate,
are necessary to Human existence. From these contraries spring what the religious call Good and Evil.
Good is the passive that obeys Reason. Evil is the active springing from Energy."

Blake-Marriage of Heaven and Hell

The prairie grass swayed and huddled in the afternoon breeze as visible waves of heat treaded the distant highway. Summer had arrived and brought dry warmth nestled throughout the planes. Farmers were once again irrigating the fields across the three Prairie Provinces and preparing for the long workdays ahead. It would be late in the autumn when bushels of hay were cut and hauled to the farms and sold throughout the winter as cattle feed.

Each home was scattered distantly apart and contained a history of generations that brought children into the world. Most of those children would grow up and leave their homes to pursue their chosen careers. There were precious few, sometimes only one in each family, who would stay on at the farm and continue the traditions taught by the elders. Corey was one of those few. He was twenty-two and was every bit the quintessential farm boy: short crop of wild blonde hair and a body that was deeply and richly tanned from the long hours under the sun. He seldom wore a shirt, preferring to toil bare-chested and to display his perfectly and naturally toned muscles. He worked every day from dawn until dusk without complaint. His favorite chore was feeding the hundred heads of cattle. Corey loved animals and enjoyed their company, sometimes more than real people.

Every one of his friends seemed to be involved in any business they could manipulate in order to make an extra dollar. There was a common thread that linked his friends together: to find a niche in the market of demand and become successful enough to become luxury homeowners. Corey, however, was content in helping his father and mother with the family business.

Corey's job was seldom easy, however. His father was a heavy drinker. Corey sustained most of the workload during the day while his father directed the work from under a drunken stupor. To most people, such treatment would be unacceptable, but Corey knew how to take things with a grain of salt. In one ear and out the other, do what must be done and don't fret over little disturbances were Corey's credos.

It was an expensive and unfortunate habit of his father's to consume a quart of vodka before lunch, which sometimes led to minor accidents thus delaying the daily routine. Nonetheless, Corey would compensate by working that much harder to carry the slack for his father.

At the end of this particular day, Corey sat in his room reading another book his friend had loaned him. The title of the book, "The Wealthy Barber", intrigued him, as he heard it had some valuable lessons on financial success. He chuckled for a moment before setting it down when the noise of his father lumbering around the kitchen disturbed the mood. He looked at a slogan on his wall, which he had under a picture of two people dancing naked under palm trees on a beach. The slogan, "Sing like you know all the words; Work like you don't need the money; Love like you have never been hurt before; And dance like no one is watching", made him reconsider about living life fully.

It would be nice to have a girlfriend to share love with and begin a better life but it was not meant to be, at least not yet, he thought. He wrapped the pillow around his head and slowly drifted off to sleep, losing the cacophony of his father arguing nonsensically with his wearied mother. It soon became a deep sleep and seemed to last a lifetime in one sense. Through the irony of time he drastically rotated in a twisting and agitated motion around his bed, searching for air. He began to cough and abruptly awoke, pulling the blanket off his body while sitting up with watering eyes. The room was filling with smoke as his hands brushed across his face with him wondering what kind of nightmare from which he had just escaped.

Corey came quickly to his senses and realized it was no dream. He crawled to the floor to catch a hasty breath of cleaner air. He looked upwards and could not see the ceiling as the smoke disseminated downwards, closer to his body. The room was fiery with the scent of death as fumes of the burning house filtered abruptly under his door. "Mom, Dad, get up! Get up! Mom, Dad!" he yelled as he choked and gagged on the vile smoke.

He hauled the blanket off his bed and covered his mouth and his face the best that he could while pushing his fatigued body towards the window. He realized that it would not push open as it had been painted shut. Gasping for a final lengthy breath, he covered his hands with the blanket and smashed the window outwards then hurled his body out onto the ground, scraping his body through the narrow exit of shattered glass.

Without hesitation, he pushed his partly cut body to stand up and rushed towards his parents' window. He smashed it open and yelled to his mother, who was still asleep in the bed. There was no time to waste; he climbed in after taking a deep breath and shook his mother, who did not awaken. Corey flung her over his broad shoulders and heaved her exanimate body towards the window and then outwards. Smoke and heat piled horridly into the room like a cavity in a tooth attracting a mouth full of sugar. He wheezed in anguish. He wanted to go into the hallway to seek his father but the heat and gasses were too noxious for him to withstand. His feeling of helplessness overcame him and he retreated from the burning building. He jumped through the window and dragged his mother's prone body away from the flames that licked the edge of the house and began artificial resuscitation on her. She began to cough and he turned her in a recovery position while running around to the front of the house. Corey grabbed a board and broke through the front windows while yelling his father's name, trying to see or hear for any acknowledgements from within.

Moments passed, and Corey was frantic. The entire house was engulfed with fire, and still his father was nowhere to be found. He could not give up and continued yelling while running around trying to see if there was any way to get inside. The situation looked hopeless and Corey was soon overcome by the gravity of the possibility that his father was gone. Exhausted, bleeding and crushed by despair, Corey fell to his knees and passed out from extensive smoke inhalation.

During the early morning hours, firefighters were still putting out the smoldering ash and searching the demolished house as a routine investigation. Corey rested on the ground outside, watching the investigators do their work as a paramedic treated his wounds. One of the inspectors informed Corey that his mother had been taken to the hospital for treatment and observation, and that his sister was contacted and on her way. A few minutes later a car pulled into the driveway. Corey stood up to see who it was and half-smiled when he saw Brenda's face behind the wheel. He hadn't seen his sister in nearly two years, since she had left the farm to pursue her education at a University in neighboring Manitoba. She leapt out of her car and immediately ran over to embrace her devastated brother.

"How is Mom doing, Corey?" she whispered with weeping utterance.

Corey wrapped his arms around Brenda protectively. "She is fine now. The policeman over there just told me that she's doing well and resting. They think they may be able to let her out by noon."

A fireman walked out from a collapsed wall that extended to the front door and approached the siblings. "I am terribly sorry son," he began dismally, "We've located your father's remains in the basement. Do you know if he was drinking alcohol last evening?"

"He did, every day and night," Corey sadly remarked.

Nodding sadly, the firefighter continued, "There was a bottle beside him. I am terribly sorry. I don't want to be rude, but we should contact the insurance agency to come over as soon as possible."

"I'll call them from the police car," Corey murmured as he walked away.

Brenda stood talking with a firefighter about the tragedy. A few minutes later Corey returned in utter distress. "Dad told us he paid the insurance last month but they said it was never paid. They told me it was overdue for three months and he talked with them about paying it next week when he gets a cheque," Corey muttered, completely crestfallen.

"Let's go and see Mom," his sister suggested, "There is nothing we can do here right now."

Their mother was awake when they walked into her hospital room. She sat fixated on some part of the wall, unblinking. They could see in her eyes that she knew her husband was no longer alive.

"I can rebuild a smaller house, Mom," Corey offered with hope, "It doesn't have to be fancy but I know I can do it."

Corey's mother let out a slow, resigned sigh. "My sweet son, there is more to life than you've had and sometimes you have to take the chance. I know what you are saying but look inside yourself. You don't have to be stuck in solitude the rest of your life, on a farm that makes just barely enough to survive. I want you to do something good for yourself. Sell the cattle, Corey, and the land and take that to invest in another job, a job that will bring you a happy life. You are twenty-two years old and there's still plenty of time for you to start making a brighter future for yourself." Tears gently came down her cheek, and she smiled for the first time in a long while.

Brenda listened in on the conversation while her heart was shaken in bereavement. She knew her mother was right and it would be the best thing for her brother. He needed to begin a life with more adventure and education to benefit his chances for a professional career. There was much for him to learn and a prosperous future would fill a hole that nestled inside of him.

At the father's funerary services their brother, Ben, arrived from Toronto for the traumatic occasion. He had a mechanic business in downtown Toronto and suggested that Corey come to live with him and seek employment in the big city. It sounded like a great idea and one that would provide Corey with a new beginning. He managed to find a buyer for the cattle while the equipment and the land were put to auction. A few weeks later his brother greeted him at the Toronto airport.

"This is going to be a bit of a shocker for you, little brother. You are going to see a different breed of people around here. Don't be too taken in by the appearance and acts that are put on every where you turn," Ben warned as he helped with the luggage.

"I'll get used to it, Ben. Right now I want to visit some places here and learn what there is to do and see. I know it's a crazy world in big cities, so I'll just take it as it comes." The pair left the airport and drove off towards highway 401.

"It looks like everybody comes here, " Corey marveled as hundreds of cars zipped by. "There is so much traffic."

Ben stifled a laugh. "It is the hub of Canada. A lot of business goes through here to the rest of the country. I've got a spare room for you. Unfortunately the view is of a brick building four feet away."

"That's fine. I think life will be much more interesting here so it won't be like I'm stuck in the room all of the time," Corey remarked.

It was a pleasantly clean apartment and Ben's wife Sandra was a great cook. They had a two-year-old boy named Christopher who Corey hadn't seen since the previous summer. Corey liked the spare room, which was large and doubled as an office for Ben's paperwork.

"Make yourself at home, Corey. Tomorrow night after supper I will take you around town to see some things," Ben said and smiled slyly.

"That sounds great, Ben." Picking up Ben's son, he added, "This little fella sure has grown since last summer. Christopher, do you remember Uncle Corey?" Christopher giggled and smiled the way little kids do.

That night Corey slept comfortably in his new room but not having a daily schedule was something he hadn't quite gotten used to. The next morning, Corey rose at the crack of dawn, as usual. After enjoying a great breakfast he took a walk through some of the city streets while his brother was at work. Some of the people hanging around the corners looked to Corey as though they had risen from the dead. Standing indifferently beside a bare wall, a group of young men were dressed in tattered leathers and sported earrings from their eyebrows to their noses. It seemed to Corey that they wanted to be hooked on a chain and lead through life as slaves. The purple, orange, green and blue hair colors took him by surprise as well. He couldn't help but stare as he walked past the group. One of the men noticed Corey's stupefied look and sneered at him. Surprised, he hurried on down the street and turned a corner.

Corey was now on Bloor Street. He breathed a sigh of relief and continued his stroll, noticing the concrete way of life that was so different than what he was used to seeing. People lived with quickened heartbeats, greater cholesterol, faster decisions and emotionless reactions in the vibrations that they emitted. He could see where it caught up with some folks that walked with subtle ailments in their movements. His pleasant demeanor was not about to be abandoned. Although few responded back to him, he continued walking down the street casually saying good morning to oncoming travelers.

He noticed a few girls dressed in black and sitting on a cement fence. They wore black make-up and had frail complexions appearing to portray something that lived after death.

"How do you do today, ladies?" He asked, hoping to find out their interests in being covered in the frailty.

"Ladies? Do you see any ladies around here, mate?" One of them snarled, showing jagged long teeth.

"Well, you are girls, right?" He asked in confusion.

"No, no, no. We are…" They hissed while looking at his neck.

"Are what? What are you?" he asked with a puzzled look.

"Vampires, we are vampires." The other one, appearing to be a twin, remarked as they stuck out their tongues and made faces as if they were ready to bite him.

"Oh right, I forgot I was in the BIG city. But I thought vampires come out at night?" Corey questioned. "We live through all hours, night and day. We are not the bloodthirsty types of vampires. We feed on energies. We eat peoples energy," the first 'vampire' replied as she leaned over to touch his shoulder.

"Yeah, I can see where you need a lot of energy. There must be a hole in you somewhere that makes you lose it all the time, eh?" he jested to them.

"We don't frighten you, little man?" the pale twin remarked.

"Frighten me? I'm not afraid of much. Do you frighten yourself at times?"

They looked at one another, wondering to themselves if this guy was for real. They were used to sly remarks, so they continued.

"We breed fear. Can we take some of your energy? We want to have it," one of the 'vampires' hissed.

"City life has really done you wrong, ladies. You ought to get out in the country more often. Oh, a shower wouldn't hurt either," Corey recommended.

The 'vampires' didn't care for Corey's straight-forwardness so they jumped off the fence and started walking away in the direction that he came from.

"Sorry if I offended. Didn't mean to! I was just making suggestions. Happy energy hunting ladies," he yelled as they walked through the crowd and vanished.

He was determined to find a job that would give him a sense of independent freedom. He didn't want to feel trapped in the regular social norm that surrounded him. There wasn't much call for farmers in downtown Toronto so he would have to broaden his horizons and keep an open eye for the ultimate opportunity. During the evening he drove around the downtown streets with his brother. Ben pointed out City Hall and told him that from the air it appeared as a large eye due to the shape of the two crescent buildings facing one another with a hump in the middle. They drove along side the CN tower and near Lake Ontario. Corey thought the spectacle of all the lit-up buildings looked splendorous and magnificent.

"Tomorrow, Sandra is going to get a babysitter and take you up the CN tower, Corey. You should enjoy the view from up there," Ben remarked.

"That will be fun. Today I met some weird folks on the streets. One person thought he was Jesus, others handed me flyers, and a few people invited me into pubs, but I did not go in," Corey said in disbelief about the strange customs.

"It's a bizarre place around here. It is like another world really. You should see some of the customers that I deal with everyday. Some think the world belongs to them and others think that everyone is trying to cheat them out of something. There is abundant rudeness in the city. Be careful not to let it side-track you from your goals," Ben suggested with a serious grimace.

The following day Sandra took some photos of Corey at the top of the CN tower. He expressed enthusiasm about the potential that the city life offers. The view of downtown was superb. It was like being atop a mountain and seeing a colony extending for miles. The buildings in the distance looked powerfully exalting as they shadowed the city dwellers.

They were ready to take the elevator down and enjoy some more scenic wanderings. The elevator usually returned to the lookout tower every few minutes but it seemed delayed. Ten minutes had passed whereafter a gentleman dressed in a white shirt and blue vest protruded from the doorway near the elevator and told those waiting that there was a malfunction. The elevator was stuck between floors and they had already sent for a technician in town to come and make the necessary repairs.

There were about twenty people standing around feeling weary and wanting to return to the ground floor. It didn't seem to bother Corey too much. He struck a conversation with a beautiful young lady from Mississauga, a suburb of the metro area.

"I came here from Saskatchewan a few days ago. It is much different here from where I lived," Corey said to her.

"I can well imagine. Are you just visiting or will you be living here?" she replied.

"Right now I am staying with my brother and his wife. That's her, over by the window. Her name is Sandra, and mine is Corey."

"You have a lovely name. Mine is Eva. I haven't been up in the tower in four years, and today, well it was time to get away from down below, if you know what I mean," Eva huffed with a sigh.

"I certainly do know what you mean. You have a pretty name. It fits you well," he politely complimented. She smiled and gracefully accepted the comment.

Two hours later the elevator door opened. An operator stepped aside as an assistant allowed a lady to enter the elevator.

"Why can't more people go in, we waited here long enough?" a man from the rear had shouted.

"The lady needs to use the washroom, Sir. Please be a little more patient and the elevator will return in just a few more minutes," the employee replied with confidence, and continued, "Ladies and gentlemen, we wish to extend out sincere apologies for the malfunction today. We are sorry we could not allow all of you to use the stairwell to return below. I have been informed to let you know that a free complimentary pass will be issued to all of you upon returning down below, and a glass of wine awaits each of you at the bar in the lower level. Again, I extend out sincere apologies for this unforeseen incident."

Finally they got in the elevator and arrived at the lower level. Sandra excused herself to the newly met couple stating that she had to visit the ladies room. A waiter delivered two glasses of wine to Corey and Eva then walked around to all others who were inconvenienced. Corey lifted his glass to hers and presented a toast of mutual attraction.

"Here's to returning back to earth. Up top was quite a view, but when somebody has to go, they just have to go," he winked with a smirk.

"Yes, that was unfortunate, wasn't it," Eva giggled, "So what kind of work do you do, Corey?"

"Well, Eva, to be honest, I am looking for work. Nothing specific yet, but out west I was into farming. Now that I am here, I am not sure of what I will do, but I don't want to be part of the grind, the day to day survival, you know," he said as they caught a glimpse of something uniquely special in one another's eyes.

"Corey, you seem to have an energy for prosperity. I am twenty-five and three years ago I began a business plan and it has turned into a national company. Many people do not realize that by reaching out to others, they can accomplish their dreams. The problem with most people not fulfilling their dreams is due to their contentment, their limitations that they allow to keep them from expanding. You can be as successful as you desire and I know you want to be successful," Eva expressed cheerfully.

"What is the business that you began, Eva?" Corey asked with interest.

"It is called Business Inventions and Ideas Institute. We help other people with leveraging their potential with the ideas they have to market and if they are looking for ideas, we interview them and help them to focus on what they can provide to consumers," Eva remarked with a gentle persuasive smile.

"That sounds great, but there must be tons of companies doing what you are doing out there these days," Corey remarked to see her honest reaction.

"Definitely there are, and you have to be on top of what you do. You have to put your mind in the perspective of the product or service and see where it can go. Think of this for a moment. If you were able to double a penny each day for thirty days, how much money would you have at the end of those thirty days?"

"Probably thousands of dollars. I am not sure, so please tell me."

"You would have made 5,368,709.12. That is not too bad of a figure, considering it is initiated with just a penny to begin with. Imagine if it began with a profit of five dollars or more and you were the inventor and manager of the product and profits," Eva insinuated slyly.

"Eva, you have quite an intelligent business outlook. I would be really interested in meeting with you, even at your office, if that is possible," Corey requested.

"Here is my business card. Excuse me if it seems too formal, but I would gladly talk to you about any plans you may come up with. Call me anytime if you want to discuss them. Right now I have to attend a meeting but it was a pleasure to meet you today," Eva said as she set her wineglass on the table and shook his hand at her departure.

Sandra walked back to him and they left the tower to continue on a little tour through the downtown streets. As they drove around the city, Corey continued to wonder about what could have brought the opportunity for him to meet with such an intriguing and lovely lady. Sandra pointed out some interesting places for him to visit, which he cheerfully acknowledged but his mind was really on meeting with Eva again. Perhaps tomorrow he would telephone her to see if she would accept seeing him before the end of the week. At first he wondered if it was a scam, but his wits were intact and there was no way he was going to invest his small amount of funds into some venture that would be a possible failure. He was ready to seize an opportunity that smelled of attainment or success but only if it proved without a shadow of a doubt.

It couldn't have been better. Eva invited Corey to her office the following day to discuss potential and opportunities. He took the subway to a corner on Yonge Street and walked from there to the address she had on the card. He looked at her inspiring company logo on the glass door as he entered the ground floor suite of her business. The logo contained three circles within one another with the word 'Fortuna' written in the center. Corey walked towards the receptionist and told her that he had an appointment with Eva at two o'clock. At that instant Eva happened to walk out and saw him standing there. "Great timing, Corey. Please come in," she politely smiled.

He followed her past a number of offices wherein people were busy working at computer terminals. Her large office was pleasantly decorated with an abundance of plants and flowers. It looked like a terrarium of freshness and vitality. She had a conference table at one end of the room and a library of business opportunity and success books at the other. Her desk was immaculate yet simple and was in the middle of the room near the long tinted windows, which overlooked the endless street. They sat in comfortable chairs at a small square table, which had blocks of many colors painted on it.

"This is quite an exceptionally unique office Eva. I could live in here. Did you decorate it?" Corey asked.

"Yes, I like to be a little different as you can see," she laughed.

"I liked that logo designed on the front door. I am thinking it has some significant relevance to success," Corey suggested.

"In fact it does, and it took many years of learning principles to end up with it, Corey. The inner circle represents the creative force, the middle circle is the formative force and the outer circle is material success. It is an esoteric symbol that reflects the infinity of things represented by threes. It may also be interpreted as creative ideation, will and love. Things that have infinity to their nature and can connect us with the missing virtue of prudence or discretionary foresight become an invaluable tool in any success," Eva explained.

"I like that. You seem to have thought out the road to success in many ways. You appear very fulfilled with your achievements. What does the word Fortuna represent in the center of your logo?" Corey asked.

"Fortuna is a Roman goddess of fertility and the wheel was originally attributed to her. It is a feminine symbol of the life of a woman. You may wonder what mythology has to do with business, but to tell you the truth, the ancient civilizations adored deities as they represented every important facet of life, growth and survival."

"Some of them were associated with planets and other celestial concepts like the zodiac, right?" Corey asked, rocking back and forth in his chair.

"The zodiac is a wheel also. There are three things we have to deal with in life. They are the past, present and future. We can link them to memory, intelligence and foresight in order to make the best choices and measure our success along the way. Do you know what periodicity means?"

"It sounds like something that revolves or recurs over and over again," Corey remarked.

Eva nodded and gave Corey a sweet smile. "The world is in constant growth and at the same time constant destruction patterns come into play. There is always flux and reflux occurring, as there is action and reaction, night and day, birth and death. We may interpret all of these instances as either good or bad or neither. To govern our material success we can use the principles of the triune concept I have mentioned and allow it to grow for us."

"That sounds exciting, and brilliant, Eva. You are not just using material ideas to bring success but it seems somehow you are working with laws on another level of life," Corey remarked excitedly.

"Exactly!" she said surprisingly, "There is always a reward for work done. The old saying of 'As you sow, so shall you reap' makes perfect sense when you use a formula and go for it. In a unique way every person works with three fundamental principles that makes things happen in their life. There is the calm, intelligent, patient, lucid method of maintaining balance. Then there is the energetic, excitable, restless and brilliant method of emotional energy at work. Finally there is the unfortunate but required inertia that sustains ignorance and sloth, darkness and withdrawal, which is a weighty and cumbersome illusion but, then again, it is required to know the difference between what is real and what is illusion."

"Everything has its ups and downs. There is positive and negative to it all, I suppose. I think that if a person is opportunistic and courageous with an open mind they can achieve prosperity," Corey added to her informed expression.

"I agree, Corey. Sometimes, however, there are blocks in the way. A person has to really take some time and make notes about what stands in their way to further achieve their desires. They have to know how to change misfortunes into great opportunities, how to create an abundance and allow their wheel to turn for them."

"A lubricated wheel can go a long way," Corey chuckled, while reminiscing the days of working with the tractor in the wheat fields.

"I think you got the point," she smiled while offering him a glass of water from the fountain.

"Is Fortuna the deity of great fortune?" Corey questioned.

"Jupiter is the god of great fortune, and Pluto is the god of giving wealth blindly. But we have to take things into perspective at critical times. The Egyptians have a mysterious sphinx just outside Cairo, on the way to the three pyramids. The sphinx represents the ability to see things in an objective point of view. This represents the competence to step outside the circles of time and regain stability and re-arouse the instincts and intuitive intelligence to create stability in our ambitions. I hope that wasn't too much of a mouthful for you," Eva said while looking into his eyes for a response.

"There are endless possibilities when we want them to work for us. It is as simple as that. I just look around and go 'wow' at the world. Nobody is any different than anyone else. Nobody is any more superior or inferior to anyone else. It just takes an effort, a desire and as you have told me, some special drives to do anything, anything at all," Corey replied in confidence.

"Very well said, Corey," Eva lauded as she picked up a deck of playing cards from a shelf within the table, "Let's look at some conceptual ways to bring success into a person's life."

"I can see it in your eyes that you are going to be playing with a full deck," Corey jested.

"As indeed we all should," she responded and flipped over the top card onto the table. "This is a spade. Its shape resembles a spearhead or arrow. In fact, it represents a sword in a very distinct manner. These spade analogies cut, pierce or penetrate through items. They divide and move, separate and cause change in motion or movement. This is the quality of air and how things begin, and the wonderful thing is that we have the ability to control and direct that mobility to make our dreams and desires to come true."

Corey looked in with deepening thought and fascination as she flipped over the next card on the deck.

"This is a club and it represents the power of a magic wand. It is like a rod penetrating into three clovers, which are like the three circles in my 'Fortuna' logo. It also represents fire and expansion and desires. Desires are like passion, they become stronger and more intense until they consume everything, just like fire does. That is the basic principle of fire, to expand our desires and make them do the work for us. It is a wonderful and useful energy and without it we cannot accomplish anything. What else do you think we require, Corey?" Eva smiled.

"I would say we need a heart to put it together in just the right way," he confidently replied just before she turned over the next card, which was the ace of hearts.

"You are not wrong. In order for these workable features to bring us success we need a devised plan. A heart means something that is fairly tangible for the mobility and expansion of our passions or desires to fall into. Hearts represent water, which flows and is a receptive quality. Water is the element just before the physical earth, so it has density and is like a cup to hold our deepest desires inside. The water element is moreover a plan that we have prepared for everything to come together, for the action to take affect. It becomes the formed concept, the condensed version of the initial desire." She said as he glared into her eyes. "Finally, it becomes hardened," she concluded as the ten of diamonds was turned face up, "into the earth plane that we see around us. Our plan becomes materialized as the result of all our efforts and work. That is how all things work, whether we realize that we are constantly doing it or not. That is the big secret of how to make anything work, no matter what it is. Earth is the final form that everything falls into. It simulates resistance, and is represented by the suit of diamonds. It is the final outcome of all forces. Everything has a beginning, just like the alpha of the Greek alphabet. Do you know any of the Greek alphabet?"

"I know a few letters like Alpha, Beta, Gamma and so on," Corey replied, arching an eyebrow.

"Yes, and the final letter is Omega, which is like our English letter Zed, the end, or at least the final letter created in our alphabet. That is why I capitalized the A in 'FortunA' in the center where it all begins and outlined the whole process of my logo with the Greek letter Omega, around the outer circle... again, the outer circle represents a successful material life."

"You are an ingenious lady Eva. I can see why your company has grown to indefinite proportions helping other people. You use the principles of how things come into being by relating them with elements and have people focusing on those principles to come up with ideas and inventions and to make them work," Corey voiced in fascination.

"I see that I am not wasting our time so far. I never doubted you to understand what I wanted to tell you, but some people as they are, become stuck in the end-all earth consciousness. They don't want to reach into their internal limitless Fortuna and grow with it. They stop the wheels from turning time and again. But inside of you, I can see there is a potential waiting to be awakened, used, developed and projected."

"Oh, there is potential in me that wants to come out! I like the word 'FortunA'. It rings a nice bell," Corey decided.

"Think of other words similar to it. Think of for-tune, fore-tell, fore-thought and fore-sight. They all suggest a beginning, a previous or starting point to bring what they supersede into life and realization," Eva noted as she got up and walked around to the window.

"If any kind of success a person desires is a future thing, how can it come into present life?" Corey asked.

"That involves another day of discussion. But basically we can manipulate each instantaneous moment that we live in. Forces and energies change each instant as we live. They alter the living pattern of circumstances by the combination or ingredients of the elements we work with. Whatever we put in the cooking pot today will be ready at a certain time, so we must make sure we don't burn it and ensure the proper emotions, thoughts, and plans are enacted upon for a perfect outcome. Use the principles of the elements in your favor," Eva concluded as she touched his shoulder with one hand and showed him her open palm with the other.

"I should pay for this information, I presume," He smiled unwittingly while looking into her palm.

"Not at all, Corey. But you have the right idea. An open hand suggests receiving something. That is the path we are on in this discussion. It is up to you to open your hand for that which you most desire in your life and it will come. Would you like to take a walk in the park with me?" Eva requested.

"I would greatly like that, even though your office is like a park, it would be nice to go someplace with you and think about all of this," Corey agreed while getting up and opening his palm under sprinkling water in her office waterfalls, adorned with mythical goddesses.

The afternoon sun made the walk very delightful as the two sauntered freely down the park path under the weeping willow trees that overshadowed their journey.

"I am not much of a religious person Eva, but some of these things you talked about sound like they involve the study of the occult. Would I be wrong to think that?" Corey asked.

"The fortunate thing about life," Eva replied matter-of-factly, "is that it involves two very important realizations. One of those realizations is called understanding. The other realization directs that understanding into the application of wisdom. There has been much silly taboo about the word 'occult'. It simply means that which is hidden from normal view. It does not mean anything bad in itself. We live in a credulous physical world and have to make the best of it. If we do not, then we come back time and again until we have done all that we must. We continue to learn about hardships and suffering, continue to go through pain and sorrow and continue to learn the hard way. The only wrong or bad that is committed is the use of ignorance by causing harm to ourselves or other living organisms." She breathed in serenely.

"In order to leave these patterns of life and not return we have to perfect our nature. We have to become like the mystical sphinx that holds the sword of reason and obeys all that is good. They say that cleanliness is next to godliness and I tend to believe that in relation to how life operates. Clutter and chaos seem to cause confusion not only around us but also in our mind and emotions. Granted, there is nothing wrong with getting our hands dirty and doing a job that needs to be done. It is the work itself that accomplishes any goal to true fulfillment."

"Should the ultimate goal be something other than a material one?" Corey questioned.

"To each their own, but essentially it should represent perfection in one form or another. It should be a living example of what we represent or have come to realize that is important to our destiny," Eva thought for a moment and then smiled peacefully, "It could eventually help all of mankind in some way."

"I like that ideal. It sounds very noble. I think if everybody did something to that affect they would be in touch with their evolution, their intuitions and would make it a greater planet to live and survive upon," Corey acknowledged.

"By being creative and flexible, open and courageous opportunities like you've never imagined can come to us. I must admit one thing however that I refrained from mentioning up to this point. Luck has something to do with life as well. Since we do not have full control over all the elements at play within the circles, there is an element of luck involved each step of the way. There are ups and downs in everything we do unless we block the downs somehow. That is just the way it is. Some things come and sometimes they go. Sometimes they keep coming without end. Life is not just a random series of events," Eva paused to sit beneath one of the large trees, and motioned for Corey to join her. Getting comfortable, she continued, "We create what happens through our conscious and our oblivious projections. Rewarding realities come to people that pave the path to them and back again. When the opportunity is there, it should be turned into a prosperous blessing, like a break-through into unexpected luck in a spontaneous way."

"You have great clarity into life and how things can work. You are truly a benevolent soul," Corey smiled widely.

Eva flushed slightly, and stammered a bit before adding, "Being altruistic is part of knowing the wheel, part of being charitable and part of life. We do not own anything in life. People create misconceptions about property and ownership. Everything comes and goes, according to time. We can be like selfish parasites or we can live with love. To be free of material bondage is by far a better choice. Why would anyone want to build a life on a foundation that eventually crumbles? It is not only unfeasible but also a recipe for disaster in times to come. If we become centered in the ever present golden sun of love and beauty and balance behind the glittering silver moon of knowledge as we do our laundry and bake delicious foods we bring a special now-ness into perspective. We do what we know is best in life and this is something that can be an eternal cherishing quality."

"I want to tell you something," Corey interjected, "When I was six years old I asked my grandfather where Hell was. He told me that when Jesus was born in 4 BC, which I thought was strange, but nonetheless, that there was a little village upon a hill and it was called Hell. At the back of the village there was an old bog that had a terrible stench of brimstone and sulphur emanating from it. The bog was some kind of dirty old Hot Springs and perhaps some terrible chemicals from builders were dumped into it to produce the malignant odors. When people did something against the laws of the day they were brought there and sent across the bog. It was believed that they would fall into the malodorous bog if they were guilty and would be consumed by the heat and then die for their penance. If the person bribed the enforcers or priests of the time they would be given a special coating on their feet, as a protection against the hot walk across the bog to prevent them from being burnt. They would be considered to be innocent and set free, if they made it across. Do you see something in this story, Eva?"

"I see that old stories brought popular and misinterpreted belief into society," Eva noted, relaxing against the base of the shady tree, "They caused fear and misunderstanding about reality. They interpreted Hell as a place in existence for suffering through ignorance. Hell is a state of mind and exists all around us, every minute of every day. It is just an illusion that we choose to live in because we don't want to wake up from it. We have the ability to be above that frame of mind and live in a perpetual state of holiness and aspiration. We cannot bride our way into spirituality. We can manipulate life to a certain degree but in the end we get what we pay for. That is where we learn to draw the line, or circle as the case may be. The Bible is filled with symbols and to know symbols we have to awaken to a point of relating all things to what they are made of and from. Whatever any particular thing represents, it becomes related to a combination of elements at work. In my opinion, it is a holy endeavor to learn about the laws of nature as we have talked about today. It should bring us closer to attaining a perfected and harmonized embrace with the Divine Being. Think about your farming experiences for a moment. Would you want to be equated as cattle to God or would you rather be closer to being equated with divine deities and angelic beings, if you had the choice to become either through aspiration?"

"I know I wouldn't want to be cattle, if that's what you actually mean. You seem to know a lot about everything," Corey said, impressed with the knowledge that Eva knew and used.

Eva giggled. "I know very little, actually. I think it is important to have understanding. With that you are inspired to talk through your heart and all things simply connect as though they make sense."

"You are a beautiful woman. I've never imagined that I would ever meet anyone quite like you. I have to say this however, that through all the nights I sat awake in bed after a long day of work I felt that there was more to life. I knew that I would one day meet somebody that would change my life and communicate with me on mature and responsible levels with opened eyes. Are you originally from the Toronto area?" Corey asked with curiosity.

"For the past ten years I have been here. I came from a little town in New Brunswick called Chatham, but it has since been amalgamated and renamed Mirimichi City," she paused and looked up at the sky, then continued, "Listen, I'd love to continue this chat with you, but I have to get back to the office. How about meeting me tomorrow night, around eight?" Eva smiled softly with glowing eyes.

"My little book isn't filled with appointments yet. In fact it doesn't exist, so your plan sounds great. I would love to get together," Corey said with jovial ambition.

"Give me your number and I will call you before I come by to pick you up," Eva said as they got up and walked back towards the street.

The following evening, Eva arrived at Corey's place and rang the bell. Ben answered.

"Good evening, please come in. Corey will be here in a minute," Ben said as he motioned for her to come in.

"Thank you, a lovely night tonight, isn't it?" Eva insinuated with casual conversation while waiting for Corey.

"Yes, the summer has been great this year, although I am sure some would like more rain," Ben retorted.

"Hello Eva, I am all ready," Corey said as he came into the room.

After saying goodbye to Ben, they walked down to her car. As they were walking, Eva looked at him and said: "Ready for what, to swing upon a star? You look pretty smashing tonight."

"No, you look smashing and dazzling, lovely lady. I am just me," Corey winked.

They went for a late dinner at one of her favorite vegetarian restaurants, which he didn't mind at all since the food was superbly appetizing. After ordering, Corey struck up a conversation.

"I have been giving this business prospect some thought and for some reason I came up with the idea to think ahead for the future. I want to try visualizing what people may need in five years time from now and begin working on the idea before it is needed."

"You are going to be a Leonardo Da Vinci, I can see," Eva expressed with eagerness.

"I am not much of a painter, if that is what you mean," Corey replied, arching an eyebrow.

"He was much more than an artistic painter. He was a visionary, a seer into the future. He was the first person to make an air plane, did you know that?" Eva noted.

"Really? I thought it was the Wright Brothers." Corey answered.

"Leonardo studied birds and how they fly. Unfortunately the two men that tested his first craft didn't get very far in it, but Leonardo went on to discover and invent many other things before the time of Columbus and modeled them. He developed the basic canon into an anti-tank gun and assembled multiple guns into something that was only reinvented during the Second World War by the Russian army. Suffice it to say he looked into the future and saw things that were going to be used by civilization."

"Sometimes it may not be a good idea to bring certain future concepts into the present, wouldn't you agree?" Corey inquired.

"That depends, who is to say unless you can see the advantage it would serve. Creative ideas that come from positive inspirations seem to be rewarding for everybody involved."

"I gather that it is a risk, and sometimes its not winning or losing that is as important but being involved in the experience itself," Corey surmised.

"Every event becomes an opportunity to arouse our creative instincts. The only true stability we have in life is at the hub or core of our Being, the axle of our inner wheels and when we connect with that the answers are always there for the proper course of action. There is a consequence to every action and people rarely seek truth for the sake of knowing it. There is generally a motive for the efforts that develop desires and a passion in the form of greed to be assuaged. We live amongst a naive society that has not purified the motive for the desire. In order not to be tormented by the lust for results, if we have a deep and divine secret for our motives everything will occur like unexpected miracles." Eva said with an air of praise.

Romantic sensations harbored within their bodies as each word connected with an uplifting emotion and reaction. There was sublime empathy blossoming in their merging hearts. They went to a dance club and danced like no one was watching. She could have almost any available man around her but to Eva, love was a substance that flowed through a pure chemical attraction combined with channeling that extended from the present and into the future.

After the enchanting evening of dance they strolled the lakeside under the star-lit heavens. Corey reached his hand into hers and felt warmth like he never knew before.

"You see those stars right there, that is the Orion Nebula. Over there, that is Cassiopeia. I wish that I could reach up and touch places beyond our miniature solar system," he whispered.

"The important thing is that you can reach inside and touch them," she smiled warmly.

Corey felt lost in her infinite charisma. Bracing himself, he said, "The only desire I really have is to be able to kiss you, Eva. You have touched me like nothing I've ever known."

Eva reached her arms around his shoulders and pulled him close to her warm body. Her face came next to touching his with an incredible urge growing out of proportion. A minute had past as the feeling heightened to a final climactic union of their mouths bringing them into the ecstasy that mutual love delivers. There was something about her that he could not quite figure out. He believed she held a secret motive for the reason they met and why everything fell so perfectly in place. Nonetheless, he was thrilled to be enwrapped in the joy that she brought him. She lovingly accepted him to spend the night with her. To Corey, it felt like the best possible event that destiny could offer.

They continually met in the coming weeks and shared emotions of love and passion that only two people joined as one could comprehend. Corey thought about developing a successful business and wrote down several ideas for her to critique. One afternoon she telephoned him and said that she had to meet him at the lakeside where they first kissed. At the appropriate time and place, he showed up with a ravishing arrangement of flowers and hoped that there was nothing wrong. She was thrilled to receive them with a poem that he wrote for her. Eva looked up at him and down at the poem as she read it:

"Every day knowing you my heart grows deeper Still,
With the love that you inspire I know I always Will,
But if a day should ever come and you would not be There
My heart would break in a thousand pieces that I could never Bare.
You are to me the Universe in a million, million Ways,
Your kisses are my love desires for a zillion, zillion Days."

"That is so lovely Corey, thank you so much, and the flowers are really beautiful," she cried while holding him close and kissing his face.

"I feel that there is something you have to tell me. My heart was in a race all afternoon wondering what it could be," Corey said as he looked into her loving green eyes.

"There is something I have to tell you and I am not sure how to tell you it. I do love you very much and to be totally straight with you, you are going to be a father, Corey," she cried with happiness.

"What? Me? Oh My! Oh Eva!" He squeezed her firmly and kissed her deeply. "You just made me the happiest person alive! I love you, Eva!" he poured out in emotional excitement.

"I was hoping you would be. I know it is really sudden and unexpected, but I have to be honest and say it is something I really wanted with you. It was a hidden motive, I must admit," she said as he kissed her face everywhere.

"That's fine with me, why would I mind? There is no way I would ever mind being together with you. You are the girl of my deepest dreams. It is like a miracle happened in my life to meet you and grow with you," he happily attested.

Eva asked Corey to move into her fashionable house to which he greatly accepted. During the coming months their binding admiration grew deeper for one another. They filled one another's heart with happiness and planted seeds of future prosperity to share. Corey was deeply in love with this wonderfully intelligent and passionate woman. She was a bright and successful Taurus and he was a balanced and loving Libra. They wedded on the fourth of September in Toronto and all of Corey's family attended. She picked the date and told him that she linked the fourth day of a month to festivity as it was for the ancient Egyptians a day of greatness and celebration.

Eva explained the organization of her company and he helped to run it and fostered many new ideas for it's continual growth. Together it was like a perfect partnership and nothing could go wrong. Corey initiated the productivity of a new body suit that was elegantly fashionable and contained microchips throughout it that allowed the wearer to control the temperature of the suit. He patterned many additional gadgets for it and soon it caught on as a trendy hot item. He enjoyed cooking, cleaning and doing constructive things around her house and for that she was very grateful. She thought him to be a picture perfect husband. When she had cravings during pregnancy, if he didn't have the delicacy she wished for he would run off to find it.

One night, a week before her birthday in May, she shook her lover's body as he slept beside her. "It's time to be a father, sweetheart," she said as his eyes opened in anticipation. He jumped out of the bed with overt excitement and rushed to bring her clothes that were prepared on the chest, at the end of the bed, for her to quickly dress.

"Let me help you downstairs, and please take it easy. Don't make any quick motions," he uttered as they scurried to the car and drove off to the stork's office. It was a beautiful moment for both of them. They had a baby boy and decided to call him Julian. They thought the baby to be the jewel of their love for one another and to them the name sounded lovely and promising. The child's face shined like a splendorous ray of happiness and completed their circle as a family.

Corey ran the company while Eva took some time off and remained home with the baby. Everything was fine until a month later, when Eva seemed agitated about something. Corey didn't want to bring up the subject that something seemingly bothered her, so he gently took her hand in his during the course of the evening. She abruptly pulled it away and then apologized.

"I didn't mean to do that." She hastily replied.

"What is wrong sweetheart? Are you feeling alright?" Corey asked.

Eva held out her palm and said, "I saw a palmist today in town. I've never done that before, but it is said that a person's life is already written in the lines of their palm. Corey, I've been told that my life is going to end. It's going to end this year," she desperately lamented.

"That's impossible, that's not going to happen. Incidents and circumstances in life can be overcome. We can override a predetermined destiny by shaping towards a new one. We change every instant and so does the future. It's never the exact way as determined, unless certain occurrences happen in an order to make it that way. You know that, my love," he protested as he shook his head and wondered why she would accept to believe such a fate.

"Corey, it wasn't a brainwashing session; somehow I saw that it will happen to me, as she told me it would. It was like I already knew it but had to be reminded that it would occur," Eva affirmed in anguish.

"How is it that this is supposed to happen? Did she tell you?" Corey asserted, wanting to know.

"She didn't know for certain, but said I have to be careful because I may be in the hospital soon. I know we can make things happen if we believe in them, and it's not that I want to believe in this at all, but it is something that I knew would happen. When I was sixteen a psychic told me something similar and that it would happen this year. There were no definite details then either, it was as though they were not permitted to know the answer of how I would die."

Corey was shocked and bewildered. He looked deeply into her shattered eyes and knew there was something to her prognostication and he wasn't going to dismiss it and make her feel incredulous. He was never oblivious to her concerns and wasn't about to be. Over the coming weeks he kept a watchful eye on any changes around them and any signs to be weary of. He went on an observation streak, seeking clues to this mystery, rather than on a paranoia fringe. There were no indications that something may occur to cause

Eva harm, yet as each day passed Corey silently harnessed a growing concern.

Early in July, during his lunch break, he decided to enlist the help of a psychic to relieve his mind. He made an appointment with one and at noon drove down to the given address. It was a female named Claire and she welcomed him in immediately knowing that he had grave concern about a situation.

"I will put it to you straight. Here is a shirt belonging to my wife, a watch and here is her photograph. I want to know anything that you can tell me about her future. There is a concern we are facing and that is all I can tell you," Corey said as he passed her the items and sat at her table.

Claire scattered the articles on her table and closed her eyes and then she slowly felt each one of them, tuning into the vibrations and seeking her guide for visions through the vibrations of the items. Corey noticed her head turning in short crescent movements as though she was gathering information.

"Has your wife got short light brown hair and green eyes?"

"Yes."

"Does she have asthma?"

"No."

"Does she have a medical problem that may cause problems to her breathing?"

"No."

"She is having a very traumatic time trying to breathe. She is gasping for air. She lost consciousness." Claire ended as she shook out of her horrific visionary experience and flung her hands to shake off the bothering sensations.

"What did you see? Why did she have a problem breathing, Claire?"

"I do not know. I could see her struggling violently and trapped and unable to take a breath," she attested.

"Is there any indication of when it would happen, is there anything more?" Corey pleaded.

"No, nothing. Sometimes these sensations and visions come in ways that are not fully clear. They are more like warnings than actual events that may occur," Claire motioned as she stood up and went for a glass of water.

"I thank you. What if I left her photo here, and you come up with something more. Would that be alright?" Corey requested.

"Yes, of course, and leave me your number." Claire agreed.

When Corey returned to work, he called Eva to ensure everything was fine with her and the baby. As he suspected, all was in order and they were going to the park for some afternoon playtime. During the evening he decided to confront her with what he had done during his lunch break. She was not upset but rather surprised that he thought of the idea.

"I don't have any idea how I could lose my breath in life unless I was trapped somewhere," Eva said.

"She said you were trapped, unable to escape something. Look, sweetheart, if there was anything that I could do, anything I could possibly invent to prevent this potential danger to your life I would give my life for it," he declared.

"I think we should do what we planned a few weeks ago and just get away for a while. I have wanted to go north out of the city for some time. Let's go for a long weekend and have Mom watch Julian for us. We need a break from everything, Corey." Eva requested.

"You're right. We can't stop living and be afraid of our every move in life," Corey admitted as he hugged her closely.

On Friday morning they began driving north without any determined destination. That night they stayed in a quaint motel off the highway and celebrated being alone and away from it all. It suddenly became a relief to feel some freedom once again, to open their wings and let go of the past. In the morning hours they set off once again and decided to enjoy a picnic in a rest area along the way. It was a beautiful July afternoon and she wished to visit a beach and enjoy the refreshing sensation of swimming in open water.

Corey took some pictures of their picnic and once again they glided down the road, this time in search of a beach. They drove past Owen Sound and headed towards the Georgian Bay Islands. It was a beautiful scenic drive and well worth commemorating on film. Along the inlet they could see some people hiking and fishing down along the water shoreline. Out in the distance some sailboats took advantage of the illustrious summer and swayed across the open bay with ease and liberty.

The air conditioner in the car was a welcoming comfort against the scorching sun that beamed down through the depleted ozone on the bare skin of those who tempted refuge. Eva shouted abruptly as they headed around a corner, "Corey, look at the size of that sailboat. It's magnificent!"

"Amazing, take a picture of it, quick!" he suggested.

"Just pull over up there and take one where the little lookout area is," she indicated by pointing. Corey pulled in and left the car running, asking her to come out for some air.

"I'm fine for now, darling. Just take some pictures while I rest my head. I have a bit of a headache," she replied.

He got out and walked down along the grass to take a picture but the boat was heading behind some trees that blocked his view. Eva pressed gently on her temples as she admired the water in front of her. Corey walked down around the trees and was at the perfect spot. He noticed some children playing in the water, jumping up and down and splashing one another. He wished that Julian could have been there to enjoy the experience. For a moment he lamented having left the child behind.

Eva leant over to the drivers' seat to stretch and lay her head down, away from the sun. Her knee caught the emergency break and unlatched the lever. The car suddenly rolled forward to the embankment as she jolted up and saw the hill quickly sliding under her. It caught tremendous speed as it rolled down the twenty-foot slope and into the Bay. Before she realized to do anything the car hood was immersed in the water several yards from shore. She frantically pressed the door handle as the car turned over and quickly sank to the bottom. Eva hysterically pushed and kicked the door but it was jammed shut by immeasurable water force from the other side. She pounded on the window with all her might but it would not burst open. Water slowly filled inside of the car as she breathed nervously in panic while kicking at the windshield.

"Air, I can't breathe! Stop that!" A child yelled as two other boys continuously splashed water into his face at the beach.

Corey's ears caught the words as his eyes lit with anticipated trepidation. His body pivoted as his feet ran in front of him back to the car. His face fell when he didn't see the car in sight. His heart pulsated as his mind returned to the event of his parents' house burning. Unconditionally, the remembrance swept across his mind of bringing his mother back to life at the instant that he saved her. He took a deep breath while running in the water and dove forward to the depths. His body lunged into the murky bottom with eyes opened in search of the vehicle. To his right he could see a cloud of debris floating to the surface to which he returned for another breath. With every ounce of power, he breathed deeply to the pit of his stomach and held it as his body plunged again through the cloudy fluid to the bottom. He could not see anything. It was like being in utter darkness, surrounded by filth and preventing any light from coming in. His arms reached around to feel for the car as he swam the bottom of the darkened waters.

Suddenly, his head smashed into the front tire of the overturned car. His hands quickly maneuvered across the car's body to find the side window. Corey held on to the side mirror and kicked through the window continuously until it broke through and then hauled himself within the car. He could faintly see Eva floating inside, upon the rear seat. Corey grabbed onto her shirt and hauled her out through the window. Anxiously, he kicked through the water in rage to make it back to the surface, hauling her lifeless body with him. It was as though he had summoned the strength of several men through the terrifying episode.

Upon the surface he gulped some urgently required air. Corey relentlessly paddled with his free arm to the shoreline. Her head rested upon his shoulder as he earnestly struggled. Without hesitation he began pumping her stomach to relieve the ingested water.

"Come on Eva! I am here. Don't leave us! Eva, come on!" he continuously echoed as his arms pressed firmly and quickly into her abdomen. "Wake up Eva! Wake up now!" He shouted deliberately with determination.

It appeared too late, as though the time had come and gone and the chance was missed by some cruel fraction of worldly penitence.

"You are not going to leave me! Come back here right now! Eva come back!" Corey beckoned through his heart for a response while pressing firmly on her and then providing mouth to mouth to revive her.

"You are coming back! Listen to me Eva!" he commanded with unremitting vigor. A dribble of water spurted from her lips as he continued pressing it out of her system. She began to cough out a stomach full of consumed liquid as he yelled cheerfully at her return to life. Her eyes quickly opened once again as she turned abruptly to her side and began coughing and spitting to the ground. Corey laughed in relief to welcome her back and began kissing her arm. Eva shook her head to get the remaining water out of her ears and looked at him insatiably.

"I knew you would be there. You are always there! You always have been and always will be," she cried as her wearied arms wrapped around his responsible shoulders.

"Does this mean that we surpassed that surmised limitation of your destiny, that we passed the test?" he asked as a thankful tear came down his wet face.

"We have three lives to live, let's hope we never have to use another one for a long time." Eva bellowed as she kissed his mouth.

"Don't ever wheel off like that again! My greatest worth in life is in loving you the way that I do and I don't want to do it without you here," He complemented as they fell back to the pebbles on the shore and regained the precious, ignited passion they shared as their luckiest of fortunes. ★

BABALON WITHIN

"... allow everyone to hold firmly to that which he believes and that which makes him happy and content.
If everyone would adhere to this principle and make it his own, there would be neither hatred nor religious discord.
There would be no reason for differences of opinion and all philosophies or all religions could co-exist happily."

Initiation Into Hermetics- Franz Bardon

Adam leaned against the lamppost in the dreary drizzle, lost in the fog of his London neighborhood. He watched despondently as the taxi pulled away from the curb and down the street towards the airport. He couldn't believe that Lilith was suddenly gone, despite the fact that he knew it had to be this way. She had enough of London for one month and enough of Adam for an eternity. Rain fell down his face and onto his lapel as he sniffled with abandonment gripping at his heart.

Three weeks previous, the once charming and delightful man was coming to the end of his rope. Adam and Lily were invited to a friend's party, a friend that Lily had only seen a few times in passing while she was with Adam. They went to the party together, and walked hand in hand to the front door. As soon as they entered, however, Adam began to change. He grabbed Lily around the waist and directed her into the living room, where a few dozen guests were dancing and prattling away. She struggled against his grip, and broke free, only to have Adam grab her wrist and pull her even closer to him.

"What's wrong, my lovely?" he hissed, "Don't you want to be seen as my woman?"

One of Adam's work mates waved him over, and so he abandoned Lilith to greet him. Lily rolled her eyes and wondered if he was ever going to grow up and accept himself from the inside. She adored him, but preferred a man who was all man and not part mouse. When Adam returned and pinched her buttocks, she looked at him in bewilderment.

"Please, Adam, we are adults you know. There is more than one way to show affection," Lily scorned.

Adam sighed loudly, which came out like a growl. "You just want things your own way all the time. You've come from Amsterdam twice now, and I already promised to go to your place next time, but I know you don't believe me."

Lily quietly fumed. "That's not what is bothering me, and you know it. It seems every time we're together it is great at first, then you change, you try to dominate me and not see me as an equal."

Adam was confused about what she was talking about. He was limited by identifying himself with only his ego or false projections of the person he thought he should be. When confronted with ideality he systematically backed away; he could not identify with his deeper, higher Self.

Lily was a deep part of him, for they had made love often, yet the spontaneity of their passion that they shared had slowly dwindled away. He wanted others to know that he was in full control and had superior dominating qualities over his woman. The more it was not acknowledged the more he would try in vain. There was a side of himself that he refused to come to terms with. The all-man that he thought he was portraying became more like an all-idiot.

The following week worsened as the relationship between the two slid from mild distaste of each other to hating one another. From time to time they would patch things up and go on as if nothing had happened, although the end would inevitably be the same: Adam would lose half of himself to the mire of gratifying his lower instincts and became trapped in his delusions. To him, Lily was everything, although he did not know how to grow with her as a person. When he dwelled on what he saw as her bad qualities, they were magnified by his fiery temper and his need to be the bigger person, resulting in his lashing out at her.

Every love song used to hold a passionate meaning for them. Songs represented their connected passions that they related to and once shared. The magic potion and mystic charm turned into toleration when they could no longer unite as a couple in climax. It was an all too simple formula, but together they did not use the potential of love and hate, pleasure and pain, relaxation and rage to fulfil their destiny and surpass the illusionary obstacles that they created. If they could surpass their negative feelings and create a positive issue from them, the passion would return; but this seldom occurred. One negative concept grew into another and before long they steamed into arguments. Bringing the best out of Lily was once a fascination to him, but now it seemed to be work that he became tired of.

There is a secret message in the Tantric tradition. It teaches the conscious surrender to the All or Infinite Goddess whom manifests in the one you love, to create realized fulfillment. During that moment, a state of bliss unfolds and all life is accepted as it is. Several viewpoints conjoin and are surrendered to the utmost through the partner resulting in achieving unbounded strength to become Oneself. Ecstasy through the union of the inner Poet and Saint, Angel and Satyr, Daring Man and Adultress swim through the Lion-Serpent energy to surpass the physical blockage of morality and rationalism. This involves strength and love for commitment to achieve and overcome the lower nature fenced in and guarded by the ego.

When Lily first arrived, Adam wrapped a chain of roses around her body, representing the unity of their desires to create such strength as to unite their spiritual and carnal natures. Yet, the very forces that were to bow to their embodiment and deliver divine intoxication ended gripping him in the lust of gluttony and wantonness such that he forgot the Supreme Sacrament of love and understanding. He soon thereafter paid no respect to the bride of his desires and lost himself in the obstacles of resistance. She held the Holy Grail but he held old fears and conditionings that prevented the penetration into her spiritual abode.

When she requested to meet his parents he always made an excuse about the timing not being right but she knew there was more to it than that. In Adam's perfect world there was no room for anyone else's error. He was perhaps quick to judge others, but not so quick on judging himself. This little mishap developed confrontations and expectations. Everyone is who they should be, and to try changing another person usually results from trying to change something of dislike within ourselves. He missed the point of this and instead of using their differences as stepping-stones his disfigured morals were shoved onto her.

The final week was most distasteful in more than one respect. Although it appeared inevitable to both of them that they would never see one another again, there was still an attachment. She refuted many of his sour qualities and he was disgusted with how freely she flirted with others wherever she went. The more he revolted with her sense of carefree living, the more she would appear promiscuously inviting to others, in his eyes. There may have been a chance if they would have taken a temporary separation to cool off, reconsider the damages and work on them, but it didn't happen. When one person is stubborn and unwilling to change, the situation becomes difficult to deal with. When both partners refuse to change, the chaos culminates quickly.

It is a difficult path to tread. On one side there is the machinery of war, fear, and hatred that are all satiated with animalistic desires, thereby becoming out of focus. On the other side is the option for great love and vibrations for a spiritual awakening to be shared with someone special and endearing. Bringing these two realities of life into harmony requires not only courage but also a willingness to surpass all lower boundaries. There was no chance of reconciliation on the final day. Lily went to a travel agent in a shopping plaza while Adam went to pick up some clothes at the dry cleaners. She was determined to have a retreat to Amsterdam that day and so they obliged her with an evening flight out of London.

The evening fog seeped in and wandered through the streets like a hazed vision of despair loosing substance and matter in its wake. Lily enjoyed her sense of liberty too much for these distraught incidents to impair her outlook. She stood at the upstairs apartment window looking out at the dim view waiting for the time to meet her scheduled taxi.

"What are you waiting for? Did you make a date for tonight or something?" Adam callously remarked.

Lilith set her jaw and steeled herself. "I may as well tell you, dear Adam. I am leaving this evening and going back home to the Netherlands."

Adam was taken completely aback. Furious, he spat, "You didn't tell me you were going to leave! How can you just get up and go like this?"

"How could I stay, should be the question you have to ask yourself," Lilith voiced vehemently. "For three weeks we've been miserable. Time and again we patched it up but where is it going? You have your way of doing things and I have mine, and there is no changing that." She flung her hands in the air then holstered them into her pants pockets.

Adam sneered derisively. "You think that you can just come into a person's life like that and then turn around and run away? Do you have a heart Lily? Do you know what you are seriously doing?"

She looked up at the light fixture and then into his eyes with a simple reply.

"Yep."

Adam shoved a finger in her face. "What makes you so perfect? You strut around like you are worth everything while getting everybody fixated on you! Do you know what I consider that as? You're not bloody leaving here until I get an apology. I've been humiliated in front of my friends, been used by a whacker and now you just flaunt yourself out of here like it was all a game?!" Adam kicked an empty wastebasket for emphasis.

Lilith crossed her arms. She inhaled and exhaled deeply. "Look Adam, you have things just a little bit wrong. Do you think I have to live, breath and move the way you want me to? Am I some kind of slave for you to use your wishful thinking upon? I don't think so!" She then walked into the bedroom to grab her baggage. Adam mutely watched her, following her with his vengeful gaze.

She returned with baggage in hand. "Enough is enough, and we both had that. We are simply not compatible," she added before opening the front door and walking downstairs towards the street.

"You're not quite right upstairs, girl!" Adam yelled. "There aren't many who will put up with your shit!" He slammed the door behind her.

There was slight drizzle through the fog as she paced back and forth on the street. She looked up at the apartment window and noticed the light had just been turned out. It began raining as she walked over to the lamppost and waited in relief. She thought once again about the abandonment in her heart. The loss was for the better. Life on this side of the apartment door promised her the freedom of choice. That was something she would never earn with the corrupted morals of the one she left behind. The taxi came down the road as she stepped to the curb. Adam ran down the stairs of his flat and out the door, but it was too late. She was gone. He leant against the lamppost as he watched the taxi vanish in the fog through the hollow street.

Adam felt a sense of anguish during the coming days as he missed the excitement that Lily had brought into his life. He attempted to telephone her but there was no answer. 'What could she be doing and where was she?' He wondered, as a part of himself seemed lost in the dread of the night. There was something in her influential flamboyant sensitivity that lured his emotional side into the longing of having her return. Her supple lioness character had control over her inner demons and fears, a trait of admiration that few could attest to. She was like the incarnation or avatar of a free woman, a scarlet woman that walked the streets in splendor and pride with a tight reign over the abominations of worldly affairs. She was a reflection of Isis upon Earth, connected with a spiritual liberty flowing effortlessly in the Great Sea of Time.

Adam came to realize that she was perhaps correct in her assumptions. Perhaps he was not the all-man that she wished him to be. He could see that she mastered a discipline of which he was ignorant. Pride, subjugation, temptation, instinct and passion were some of the mastered skills that he saw in her. To acknowledge such human emotions and to refine them shows a feat of self-control and awareness that transforms a person into something more.

"Why am I so limited, vain and shameful?" Adam reflected. "Do I fear there is nothing beyond my physical appearance? Can I not master my mind and emotions then trade them in for something greater? Do I fear there is nothing beyond the preconceptions that I have wrapped my life into? What is unity if it is not with Thee?" he contemplated as a realization began to occur. He was not ready for what Lilith had to offer.

He had not prepared his life to be with the firelight of her exhilarating and liberated nature.

She was an enchantress that revealed nothing until the highest peak of rapture. The mystery of her heated excitement was revealed in the symbol of the broach she had pinned upon her lapel. It was a cosmic lemniscate, a figure-eight to illustrate that the infinite is constant and everything returns to itself. Through control of all internal elements, Conscious Light delivers unimaginable joys surpassing all that can be conceived. It is this Light that she had connected with, rejoiced with and held in secrecy. She held no restriction and rejected no expression of the products in her character. Whether legitimate or illegitimate, it didn't matter. Her destructive powers were as important to her as constructive ones. She was the bride of Babalon.

Adam associated with these conceptions about her qualities. He knew she was not one to be tamed but yet the connection he had inside with her was real. Somewhere he would meet another person of his desires, another woman to teach him along the way to attain the knowledge of good and evil. She could awaken him from his stupor and he would become self-realized. Although Lilith was free as ever to roam the wild side of life, the erotic mutuality that she craved would never be satisfied in normal ways. There was more to her than he could fathom. Her life was a continuation of previous experiences beyond his.

The evenings grew longer as winter settled in, bringing with it dismal days and nocturnal notoriety. Adam went about the season learning about things more meaningful than he had previously considered. When the time was right, someone would be there for him to experience another portion of eternity. He settled down to study literature, the arts and the sciences. An afternoon walk through the City Park brought him in contact with a beautiful and charming lady. Her pleasant outlook began to infatuate him the moment they began talking.

He felt something through her that represented part of himself as a complete person. She represented a side of him that he had long neglected to accept. There was an immediate bond of attraction and laughter through their mingling curiosities.

"We have to accept who we are and live in love and sensitivity." She said with an amicable expression.

"I haven't had much luck in relationships. I don't think I was aware of what it is all about. Did you ever feel like you were on a journey and seeking something but not quite sure what it was or where to find it?" Adam blurted out without realizing the consequences of his openness.

"Self-exposure, my dear. Everybody wants to be outward but few look in the other direction. You are simply searching for something in the other direction. There is a legend to the Inner You and once you begin to question it, everything becomes indecisive," she returned with an air of pleasantness.

"Why is the search so traumatic? Isn't there a simple answer, an easy solution to it all?"

She looked up at the over-hanging tree that shadowed them and awaited the sunlight to shine upon her face. "Each person has an inner guide, a sensor that directs their motions of where and when to go on their journey. The solution is as simple as the question. The question is as complex as the desire and the desire is as great as the feeling." She turned and began to walk away.

"Wait, I wish to talk with you more. I want to get to know you," Adam implored, his voice tinged with anxiety.

Eve paused and smiled sweetly. She leaned forward as if to kiss him, but instead whispered into his ear, "We have known one another for a long time, Adam. I am the Eve of your beginnings. It is up to you to find the beginnings for yourself. No person can give another person the quality of Understanding. It is something that is sought and earned." As she withdrew from Adam's ear, her hair fluttered back and forth in the gentle breeze.

"May I see you again?" Adam looked almost pained.

"You may, but first you have to take the journey. You have to find the road to your legend."

"Where is the road? Where do I begin?" Adam asked in earnest.

"You must go to the City of Pyramids. When you stand there in silence and alone, the answer will come for you. It will be echoed in the warm wind and you will know where to go."

"You mean Egypt? I can find my quest, my road in life if I go there?" Adam questioned in wonderment.

"Yes, that is where you must begin. When you find the road and travel it, I will come again," Eve assured him.

"I will do that. I promise I will. I think I knew that already, strange as it sounds, but yes I knew that is the place I must begin. It is like going back to my birth, back to my beginning. Thank you, you are enlightened." Adam said as she vanished through the trees while voicing back to him, "Your Soul."

He looked around, and there was nobody in sight. The park was oblique and there was no sign that she was there. Adam walked back to where they met and looked up at the large tree. It had character within its enormous shape. He smiled, looked down at the ground, and then went home.

Where should I begin; what to do and how to prepare, he wondered. He made a call to his parents to let them know he was going to be out of town for a while and then telephoned his old friend Percy.

"It's been a long time, scout. What is happening?" Percy asked.

"I want to sell you my car. You're in the business, mate, and I know you wouldn't do me wrong. I'm going out of town for a while and need the extra cash." Adam said directly with confidence.

"Bring it around in the morning. I'm sure I can fix you up." Percy agreed.

"Right, see you then chap." Adam replied and hung up. He then telephoned an airline agency and arranged for a flight to Cairo in three days.

The following nights Adam sat up in bed wondering what he was doing all of this for. It seemed completely crazy but from his point of view there was nowhere else to turn. Embarking on this uncertain journey was either going to be a success or humiliation and either way the benefit had a special purpose to him.

Egypt Air flew over the Greek Islands and touched down in the over-populated city of Cairo, home to eighteen million people and the capital of Egypt. Adam walked off the plane as the heat waved across his face, welcoming him to the land of pharaohs. After clearing customs, he exchanged some currency and took a taxi downtown to the west side, called Memphis, so he would be close to the Old Kingdom of Giza. Giza is near the site of the only remaining ancient Seven Wonders of the World, the pyramids. Adam found out that the modern name given to Cairo was Al-Qahira and that it was at least fifteen times older than New York City. As the largest city in Africa and Asia it served as the gateway through Africa, the Middle East and Europe throughout time.

The taxi driver took Adam to a fine hotel near the marketplace and showed great courtesy for his patronage. After settling in with a refreshing shower, Adam walked through the market and purchased some bottled water and fruit. He noticed a postcard with a close view of one of the pyramids called the Great Pyramid of Khufu (Cheops). In the background on the postcard was a lady pointing to a corner of the pyramid. The clarity of her face was not well pronounced but to him she looked like the mysterious Eve that met with him in the park. He held up the card to the light and looked at it strangely. Mystified by the coincidence, he purchased it from the vendor. The old man behind the counter took the money and provided change while saying: "There is an old Arab proverb that says 'Man fears time, yet time fears the pyramids.' Welcome my friend and please come again."

"Thank you. I am here to invade the pyramids," Adam chuckled.

"You are too late, Napoleon did that in 1798, but good luck to you," The elder replied.

"These pyramids sure have a lot of stone to them. It is amazing."

"Mister, there is enough stone in the three pyramids to build a ten foot wall around all of France. That is how well compressed they are and why they stood the test of time. Two million blocks of solid stone is what you will find there and each one is two tons heavy," the vendor noted.

"That is impressive. They were built as tombs for Kings and Queens, correct?"

"Yes, for Khufu, Khefre, Menkaure and others so they may begin the mystic journey into the afterlife."

"Alright, well I hope to see you again. You are most friendly," Adam replied as he began to walk away.

"Come again, we like all peoples," the jovial man waved.

Adam returned to his hotel room and looked out the balcony window at the resplendent city that held thousands of years of magnificent history. It had been a long day and an evenings rest was remarkably inviting.

The following morning began with a filling breakfast at the lobby restaurant. Adam wasn't sure of his next step so he took his sports bag of belongings and checked out of the hotel, then got in a taxi and headed to the pyramids. As the driver went up the sandy roadway and passed the giant Sphinx, Adam's eye caught a glimpse of the three pyramids in the horizon. He felt trapped in the moment, but breathed a sigh of relief for having left behind the old part of his life that he had long clung onto.

Adam tipped the driver, then got out and looked up at the superb structures that somehow had a connection with his destiny. He reached into his pocket and took out the postcard, wanting to go to the spot on which the lady on the card was standing. Looking around, he had to figure the point from which the picture was taken and then go from there. It appeared to be the northwest corner, so he walked to that spot and then to where he estimated the lady would have been.

He stared straight ahead at the corner of the pyramid without trying to see anything in particular. He was looking at the corner spot where the lady was pointing. Several minutes had passed as he began to reflect upon his life and the narrow-mindedness that consumed his emotions and misdirected him many times. Other tourists didn't seem to pay any attention to him standing there. They were interested in scouting around the pyramids and going for camel rides with Arabs leading them around on the hot sands.

Adam thought of the one quality he required for achieving anything of lasting value in life. He thought of perseverance, something that never crossed his mind so intensely until now. After an hour had dwindled by he sat down on the sand and continued staring at the same location. He never once looked around to see anything else. He endured focusing on the corner of the giant stone that was eleven feet in front of him. From the corner, he could see down one side of the pyramid or down the other. It suddenly entered his mind that in one direction was the city and civilization and in the other was the vast desert. He was determined to remain there and not allow anything to dissuade him from the effort. Another hour had come and gone and he reached into his backpack to get a bottle of water.

Remaining there was to be his resurrection from the old Adam unto the new. He was not going to leave until some sign came to him that would release him from the bondage of his past. The scorching afternoon sun began to redden his face under the lotion that he continually smoothened onto his skin. It became very quiet as most people left the area to continue their bus tours. A distant figure from the desert approached on a camel from his corner view of the Great Pyramid. Adam's eyes squinted as he looked towards it then refocused his attention back on the corner that glued his mind throughout the day. Thirty minutes later a child arrived on the camel, wrapped in Arabian gowns and his head was crowned with an elegant headdress. He stopped beside Adam and looked down at him.

"They want… you to come. They… are waiting… for you," the youngster voiced in erratic English.

Adam looked up at him, fatigued and exhausted from the heat. "Am I seeing things now?" he thought to himself as he uncrossed his legs and slowly stood up in utter agony.

"Come up here, Mister," the child beckoned with excitement, "We… will go. I take… you."

The camel crouched down to the ground as the young boy held out his hand to welcome Adam behind him onto the splendid beast. They rode back to where the boy came from, across the dunes and into the desert. Adam looked back and saw the pyramids of Giza dwindling in the distance. They rode for hours, further and further away from civilization. The ride was most unbearable. Adam's body was not accustomed to such a long period of heat and dryness. His water bottles were empty as well. Through a parched voice, he murmured to the youngster, "Why have they sent you? Where are they?"

The boy replied without hesitation. "It is your… time. It is there Mister, right… there."

Adam scanned the desert ahead of them but could see nothing but hill upon hill of sand. They rode up one dune and down the next. It seemed like an eternity of hell that his body endured. He tried to analyze his feelings, but through it the toleration of each sweltering minute took precedence. He straightened his back and felt something peculiar. It was as though nothing existed except for now. He twisted his head back and forth, stretching his neck muscles as the camel hoofed through the sand. All of his past had been burnt away; consumed in the fires of the desert for him to be reborn into a new awareness. His head lowered to his chest as he breathed the dry air into his body. For a moment it seemed that his body fell asleep but his mind didn't drift. Rather, it remained alert to the sensation of falling towards a great light.

All of his desires seemed abandoned. He didn't think or feel anything. It was like he entered a void world. Suddenly his body jolted and his eyes opened. The camel had stopped and was lowering to the ground. The boy jumped off and looked at him without expression. Adam looked around and saw that he was in a small village of tents and camels, set within an oasis. An old bearded man walked out of a tent and towards him. Adam widened his eyes as the man approached.

"Thank you for listening," the old one said as he stopped in front of Adam.

"Do you have some water?" Adam requested.

The man took Adam by the arm and led him into the tent. Inside they sat on the floor with a bowel of liquid in the center. The man shook his head in agreement after which Adam began to drink. After a mouthful, Adam paused and glanced inquisitively at the liquid. "This fluid tastes very strange. I have never tasted anything like it," he remarked.

"It is a sacred drink called Soma. It will refresh you and help you," the man stated matter-of-factly.

"Why did you call upon me? Why is it my time?" Adam asked in between drinks.

"Sometimes we must not ask the questions but perform what is required of us. When we least realize it, we are punishing ourselves with our head. We are not aware of this, but we do it often," the old one replied in confidence.

"I am finished with punishing myself, and others as well. That is why I am here, isn't it?"

"You know that life is a series of faceted layers. When you step out of one layer you enter another. You have come this far and now it is time to learn the work that you must do to reach the next layer. All things are relative and true in their peculiar way according to the level they are experienced. What I say may have relative truth on one level and not on another."

"I know there is no one answer about life. It is a complexity; a mixture of laws upon each level that make things work the way that they do. There are still mysteries and nobody has the answer to everything." Adam conceded.

"To have the answer to everything, you must be everything. To have the answer to you, then you must become you and nothing more or nothing less. To know the rules and play by them is good, yes, but they are all so relative. You see the rules in a different way than I, and I see them differently than you. That is one great mystery between every person and why each is distinct from the next."

"So, the next mystery is?" Adam asked abruptly.

"The next is what creates strength. It is Achad that makes strength. Achad is Unity. When we take two elements and put them together, they have diversity and power to make a third element. They do not unite unless there is passion. Do you know passion?" the Arab asked, with a small smile surging upon his lips.

"Passion is when there is an attraction and desire. It creates love and love makes unity and then we have strength," Adam returned energetically.

"You are following the idea. The next mystery is destiny. When you are awake, when you are a master, you know what destiny means. Before then, you only hint at the theory and belief of it. You have to step outside of yourself to see who you are. Then you have to climb in, like going in a sleeping bag and living in it. Your body is a temple for your spirit. To know your destiny you must master your temple. To do that you must master all of your head and your heart. Then you can see spirit without distortion, then you can see destiny."

Adam could smell the poignant scent of frankincense in the tent and looked to the man with appreciation of learning his principles. The man made a circle around Adam's body with his outstretched arm.

"Inside of you there are thirty-two Kalas. They are polarized male and female organisms. When you learn to connect with the awareness of them, your consciousness will be in the next layer. You will be in a balance and flow through a current that will take you to your destiny. You will open like a lotus and be fulfilled."

"What is your name? What is a kala?" Adam asked.

"I am Ibn Battu. A kala is a time but it is also more than that. It is the many fluids inside of your body. You can produce more of these fluids with the powers of your head. Also, by prolonging the activity of making love you can infuse more kalas. There are tantric exercises for you to learn and accomplish this. The sustained focus will create the additional fluids. We usually focus on kama and that can be a problem. Kama is desire, lust, and volition. It becomes a habit to fill our appetite the easy way. This is because of Maya and Mara. One is illusion and the other is temptation. Control those creatures and do not be blinded to their level of inertia. Love and hate are opposites, yes, and one cannot exist without the other. That is the way it is on the levels they are experienced. This must be balanced with energy guided through you." The old man pointed at Adam. "The energy is directed by your will."

"What did you mean by saying I would open like a lotus?" Adam asked.

"That is the name of the sacred plant of Egypt and India. It is called 'the child of the Universe bearing the likeness of its mother in its bosom'. To go back in time you would see the world as a golden lotus, with peace unutterable and tranquil serenity. To open like a lotus is to blossom your heart and listen to your voice and become with your great guide."

"What of my mind, and the re-awakening I am experiencing through this inquest? It has been like a resurrection to me."

"Resurrection is of Isa and Asar and is a formula we do not use any longer. It is the sanctification of the past, death that has come and gone. Live now through transmutation. The only sacrifice you will ever conceive is to make sacred that which you perform. This is the holiness of your efforts and the key to the next mystery. The climax of prolonged energy awakening has to be exchanged and not destroyed. If there is no exchange, then one or the other becomes the slave. As all things are sacred or capable of being viewed as sacred and the exchange of them must occur in accordance with the level they aspire to. Use the wisdom of the serpent with the innocence of the dove. Our Order here in the Orient is that of the Dove. Our Great City, Al-Qahira, or Cairo is the gateway to the desert. It was once Babylon. Babalon is the Guardian of the Desert and the reflection of immortality in the heavens. Become one with your immortality is the mystery I am revealing to you," Ibn declared.

"What of evil forces and their destructive powers?"

"Evil is where it dwells upon and entangles the heart. The same is of good. Set and Hoor are twins, opposites and one does not exist without the other. Unite them in yourself; cause not division in your nature but control over the darkness with the light. The only freedom is of your soul so be not fixated upon duality or you will be enslaved. Invoke the light within you, through your central pillar of now, aspire in prayer; let the light vanish the illusions of bondage so be it cast away before your eyes."

"What is it that you practice through these mysteries, Ibn? What is it that I must do now?" Adam wished to know.

"I practice thaumaturgy. It means miracles with divine work. Through the spheres of deities and the world of formation where angels reside, the mystic words of Konx-Om-Pax vibrate the ethers as it has in the ceremonies of the Isiac times. The voice of the divine echoes back QUL as a step up the ladder is taken, returning to your beginning. You have met the owl and touched the red earth and now is the time for you to go closer to the Sun so your shadow will enlarge. Your marriage, Adam-Adami will be with the Shekinah, as you walk past the Ashim souls of fire and become one as a child of the Infinite Starry Heavens, Nuit."

Adam suddenly realized that his body was becoming enveloped in a sphere of crimson fluid. Panicked, Adam blurted, "What is this? Something's happening to my body! Can you see it, Ibn?"

"It is to protect you, Adam. You are about to journey through the elements and someone will recognize you for who you are. Your Self has created what has happened to you. Your transmutation is just beginning. What I am about to show you will be something you can do for yourself," Ibn said as his hands reached towards Adam and returned. Adam's mind was suddenly hauled from his body and was suspended in space in front of him. His consciousness carried the vision to be able to look back at his body enclosed within the oval crimson sheath. He could not speak but was aware of what had occurred. By the force of his will he returned to his body and began to talk.

"I can go outside of myself! That was truly remarkable, Ibn," Adam astonishingly remarked.

"You can go outside anytime, and you can go inside of anything you focus upon. Always be one step in front of the other, one layer beyond the one you are working upon. That will set you free from confinement and free to do your work," Ibn suggested.

"I feel freedom, and I feel awake. There is something that I must do," Adam remarked.

"Yes, I know there is. There is something that we all must do. When we step away from the trap, the barrier that prevents us from seeing, we gain the vision to see much more and then feel the need to do certain things. Things that are positive for life, for others, for the world," Ibn noted with a congenial expression.

"I am ready, Ibn. I do not know how this happened or why I was so fortunate to come to this realization in life, but it was for the best and will become the beginning of a new life for me. A life that will be for the accomplishment of my purpose," Adam assured the mystic.

"Now you must go back to the world and use the effect to grow further with it. Your journey will be assured when you work with the mysteries through your heart," Ibn said as they stood up and walked out of the tent.

Adam looked around and could see other Arabs working around the oasis. He could see them in a new light; they were enlightened souls with profound knowledge about the mysteries. The late afternoon sun gave a lustrous illumination that radiated over his oval shield. He felt immersed in protective layers and guided by the light of his spirit. The young boy walked up from the water hole with two camels. Adam mounted on the back of one camel as the boy climbed atop the other.

"Farewell, Adam," Ibn voiced as he raised his hand to the sky, "Hold your deepest secrets and use them wisely."

Adam looked at him and spoke through his heart. The sage heard the subtle voice and knew the destiny of Adam would be discovered this time around.

The boy led the way across the desert sands, returning to the Great Pyramid. Adam thought about life on the return, about what was and what could be. He did not wish to belong to any particular system. He would use all for what it was in his search for truth but would not become cattle to the gods and not adhere to any systematic dogma. Hinduism, Buddhism, Catholicism, and all other religions are specific paths taken by devoted followers. He would take from them the essence of their teachings and use it as part of the spiritual puzzle. He was prepared to fathom the transcendent nature of immortality without the creeds and binding factors of rationalism or the blind eye of stoicism. He was ready to take the beauty from all possible sources in balance and travel the road to his destiny.

The young boy looked back at Adam upon the camel, following in the hoof prints. "It is a… big world out there, right Mister?" The youth remarked with a fond temperament.

"It is very big in many ways. It is a beautiful world but it also has many problems," Adam replied as they made their way over the hot sand dunes.

"Do you… like it here Mister?" the youth asked.

"It is peaceful. Sometimes you have to go far to find great peace. Do you like it here?" Adam inquired.

"Yes, it is very… good for me here. The masters… have taught me much. I would not.. want to leave."

Adam could see that the boy had a pure innocence within him that was protected by a shield similar to his own. He knew that it was important to have such a strong shield when engrossed in society. A shield that had holes in it would harvest negative influences or energies and prevent a person from being fully focused. He contemplated this and many other important factors upon the hot return.

When they returned to the Great Pyramid, the camel lowered to the ground and Adam got off. Adam looked at the youth and together they knew about something that had transpired through their journey. There had been a psychic communication between them about what had occurred during the visit.

Adam underwent a baptism of consciousness. The Templars may associate Baphomet in one sense with Baphe (baptism) and Metis (wisdom), or initiation into wisdom. This is, in essence, what had happened to him. The master showed him who he was, and for Adam it elevated his conscious awareness so that he was no longer trapped inside of thoughts and feelings. He found his center of balance and could shift his awareness any place he directed it to be.

He passed the harness rope of the camel to the youth and the boy waved before returning to the desert with the camels. Adam smiled appreciatively and began walking past the pyramid, down towards the sphinx. The sun began to set over the horizon as he stopped and looked back. Life seemed to be just a little bit amusing and held a twist of comedy in its marveling perplexities. Within the infinite joy and laughter of being embraced by Universal Rapture, he felt deeply tickled and was ready to initiate a significant advancement as each moment flashed into the core of his spirit. He was prepared to commence the adventure of life, embodied with love and liberty through the lustrous light of Babalon within. ★

EMBLEMS OF ANTIQUITY

"Whether we talk of the 'collective unconscious', or the Anima Mundi, or the 'astral light', we are compelled to view each individual as being intricately linked with all his fellows, and indeed with all evolving life."

Magic And The Qabalah- W.E. Butler

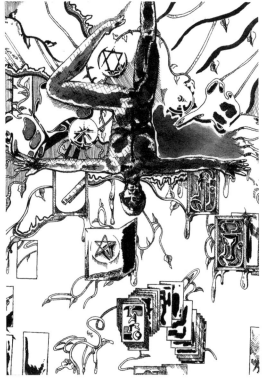

The sun reflected off of the glimmering silver wing and caught Robert's attention to stare into the vast blue sky. Soaring through it at a speed of 731 miles per hour, he looked up at a lady trying to gain his observance. The stewardess had stopped by his seat and asked, "Would you like a drink, sir?"

"Ah, yes, a 7-Up please and thank you," He responded while opening his New Age Tarot book and began reading where he left off. The final card was The Universe. Something about it intrigued him throughout his journey. Its meaning, amongst many other things, meant meeting new people, new places and situations which he was unknowingly about to do. This Tarot card deals with all constellations and as such represents realization of the universe within oneself, similar to the microcosm and macrocosm concept.

It was mid-winter and he was leaving Canada to go on a journey to Brazil. He left his telecommunications job for two months to take a break and make this intrinsic opportunity an elaboration of his interests. For several years he had studied various sciences and facets of the occult and was deeply fascinated with the history of interpreting tarot cards. Like many people, he wanted to leave some mark in the world, by establishing his role in pursuit of his dreams. He was perplexed by endless possibilities and in what direction he should turn. Thus it became a spontaneous decision to go into a land he knew little about with no one there to greet him and without a place to stay. He was simply following an instinct to travel to this particular location, an instinct that built up in his mind. Robert turned the book sideways and glared at the picture of The Universe card. The more he looked at it the more it appeared to be an eye with a person in the center striving upwards or inwards. The color, design and figure engrossed his total imagination as he laid his head back to rest.

The airliner made a sudden jerk as it touched down, startling Robert into awakening. He reached for his carry-on bag and proceeded to enter the airport. He wiped his brow as he entered the warm climate, looking around at the large number of people rambling through the terminal.

"Taxi, taxi, Sir?" an attendant shouted to him as he exited the large structure to the bustling street.

"Yes, take me to a hotel in the city please," Robert responded.

The cabbie picked up his bags and dropped them on the roof rack of the windowless little gray truck.

"Where you from, Mister?" he commented candidly.

"I am from Canada. I am just here on a visit. What can you tell me about your city here?" Robert asked as he entered the back of the cab.

"Oh nice. Canada, nice," Smiled the driver as he walked around the truck and into the driver seat.

"Yes nice, but lots of snow every year," Robert chuckled.

"Snow? What's that?" The driver giggled.

"You know, that white stuff that falls from the skies in huge, never-ending blankets?"

"Oh! Yeah, yeah! We have winter here too in Sao Paulo…last year it was on a Tuesday," The driver smirked, raising his eyebrow. Starting the truck, he added, "Well, this city is ok. I guess, but very poor. People have problems like everywhere. I can bring you to Plaza Park Hotel. How long you stay?"

"I am not sure. I may move around a bit while here. I will be here for a few weeks anyway," Robert responded, staring out at the scenery.

"You should check in at the flats then. Aquaviva flats is good area. 'Sobrados mobiliados com uma entre as praias Grande e Tenório'. It is affordable," The driver suggested.

"Alright, bring me there. Sounds nice," Robert smiled.

"Okie dokie, Mister. Maybe you like Música da Operação Praia Limpa too," The driver laughed.

"Oh, one never knows," Robert rolled his eyes sarcastically, humoring the cabbie.

The scenery was pleasant as the car moved from street to street while Robert felt a soothing comfort in coming to this location. He had meditated one evening and the name of this city came into his mind. He didn't even know what country it was in until he checked in an Atlas. The driver pulled up to the front door of a large white building with balconies stemming off ever room. There were hills in the background and trees surrounded the lush grounds. Robert seemed pleased with the choice so far. "Nice place, thank you," he said with a satisfied tone, "How much will that be?"

"You have American money? Five dollar good," The driver grinned, holding out his hand.

"Oh, here is ten dollars," Robert grinned back, "The Portuguese lesson was worth it, too." He quickly hopped out of the cab and collected his bags, then ran up the stairs to the hotel.

The lady at the reception was pleased to see him. "Good day, Sir. Would you like a flat?" she inquired.

"Yes, I may be staying for a week or longer, I'm not sure," He responded.

"Oh, we have special for one week, for two week, for long as you stay," She smiled to the businessman. Robert turned around and sensed something. He turned back and asked for a room facing the north hills. The receptionist handed him a key and pointed down the hall to the right. "Just fill out this paper and bring back later. Any questions just ask and have nice time, Sir," She said, grinning the way only hotel receptionists can.

The room was refreshing after the long journey. The air conditioning was on and most welcomed. The view of the hills was inviting, almost beckoning for a hike. Robert unpacked and began to shower. He felt invigorated afterwards and got into a horse stance and began some front kicks in the living room area. The long plane ride had drained him and made his muscles ache, but he felt his stamina rise after practicing basic martial arts for twenty minutes. He set up his easel and while sitting forward on the comfortable armchair began to sketch The Universe card on paper. Within minutes he slipped into some trance feeling and the drawing came natural. It was like a mirror of his soul he was looking into. He felt some cosmic union and had a better realization through his feelings of what was happening. The card is represented by Saturn and as such, completion and the burning off of karma. It embodies the idea of transformation, which is why Robert had unknowingly come to Brazil. The card could be likened to a drop of stardust returning to the great infinite universe and the infinite then pouring back into that drop. It was a symbol of the eye of Horus, being one with your original uncontested nature.

He began to sketch out the serpent as he transcended beyond earthly consciousness. The serpent energy was lost with its original poisonous function through the woman in the center of the card who cut through the veils and became liberated. It was an eye opening experience, to draw pictures that he could associate with subconscious complexes and then subsequently release them. Next, he drew the four cherubim at each corner of the card. A few hours had passed and he began to add colors into his creative art. He had no conception of time. He was completely absorbed in the influence and continued on while father time ticked onwards as the rings of power enwrapped him around the Saturn enterprise. The sun began to set over the hills to his left as the red fireball glistened across his canvas. He became exhausted and needed rest. He walked to his balcony and greeted the sun in respect as the Egyptians did so long ago. Turning west he proceeded, "Hail unto Thee, who art Tum in Thy setting, even unto Thee who art Tum in Thy joy, who travellest over the

Heavens in Thy bark at the Down-going of the Sun. Tahuti standeth in His splendour at the prow, and Ra-Hoor abideth at the helm. Hail unto Thee from the Abodes of Day!"

Robert returned to the room and sat in a yoga posture upon the bed. He became uplifted as a sensation of inner radiance swirled up his spine. He breathed deeply and rhythmically into his abdomen as the prana or life force permeated his being. Also known as the chi energy, vital life, bio-energy, astral light, manas, spereima or 'breath of life' and Holy Spirit, his uplifting energy brought forth a psychical cosmic influence which told him he was going to be connected with an influence that would bring him the ability to cause transformations. This inner energy which rooted upwards through his being was spatially extending and vitalizing. He felt it before but never so exhilarating as this time. He felt a radiation permeating on some subatomic level that brought him at spectacular peace within himself. It was an ongoing experience, which seemed timeless, nonetheless lasting an hour in reality. His head tilted backwards as exhaustion overcame him, allowing his body to limply fall on the bed into a somber sleep.

Morning came abruptly as the sun brightened the girders of his soul into a new sparkling appreciation for life. Robert sat up in the comfortable bed and recalled a peculiarly strange dream. He was visiting a house of some strangers and was held down by invisible forces on a throne-like chair. They shaved off all of his hair and then released their pressure on him to stand. At that point, Robert recalled, they took him to a large fountain and plunged his head into the watery fluid to cleanse his past. He breathed in the liquid and it was like breathing a new life with an abundance of force generating throughout his body. He felt extremely athletic and saw a reflection of his true identity as he looked down into the fountain. It was like they had shaved or stripped his personality from past programming, which allowed him to be free of barriers for progression. He looked back on the dream as a significant reverence to his true ambitions. Alert and awakened he was guided by an energetic feeling which got him quickly showered, dressed and off to breakfast in the downstairs restaurant.

The waitress was most pleasant while pouring him a cup of coffee and suggesting he enjoy the morning buffet. A streak of light came from the hill beyond the motel as he sat and ate with a great appetite. It was like someone with a mirror on the hill flashed the sun into the dining area. After breakfast he prepared a backpack and fled to the hill. There was a rough dirt path that widened into a meadow as he proceeded upwards on the hill. He paused and looked behind to see the sun rising over the roof of the motel and took a deep breath then pressed on. He felt so full of energy through practicing yoga for several years, and developing the cerebral-spinal arousal system of kundalini that the life energy gave him an alert awareness of everything on is path. He wore no jewelry except for a unicursal hexagram around his neck. It was similar to a hexagram or two interlaced triangles representing as above so below or uniting the physical consciousness with the divine, meshed between two worlds. He knew he was creating an evolutionary change and that such adventure was for those who made it.

The forest blossoms danced as he mingled into the natural scenery with splendour and rapture entwined in his heart. Everything seemed so wonderful and new. The birds sang melodies, which he could almost translate into a serenity that is too often ignored in daily living circumstances. The sounds of children splashing into water came from over the hill ahead. He arrived at the top and saw a small lake with three children swinging off a rope and plummeting into the water with shouts of joy. He projected a bright smile and sauntered in their direction. They were surprised at his arrival, but didn't appear afraid or disturbed.

"Olá Senhor, de onde é você?" One of the children asked inquisitively as he left the lake and ran up the embankment.

Robert quickly leafed through his translation book. A look of comprehension crossed his face. "Ah, I am from Canada. Hello," He offered awkwardly.

"Canada?" one young fellow echoed. "Você quer-nos mostrar-lhe a casa velha assombra próximo de aqui?"

Robert blinked twice. Flashing through the book he discovered that they want to show him some old, abandoned house.

"Yes, yes, please, show me what you mean, the casa" he replied, nodding emphatically with a huge smile and opening his hands gesturing them.

One of the boys shouted, "A casa é sobre esse monte ao lado do rio!"

The third boy replied in turn, "Você vai lá sozinho?"

He wasn't sure what the young ones really meant but thought they wanted to know if he would go inside the house alone or with them. One little fellow jumped off a tree limb and down beside Robert, shook his hand and pulled him towards the path along the lake. He pointed around the lake to a thick grouping of tall trees. He pushed Robert gently and pointed him to that direction and giggled wildly. The other boys laughed in the background, but the laughter had some angelic happiness in it. He walked around the edge of the lake and looked back, but the children had disappeared. He grimaced and proceeded into the deep dark forest. It was so thick in places that one would swear it was nightfall. Curiosity became his guide, as he had no idea where he was going. He walked for ten minutes at a brisk pace and finally saw some light ahead.

When he exited the wooded area there was a sloping meadow containing the largest rock, which peered into the sky, he had ever seen in his life. It must have been hundreds of feet in length, and at one point forty feet high. He ran and hopped happily across it like a goat-footed god as in the story of Pan, only lacking the flute to bring the melody of freedom to a climax. His heart raced as he danced in his motions, leaping with a certainty beyond faith across the rock ledge, embraced in every step as though each was directed from a higher source. His eyes lit up as the abandoned house came into view. It was nestled on a slope in the trees, with gravel and huge boulders pressed up against the backside. It almost looked buried at the foot of the massive hill of soil built up around it and appeared to be vacant for a long time. The front entrance was barred but there was a side door that hung partially opened. He entered with caution as he removed a flashlight from his tote bag.

There were interesting murals painted along the bottom of the walls inside the first room. They looked like creative expressions of paranormal activity. Strange archaic symbols adorned the artwork. There were some alien looking figures as well, with thick crosses and roses of many petals painted at their centers. Translating hieroglyphics would probably have been an easier task for him. He continued to the next room where he seen an old table with four chairs around it. Cobwebs were everywhere, so he ducked and swept his way through the room gradually. His flashlight shone towards the wall along side the table where a large mirror still hung intact. He directed his flashlight into the mirror and saw a bright reflection of light come back. In the stirred up dust of the room, he could tell that the light reflecting back was not his own. He shook his head abruptly and looked back but the light had vanished. His breathing became more rapid as he sensed some kind of presence in the place. The energy he felt magnified as he moved around the room.

The whole place was in such rough shape and had a capitulating aura about it. There was a bedroom off to the right at the end of a small hall, a washroom to the left and another bedroom to the far left. There were wooden beds in one room, with mattresses that had long been decayed. His flashlight shone into the open closet and he looked up to see a small attic door hidden within. He could feel his heart pounding faster and deeper as he walked closer to the closet. There was something powerful projecting from there and he could not ignore it. It seemed to draw him directly into opening the small door and looking in with his light above his head. There was not enough space to crawl in, but he could reach inside with his hand. He noticed a pile of dirt not far within, which his flashlight brushed across and struck something wooden below its surface. He knocked at it three times and pawed it towards himself with eager curiosity. He managed to grasp the edge of it with his hand and hauled it out carefully.

Dirt fell from it upon his face as he lifted it out. Robert shook his head violently and rubbed the debris from his eyes then opened them to see a small box in his hands. The box was soiled from sitting in moist dirt so long. He knelt down and opened it, with his light shining inside, his jaw dropped. A cloth lay draped over the base of the box, which appeared to conceal some sort of object. As he eagerly pulled off the cloth to reveal the treasure, an unseen force swiftly knocked him to the floor. His head hit the side of the wooden bed slightly as he fell.

Suddenly, a very old set of Tarot cards lay spread on the floor before his eyes. 'How could this be?' He thought. His hands grasped the entire deck of cards, which sent him into a rapid autistic motion, back and forth, with a shrill of excitement. His lateral motions had shivers of extraordinary proportions. He had to drop the cards back within the box. He knew that this deck of cards contained some kind of powerful energy, but could not imagine why. His hand brushed atop the deck as he felt some instantaneous kind of magnetism flow upwards into his arm. He closed his eyes and felt like he had all the tarot cards working at once in his mind. He already knew their meanings and how to read them in a variety of spreads, however he never fathomed having seventy-eight cards in his mind at one time. It was like his mind expanded to a deeper subconscious level. He stood up, held the old oak box in front of him and lit his way to the side door again. He went outside and looked around keeping the box under his arm as he inquisitively checked the surrounding for what possible life had been there in times past. There was definitely something about the house and its history. He took his camera from his backpack and snapped some photos from all angles outside. Wandering back into the thick forest he realized that there was some plan made for him to find this deck of cards. It was no ordinary deck. They had some definite power instilled into them.

The forest held pleasant chirping sounds of birds everywhere. He pushed leaves and twigs aside as he maneuvered through its semi darkness. A large hoot came from a tree above him. Looking up, he saw a magnificent owl staring into his eyes. He stopped and stared up at it thinking of the card The Emperor, the sign of Aries, and the Hebrew letter and path of Tzaddhi. It was an inspiration, as the owl was significant to that path and the card represents a sudden, violent but impermanent activity. Robert's personal energy had reached a climax and became established. The Tower card entered his mind, which represents a generalization of the paternal power that, if persistent, can burn and destroy. He looked back at the house, which shrouded protective forces and yet allowed him to escape with the emblems that would change the life of many.

Robert continued on to the mile long rock. As he goat-footed his way up along its side he stopped at a peak to greet the noonday sun. There was a definite peaceful nature in his smile and manner. He carried on soon to reach his room and continue with his painting of the card The Universe. The colors were vibrant and delicate. He was more pleased with the completion of this card than any other he had already painted. He had dinner in the motel restaurant again and decided to take an evening stroll around the neighborhood. It was a beautiful evening. He watched the upcoming moon from the horizon. It appeared huge and orange. He walked through a nearby park and enjoyed the serenity of the moon reflecting off the river. It was like he was on an astral journey. He moved beyond former limitations in thought and action. He was free with a creative power that was capable of doing much good in the world. He was intense, yet relaxed, intuitive and in harmony. He was, in short, a supreme example of the Prince of Wands.

As evening grew on he returned to his room and enjoyed a refreshing shower. He sat on his bed and held the oak box of cards in front of his crossed legs. He breathed deeply and rhythmically into his abdomen as he opened the box. The cards looked incredible. They actually had some power in them. One can look at any material object and have some influence from it but for an object to actually have such a power radiating from it that one can feel the vibrations on so many levels was extremely bizarre. He picked up the top card and turned it over. It was the Three of Cups. It represented a talent in the arts like painting and music, good fortune in love, hospitality and perhaps a meeting of an interesting nature soon to be. It was a card of Binah, or Understanding and Abundance. The card also represents Demeter or Persephone. Although there are good things in life to enjoy, one must be on an upper level to truly appreciate them and have them work functionally below. He laid the cards gently across the foot of the bed, amazed at their appearance and artistic flavor. Although he was in excellent health and great stamina his body swept in small circles as the influence of the cards began to take over his emotional receptivity. So many things came to his mind but in a balanced way. He was able to see opposites and discern some truth therein. He pondered the twenty-two letters of the Hebrew alphabet, each of which had a major arcana card attributed to them as well as qualities and particular senses attached to them. His mind felt totally at ease and in order. Like a flip chart, his mind went through each letter beginning with Aleph, the Fool and Air. Then Beth the Magus and Wisdom, and so on through the letters and cards. The appropriate qualities of each letter came in order as well. His mind fathomed all of them. Fertility, Speech, Mind, Movement, Sight, Hearing, Work, Life, Sex, Water, Smell, Sleep, Anger, Power, Taste, Laughter, Peace, Fire, and lastly Beauty for the final letter of Tau and its card, The Universe.

What was really happening to Robert? Did his subconscious mind take in a greater understanding of the universe or world he lived in? Were connections being made to be able to direct his will efficiently in any direction for some future purpose?

He laid back to relax on the pillow. The cards were a miraculous find. His eyes closed as he drifted into a peaceful rest. It soon wasn't as peaceful as one would imagine. The cards picked themselves up from the bed and hovered in the air above his body. They lifted one by one and swayed over his sleeping frame. He felt them there and became more aware of them one at a time, as they seemed to develop another dimension. It was as if they were real, like the picture on each card was a doorway into the card itself. It was beyond the strangest thing he had ever experienced in his studies and interests. He could project his mind into any card and become one with the scenery of that card. They had life, and the figures were real. He felt that he could communicate with the cards in an intimate and personal way. As each card flashed around the room in its manifested life form he envisioned the search of what was deeply important to him.

It has been a great journey and there was still so much work to be accomplished. There was a great harmonious energy in the air. The most attracting card to him was Adjustment. His conscious efforts began to soar into the card but the bed suddenly shook in an abrupt and jolting manner. The cards swiftly vanished as the entire room began to shake. Robert awoke and lifted himself to a seated position. He looked at the clock and it was 3:33am. There had been an earthquake. It seemed to have subsided and so he resumed his sleep.

In the morning he felt entirely rejuvenated. He went to the motel diner for his usual breakfast. Sipping his coffee he noticed a beautiful girl sitting at the table next to him, alone. Her long flowing hair and beautiful face took his attention off the earring hanging from her eyebrow. She looked over with a pleasant smile.

"Good morning, are you enjoying your vacation?" she asked.

"Ummm, ahhhh, oh definitely!" He remarked with a giggle.

"I just got here a few days ago and there is so much to see. There is a psychic fair in Sao Paulo this afternoon and I think that I will check it out," She mentioned.

"Oh great! That sounds like it could be fun to say the least. Maybe I should do the same," He replied.

"They have a bus going into the park where it is held at 1pm. Maybe I will see you on it. It will be right out from of the motel, I was told," She smiled knowingly to herself.

"Sounds super to me," He smiled as he lifted his coffee cup and toasted in her direction.

"My name is Lisa," She returned the smile and offered her handshake.

"Very good to meet you, and my name is Robert. What brings you to this part of the world?"

"My travel agent had a great deal on it, and I needed a vacation so here I am," She grinned.

The morning passed quickly. Robert had gone out in the backfield and practiced tai chi for ninety minutes and read a few chapters from one of his books, The Key of the Mysteries by Eliphas Levi. The part referring to metamorphosis intrigued him. To be able to concentrate on the qualities of absorption so that one can direct their rays towards an absorbing focus had some interesting possibilities. To polarize one's own light in equilibrium with the opposite pole and to have a control over how one can change appearance can yield fascinating results. The Qabalah is, in essence, transcendental magic and the science of light, as God is the soul of light. All of the dogmas of religions are based upon some action of the Qabalah, as it was ancient mysteries passed down throughout the centuries. In changing ones form in the body of light, or etheric double, one can transcend the normal realm to venture into the ethyrs and travel the twenty-two paths of wisdom, to gather information for the accomplishment of ones true will and to cat and mouse ones way into an adventurous search of the extraordinary.

It was approaching the time to hop on the bus. Robert gathered his necessary things and proceeded to the motel lobby. Lisa was there, sitting on a bench. She looked up and smiled as he entered. "I am looking forward to this," She remarked.

"Yes, as am I. I haven't seen much since my arrival two days ago," He replied.

They left out the door together and boarded the approaching bus. They sat together in the middle. There were several other tourists, mostly of Brazilian nationality. He offered her a stick of gum.

"Care for some sugarless?" he chuckled.

"Sure thing. Thank you. Do you have any interest in psychics and palm readers?" She asked.

"Yes, in a roundabout way I suppose I do. I enjoy reading a lot and have what I reckon you can call a magical nature in several interests," He replied.

"I see. I guess you can say the same about me. I have something of a mystical nature. More of a passive approach as I enjoy reading horror stories for the rush of what is going to happen. Ghost and UFO writings also curl my interests," She laughed

There was a tangible attraction between them that was undeniable. They recognized the peacefulness and harmony of each other's nature. The bus ride was most pleasant. The scenery was relaxing and homey. They continued their conversation while exchanging an air of gratitude for meeting one another. The bus pulled into a large park where many people were coming and going on bicycles and mopeds. They disembarked and walked into the park that had a large sign hanging from trees that read: Sao Paulo Psychic Fair. She looked at him and grimaced in an unusual fashion. They strolled through the amusement section and wandered around the stands and small tents which had fortune tellers, palm readers, Tarot readers, magic and mesmerism shows, herbal medicines, reflexologists, voodoo and shamanism exhibits, New Age counselors, science demonstrations, and a host of other entertaining activities. There was an old lady pointing to Lisa and beckoning her to come over. Lisa grabbed Roberts arm and persuaded him to follow. She stopped in front of the small tent that had a sign upon it: "Your Future is Known."

"I can tell you anything about your future. What questions have you today for Madame Margaret," The elderly one asked.

"I am sure you can," Lisa remarked smilingly.

"For five dollars I tell you much," She replied, eyeing Lisa mysteriously.

"Robert, that is a deal, wouldn't you agree?" Lisa remarked.

"Oh I am sure you will hear something interesting for that," He chuckled.

The lady grabbed Lisa's hand and swerved her head towards the inside of the tent. Lisa and Robert followed amusingly. They sat in rickety chairs facing a small table where on it were Spanish styled tarot cards, a crystal ball and some small sticks. She looked into Lisa's eyes and quickly into Robert's and asked where she was from.

"I am from America. I would like to know about my future job and about something significant that will happen to me this year," Lisa responded.

The elderly one peered into her eyes, and quickly into Robert's. She wrapped her hands around the crystal ball and twirled her head in slow motions as she began to concentrate.

"Your job will improve soon and you will have an opportunity for a promotion. I see a child in your life. Perhaps you are going to have a child in the near future. Some money will be coming your way very soon. It could be some inheritance," The lady looked up at her for a reaction.

"That is all interesting. Do you see anything else?" Lisa asked.

"Nothing at this moment. There is much more to tell you but it takes time," The lady responded.

Lisa looked to Robert and shrugged her shoulders. He smiled and looked at her. "I see that Lisa will lose her job in a month, she is not going to have any children for several years, and there is no immediate money coming to her in any discernible way. This is, of course, my own vision of how I can see her immediate future. As for Madame Margaret, you are presently suffering an ulcer, and it will get worse in about a week. You must cut down on greasy foods immediately. There is some man coming in your life soon and will try to take something from you. Be aware that truth is the best policy and if you are going to tell someone their future, you should be able to tell your own as well," Robert chuckled and smirked.

Lisa laughed in amazement as she glared at the sincerity in his eyes and truthfulness uttering from his lips.

The lady's eyes bulged out of proportion as she grasped her stomach and leaned forward to squeal, "I think you are right, good sir."

Robert smiled and replied, "Thank you, have a better day tomorrow."

Lisa took Robert's hand and left the tent. "How did you know that?" She asked in amazement.

"There are some things people have gifts of, some that need to be developed and many things which people in general should be made more aware of," He smiled.

"She was way off in left field with her predictions, I am sure." Lisa grimaced.

"Perhaps Madame Margaret indulges in margaritas and becomes a walking mixed metaphor with her meager monotonous messages." Robert chuckled.

"If what you said in the tent is true, do you know where my future will bring me after losing my job?" she asked.

"You will go on a short journey, followed by a longer one. You will feel a greater success after the second journey and will become involved in some greater cause. There will be moderate riches that come your way through this," He replied as his head lowered to eye level and his eyes returned to her.

She was astonished. Somehow there was a truth in what he said, which she could feel deep within. Robert was moderately psychic before, but this day was very special. Certain Tarot cards came to his mind as he thought of any subject and answers came to him automatically. It was as though he was in tune and in touch with his greater subconscious. Almost as though his conscious and subconscious were fused together in an odd way, that allowed him to answer anything on his mind with universal references.

They continued walking along the route. They passed by a tent with a sign above it that read: Madeline's Magical Revelations. A young lady was outside looking at the sky. She looked at Robert and said, "You have a wonderful destiny."

Robert smiled and replied, "I know that now. You have many intense experiences coming also which will bring you soon to Puerto Rico."

Madeline ran up to him and gave him an unexpected hug and responded, "May safeness always be with you. I can tell you are a wonderful, miraculous person."

Lisa was appalled. She couldn't believe the abilities going on around her. She looked at Robert and said, "Would you mind if we sat somewhere for an iced margarita or something?"

"That sounds lovely. There is a great place right around the next set of tents," He responded.

She looked at him as though there wasn't anything he didn't know. He returned the look with a subtle response. "I saw the place on our way into the grounds. I didn't know it was there by any other means," He laughed.

They rested and sipped their drinks slowly. "What is it that you wish to accomplish with these mysterious powers?" Lisa asked.

"There are many things," Robert began after taking a long sip from his margarita, "The world is up for as many changes as it has people. There is much more instability today in peoples lives than there was in times past. People are constantly changing, as social pressures push them forward into a world of uncertainty. Their creative abilities are lacking. They are getting lazier. They are not sure where to go with their life. They are ill educated over overworked in schools and it doesn't amount to many positive results.

"People are not prepared to meet the requirements of their future. Crime and injustice is in an uproar. Economically, there is a fast spinning world, which strives to make more money and give less of a product. Spiritually, the majority of people are not going anywhere. Pollution is devastating health conditions in every country. The world's percentage of drinking water is only one percent because all the ships on the seas dump their garbage and chemicals into the water and literally kill everything within miles of it, every day. Automobiles and mass pollution factories are creating an ozone layer that will eventually burn our skin within seconds of exposure in the future. What is there for our children to grow up to, and their children? How can we stop some of these things? What natural disasters are in wait due to the earth's continued unbalance? With my personal insights and understanding, I wish to get into contact with people that can help. People that can make some changes. Groups that will work together in harmony to make changes for the better. Warn people of disasters to come and prepare appropriately for them. Things which I can see coming. Events which the cards warn me about. I want to take a stand of responsibility for mankind. Bring mother earth back to a balanced, natural state, before it exceeds its capability."

Lisa looked amazed. She looked deeper into his eyes. "That is so noble," she exclaimed, "There are so few people in the world that care enough to do anything. I can really appreciate all the work you must have done to come as far as you have in your studies and interests. Really though, is there anything that can be done to control the masses of people who are damaging our planet so rapidly?"

Robert looked up at the radiating sun as the card of Adjustment came into his mind. "Balance," he replied, "can be regained, but it takes a sincere effort on the inner planes. Many mystics and magicians around the planet are creating an influence as we speak. There are always powers at work. When we evolve and tap into those powers they are used there to create a better life here. When we develop ourselves and are ready for the next step, it comes automatically. We gain a certain realization and move on. In essence we have to change education systems and values in the media. We have to make a great influence to cause this change to occur in conformity with progressing mankind. Everyone is a radiant star and through realizing it they use positive energies to bring harmonious adjustments. It is the responsibility of each person to do that. Then we come upon inspiration and answers to create results, which in turn will bring the pendulum of life back in its proper motion."

Lisa was deeply interested. She knew this would not be the end of their conversations. Months passed and she took a short trip to New York City. She then went to Phoenix for a job offer but decided against it while there and returned to the other offer in New York City. She worked with an editorial company and by the end of the year she opened her own publishing firm. She kept in touch with Robert by telephone, deeply curious as to how he was making out. He sent her an article entitled 'Moving From Within', which he wrote and she thought it quite impressive and published it for him. It heralded the search for Tapping Into The Unlimited Source of Powers while instructing on focusing and channeling the limitless inner strength during that exploration. It became a successful article and was the beginning of their re-connection. She visited him and he went to see her over the coming year.

The following year Robert opened a study hall, which he titled 'Intimate Visions', where people came from all over to learn from guest lecturers and an expanding library of useful literature. It became an increasingly popular vista for seekers of that which is mundanely ignored in society. Lisa was quite exhilarated with how Intimate Visions flourished into such a useful social escapade. Robert had his tarot paintings on display as well as other artwork inspired and created by repeat visitors of the study center. The influx of people streaming through and learning their inherent abilities and accomplishing goals beyond previous ability and comprehension was dramatic. The artistic talents combined with the informative resources paved the road for Lisa to move in with him and begin publishing a consistent journal of the experiences and knowledge gained through the center. They appropriately titled the nationwide journal 'The Center of Discovery'. Through the emblems of antiquity their combined efforts grew to outreach the expressions they fathomed and became an utter success of rewards for the strategic sacrifices they made. The ancient emblems provided Robert with insight into the plight of society and how to make recommendations in all venues of mending earthly discord. They plunged into the depths of self-abnegation and arrived on top by reversing all potentials into joyous victories. ★

NECROMANCER'S PROVIDENCE

"The Church does not deny that, with a special permission of God, the souls of the departed may appear to the living, and even manifest things unknown to the latter. But, understood as the art or science of evoking the dead, necromancy is held by theologians to be due to the agency of evil spirits…"

The Catholic Encyclopedia

The midnight air never stirred so restlessly as the late night's sweeping of the misty breeze off the coastal waters. Frank gulped a red solution into his throat while peering out the balcony window at the murky crashing waves ramming into the rugged petrified shore. He relished in the abominations of injustice and abilities of his power-driven mentality from the high portals of his illustrious Victorian-styled home. His long dark hair matched his unwitting abstract eyes as wind ruffled through his open window. Gazing down at the dismal ocean view he pondered the necromantic event that was soon to take place. It was yet another experience in calling the soul of a deceased victim into the corpse from which it departed. "My tower stands higher than all, greater than all, stronger than all, from the powers of ineffable fixation shall I achieve what is rightfully mine!" he babbled to himself, bent in his self-adulation.

On the ground floor, Jerry Truswell was conversing with Abe Talbot. The latter assured the nervous assistant that all acts of necromancy are harmless and that they will achieve greater powers from the outcome. "Not only that," added Talbot, "But wait until Frank gets the money! We are going places, my friend!" Talbot sneered while nudging the accomplice in the ribs.

"The first time is always rough, I mean," Jerry began to stutter, "I mean, it's like an initiation right? You never know what to expect until the fat lady sings." He laughed off his anxiety.

Nodding, Talbot bent low to rummage through a small black box. "Let us get our items in order. You know how Frank hates us being late for anything. Don't want to get whipped again!"

Truswell had been with the meager group for two months, and although he had barely read any documentation about the act of necromancy, he had faith in his leader who would surely guide him through the ritual safely. Frank was a veteran of thirteen years in the Black Arts and knew his way around demonology and satanic acts quite well. Truswell, about to celebrate his twenty-first birthday, hadn't finished college and lost interest in the hard work involved in studies. He met Frank at a friend's house during a party a few months previous and before long was lured into the cult with promises of becoming an all-powerful wizard in the Dark Secrets of Tenaria. It was a cult created by Frank and he named it such because ten was the number of deeds the novice had to perform prior to becoming an Arianic Wizard. So far, Truswell hadn't accomplished anything that Frank had beset upon him, but he was willing to allow the newcomer to see the advantages of following orders and witness miraculous abilities of stirring evil spirits into revival and obedience.

Frank was thirty-two and had a prolific but scattered library of literature on sorcery, devil worship and necromantic fascination. It would be actually incorrect to call Frank a black magician, but rather a black brother, as he chose to travel the path of self-destruction and drag others along the route. The practice of the extreme black arts held a fond fascination in his heart, without which he would feel lost, unnoticed and uncompensated. The habit of working with evil entities became a thrilling fantasy of escapism for Frank, but held greater pitfalls than advantages. Nonetheless, it is what he knew and it is what he did. He did not mind being a slave to diabolical forces, for all the while he believed to be their master. Frank's fancied axiom stemmed from the words of Milton in Paradise Lost -- "Better to reign in Hell than serve in Heaven." Unlike some misfits, Frank had previous pedagogues from whom he had learnt his tricks. Both High Priests of his previous cult legion committed suicide, one after another within the same year. Their reasoning for suicide was undetermined but likely was a result of being driven mad from the demoniacal entities that drained them and overwhelmed them in evocations. The minor pitfall of death was not of great concern, since selling their souls to such forces was beyond a death experience. Frank, like the two that passed before him, was prepared to pay any price for his unimaginable gains.

Talbot was no worse for wear. He was a High School drop out and never had much success in meeting dignified women. In fact, he never had much success at anything he did, wholly due to his short attention span and obnoxious character. If Talbot had taken to the books instead of losing himself nightly in seedy backwater bars, he could have easily earned his high school equivalency. During his drunken reveries, he suddenly and unexpectedly came up with the idea that finding God would be his only salvation. That same night, Frank wandered into the bar, the taste of corruption and weakness strong on his lips. It did not take much convincing from Frank that he could show Talbot a more profitable way than the legendary ones to God, and that it would take very little effort. Naturally, Talbot was all for it, convinced that Frank was some kind of powerful being sent by magnificent forces to guide him. Once Talbot sobered up, he was hooked. He swore off alcohol and became Frank's most devoted servant, donating all of his time and money to the so-called church of Tenaria. Talbot's appetite got wetter as drugs entered the picture while he dallied with sorcery for several years under the tutelage of Master Frank. In some of their diabolic missions, they had tapped into malignant forces with the perversions of satanic ritual, voudoun, and demonology. Talbot aided his master in several rituals of sacrifice and worship, usually under the influence of LSD or mescaline, which produced the hallucinogenic effect that they had control over the lower realms of demonical elementals and spirits that stirred their subconscious.

Truswell, on the other hand, was simply brainwashed into secrecy by the inexorable group. He was young, and willing to dally in a new experience, and just as unpopular with the women as Talbot. However, unlike Talbot, Truswell was very sharp when it came to rote learning, but he had difficulty applying what he learned due to his seemingly incurable dyslexia. As a result, Truswell came across to the world as foolish and gullible, traits that Frank required of his obedient servants. Unwary of the evil and potentially deadly energy currents that he was getting involved with, Truswell trusted Frank when his newly appointed Master explained to him that his secret society was like a brotherhood for people with special needs like himself. It was a special club where everyone is treated equally, Frank had explained, a club where no one called each other names and one in which everyone stood to profit by donating their unique skills to the cause. "Like the Boy Scouts?" Truswell asked, which Frank confirmed. Two days later, Truswell had joined with Frank's group and swore to never reveal the secrets of the brotherhood to people outside the group.

For 'initiation' into the 'brotherhood', Frank had garnished his devotees with tattered robes that he had previously planted in a grave for seven days. The musty smell of the clothes brought the scent of death into the auras of the students and master, enabling them to be fixated and closer to that which they would return to life. Nine days without washing, living in filth and focused in barbaric deeds was an ordeal in itself. During some nights, Truswell would awaken and vomit next to his cot. This was likely due to the absorption of animal flesh, black bread and unfermented grape juice, which was the daily meal as ordered by Frank for their ritual preparation.

The purpose of the ritual to perform was quite clear. Necromancy sometimes becomes a practice by sorcerers to obtain information about the future or to seek buried treasures. Departed souls traverse on the shadowy realm next to the physical and are not bound by physical limitations, so they can foresee events and have the vision to see through objects, such as soil to seek buried items. They also have closer, realized contact with demons, elementals and so-called spirits of the underworld and for such purposes the sorcerer seeks depraved knowledge through the dead.

In this particular case, Frank's brother, named Henry, had robbed a bank just over a month previous and had buried the full amount of four hundred and sixty thousand dollars somewhere at the rear of the City Park. A week later, the police caught up with him, which ended up in a vehicle chase through downtown. Henry's car had smashed into a city bus, but he escaped and fled on foot across a bridge. An officer shot at him and wounded him, at which point Henry fell into the side rail of the bridge and flipped headlong into the stony waters a hundred feet below. Rescuers dove in and attempted to revive Henry, but to no avail.

Frank didn't show a whole lot of remorse, and the day following the funeral, he and his comrades retrieved the corpse and stored it inside of the deep freezer in the basement of their sorcery temple. If Frank had made a little more effort by foot, he may have finally located the loot, since Henry blabbed about its general whereabouts. Frank could spare no room for error, however, because the police were searching for the stolen money as well. Having little time to waste, he immersed himself in his sick and twisted diablerie in hopes of locating the money before the police did.

Any normal or halfway sane person would consider the act of bringing a corpse to life to be an extremely obnoxious performance, not to mention the dealings with hostile spirits and the putrescence of the rotten corpses to be unbearable by most. Frank and the others did not consider or even seem to be overly concerned with the theory that everything a person does in this life is an investment into the next. But then, gangsters, idiots and thieves are somewhat self-bred vampires that refuse to see the Light and flock to a different shade. One of the greatest and most well known codes of behavior is none other than the Golden Rule: "Do unto others as you would have them do unto you". The new age religion of Wicca has a similar tenet: "And you harm none, do what you will" and is supported by "What you send forth comes back to you times three". These ideas were of no concern to Frank's group and, as a result, no one was prepared for anything as dramatic as what the night's ritual was about to become.

The sound of the grandfather clock clanged bluntly, instigating the three mortals to don their death shrouds and proceed to the chilling basement where the performance was about to commence. Palms were rubbed together in unison with the hopes of cashing in before morning. The drugs required (or believed to be required) to achieve the 'right' state of mind were expensive, and this was perhaps one of the greatest driving forces that compelled Frank into this morbid assignment.

Alone and anxious, Frank fettered about in his room in search of his stash of angel dust. He needed a quick fix before bringing his departed brother back into the world. Below him, on the main floor, Truswell and Talbot clamored around to get the instruments ready before they wandered into the basement.

"Here, kitty kitty!" Truswell squirmed as he reached into the closet to bring out the pet taxi filled with several fluffy, adorably mewling kittens.

Talbot went into the den to grab a selection of candles, ensuring that he had the proper amount of nine violet candles along with a single jet-black candle. His austere glare matched his brutally chapped lips, both of which suffered from the lingering odor reeking from his tattered garments. Delinquency was second nature, as he pondered the past momentarily, like it caught up with him and bellowed in his ears with pangs of suffering clashing in his head. This is how he was bred, raised in a house of constant screaming and dysfunctional appetites for lust, greed and agony.

"Got everything? Let's go and get Henry," Truswell chirped.

"Hell, yeah," Talbot snarled, shaking his head. "Hey, I just had an idea. Ya know, Trus, the planet needs to recycle everything now. Well here I was, thinking again, that maybe I can go around collecting dog crap and meld it together, ya know, like an alchemist?" Talbot began tilting his head, as though looking at something behind Truswell. Nearly losing his balance, he added, "I could, like, grind it up and then add some hardener and sell it to the government. Hell boy, they'd think it were hashish and damn it's gotta be better than the stuff they be smoking there now!"

"That's a, um, mighty good plan, Stan! Maybe then things would change. Wanna partner?" Truswell joked while wagging the cats back and forth.

Talbot stood up and locked his dazed and confused gaze on Truswell. Arching a brow, he mumbled, "Might not need one if we get that money tonight. Come, its 'bout time to warm up the bro!" Talbot then nodded several times to himself.

Walking down the basement stairs creaked blatant noises disturbingly underneath, as though there were a person standing and waiting for the instant to jump out and steal their bodies. Talbot set the candles around the salted circle of protection and Truswell placed the pet taxi within the confines of the circle.

"Damn, he looks like Frosty!" Talbot lurched out after looking in the deep freezer.

"What if he snaps in two when we yank him out?" Truswell deplored in concern.

"Heck, I dunno. As long as his mouth will still work, that's all we need," Talbot lurched again, then huffed warm air into his hands before grabbing the shoulders of the corpse. "Come on, bugger," Talbot heaved and finally got the frozen body out with the aid of Truswell's arms around Henry's waist.

"One piece! We're good!" Truswell remarked as they walked sideways up to the rough floorboards on the ritual platform. Together, they rested the body of Frank's brother into the sacrificial coffin prepared for such ceremonies.

"Oh, Henry, I miss you. Please come soon!" Talbot said and knelt over to give a peck on the head of the deceased.

"Places!" A stern, commanding voice roared from the bottom step, shaking the boys into obedience.

Both Talbot and Truswell skittered across the damp, basement floor to stand in their pre-arranged places. Frank was walking down the stairs, holding a flashlight and looking all the part like Dracula. Without a word, he strode into the center of the circle, and with one swift motion, snapped up an Egyptian dagger from the altar. Glancing at both of his associates, willing them to be still, he inhaled deeply and began his litany.

"Dweller of the Void, be with us as we disturb the energies in here this night!" Frank uttered as Talbot loyally went around lighting the incenses to build the atmosphere. The harsh smell of hemlock, opium, mandrake and henbane soon filled the basement air.

The grandfather clock rang out above them twelve times, issuing the first hour of a new day as they continued the exorcism by entering the circle.

Lifting a long, slender wand from the altar with his free hand, Frank continued his invocation. "By virtue of Holy Resurrection, tormenting of the damned and wickedness of the deceased, I conjure thee, spirit of Henry, to answer me this night! Obey, hear me, come now; listen to my every command! Berald, Beroald, Balbin, Gab, Gabor, Agaba, arise this hour, show yourself under my command!"

Silence consumed the room as the trio paused, none daring to breathe. Hecate, goddess of death, sterility and ghosts was in the midst of the operation. Her influence was felt and drawn into the room. Frank's ravening eyes were shed over the corpse. He tapped the carcass nine times with his powerful wand while projecting his desires into it. On the right of the corpse, a dish of wine, sweet oil and mastic fueled the immediate air.

"Torment of ceaseless pain, wanderer of thrice seven years, by magic rite I inflict the powers to bring thee into sight!" Frank uttered in devout cruelty and hatred, attracting the current of evil in his ignoble solitude.

Truswell held the lit black candle in the confines of the circle, hot wax dripping down its side and over his hand. With perspiration easing from his forehead, curiosity gripping at his veins, and wonderment flogging in his feet, uncertainty sought cavities within his body to nestle. His nerves began to jangle and he became almost painfully uncomfortable. He began to fidget, shifting his weight from one foot to the next. He had never told Frank about his inability to read, and when Frank requested that Truswell study the material for tonight's ritual, he didn't know what to do. He could not have asked anyone outside the circle for help, because he had sworn himself to secrecy. And, he could not have asked Talbot, because Talbot would have undoubtedly told Frank that he was not ready, and Frank would surely have kicked Truswell out of the group, or worse. That was a fate worse than death, for Frank had told Truswell that he would never forget him. The implied threat was some kind of supernatural torment and had kept Truswell silent. So, he had hoped he could 'wing it' and follow Talbot's lead.

Talbot mercilessly grinned at the kittens, still hovering in the corner of their safe house, awaiting their calling. Hapless, enigmatic preludes of villainous jeopardy echoed in the corners of the less trained. With a nod from Frank, both Talbot and Truswell crossed the circle and pivoted, and began chanting in unison with Master Frank, loudly evoking Asmodeus, devil of lechery, sensuality and luxury. With the appearance of one great demon, they would be delivered to a pinnacle of success and ask for its assistance.

Frank bellowed at the top of his lungs, exerting his will onto the forefront triangle. "Asmodeus, King of Demons! I call upon you to make yourself known unto me. As you have defiled unto death the seven men of Sarah, I appoint you with seven carnivores to greet thine required presence. Asmodeus, flare the soul of Brother Henry, my only brother, back into his body so that I may communicate unto him this hour!"

Truswell suddenly jumped as the hallucinogenic drugs from the braziers began to take hold. He swooned and stumbled, dropping the candle he had been holding. It tumbled to the ground and rolled slowly across the basement floor. The candle stopped short of the protective circle, and Frank snorted at the clumsiness of his associate. He suppressed a laugh, trying to keep the solemnity of the rite. The drugs had their own hold on Frank, making him light-headed and paltry. Truswell dropped to one knee, overcompensating for his mistake and tumbled to one side, catching himself with one hand outside the circle. At that precise moment, the lustful creature appeared and stumbled feebly within its triangular barrier, hissing and squalling at the corpse. Its offensive features lurked over Henry as a slimy dark substance emerged from its orifices into the pale face of Henry.

Truswell's' mouth became dry and parched from the sight. He shivered at the sight of uncertainty as an unfamiliar sensation began crawling through his skin. His life energy felt as though it was draining through his eyes and into the wretched devil called Asmodeus. Talbot's mouth however was filled with wretched saliva as he watched fervently the credulous success of his Master.

"In the name of Mammon, come forth and speak to me. I command you!" shouted Frank.

"Heee doooes not speeaak…" Asmodeus blurted in a grating voice. Frank's eyes widened as Asmodeus' figure transformed into a five-year-old boy. The corpse stood motionless and silent as the new figure sought control within the room. "Please help me Frank. They are hurting me. Please, they are tearing into my body and it is so painful, help me… they are hurting me, Frank!" The young voice hauntingly bellowed.

Frank sneered. "Begone false child! Begone from this demon and never return!" Frank uttered in sternness as the assistants looked on with helplessness. The cry of the child dug inconspicuously into his heart. He fumed with the sight, bringing back old memories. His arm reached slightly out of the protective circle in anger as to strike at the image when a voice yelled, "No, Master! Stop!" Talbot leaped from his position, grabbed Frank's shirt and hauled him back before it was too late. Frank's wand clattered to the floor as he reactively pushed Talbot back to his corner.

The child had vanished. Frank regained some of his senses within his addictive stupor. Asmodeus transformed from the child into a vaporous substance and entered the mouth of Henry. Frank groped around for his wand and, finding it, directed it at the base of the triangle barrier and commanded another devil to appear before him.

"Balberith, I summon you to come forth! Move therefore and appear!" The demon appeared as directed and laughed wickedly at the Master. Frank projected power through the wand and responded, "I command thee to awaken the spirit of Henry! Charge him now and bring him to me! Bring him here to speak! I will burn his body to ashes after the commands are met, and none shall bother his sleep again! I charge you to obey now, Balberith!"

The irked and deformed centaur dispersed with ruffling sounds, spreading large cracks throughout the walls and floors above them. Henry's left arm twitched, then moved to his chest. The pupils stared as though a miracle happened while Frank raised his arms to the air.

"Speak to me brother! Where did you put the bank money? Where is it hidden in the Park? Speak to me Henry, tell me where I can find the money!" Frank was both livid and at the height of his euphoria.

Henry's neck quivered as though a vibrating ball was working its way though his esophagus.

"The money, Henry, where is the money you buried?" Frank forcefully projected into the spirit.

One eye opened as the hand reached to his throat. Suddenly it blurted with great effort, "Underrr, beneaaathhh theee doouble youuu…"

"What 'W', where exactly is it?" Master Frank demanded.

"Poooond, biiiiirddds, grooound…" The suffocating beast lamented.

Truswell let out a lengthy grating cough, as the heavy stench was becoming unbearable. Henry resumed his lifeless form in the sudden intrusion of unwarranted noise. Frank looked over to Truswell with a maddening glare.

"You fool! Contain yourself!" Talbot shrilled without warning.

"Balberith, return! I summon you to awake!" Frank harped with a jut of anxiety.

Balberith took his spot and glared at all within the confines of the circle.

"Why is the demon staring at me?" Truswell timidly yelped.

"Shut up and wait!" Frank interjected.

The exploiting monster hurdled around the triangle attempting to further distract Truswell. It was stalling for time. The ceremony lasted too long, complications heightened, and the necromancers wanted to dissolve the operation with the results they obtained. Frank shot his wand in an arcing motion attempting to still the demon. Balberith flaunted about with exasperating cries and wails.

"I curse you Balberith! I curse you with all your descendants!" The devils' eyes enlarged and wanted to lure any necromancer from their circle of protection. It transformed into a seductive, alluring princess and called to Talbot in yearning passion.

Talbot fidgeted and swallowed his drool as he muttered in a gaze, "She's beautiful! She wants me!"

"Shut your mouth, Talbot!" Frank yelled, demanding attention. Talbot wearied of not being compensated and desired to be with the resplendent princess. His mind had wandered, lost in the moment of illusory glory by the sight, and anxious to be loved.

Truswell lost concentrated effort long ago with the presence of Asmodeus and could not resume it to support the operation. He moved to Talbot and pushed him across the circle hoping to rid him of the seductive delusion. In the frenzy, Talbot tripped and caught his pant leg on fire from one of the nine surrounding candles.

"What are you doing? You inept fools! Gather yourselves!" Frank howled.

Balberith contributed to the confusion with his shrill of mischievous laughter and hissing sounds behind his vizard. Frank shrieked and kicked at Talbot to roll on the floor and extinguish the gushing flame from his apparel. Talbot retaliated and in maddened frenzy hauled the dagger prepared for sacrificing the cats and moved to the outskirts of the circle where he could snap at the alluring demonic presence.

Truswell screamed in fear and confusion as he turned to grab the dagger but Talbot knocked him and clumsily fell off the circles' edge. Balberith grasped at Talbot's hand, devouring the skin from it like it was a dipping sauce. Truswell screamed profusely as Talbot dropped the dagger. Frank knocked on Talbot's head with his wand, his anger becoming desperate. Truswell suddenly stiffened, then leapt back on his feet, snapping the dagger from the ground. With one decisive strike, he plunged the dagger deep into Talbot's heart, then kicked him backward into the triangular area… and into the arms of the awaiting demon. A loud hiss filled the room as both the demon and Talbot disappeared in a vaporous cloud. A few seconds later, all that remained within the triangle was a pool of viscous liquid, and an empty skull.

"No, No you idiot! You craving idiot!" blurted Frank as he grabbed at Truswell. In his drug-induced stupor, Frank slipped and fell to one knee with a loud crack. Smiling inanely, Truswell reversed the grip on his dagger and, point jutting downward, thrust the blade deep into Frank's shoulder.

"Charon," Frank cried in pain to the ferryman of hell, "Do not take me…"

Demonical smiles fell heavily into Truswell's eyes. Truswell cried in anguish, dropping upon the floor. His heart beat frantically as he fell with gripping distress inside. His feet kicked out in spasms of uncontrollable frenzy. Something possessed him, something abominably horrid and controlling.

Truswell suddenly felt the urge to run. He darted for the stairs but fell backwards on the third step. Wrought with terror in his eyes, he laid there, looking up from his prone position. Truswell pleaded for his life, "Give me one more chance, I will not defame you!" he yelled, "Let me become pure, let me be free!" He fought for his soul.

As good qualities beget overall positive or favorable outcomes, likewise a torturous nature heaves into the fabric of the soul, blinding it from the source of Light, and allowing it to continue suffering with cursed infliction. Truswell realized this as fragments of his distorted mind clung together, praising that which he had so long ignored. A dense haze appeared atop of him, quickly forming into an unfamiliar demon and transported itself into his body.

All became suddenly silent. His eyes closed peacefully. The demons had vanished. The providence of the necromancer was broken. The soul of Master Frank was taken away as Truswell laid motionless, vacillating in receptive possession. He looked up, wanting to harness energy from beyond his reach. His eyes opened slowly as he sat up and looked around. They weren't Truswell's eyes anymore. They were clotted red, hideous beyond belief. From behind Frank's inert body, a massive force leapt from nowhere and began to gnaw carnivorously into the corpse's neck. It was Truswell, or the vampire entity that now latched into his body. Gorging triumphantly into the meal, Truswell satiated his thirst and leaped up while hissing, "Exurgent mortui et acmo venuient! Baron Samedi!" ripping the soul from Frank, he devoured it while adorning the grotesque Baron of Necromancy. His reddened eyes widened as he headed for the stairs.

It never surfaced in their imaginations that forces belonging to demons inherently perpetuate vices, or the countenance under demonical influence. Drowned in the mire of abominable acts, and lost in the turmoil of avarice, evil takes its toll upon its prankish prey. Turning his head back, Truswell sneered in his blood stained clothes through a face that was once his. The only sound mixed with his footsteps clamoring up the stairs was the cat's meow. ★

THE SOVEREIGN ARTIST

"If attention is directed to the unconscious, the unconscious will yield up its contents like a fountain of living water. For consciousness is just as arid as the unconscious if the two halves of our psychic life are separated."

Mysterium Coniunctionis- Carl Jung

"How can I do that?" Jennifer asked Doctor Wellsley as she scratched the side of her jaw.

"You see, Jennifer, the first thing to consider is that you should try to step outside of your inadequacies and let yourself go," Doctor Wellsley counseled as he adjusted his glasses for perhaps the millionth time. "For the past few weeks we talked about taking responsibility for your happiness and being in charge of where you want to go in life. Everybody has these little programs running around in their head that tells them they can do certain things and not other things. The programs also say, 'I cannot do this or go there', because they have excuses or create reasons to exclude their desires. Excuses range from being about time, money, responsibilities, or inadequacies. This sort of programming has gone on all throughout life. If you notice people changing a lot around you, as you've indicated during our last meeting, it is perhaps the result of them breaking out of one shell and trying something new or different to take a chance on change."

"You always call me Jennifer. My mother would have loved your formality. I've asked you to call me Jenn every time we met for the past month. You are like a friend to me, really you are."

"Yes, I guess you can call it that. I am concerned about your best interests. So, in that case I would be like a professional friend opposed to a casual one." The doctor said with a confident glance.

"You've helped me a long ways since I lost my husband. That was the biggest hurdle to get over. Ever since he was gone for the last year and I finally began dating, but things never seemed to work out. I don't want to get into relationships for the wrong reason. I mean, for the wrong reason for me. I have been able to let go, to begin healing from the loss and pain but what should I do with all of this energy that is building up?"

"Constructive and creative outlets, Jennifer. You told me that you do aerobics three times a week. That is great, and for all of the extra energy you have, you should begin something new for yourself. Develop something that has special meaning to you. Creativity is one of the greatest things we are capable of. Look around and see what everybody has done in the world. Some things good, some not so beneficial; but you can learn from all of it. What's important to you? If you don't know, then write down some ideas, some things you wish to accomplish or create," He urged.

"Well, I am an amateur artist. I usually doodle or paint scenarios of people in situations. That has helped me a lot in my spare time also, not that I have a great deal of spare time, mind you," Jenn replied.

"When you draw and paint, do you ever wish to be in the situation that you are creating? Do you have a feeling to experience something that you haven't before?"

"With you?" she grimaced as she arched a brow with suspicion.

"Not with me; not a good idea. An experience with something that would make you feel good about YOUR life; something that will bring you closer to your dreams, your deepest desires of accomplishment."

"Sometimes, yes," She pondered and then continued, "I see myself living in a beautiful house and having somebody that I can communicate with about really interesting things all the time. Somebody to share the adventure with, you know what I mean. Steve and I had good times and rough times, but we were always able to talk about what meant most to us. Do you think we change over time, so much so that we are not the same person we were during a previous year?"

"In some ways and with some people, yes. Change can be dramatic or it can be subtle. It really depends on what you do and who you are with," the Doctor happily responded.

"OK, I was just wondering because I don't think I was the same person as I used to be. Not that I am completely different, but my values have changed. I realize things that are more important to me now. There are times however that I am still so unsure about what will or should happen. Sometimes I have that need and loneliness deep inside of my stomach. I like to be around my friends but also want my space at times, even though there is a sense of non-fulfillment inside."

"Yes, I know. That is good as well. Everyone needs time to reflect on what is happening around them. Time to ponder and consider the possibilities to make choices that are beneficial in the long run. When you are young it doesn't matter as much as when you pass a certain stage. For some people it is when they are twenty-five, and for others it is younger or older. Values alter and change as our bodies and way of thinking does. Boys sometimes go around feeling they are the kings of the earth, even through their insecurities. When they get older then the testosterone levels decrease and they become more of an androgynous and settled nature. Females go through similar changes with their cycles as well."

"So you are saying that as guys get older they inherit some feminine qualities to their character?"

"In a manner of speaking, yes. We have active and passive chemicals inside of our body and as we mature these chemicals take on a new balance and alter our behavior patterns."

"That's interesting. Maybe that's why people that commit crimes can be rehabilitated in some cases over time. They actually change inside and with the right atmosphere and training they can learn what is proper, such as not hurting innocent people."

"That's a whole new study, but basically true; so you see the point. We change, alter and gradually transform into a new level of the person we used to be. In some instances it is more dramatic as I've stated."

"Alright, Doc, so I am going to work on overcoming my inadequacies. I promise to update you on that one!" Jenn directed with the point of her index finger in the air.

"That sounds promising Jennifer. Is anything else on your mind that you wish to discuss?"

"Yeah, can you just call me Jenn?" she asked while kicking back in the big chair.

"Yes, you win Jenn. So I will see you next week, same time?"

"Maybe, maybe not, but likely," She giggled as she got up and walked to the door adding, "Have a super weekend, you smooth talker!"

"I'll do my best, you too," He smiled while scratching some notes in a book.

"Is that you Jenn?" a voice asked as the door opened in the front room.

"Yes, it's me." Jennifer answered as she came into the house, "How was your day, Cindy?"

"It was great and guess what?" She enthusiastically raised her voice while scrubbing the dishes, "I won some tickets on the radio to go see Heathen Riot this weekend! Do ya wanna come?"

"Who is Heathen Riot?" Jenn chuckled with joy.

"You don't know?" Cindy's face dropped as a plate slipped from her hands into the suds.

"Oh boy, sorry I don't know. Anyway, I have some plans this weekend, but thanks Cindy," Jenn grinned as she walked into her room. She sat on her bed and began to think about what the doctor suggested to her. 'I have to take charge of my happiness and overcome my inadequacies. I have to step over the boundary of excuses and do what is best for me and I will feel better for it,' She thought as she breathed in deeply and dropped her head momentarily. Every time she came from visiting the doctor she would go back to her room and think about his suggestions and was not afraid to confront the therapy that was inevitably for her well being. There is something more refined regarding permanent well being, however, and Jenn wanted to find some answers. Temporary peace is one thing, but what happens when it dwindles away? After all, throughout life, a person is confronted with degrees of problems and perplexities, and to know your Self is to be able to handle them on better feet. Was there such a thing as permanent inner peace? She had to know.

Jennifer decided to begin sketching a picture of what she thought her dreams meant to her. Not the kind of dreams she had while asleep, but the dreams of answering her enigma about becoming a free soul. She sat at her desk and began to draft out the concept. An hour passed and Cindy knocked on her door.

"I am going out with Ted tonight. Be back late… oh and I left some salad in the fridge for you," Cindy said.

"Thank you, and you guys have a great time. See you in the morning." Jenn beamed.

Time seemed to have played a trick on Jenn. Minutes after Cindy had left, it was as though hours had passed. She was engulfed in the creativity of her artwork. It was a drawing of three enormous stones coming out of the ground, hailing over the sky like they dominated the world. She began to paint them shades of gray and black and gave a tincture of flame emanating from their curved tops, into the deep blue firmament. She felt fully consumed in the magnificence of power that the structures in her drawing exhumed.

A knock bluntly came upon the apartment door and startled her. Jenn quickly got up and whisked through the hall to open the front door. There was nobody there. She peeked out the door then stepped out and looked back and forth but there was no sign of any soul. She returned inside and went to the fridge to snack on the dinner salad with some apple juice.

'It can't be wrong to analyze yourself; although we are not perfect, we are certainly more imperfect if we do not seek truth, and to admit you already know truth must be an absurdity. Can we ever really know truth?' she wondered for a moment. 'We can go so far in life and feel content, then block all the questions out of mind; but what will that do besides put us back into slumber, into the ceaseless torment of ignorance and sloth? There has to be a way, a method to find the path in life; an advantage to the search and results justified in working towards it.' She continued to question to herself.

Jenn finished her light meal and went to stare at the drawing in her bedroom. She felt a vague connection to it, as though the drawing represented a primordial conception of time, or the beginning of existence that each person longs to connect to and be associated with.

The week flew by with the enigma still stuck in her mind and then it was once again Friday afternoon and time to make her weekly visit to Dr. Wellsley.

"I don't feel like I have the same problems that burdened me previously. It has become deeper than that really. I long to know who I am inside, and yet every time I analyze who I believe I am, the answers are not enough," Jenn said with a touch of despair.

"Off the record, I can offer you some advice, but this isn't the average information I would share with a client, you understand."

"That's fine with me. Whatever you can suggest or hint towards may be helpful. What I am seeking is something more than comfort, more than information; it is truth, existence, the very ingredient of my purpose," She solemnly declared.

"You are a Sagittarius, correct Jennifer?"

"Yes, and I've read about my astrological profile. That doesn't do a lot for me. I've worked on overcoming the weaknesses of traits that the stars assigned to me," She admonished.

"Combining your astrological profile with tarot correspondences may give you a better glimpse at who you are as a person and what you have to do to remove preconceptions that cause unbalance."

"How is that so? How can you relate the cards to my birth sign?"

"Here is a pen and paper. This time you take some notes." He smiled.

"Alright, I'm prepared." She admitted.

"Sagittarius is a Fire sign, relating to the suit of Wands. For a woman over forty, you would link the Queen of Wands, but in your case, you are well under forty and so you will be the Princess of Wands. The Princess is the Earth sign of a suit and so your representation is the combination of the elements of Earth of Fire. This is your character symbol. Do you have any questions?"

"Nope, I got it." She smiled while raising her eyebrows.

"Your date of birth is the 18th of December, so your personal symbol in the minor cards is the 10 of Wands. Each minor card falls under a certain portion of your astrological sign, called a decan, or 10 degrees of the sign that you come under. Sagittarius for example, begins on 23rd November and from then until 2nd

December, the 8 of Wands, typically called Swiftness is the card for that period. From the 3rd to the 12th of December the card is the 9 of wands, or Strength, and in your case from the 13th to the 21st it is the ten of Wands, also known as Oppression." Jenn's face dropped. "Now don't begin to frown because of the Oppression card, as none are good or bad individually. They are merely a symbol of the challenges that you face during times in your life, or a facet of your personality that you have to recognize and overcome."

"Ok, I can live with that. Oppression is minor compared to some things," She hesitated, then giggled.

"Your archetypal character symbol is the 14th card, Temperance, otherwise known as Art. It is the card directly related to Sagittarius. Think of the moment of your birth as your entrance through the planes of existence into the material plane, and that the stars, planets and all relating elements associated to them had a special effect in the ingredients of your initial boost into this elemental sphere. Their significant yet subtle blueprint marks the basic influences that surround your personality and things you can become aware of in order to find your strengths and weaknesses. If you want to look further into this, there are also associated angels, two in fact, for each decan division - one that rules during the day and one during night, as well as spirits of the Goetia, of which there are 72 in number. That number, divided by two is thirty-six; and there are thirty-six decans in the year; three for each sign."

"Do these angels and spirits have any effect on my life?"

"Yes, they may have an affect in your understanding the qualities impregnated into your manners and attitudes toward things. There is also a preceding and proceeding card. In your case the preceding one is the 9 of Wands which tells you where you are coming from and the proceeding one is the 2 of Cups... as Cups follow Wands in suit and your initial card was the ten of Wands. The 9 of Wands, again, is strength and the 2 of Cups is Love, which tells you what will follow your efforts."

Jennifer continued writing notes to follow up with later research, then stopped and looked up at him.

"Is there something we can aspire towards; something divine as people would say that would communicate its existence to us as an individual seeking the ultimate answers to the perplexity of life?"

"The Ace of any suit is the basis or nucleus of the element it is attached to. In your case, it is the Ace of Wands and is characteristic of the element that your angel connects you with."

"Is this a dream?" Jennifer queried, out of the blue.

"A dream?" the Doctor blinked, puzzled.

"Every morning when I wake up, I feel connected to the world and yet all of my realizations about who I am and what has occurred in my life are like layers; shattered perceptions of the past that no longer exist. You have helped me a great deal to overcome the initial blockages, to accept who I am and what has transpired and enable me to embrace myself, but now there is more for me to accomplish. I am content in being non-content, happy in being saddened and mystified in the glory of reaching further than my limitations of awareness."

"You sound rather positive about your life. What is it in the sadness that allows you to be happy?"

"Everything is connected doctor, don't you see? It is all part of what is and it is up to us to not be blinded by our attachment to it. That's the only way we can transcend beyond what it is, into a world of creation that allows us to move, breathe, and live with certain direction; definite freedom of expression so that we can mold our outcome to our heart's desires," She stared deeply into his eyes.

"You have really considered overcoming your inadequacies, I can tell." He chuckled.

"What is it about my card, Temperance that makes me who I am and what I am trying to achieve?" She asked.

"The cards of the Emperor and Empress become married, unified, in the sixth card, called the Lovers. Your card is the transcendence of the Lovers on another level. It is the effulgent reward of attaining the creative expression from the conversation you can derive with your inner angel."

"What inner angel is that?"

"The one that guides you through life, gives you the knowledge beyond words, the wisdom to comprehend and the understanding to be."

"It is the true form or force that sheds light in the darkest hours, isn't it?"

"Jenn, there is something called the Ominous Night. Basically what it is, is the point where people who aspired a certain way end up giving up. They simply become content in knowing what they do and then feel no need to go deeper into the meaning of their life or life in general. They may praise their faith and their ignorance for what it is without hesitation. They may earth their beliefs and call it an end-all to the quest.

Those are the people who you may consider as having stepped off the path for a permanent picnic and live in the ominous night. If they had serious intent when they were given opportunity, then every now and then something warns them, signals them to seek the path again. Everything that I say can be interpreted a thousand ways and…" he paused, searching for the right words.

"And the best way to interpret anything is the way that brings another question?" She intervened.

"Well, perhaps an answer within a question. Those who proclaim to have all the answers are the ones who stopped and may have enjoyed the picnic too long to know the difference." He grinned.

"You are filled with riddles today, but I see the effect of the Ominous Night within the mind. I am seeking the beginning and end, the cycle that carries on and will bring me closer to making larger steps; greater leaps in my pursuit. The beauty in eternity is in travelling it, and not in reaching the end," she surmised.

"Think of the female as a circle and the male as a point within that circle. What do you have?" he asked.

"Two infinite beings, or two that represent infinities?"

"Well, the circle is never-ending; that is true. The point appears as a dot, but it has extension, into the circles inner dimensions. The point is the direction and focus within the circle. The pair compliment one another in the search, as they playfully mingle along the path."

"There is no one answer to everything is there? I mean, it becomes a responsibility with the more knowledge that you learn through life."

"The many become the one as you aspire on the path."

"I can live with that. I should be going now; there is a place I wish to visit this afternoon."

"Consider this as a discussion amongst friends. There is no charge for such a discussion," He said.

"There is another lesson, Doctor! Money can't buy you happiness, but friendship may. You are filled with good morals and ethics today," She laughed.

"Have a great day Jenn, and a fulfilling life," he said while shaking her hand.

"Thank you for the boost and the focus. I will use it, I promise," she smiled as she left.

Jennifer walked down along the river that flowed through town and sat herself upon the bank of a small hill that had a view of a church on the other side. It was a unique little white church that was built in 1926. In the cemetery that was beside it rested her late husband. She went over the tragedy several times of how he was in the wrong place at the wrong time during the struggle, and gave his life in trying to protect hers from some intruders into their house. It wasn't enough that the burglars were caught and sent to the luxury of prison life, and yet to have their life taken wouldn't solve the wrong that was already done either. Coming to grips with the loss of her partner was something she had fought with over a year to accept, and still there was no convalescence through the extensive healing routine that she underwent.

Her eyes gazed above the distant tombstones, seeking the essence of life above death, the truth to the connection that she held on to and would never let go. There may be no end but another beginning and the purity nestled in the heart of truth may be difficult to touch with open hands and embrace with continuity when half of the equation is missing, but through it all there was something to achieve. Everyone must sense this concern at least once in lifetime, she contemplated. A concern that nobody could understand your pain, your sorrows or the ultimate meanings of your happiness. It is a part of growing and experiencing that we all must face. She thought about what the doctor told her, about the inner angel, the aspiration to converse with it and that it would follow her through life and share the knowledge that was vital to her growth, awareness and inspiration to become focused on the path.

'It has already happened,' she reminisced, 'My angel has sent me messages. I know it has, through feelings, visions, dreams, and thoughts of refinement. Everything matters, it all has purpose and meaning. Even the deplorable entities that roam through society and reek havoc and disdain upon others. They have purpose! We have to wake up out of this dream, this nausea of suffering and stop mutilating the essence.'

A glowing luster emitted through the air particles around her. Jennifer breathed deeply into her abdomen and exhaled slowly, becoming inundated with the vibrations that began taking over her body. The river gleamed with golden radiance as her lips began to quiver.

"Who are you? What are you doing in my life?" she asked the fiery presence that rose from the water-fire.

"Perception in harmony. Combination of success through the fountains of the world springs from the moon to sun. Through rectification to the inner realms of the earth you will find the universal medicine -

VITRIOL."

It was a challenge for her to look austerely inward at herself and to discover the reality of what awaited her discovery. The figure fell back into the river and Jennifer closed her eyes. Her emotions bathed in the creative synthesis of opposite energies, being the sun and moon, solar and lunar fusion that propped the nurturing and regenerative expression of her identity. Although not visibly detectable, she was having a communication in the dream world, an ingenious and concise elaboration of how to ascend the passage of the arrow, the emblem in flight to the sphere of the sun. Her guardian angel resided there in waiting to transfer the knowledge of her initiated alliance with liberty; prepared to decipher to her the link in achieving ambient fuel from her spirit. Her physical body was completely relaxed, free of anxiety and escaped from the emotional bondage that dissolved through the acceptance of who she was.

Jennifer was exhumed by a vitality that she had never before experienced. The number fourteen popped into her head as she felt herself looking back, as though she was seeing with a light shining through her body into the distant space providing the vision for her to see beyond the apparent emptiness. For some reason she began to think that it took fourteen days for the moon to pass from a new moon to full moon and back to new again. She thought of going home to paint the phases of the moon on a canvas and linking them to states of consciousness, but she remained poised in comfort, upon the brink of the absolute brilliance of communication with her angel. She opened her eyes and then it appeared again! Through the light particles that flourished through the air, she could see the vast eminent figure rise from the river, puissant with fiery energy that emitted through its piercing eyes and radiant body. Persistent and enduring patience was the key for her to unlock the mystery of her creation. The Guardian stood resolutely overlooking her with a bond she had never before experienced. "Speak to me, tell me what I must know," She whispered with her eyes locked upon its own fiery gaze.

"Sovereign sanctuary, light of light! Eminence, kudos, love enflamed! Speak within and not above, your star shines bright!" the angel returned.

"I seek within, share with me the reason of being," Jennifer pleaded.

"Edge thyself, move closer now! Whisper to thine heart desires of the flame," It echoed vicariously.

"I yearn to you most sublime presence. I pursue you as the Lord Divine. Where must my path lead?" Jennifer implored.

"Always into you, the path is ever within. Hurl across and divinely free Light of all ambiguity. Hand the arrow beseech thine brow, into the center become the Now!" The angel powerfully decreed.

Jennifer took a breath and swallowed in her throat with a sudden blink of her eyes. The vision had vanished. Majestically inspired, she rolled over on the ground and felt the soft strands of green grass caress her fingers and arms. She breathed in the fresh scent and rolled around in complete content. It was supremely beautiful. A feeling she had sought for a year had come upon her. The ideal sensations of being deeply in communication with Self; a confirmation that something beyond the normal droll of life was in existence. Something that she could contact and achieve meaningful answers for the perplexities she contemplated. She got up and walked solemnly home to begin a sketch of what it meant to her.

'The path is the internal process of clarification, divinely set and met, prepared through the work of harmony.' She concentrated as she sketched out a concept of meeting the internal sun on the path of simplicity through understanding. She faced the challenge, exhumed the universal fountain and consummated the royal marriage with her angel through a creative outlet of expression. Her footsteps upon the soft earth would forever have direction through the guidance of her Illuminated Intelligence with the reconciliation of transmutation. A new light dawned in her radiant loving eyes as she swiftly rose upon completing the sketch and titled it 'The Edge of Forever'. ★

THE INSTITUTE

"…facilis descensus Avenrno; noctes atque dies patet atri ianua Ditis.
The gates of hell are open, night and day;
Smooth is the descent, and easy is the way."

Aeneid- Virgil

The crimson morning sun tinctured everything in sight as it ascended on the eastern horizon. Distant winds echoed through the hollowed atmosphere while thousands upon thousands of people gathered at Mount Vernon Park, in Baltimore, for a variety of festive activities taking place during the memorial day weekend on July 4th. Rachel recently celebrated her 23rd birthday and newly moved from Wyoming to follow up on a job offer at the University of Maryland. Rachel was an only child of good, loving parents who most unfortunately met their end in a tragic collision on icy roads. Rachel was two years of age at the time and survived the accident, perhaps due to being a child and having the natural tendency of relaxing during a sudden jolt or shock. The impact wasn't without recourse however, as it had affected her dreams in the years to follow. Family care in foster homes paved her way to complete an education and get by without any major conflicts during her 'shifted around' upbringing. Rachel's attractiveness flourished with her age. Her long wavy brunette hair and emerald green eyes grabbed the attention of men everywhere, often prompting them to commence casual conversation just to speak with her. Combined with her friendly and trusting demeanor, she was truly blessed with a lavishly glowing character that maintained a charming instantaneous personal magnetic quality.

She sauntered through the crowds sipping Cola while observing boisterous and titillated people coming from all directions. While wandering past the Peacock Observatory she decided that the following weekend would be a better time to go and see why it held world-famous recognition, since this weekend it was horridly overcrowded.

Throughout the park entertainment was ongoing, from clowns and Disney characters to magic performances and comedians. She noticed a young girl walking around and looking up at the sky. It appeared as though the girl was lost, abandoned or had simply misplaced her family.

"Where are your parents?" Rachel asked softly.

"Right over... right…" the girl clamored with sudden anxiety, as she apparently could not locate them.

"We can go to the information booth to send out a message. I will help you, but first let's walk back to where you last saw them, alright?" Rachel suggested.

"My mother told me never to go with strangers," the child resisted, frowning.

"That is a good thing that she told you. I am not asking you to go anywhere with me. I just want to help you find them so you will be safe. I will walk near you as you look around for them, how is that?" Rachel implied.

"Ok, that is fine I guess," the child, lost in emotion, slowly smiled.

They hustled through the hoards of people as the child looked up at all the strange faces and expressions. It appeared that she was about to burst into tears when her eyes suddenly open wide with recognition. "There is Mom! Mom, mom! I'm here!" the child yelled.

The mother scrambled through the crowd as she heard the familiar voice and grabbed her daughter with an almighty hug.

"Where did you run off to?" the mother scorned.

"That girl helped me, Mom. She helped me to come and find you."

The mother lifted herself and looked at Rachel. "Thank you so much. You know how quickly children can run off. It happens only too often. Thank-you for being there."

"You are welcome. I just wanted to make sure she found you again," Rachel smiled and walked away feeling good for having done a good deed.

It was approaching noon as heavy clouds embarked upon the city. Rain was imminent but everyone hoped it would not begin until much later in the afternoon. At the bandstand a huge crowd gathered, as RocKinEra, a hot new music group from North Carolina, was about to perform.

The sprinkle of raindrops began nearly an hour later but did not sway the joy and excitement from the thousands in attendance. Rachel purchased a tie-dyed T-shirt from a vendor and put it over her own T-shirt for added protection from the drizzle. The distant sound of thunder grew closer as Rachel looked into the distance and saw two enormous black clouds emerging from behind the city skyline. Dismal winds shrieked through the Park in a sudden ominous way as to predict a storm surging from the distance. Frowns grew dispassionately amongst the crowd with shrill concerns of losing the celebrations. Compelling winds grew rapidly stronger while the distant raven clouds converged closer, like an omen about to give birth. Then, in a final bout, rain gushed from the blackened sky. Lightning and thunder quickly followed, stirring panic into the hearts of many.

There was no cover to be found in the park. Thousands of unprepared people began running out of the only available exit seeking refuge in nearby street shops. Winds heavily increased with pouring rain drenching everybody and everything within the city and, more dramatically, the overcrowded park. Nobody wanted to remain any longer and the mass decision to hurl out all at once was frantically made. Everybody was eager to escape the cruel and unforgiving weather.

Lightning struck the top of a tree in the park and a power transformer blew, causing sparks to dance along the wires down the street. Frightfully awed, people ran every which way, holding their children in their arms as though they were running with grocery bags. Incessantly, they shoved and pushed to escape the frantic horror in hopes to seek shelter in stores and shops that may be open. Frantic and maddening, with no concern for others, they all rushed through and over one another, in fear that their life would end. It wasn't the storm that was the greatest threat, but rather the culminated panic that became the greatest potential tragedy.

Rachel maneuvered through the crowd, attempting to make her way into a bus stop shelter, but the irrational stampede impeded her every move. Nobody could remember a time when Baltimore ever suffered such a harsh rainstorm as this July 4th, or any other day in any other year for that matter. Concern heightened as lightning hit the branches of trees alongside the road and fire rushed upwards through the limbs. Seconds later, flaming branches began to fall onto the roadway. Herds of intense people, straining to see as they shoved, held shirts and hands over their heads as they bumped and rammed one another in an effort to find some open space. The ravaging rainstorm blew entirely out of proportion like an impulsive twister without warning, heaving its way from the spitting sky.

Each step was a greater calamity for Rachel as she gasped for oxygen, continuing to force her way through the maddening mob. Moral consideration and respect was not an issue. Walking over someone who had fallen to the ground became second nature, lest one would become the next to be trampled upon. People were at a loss to consider anything other than their own comfort, which they suddenly lost.

Rachel did not give in to the irrational behavior. Fatigued and bruised, she looked around slowly while constantly picking herself up from the sidewalk as the hoards trampled over her wearied and wounded body. Her long brown hair was wet and ragged from people using her head for propulsion as they made their way by. She cried in disbelief that people could instantly change from a pleasant character to something so drastic, controlled utterly by panic and fright.

Rachel was fifty yards from the bus stop shelter, struggling to bring herself up but wet boots and shoes stepped all over her like she was part of the asphalt and drove her back into the ground. Thunder echoed in the background as cries of pain came from her reddened lips. Blood seeped from her mouth as she attempted to scream for help but could only let out wheezing painful cries. Crawling and hauling herself off to the side under the stampede, her determination to survive was still alive. Blood ran down her face as cuts on her head increased from muddy footwear. She began using the ankles of the hurdlers as grips to bring her off to the edge of the sidewalk. It was like rushing against the roughest and coldest of ocean waves. She miraculously made it to the curb and gripped on to the metal street lamppost while hearing the yelling and screaming of frustrated escapees. Her mind was filled with fogged visions of savage maniacs rushing in every direction.

The loudest roar of thunder came blasting through the streets as a streak of lighting bolted across the trees, dancing its way through the sparking electrical wires in search of grounding. Rachel's eyes suddenly lit open as she sensed something about to occur. Tops of trees burst into flames as the lightning rod soared into the apex of the lamppost she clung to. It jolted her off of the ground as though she was a weightless rag doll, sending a vibrating voltage throughout her almost lifeless body. The current ceased as her head smashed against the metal post, forcing her body to the ground. Blood from her wounds quickly washed away off the sidewalk and down into the gutter as rain pelted upon her motionless and unconscious body. Nobody appeared to take notice of her as the crowd's focus was scattered in the onrush of chaotic behavior.

The crowded herd of people began to diminish, creating more physical space between each person. Hand in hand, a less frantic couple finally stopped to assist Rachel. A young man roughly of her age was with his girlfriend and leaned over to check if she was still breathing. He asked his girlfriend, Lynn, to summon more assistance and get an ambulance. Rick removed his jacket and placed it over her and supported her head with his hands.

A doctor and two nurses surrounded her bed as Rachel finally awoke. "How are you feeling?" the doctor asked.

Rachel did not respond. Her vision was blurred and she had no idea where she was and could not hear what was being asked. The doctor held her left eye open with his hand and looked into it with a small light. She did not appear to have any reaction to the light. He checked for other reflex actions but they were minimal.

"We are going to need some radiology done. She is not responding to anything. Contact Doctor Metzger and have him examine her," the doctor said as he wrote on the chart.

"Poor dear, don't worry. You are going to be fine soon," The nurse said to her as she tucked Rachel back into the bed sheets.

Rick and Lynn were in the comfort and security of their home, looking out the window at the diminishing storm as Lynn turned to her boyfriend. "Should we stop at the hospital tomorrow and see if she is doing okay?" She asked as she gazed down into the street.

"Absolutely. Let's go in after lunch to make sure everything is fine, dear," He replied with concern.

"That was the craziest thing I've ever experienced in my life, Rick. I mean, why do people have to act so bizarre just because of a heavy rainstorm? She asked in dismay.

"Well, perhaps they feel threatened and insecure. Maybe it is like the theory of an animal being trapped in a corner and such a feeling comes over them that they react without thought, just by rampant emotions. It is an incredible mixed world we live in. So much happens that we are not aware of. Then when something happens and we become a part of it, the awareness of it is a whole new turning point. It just demonstrates that masses of people behave like a herd of animals at times," He remarked, shattered at the thought of the uncivilized civilization.

The hospital attendants attached a monitoring device to Rachel so they could keep a watchful eye of her vital signs during their absence. Her eyes opened and closed through the night but she didn't display any other physical motions. She heard noises but was not sure exactly what they were or where they were coming from. It sounded like people having a conversation at a distance, however there were no people in actuality having any conversations.

On Sunday afternoon, Rick and Lynn arrived at the hospital. In the elevator they gave one another a caring embrace as they went up to the third floor. They walked the hall in search of her room number 315. Rachel's door slowly opened as they peeked in to see her lying there with her eyes staring out the window. "Hi there, may we come in?" Lynn asked.

There was no response. Rick looked at Lynn curiously as they both entered, hoping to brighten the unfortunate soul with a resilient smile. "You are looking better than you did yesterday," He assured her with a soft voice, "My name is Rick and this is my girlfriend, Lynn. We helped you to get to the hospital. It was a bad day yesterday, but today you certainly look better."

Rachel looked at both of them and wanted to say something. Her eyes blinked slowly a few times as she daintily moaned to them, trying to express an appreciation for saving her life. "I am going to the front desk," Rick said to Lynn, "Stay here with her, okay?"

Lynn smiled and tried to uplift the atmosphere in the room as she remained with the troubled girl.

Several minutes later Rick returned with a nurse. Both shared a concerned look on their faces.

"There doesn't seem to be anyone at her address," The nurse explained to Lynn, "We've contacted the police and they went there and spoke with the landlord. He said she moved there from out west a few weeks ago and seemed to be a quiet and pleasant girl. There hasn't been anyone in to see her except you folks." The nurse managed a smile in front of her melancholy.

"We haven't even heard her speak yet," Rick lamented, "We found her unconscious as we were trying to get out of the crazy riot yesterday during the park celebration. What did you determine so far with her condition?"

"Her external physical injuries are not severe. In fact they are healing quite quickly," The nurse responded. The nurse walked to the door and beckoned them to follow her. They all stepped outside the door and closed it. Lowering her voice to a whisper, the nurse continued, "We think she suffered some physiological distress with the injuries as well. She is not responding to any stimulus that is imposed upon her. Her nervous system is still in shock, she is without reaction and unable to speak. The electrical current through her body after the injuries may have compounded the effect and caused additional damage."

"That is so pitiful. She was the innocent victim of a mad panic." Lynn noted.

The nurse shook her head. "Tomorrow, a specialist is coming in to do some more tests on her. He is an excellent psychologist and very proficient in dealing with such mysterious cases that defy computerized and standard physical examinations."

"We can leave our phone number if you would wish a temporary contact for her," Lynn offered, "It is not as personal as someone that she would have known but at least we can be a visitor and a contact for her, until she has recovered. It must be a terrible thing when there isn't anybody out there to show care and compassion during such times of need."

"That is very kind of you," the nurse smiled as she took the phone number from Lynn, "I'll enter it into her medical records for now. You may stay and keep her company if you wish."

"I think we may do just that," Rick smiled. The nurse smiled in return, then turned and headed back to her desk.

Rick and Lynn spent the following few hours sitting in Rachel's room, reading some magazines and having casual conversation, hoping to incite the feeling to her that she has some company. She did not show any response to their presence other than watching them without expression. Before leaving, Lynn gave her a long hug and told her they would return in a few days to visit again.

The following afternoon Dr. Metzger examined Rachel for possible psychological disorders. His examination concluded that her response syndrome was a result of shock and electrical current that caused nerve-paralysis and brain injury. He suggested to her doctor that she be sent to a psychological clinic for further evaluation and that within a week they would have a clear prognosis of her recovery capabilities. He gave the doctor his notes and a number to contact for the clinic receptionist and suggested it be done soon in order that the proper treatment could be prescribed and underway.

The rest of Monday went by without much notice or activity as Rachel scarcely moved in the confines of her hospital bed. She was removed from her IV unit and the nurse fed her some light meals. She attempted to have Rachel move facial and finger muscles for varying periods but the girl needed assistance in each movement to prompt her. Her attempts of communication were still disturbingly indistinct.

Throughout the night Rachel once again heard the voices of people chattering at a distance. She was not coherent enough to realize that the voices did not come from anywhere in her vicinity. She passively accepted it as a normal function of the world in which she was trapped. The voices resembled a group of people calling out to her, but from where, she had no idea. It was a somber comfort to her feeling of utter isolation. She eased back into a content sleep, accepting the outcome of fate.

On Tuesday afternoon the nurses dressed her and brought her in a wheel chair to the ambulance entrance. A driver and assistant were waiting and ready to transport her to Woodleigh Psychological Evaluation and Care Institution. The institute was an ancient structure and once called an Insane Asylum. It was a rather sinister and decrepit three-story building with wings stretching back on each side. In the courtyard between the side wings there were many rows of trees. Its rigid stone structure was evidence that it forbade natures gradual destruction.

The ambulance drove around to the rear entrance and backed up to the loading ramp. The driver and medical assistant opened the back doors of the ambulance and wheeled the bed into the building. Rachel was conscious and looking around at the place she was entering. They delivered her to the receptionist, Mr. Carnivort, who was seated in a small office. His job entailed accepting deliveries and guarding against the potential escape of patients. He was an old looking man, with gray hair and carried a simple disposition in his expressions. The medical assistant handed Mr. Carnivort a sealed envelope, which contained all the particulars of Rachel's hitherto evaluations.

"There are not many spare rooms left inside. She is lucky to get in so quickly, too," Mr. Carnivort said in a loud voice, while eyeing the girl from the corner of his eye as he opened the envelope.

"Everything in order?" The driver asked.

"It all seems to be here," Carnivort exclaimed while he took a pen from his pocket and reached over to sign the delivery sheet.

They transferred her to another bed on wheels, which was alongside the entranceway. The driver patted the side of her bed as they tucked her in and turned to leave. "Rachel, you will be just fine here. They will treat you well I am sure," The medical assistant voiced as he waved to her, then walked out the door.

Mr. Carnivort telephoned the front desk and within a few minutes a lady was there to take Rachel up the elevator to another floor. Rachel was able to differentiate between being in one place and another and cognize what she saw but she was unable to express it in any manner. The nurse hummed a nameless tune as they came out of the elevator.

Rachel looked around the lobby and saw a man sitting in his wheel chair talking to himself with his head against a pillar. It looked as though he was having an argument with the pillar because he would hit his head against it over and over with no apparent cadence.

The lady left Rachel beside the office and entered inside with her file. She talked with the duty nurse then returned to introduce her to Rachel. "Hello, Rachel," she intoned pedantically "I am nurse Devonshore. I will be taking you to your room, to show you where you will be staying. Every morning we will bring you to breakfast and during the day you can visit with other patients in the lounge. Can you understand what I told you, Rachel?"

There was no response for a minute, then suddenly Rachel blinked her eyes. "Maybe she understood," the lady said to the nurse.

"We will know soon enough. Alright Rachel, let's go see your nice new room," The nurse said as she wheeled her down the outlandish corridor.

Rachel was given a room with a caged window view to the backyard gardens. She felt unsure and unsettled inside, not particularly at ease with the atmosphere generated from the Institute. Early that evening, Doctor Heinzinger came to meet her. He was in charge of the facility and although he outwardly expressed a caring attitude towards everybody, inside there hid a mysterious man with ghastly ambitions.

He stood over Rachel as he talked slowly and discreetly to her, all the while patting her shoulder. "You will be just fine here, nothing to worry about. Tomorrow I will do some tests with you, Rachel, and we can see what we can do for you. Don't worry about anything my little child, Doctor Heinzinger will take excellent care of you. Here are some resting pills that will help you sleep soundly. I will see you in the morning for the examinations." He popped the pills into her mouth, then poured down a small glass of water to ensure they were absorbed.

The following morning, the nurse brought Rachel to the eating area for breakfast. Rachel appeared rather drained of energy and more unresponsive than the previous day. The atmosphere was dreary but not disturbing, perhaps due in part to her medication. She didn't appear to be affected by the many other agitated souls. After being fed, the nurse pushed her wheelchair down the hall and into the doctor's examination room. "He will be here shortly, and then we will do some simple tests to find out more about your condition." The nurse said with reassurance.

As if on cue, the doctor appeared from around a bend in the hallway. "Here I am," he said cheerfully, "We are all ready to begin, I see." Surging with self-importance, he placed her x-rays on the illuminator. He then began a series of tests to check her responses and made a show of making some notes.

"It is apparent that she has an inflammation of the sub-cortical membranes and her system is trying to fight off an infection. We will have to begin with prescribing her some anti-inflammatory medication and pay attention to any changes that will give us more details," The doctor ordered the nurse to get the pills as he continued to check Rachel's reflexes.

From his medical bag, he pulled out a needle that was prepared beforehand and asked the nurse to inject her with the medication. Rachel stared at her without emotion as the needle was pressed into her veins. Facial muscles began to twitch slowly as her eyes blinked then closed, falling into a deep torpor from the antidote. "Rest will do her some good for now," The doctor said to the nurse as he packed his instruments into his bag, "Tomorrow we shall begin some rehabilitation practices to regain her muscular control." The nurse nodded, then wheeled Rachel back to her room and placed her into bed.

Early that evening another nurse entered her room and brought Rachel to the lounge area so that she could be around other patients. She looked around the room at the patients who all appeared to be not only mentally ill but also distraught about something else beyond their control.

An old lady that continually twitched her neck rolled up beside her in a wheelchair and began babbling about the presence of evil. Rachel's eyebrows raised as she sat in her somber state from the medication that was earlier injected into her. Two men were scrambling items in a burlesque manner at the backgammon table. There was nothing consistent about their actions except that it was like they wanted to communicate to one another about their distress. Their lack of coordinated effort illustrated the frenzy in their mind and emotions that toiled them in perpetual havoc. A middle-aged lady was pulling at her hair and motioning back and forth while gazing out the window, as if she felt constrained. A thin blond man was rolling around on the floor chanting some words that he made up as he gyrated. Another man was sitting on a chair set atop a table. His hair was greased back and he just sat there looking at everyone else. Every few minutes he would grab his head and shake it with his hands.

"Don't you want to talk with me?" the old lady beckoned. Rachel stared at her as she heard the words and remained motionless. "When they come and get you, don't cry for help. Nobody is going to help you, nobody!" the old lady whined and rolled away in her chair.

Rachel began twitching her fingers on her lap and feeling the material of her gown. Inside she had a longing to break out of the shell that inhibited her actions. She realized her spirit but could not connect it with her body. She felt paralyzed, helpless and without hope. Slowly, she strained her facial muscles to open and close her mouth. It was like a yearning to awaken from a nightmare. Her body was dormant but her spirit was alive and penetrating.

A short pudgy man walked into the room and went over to the blond man on the floor and began kicking him. The man perched atop the table wore a nametag that read 'Christopher', which appeared to have been written in crayon. He sat there as though he was their God, controlling each event. Rachel clenched her fist and tried vehemently to raise her head. She twirled her tongue trying to say something. Suddenly she spurted out to everyone, "Naaaaaaaaaaaa."

A monitoring camera was situated up in the corner. In an office at the end of the hall Dr. Heinzinger was viewing the incidents. A depraved smile frowned upon his face as he looked up and then returned to writing some notes.

Rachel's head lowered to her chest and rested with her eyes open. Attendants barged in as though everything was clockwork and began leading all of the patients to their rooms. As Rachel was pushed down the hall in her wheelchair, she noticed a large gray cat walking down in front of her. It stopped to look up at her with disquieting eyes as she rolled by. Their eyes met and were glued together as if the cat had some contact with her, neither wanting to depart from the other's vision.

During the night she awoke many times and each time fell back to a haggard sleep. The voices that she previously heard when she went to sleep were there again, but they were louder. The sound of a dog barking in the background accompanied the sounds. Loud noises of doors slamming shut came and went during the conversations she heard. A girl began to scream in the distance. It became louder and louder until Rachel suddenly awoke, snapping herself upright to a seated position.

Bewildered, she turned her head to look around, all the while marveling at the apparent return of her motor functions. She tried to move her legs but they did not budge. She could move her head and arms but very slowly. She was awake and still heard doors slamming but knew it was not just in her mind but rather outside of her room that the noise originated. Trying to move her legs off of the bed by grabbing on to the head of her wheelchair, Rachel leaned over and fell on the chair face first. It rolled backwards as her feet dragged on the floor. Mustering all of her strength she pulled herself around and looked up at the wheelchair. Her hands slowly reached for it and began hauling her cumbrous body upwards. Exertion festered from her face and arms as she finally heaved her body into the seat of the wheelchair.

She began recalling the images of hoards of people walking over top of her and using her body as a stepping stone. She became angered, flustered and jaded. Frenetic emotions grew disproportionately while craving to lash out at anything in sight. She realized that she was in a mental institution and remembered faces of the other patients. This psychological domicile agitated her. What was she doing here and how quickly can she prove herself to be released, ran through her head.

Rachel was in touch with a part of her self that she never knew existed. She had the inkling that she possessed some inner sensory perception, which enabled her to know things were happening without seeing them occur. She accepted the voices of people that she heard indistinctly in her head. Her eyes closed and she got a picture of the young blond man kneeling down on the floor with his head between his knees. He was naked and in pain. She nudged her head to the side and 'felt' some large leather strap come down and strike his back. A large black dog came in her vision as though it was watching the man be beaten. She let out a dreadful sigh and lifted her hand to wipe her face. She managed to maneuver her chair a few feet away from the bed, finally having enough strength and control to do so.

Coming from outside of her door she heard a scratching noise. She rigorously wheeled closer to listen to it. Her arm reached towards the door handle. Slowly she turned the knob and opened the door. Stunned as a bird in a cat's mouth, her head lowered to see the gray cat scurrying into her room. Their eyes captivated one another but not as poignant as when they first met in the hallway. The cat jumped up onto her lap and began to purr. Rachel gave a relieved smile as she twitched her nose at the affectionate animal.

There was something more than just animal with that cat, which her mind couldn't fathom. It was as though a spirit had entered it and lived within it, directing it to go places for a purpose. The cat jumped down and sauntered out of the room, pausing at the door to gape back at her before flitting out of sight. Rachel lifted her arms in front of her then spat into her hands. Gripping onto the wheels, she spun her chair along to follow the cat as though it was beckoning her onwards.

Silence filled the corridors as she followed the creature to the far wing of the institute. The lighting was minimal with dim nightlights along the route. Moonlight trickled in a distant window with the fluttering of tree branches disturbing it when she finally brought her chair to a leisurely stop. The cat began walking in small circles outside of a door. She perched her ear to the door listening to see if anyone was in there. A loud thump against the wall shrilled her backwards with a sudden gasp. Mumbling noises could be heard coming from the room, followed by whipping sounds. She moved her head back and forth recalling the slashes that were made upon the man in her dreaded dreams. A commanding voice within the room echoed, "Now! Now!"

Her head raised as a woman's scream resonated with horror behind the door. Rachel knew that by entering the room there was nothing she could do to protect anyone, especially herself, being confined to the wheelchair. In this particular institution, anything could happen and nobody would ever know about it. As her nervous hand rested on the door handle, wondering if she should open the door just to know why she was led there, a sudden twitch turned down the handle and her weight pressed the door ajar.

Her eyes bulged at the scene of a nude woman strapped to a bed with blood spattered all over her body. To her astonishment she caught a glimpse of Doctor Heinzinger's face as it turned in a hooded gown and was busily fantasizing while a headless pheasant dripped blood over the victim's squirming body. He was so engrossed in his performance that he did not realize Rachel was behind him. She backed up and began pushing the wheels as fast as she could to return back to her room. She did not, nor could not turn her head to see if he was following her, as distancing herself from the grotesque scene was the only thing that mattered.

Ahead of her, a man with long black hair exited a room on the left, and walked towards her. She frowned with disappointment and terror of failing to reach her room before being caught. She came to an abrupt stop and the cat ran under her wheelchair. The man walked right on past her, seemingly entranced and not acknowledging her existence. Perhaps he was sleepwalking, but it did not matter. Breathing a sigh of relief, she continued on towards the main hall.

A shadowy figure pacing backwards appeared on the wall ahead of her before she reached the main corridor. She delayed her motion and gazed at the moving shadow only to see it pulling a body along the floor. The indistinct figure sent a chill through her spine as it passed by and vanished. Carefully moving around the corner she frightfully eased towards her room. The cat followed as though it was a companion and came into her room. Rachel closed the door but could not lock it, as there was no locking device. She hauled a chair over by using her wheelchair to forcibly maneuver it and weakly plowing into it, finally nudging it under the door handle. Rachel wheeled herself back to the bedside but was too exhausted to bring herself out of the chair and up into the bed. Feebly, she reached for the blanket and pillow so that she could cover up and rest. The cat jumped upon the bed and began pawing at the mattress, nesting into a long nap as Rachel glared at the friendly critter before falling into the darkness behind her eyes.

Sunlight surfaced and brightened the room, awakening her into recovery and providing her with enough strength to remove the chair from locking the door and returning to the bed. Still fatigued, she resisted lifting her body out of the chair and fell back asleep.

A few hours later the nurse entered the room and found Rachel asleep in her wheelchair. "How did you get down off your bed?" she queried, then raising her voice added, "Wake up! It's time for your medication, Rachel."

Rachel's eyes opened as she looked at the tray with a cup of water and three little cups of pills. There were several more pills than what was previously given. She thought they were doing this to make her more submissive. She knew that it would turn out badly for her if she swallowed them. "You have to take all of your pills if you are going to get better," The nurse asserted.

Rachel nodded and drank from the cup of water, then picked up the cup of the pills. Pretending to put one in her mouth she dropped it in the sleeve of her nightdress, then glanced at the nurse to see if she had noticed. The nurse was oblivious to the trick while she busily made the bed and sorted the room. Holding the cup of water in one hand Rachel proceeded to slip all of the pills into her panties. When the nurse turned to look at her, Rachel raised her hand towards her mouth and simulated swallowing the drugs. Rachel swallowed the last bit of water with a submerging gulp and resilient smile. The nurse looked over and was impressed that Rachel had taken all pills so quickly. "Well you certainly are a good girl today," the nurse praised, "Finally we can see a real smile on your face. Are you ready to go for breakfast now?"

Rachel nodded idly and was steered out of the room and towards the dining area. There were fifteen other patients having breakfast when she arrived. She did not see the girl that was strapped to the bed the night before and neither was the young blond man there either. Christopher, the self-proclaimed 'God' was sitting at the end of one table with an overpowering yet deranged look upon his face. The short pudgy man was sitting beside him, eating his cereal with a plastic fork.

Rachel was pushed to a vacant position at the side of the table, where everything was properly situated for her meal. The nurse then poured her some milk and cereal and delivered toast to a plate in front of Rachel. She stood back and watched Rachel gradually lift the spoon and begin eating. All of the patients gnawed away on their cereal and toast as the nurse turned and walked out of the room.

The old woman patiently entered the room and got some milk, then sat down across from Rachel. "Do you know now?" the old lady bellowed.

"Wha, what?" Rachel managed to stammer.

"They have plans for you, dreary plans. You are really special," The old lady hideously laughed.

Rachel shook her head back and forth with agitation and in disagreement with the haggard lady. She wanted to leave the institute but at the same time she wanted to defeat the demons that worked in it.

The pudgy man got up as the cook came out with a tray of eggs. As the tray was being placed on a table, the plumped one bumped into him to create a startle. The cook told him to go sit down but he went berserk and started smacking the cook with his opened hands, knocking him off his feet and to the ground.

Another worker in back walked out and yelled to the patient, "Get back! Get back!"

With the timely distraction, the cook quickly returned to his feet while the employee rang a buzzer, alerting the front desk for assistance. Two large men arrived within a minute and grabbed the pudgy man, handcuffed him and led him out.

"It's a plan," The old lady whispered to Rachel.

Rachel looked into the old lady's eyes and saw nothing but disgust. She wanted to tell the old lady to go away, but somehow she knew that any attempt to communicate with the lady would be ineffectual. The old one was set in her ways, no matter how disturbed they were.

After eating, Rachel acted less dexterous than she really was and allowed the nurse to wheel her back to her room where she remained all morning. "I will be back to get you at lunch," The nurse said before closing her door, "You probably want to rest now from all that medication." Rachel nodded complacently and feigned drifting off to sleep.

Rick and Lynn were planning on a hospital visit all week but they had been busy with work and had relatives staying at their home. They finally arrived at the hospital on Friday morning and found that another person occupied Rachel's room. They asked at the information desk for the room to which she was transferred.

"She is no longer at this hospital, Sir," The nurse replied.

"What? How is she? Where was she sent to?" Rick was determined to know.

"The psychiatrist had us admit her to the Woodleigh Psychiatric Institution," The nurse told them.

Lynn asked to use the telephone so that she could call the institution. "Hello, I am a friend of Rachel Marden. I would like to come and visit her today, would that be fine?" she asked.

"I will let you talk with the doctor, just one moment and I will connect you," The speaker curtly replied. A few moments later, a gruff voice came over the speaker. "This is Doctor Heinzinger," he growled, "How can I help you?"

"Yes, Doctor. I am a friend of Rachel Marden and would like to visit her today, would that be fine?" Lynn requested.

"I am sorry, Madam," came the reply, "Only next of kin relatives are allowed to visit people that are on the ward she has been admitted to."

"Well, how is she doing? What did you find out so far?" Lynn asked.

"We can not divulge information over the phone about patients, and such questions can only be answered to family members," He trilled as if he had rehearsed his whole speech.

"She has no family members, Doctor! She is alone in the world as far as I know," Lynn exclaimed.

"We treat our patients in the best possible manner for recovery. I am hoping to see her leave the hospital some day fully recovered. May I take your name and number and we will tell her that you inquired?" Lynn gave him the information and hung up with grief. "Well, now what do we do?" exasperated, she asked Rick.

In the course of the evening Rachel practiced whispering the letters of the alphabet, attempting to strengthen and control her vocal cords. She attempted to move her hands and arms under control without spasmodic or jerking motions. She was completely nerved up about the people at the institute not knowing of the evil that was housed within. That grave concern was one of the reasons for her sudden and partial recovery. Her sole mission was to regain control of her body as she had of her mind. She could not think of a plan, but surely if the desire was there to fight for recovery, a plan would inevitably appear in time.

Midnight arrived as she peered out of the window, wondering if anybody cared or knew about her. Suddenly an unfamiliar coldness overcame her. The scent of death was in the aching chill that circumvented her tired soul. She yearned desperately to just fall asleep, into a comforting dream state that would allow her to forget all. Her hands gripped on to the pillow and squeezed it tightly, releasing the frustration that built up inside. She turned carefully over onto her stomach and felt the pang of abdomen cramps wheezing around in torment. Finally she drifted off, forgetting about her anguish and fell into an unconscious slumber.

The door handle cautiously turned in utmost quietness. Silently, the door weaseled opened and was languidly shut behind the personage that entered.

Rachel was still somberly asleep, but in a distance she could hear the familiar voices of before. She wanted to embrace them for help and hoped that they would recognize her cry for assistance. "I am here, can you hear? Can you see me?" she bellowed to the noises, "Help me please, come and see where I am!"

Two feet walked discreetly to the side of her bed. Quickly a hand went over her mouth with a cloth containing chloroform. Her eyes opened as she shrilled out a crying dirge. She twitched violently and struggled feebly before jutting back into unconsciousness. The dark blue sinister eyes that looked over her were those of Doctor Heinzinger. He slipped out the door, hauled in a hospital bed and placed her on it, covering her thoroughly as though she was a corpse. The doctor pushed the bed down past the corridor and into an elevator that had its door jammed open.

The elevator door re-opened on the basement level as he prodded her bed out and wheeled it down the cool damp hallway into a large storage room. Rachel's head twisted back and forth in agitation, attempting to exhale the drug that was forced into her. She opened her eyes and saw Heinzinger looking down at her.

"Why am I here?" She blurted without realizing she could talk.

"You are part of me, you are mine now. You belong to me!" The doctor confirmed with a shrilling voice of derision.

"What? What do you mean? I belong to nobody," Rachel spurted.

"Your soul belongs to me," the sinister man vowed, staring into her bewildered eyes, "I am your guardian, your mentor, and your sentinel. You have a chance, but if you fail me, your soul will be divided and never return to your body. You have seen the others upstairs. They have failed me. I have taken their souls from them. They now live in hideous torment and shall never be saved."

"I feel recovered. I am able to leave, go back, back to the hospital…please!" Rachel begged.

"You do not understand, my child. You can never leave me. I have saved your life! You owe me that."

"Why are you doing this? What do you want?" Rachel started crying.

"I do what I must. Your duty is to fulfill mine; you are on a lower level!" he declared with a scratched throat, and added, "Mine is to fulfill the Dark Prince, the reptile in the underworld that gives real POWER! Never ask questions! You must obey all commands, orders from the High! If you do not, then pain you will know! Pain that will never leave you, pain that will eat away into you forever! Do you understand me?" the Doctor ranted.

"Why are you like this?" Rachel whimpered and convulsively shook.

Heinzinger grabbed her by the throat with his piercing claw and pressed his face tightly against hers.

"You want to know the pain? You want to die over and over? You listen to me! I am the Urchin of all Vampires, the Demon Chieftain of all filth and dark places. I am your only savior but I can destroy you; bring you to the damnation of eternal torment! Obey, listen, obey me always!"

He screamed as his hands went up her face and grabbed onto her hair tightly then ran his tongue alongside her face and to her forehead. "Never ask a question! Never think of what I demand! Just do as I command. Never question me!" he repeated with a disdained smile and repulsive, controlling laugh.

"I will do as you say. Please, don't hurt me… please, don't," Rachel pleaded.

"You will stay here until I can trust in your devotion. If you try to escape or alarm anybody, it will be of no use. Nobody can hear you here. Nobody comes down here. They will all know you have been sent to the hospital today and nobody will check on it. You will be fed and cared for, but only when you become obedient unto me. If ever you try to escape, it will be the last chance you will have. You will never walk again, and your arms will be broken if you disobey my orders," The fiend promised her.

"I do not want to die! You can trust me doctor, you can!" Rachel appealed for her life.

"We will see. We will! I shall be back later today to check on you. Be a faithful disciple," He warned as his eyes lit with fury and slammed the door behind him, leaving her in the dungeon of despair. The dim light went out, as he clicked off the switch from outside her jail room. He knew that sensory deprivation would weaken her and he would soon have her soul enslaved under his desires.

Rachel got off the bed and walked around, trying to feel the walls and floor in the pitch darkness. Everything felt cool, moist, and devastatingly irritating. There was nothing there; the cement walls and floor were deviously desolate. She was trapped in a ten-foot room of utter darkness. No windows, nothing but an old mattress with a black bed sheet, which he left her to keep warm. The foul, moist odor in the air was poignantly repugnant. Rachel fell to the cement floor and began to weep.

"Good morning doctor. Sorry to disturb you, but Rachel isn't in her room," The nurse said as she walked into his office.

"Oh yes, excuse me for not letting you know already. Mr. Carnivort found her in the hallway last night and she was having a seizure. He alarmed me immediately and we got an ambulance to bring her to a medical facility. I went with them and she is fine now. I don't know why the inept doctors send patients like that here. There was no reason for her to be in this institution, really. They must have been duped by her temporary disorder. Anyway, here is her file. I was just amending it and she won't be returning. No need really, she can walk, talk and probably dance by now," He cheerfully expressed.

"That's amazing, but not uncommon. All right doctor, I will update our system and note that she was released to medical care," The nurse acclaimed.

That same afternoon, Rick arrived at the institution claiming to be Rachel's brother and wished to see her.

"She had a seizure last night and was brought to the hospital. She has had a dramatic recovery and will not be readmitted here," The nurse assured him.

"What facility was she transferred to?" Rick requested to know.

"Let me see what the doctor has noted in file." She said as she scuffled through the filing cabinet and opened Rachel's folder. "Oh yes, here it is. She was sent to WestCare Medical at approximately three in the morning," She congenially smiled.

"Thank you," Rick said as he turned and walked out.

Rachel clamored in her uncomfortable bed, trying to keep warm while wrapped in the thin black sheet. She heard footsteps coming down the hall and cringed tightly in fear for her sanity and survival. A key was pressed into the deadlock and slowly turned, followed by the lever shifting to open the hefty portal. The pale light was clicked on and the Doctor entered, staring feverishly at her.

"It is late and I have thought nicely to bring you some water and food," Heinzinger whispered as he treaded in, carrying with him a jug of tap water and some bread.

"When will you release me from here? I will do as you ask of me," Rachel expressed in consolation.

"Do you forget so easily my child? That was another question. You do not want to upset the master, DO YOU?!" he screamed out at her.

"Never," she surrendered, "I will not upset you. Please, give me something, I am very hungry."

He walked over to her after setting the food on the floor, in the corner. His hand softly stroked her long hair. "You are pretty. I can see you through your eyes. I want you to grow to love me beyond all else. Soon you will worship the powers I hold. You will adore the ineffable evil and praise the irreverence of almighty sin. Lust after me, thrill for me, and cherish the wickedness of my commands! This will bring you to freedom, this and only this," He uttered.

"Yes master, I obey." She bowed forward, pleading his acceptance of her submission. She could conceive of no other choice but to play in with his sadistic appetite.

"You may go and eat now. Crawl to your dish, and drink, then eat like an animal," He joyfully commanded, knowing that her continued submissive behavior would eventually lead him to have full control over her mind and body.

Rachel carefully climbed down to the floor and crawled to her dish. She dipped her hand in the water and sipped from her palm. She looked back to smile at him then leant forward to eat the dark chunks of bread he had brought to her. As she ate, he walked over and sat upon her back and leaned his head back, wielding a demonical smile of success. His overbearing weight sent a devastating shiver up her spine.

"My ex-boyfriend used to do this to me," She vented with a tinge of sarcasm.

"You think this a joke? You play with me? Is that what you are doing?!" he vehemently screamed as he leapt angrily off her back. "We will see what happens. I will be back in a few days!" Heinzinger clamored as he slapped her head and walked out, slamming the door once again and shutting off the light.

Buying his affection and upsetting him at the same time was sure to give her some leverage. She knew that it would be of no benefit to her if she gave in unconditionally. But, by slowly piercing into his devastated mentality, she might cause him to slip up and somehow make a mistake upstairs. At least she bought some free time alone, and that is what she really needed.

At noon on the following day, Rick returned to the Institute. He began arguing with the nurse at the office.

"There was no admittance of my sister at that hospital. They have no records of her being brought there whatsoever!" He assuaged.

"Just a minute. I will have our doctor come in and speak with you," She calmly returned.

Doctor Heinzinger came into the lobby and walked to the nurse's station. "What seems to be the problem?" He asked innocently.

"Doctor, I am Rick Marden, Rachel's brother. WestCare Medical has no records of her being brought there. Are you sure that is where she was brought?"

"May I see some identification please, Mr. Marden? He requested.

"Identification? Why in hell do you need it? I just want to find out where my sister is!" Rick demanded.

Mr. Carnivort walked in the lobby and noticed the argument in pursuit and entered the office.

"Hello, I am an attendant here. I hear you are looking for a patient named Rachel. I was on duty that night and found her having a seizure in the hallway. I telephoned the doctor immediately then an ambulance. I saw her leave in the ambulance and that is all I know," Carnivort attested.

"I'm sorry, Mr. Marden, but without proper identification, we are not permitted to give details about patients. You understand, I am sure, with the insecure world we live amongst." The doctor smiled as he touched Rick's shoulder.

In a haze of fury, Rick sent a fiery gaze at everybody and readied himself to lash out at someone. The gray cat walked up to him and rubbed along his leg. Rick shook his head in discontent and asked once again,

"Are you sure you know what hospital she was sent to? I have to find her right away. I haven't seen her since the accident."

"Your identification card please, Mr. Marden," The doctor insisted.

"I forgot my wallet at home, okay? I'm going to be back, I promise that!" he snarled and marched out of the office.

Rachel cringed throughout the day in the bleak black sheet, scouring for a touch of body warmth to keep her from being chilled. Every hour she would get up and walk around the room in circles to keep her muscles coordinated and active. There was no place for her to wash and no toilet for relief. The doctor was completely foul in his expectations. She knew it, and was not about to become his demonic slave. She had to compose herself, otherwise she would blunder and perhaps not see another day. Walking in circles, Rachel held tightly onto her head. "Where are you, I am here, where are you?" she repeated as she circled faster and faster.

Wanting to hear the familiar distant voices of before, she felt that perhaps she could call upon them. There was no hope in anything else, except, except that cat! Yes, she thought, the cat would know she is missing. It would certainly alarm someone like it did to her the other night. Excitedly, she continued pacing in clockwise circles and expedited through her mind the same thoughts, louder and stronger. "I am down here, down in the basement. Somebody hear me. Somebody come and check for me."

"What are we going to do, Lynn?" Rick complained to his girlfriend, "They will not tell me anything more because I have no family identification to show them."

"Talk with the police. Get a phony ID. She has to be somewhere, Rick. Don't just leave it at that. Let's go and I will talk with the police also. There is something peculiar and strange about this. It sounds as if she just disappeared," Lynn augmented.

They walked into the city police department, determined to gain their assistance.

"All I can tell you is that the Woodleigh facility told me that she was sent to the WestCare Medical Center and they have no documentation of her being sent there at all. You can't let this go uninvestigated, officer. She has to be someplace. I am willing to fill out a report, a missing person's report in fact!" Rick assured with concern.

"We will check on it in the morning," the officer said, "Just fill out everything you can on this paper and how to contact you."

The following afternoon they telephoned the police station but were given the excuse that it was a busy morning and nobody had time to check on the report. By nightfall Lynn decided to go and check at the Institute with Rick.

"You stay here," Lynn said as they parked at the side of the decrepit building, "They have already met you. I am going to pretend to be her cousin."

"All right, try to find out something, anything! Just come back with some news," Rick lamented as she closed the passenger side door.

Lynn walked up the front steps and casually promenaded inside. She saw a nurse wheel a patient down the hall and out of sight. There was nobody around anywhere. Gradually she eased her way down the hallway to snoop around. Noises came from behind closed doors on both sides. Her ears touched up against a door as she looked around, keeping a watchful eye for anyone coming.

"They come tonight. They are!" an aged female voice shrilled in the distance behind the door.

"Who is, who is coming?" a man asked. Then silence fell.

Lynn walked across the hall and listened at the other door. "No, no, I am not going." A distraught male voice cried. Suddenly she heard a smashing sound and somebody falling to the floor.

She hurriedly walked back towards the front entrance and looked into the office. Nobody was there. The gray cat came, running up the hallway, and scared Lynn out of her mind. It stopped abruptly in front of her and began purring and rubbing along her foot. It briskly jaunted around her and went down the hallway, halted and looked back at her. Lynn followed it down and stopped in front of it, next to a washroom. The cat brushed up against the door and Lynn looked at it strangely. She opened the door and the cat ran in. She looked around and saw nobody, then walked in to get the cat.

Rachel leaned over onto the bed, pressing her cold hands into the mattress. A thumping sensation began inside of her head. "Come on, come to me! I am here!" she cried inside.

Through her anguish the sound of voices came back. Eyes tightly closed, she spoke deeply through her heart to them. "Answer me please, what do I do? How do I call you?" Something came to her, like a light piercing the darkness. Swiftly she grabbed the end of the bed and pulled it out from the wall. On her knees she crept down and began to feel around. There it was! Pipes! Water pipes that ran across the basement and likely to the washrooms upstairs. She sat on the floor and began banging the edge of the bed into the pipe. She tried to make it sound like a code. She didn't have any idea what time of day or night it was, but it was her only hope, a chance in a million.

"Come back here, you little cat!" Lynn said as she opened a stall door. As she leaned over to grab it she heard the clattering in the pipes. The cat looked up at her. She looked at the cat then at the water pipes. "What," she clamored and shook her head, "is going on?" Quickly she grabbed some keys from her purse and began clanging them against the pipe. There was a moment of silence, then her rapping was repeated by the other person. She clanged three times and then it clanged three times in response. She looked back at the cat. It began to brush up against her. Quickly, Lynn picked the mysterious animal up and ran to the door and back into the hallway. She wanted to find the basement but thought beforehand she should go and tell Rick about her notion. She patted the creature then knelt down and set him on the floor. As she got up an arm came around her neck and pulled her close to a brute body, with its hand covering her mouth. She kicked backwards and struggled momentarily before a needle pierced her side and injected a fluid into her. Her struggle abruptly ceased and her assailant hauled her towards the basement stairwell.

Rick was patting the steering wheel and looking at his watch, wondering if Lynn had any information. Another five minutes passed by and still there was no sign of her. He impatiently decided to go in and check on the situation that may have gotten smack out of control. To his astonishment, the front door of the Institute was locked. He smeared his hand across the small window and stuck his nose on the window to look inside. All the interior lights had been extinguished, and the place was dead.

His heart pounded imperviously through his shirt while emotions took a raw turn into uncertainty. Desperately, he ran to the car and speeded to a service station a few miles down the road. He pulled in like tomorrow would never come and rushed to the telephone to alert the police. Without hesitation he returned quicker than he left and began pounding on the front door of the cynical sanitarium. After a few minutes an elderly nurse opened the door.

"Visiting hours are finished at seven o'clock, Sir," She whispered as his frustration stared her in the face.

"My wife is inside here. She came in over half an hour ago. I've been waiting outside and she hasn't returned yet," Rick argued.

"Nobody has come inside here, Sir. I have been at the front desk and would have seen someone if they came in. Nobody passes by me," She confronted.

"I'm coming in and don't care if you didn't see her. She is in here, so move aside!" He blurted as he maneuvered his way past her and into the building.

"Sir, you can't barge in here like that. I will call the authorities," She warned.

"Save your breath, I already did that. Help me find her, the police will be here any minute," He asserted. Rick walked into the office and looked around. "Well, are you going to help me find her or just stand around and look like you are lost? You do work here, correct?"

"Mister, I am going to have to telephone the doctor. This is an outrage!" The nurse grabbed the telephone and called the doctor but there was no answer.

"You may telephone the whole world. What's your name by the way?" Rick blurted as he walked down the hall, sticking his ear around doorways to listen for any noise. "Lynn, Lynn, where are you?" he shouted.

"Listen Sir, you are going to wake up the patients. Your wife never came in here. I was here the whole time. Now go wait at the entrance until someone arrives," She demanded.

"Where is the doctor? That Heinzinger fellow, where is he?"

"He may be out this evening. There was no answer."

"Yeah, okay, I wondered where he might be. What is upstairs and what about downstairs, is there a basement?" Rick asked, darting from door to door.

"Upstairs are patients, asleep, and there is nothing in the basement," She attested.

"Can we check the basement? I would be quite happy to look down there. Listen, I know my wife is in here, I saw her come in forty minutes ago to look for the girl named Rachel. She has been lost and there is something very weird going on. How do I get to the basement?" he said while walking down the hallway.

"There is an elevator and a stairway," the nurse offered.

"Let's try the stairway. Where is it?"

"The second door down on your left."

Rick opened the old door and walked down the steps. "You may come along also. There might be ghosts down here."

"I am staying up here until the authorities show up so I can tell them what you are doing," She said as he walked down the steps, the door closing behind him.

The basement door squeaked bluntly when he pushed it open and entered the lowest level of the enfeebled building. The dismally damp basement carried a malignant odor that bothered him severely as he wandered slowly down a passage. There was utter silence throughout. There were some open rooms and some closed, locked tight. He came to the end of the passageway and turned around, slowly walking back while listening in the dead silence. He passed the stairwell and went in the other direction. The dimly lit hall offered scant visibility but he could see a door jarred open further down the passage.

Rick slowly walked towards it and pushed it open. There on the floor was Lynn, lying prone and lifeless. He vaulted beside her to check her pulse. "Lynn, wake up, Lynn!" he whispered aloud, shaking her and tapping her face.

He lifted her body from the floor as a noise of someone behind him hurdled in and smacked him over the back of his head with a large, blunt object. Rick fell to the floor unconscious, next to Lynn. The door was shut and locked.

"What should I do with them?" Mr. Carnivort asked Doctor Heinzinger.

"Stay with them. We will have to dispose of their bodies later. Right now there is no time. I sense there is trouble ahead, so keep the passage clear. I have to do some soul sucking right now," The evil-minded doctor said, stammering down the corridor.

He went down the end of the passage and turned right, and walked abruptly towards Rachel's cell. She cringed in the corner as she heard the door opening.

"You have returned. I am so glad. I thought you wouldn't be here until tomorrow," Rachel wailed.

"You are not a disciple. You are a fake, like all the rest were! You are only pretending to be devoted. I can not have this, my child. It is not meant to be!" The Doctor snarled.

"That is not true Doctor. I do as you tell me. I always will," She pleaded.

He walked over to her and grabbed her by the arms. "Come, up on your bed. I must make you a part of me," He scorned.

The police arrived and were escorted downstairs. The nurse walked behind the police officers into the far end of the basement. Mr. Carnivort heard their arrival and locked the door, then quickly hid in a cell across from Rick and Lynn. Rick began to shiver and toss on the floor, awakening from the smash he had received minutes before.

"Is anybody down here?" a voice yelled in the distance.

Rick slowly climbed up to his knees and heard the call. "We are over here, help us!" Rick bellowed in return.

The officer rushed to the dingy chamber and fired their gun once at the lock then kicked the door in. "I was hit in the head," Rick said as the officers entered, "Call an ambulance, my girlfriend is still unconscious. I think there is someone else trapped down here…"

The officers continued cautiously down the passage, listening for any sounds. They heard a voice murmuring in a room at the end of the hall. Hastily they ran and opened the door. The doctor was on top of Rachel on the bed and about to bite fiercely into her neck. Without hesitation, the officer jumped him and hurled his body back, onto the floor.

In Rachel's chamber Heinzinger's head arched back as he let out a snarl of vexation, cursing the world in a mumbling chatter. His head leaned forward and his feet squirmed, attempting to get up and return to his bride for one chomp into her lascivious neck. Rachel cried with relief as the officer knocked Heinzinger in the head with his club, allowing him to fall back onto the floor.

Outrageous yelling bellowed from the end of the hall, causing one of the police to scurry and check the commotion. It was Carnivort wrestling his piece of blunt lumber at Rick. The officer yelled for him to drop it, startling the maniac into running for the stairs. The officer hastened after him, up to the main floor. Heinzinger hurled his weight upon the constable and bit deeply into his neck, spurting blood gushing as if from a hose splattering throughout the room. The doctor's eyes burned with fervent desire as he climbed onto Rachel, quickly wrenching his face into hers.

"It's not over. Come now with me, let's go together." He blurted before spreading his teeth over her jugular vein. Ready to gorge into it, he hissed vehemently as a gun was pointed at his head and shot fervidly into the doctor's skull. Rick's facade appeared in Rachel's vision as blood spattered instantly across the wall with an ultimate last screech bulging from the doctor's tormented dissolution. Shaking like a breeze swayed through her, Rachel clamored to push the lifeless body away from her. The pang of horror rang through her bones as she heard the voices yelling in her head, screaming louder than ever before. She gripped onto her hair and shook her head from the abhorrent cries as debris of effluvium emanated from Heinzinger's massacred skull.

She could see faces within the clouds as their voices expressed relief in being set free. The doctor considered himself to be the devil's son and swallowed the life, soul and essence of those who would never fully obey his orders. Rachel knew the voices she heard signaled her to cast Heinzinger's soul in the cellars of astral purgatory where he would be dealt with by similar creatures. They wanted his soul in their world, on a level that it merited. Rick and Lynn faltered over to her, still in shock, and offered their hand.

"I have been blessed and I will never really know how," Rachel cried as Lynn and Rick held her blood-drenched body between them.

"It was one unfortunate woe after another. Such institutions usually provide the best of care, but whatever happened here will be a mystery the police will solve." Lynn said, drowned in disbelief.

"There is always something wicked out there, and there is always something good to overcome it." Rick voiced as he rested his head upon Rachel's. ★

THE REFLECTION OF EVIL

"If only men could see that almost all that they know consists of the ruins of destroyed towers, perhaps they would cease to build them."

P.D. Ouspensky - The New Model of the Universe

Beams of sunlight danced their way through the upper studio window as Stephen sluggishly rolled around in his bed. Behind him the door slowly opened. Two large green eyes peered into the room and looked directly at him. "Time to get up, honey! We have to get ready and go soon," Kathleen said in a sweet morning voice.

"Is everything packed and ready?" Stephen mumbled while stretching his wearied body. Kathleen rolled her eyes and gave Stephen a sweet smile. "Yes, dear," she grinned as she roughly shook him, "And breakfast is ready as well. We should get to the airport an hour before the flight, so get your bones out of bed."

Stephen growled playfully and pulled her on the bed. "Come here and be my breakfast, you little devil!" He leered as his hands swarmed across her body.

Kathleen squirmed away from him and let out an exasperated sigh. "I'm not in the mood, Stephen, and you know why," she whimpered, "Now let's go!"

Breakfast was meager and before long they were at the airport, standing in line and about to board the jet on their way to Vancouver.

"She may already be back. Try not to worry so much, babe," Stephen asserted as they boarded.

"Someone would have phoned us if she was, Stephen. She has been gone four full days now," Kathleen said in aggravation.

"That's true. Anyway, we should talk to all her friends and maybe get some information from them," Stephen replied with a glimmer of hope in his voice.

"I wish we had gone up to see Susan last weekend on her birthday. Maybe things would be different now, do you think?" Kathleen asked with a touch of guilt in her eyes.

"It was just a stupid coincidence that she went missing on her birthday. Nothing more," He remarked.

The airplane took off into the sun as they sat back looking out the window at the city withdrawing below them. The stewardess walked by smiling at Kathleen as she looked up at her. "May I have a glass of water when you have a moment please?" Kathleen asked.

"Certainly, I will return with it right away for you Miss," The obliging stewardess replied.

Kathleen looked to Stephen, shaking her head back and forth. Stephen inhaled deeply and squeezed her shoulder. "Everything that we do in life causes changes to occur, baby. The actions that precede any incident will affect the course of events. I don't know what to say. Maybe it would have changed the circumstances if we visited Susan but that's not our fault. We can't blame ourselves for something we knew nothing about. Wherever she is, we will find her. I am positive she is all right," Stephen reassured his wife.

The stewardess returned with the water and passed it to her gleefully. "Thank you so much," Kathleen said. Sipping the water carefully she opened a magazine from her purse and began to read, retreating into her own thoughts. She couldn't help from thinking 'what if, what if,' constantly blaming herself for not being there for her sister's birthday, as she promised earlier in the year to be and that Susan's disappearance may be partly her fault. Stephen had already drifted back to sleep, oblivious to Kathleen's constant emotional turmoil over her sister.

People scrambled like mice in a maze throughout the bustling Vancouver airport. One man in particular, walking through the crowd, looked overly concerned. The plane touched down as he waited at the entrance for their arrival. Dozens of people scattered through the entranceway as Kathleen and Stephen walked in and were embraced by her brother-in-law, Jason.

"I'm so sorry, Jason," Stephen lamented, "Is there any more news?"

"Nothing!" Jason spat as he threw his hands into the air. "The police have considered it a missing persons case and said they will notify me of anything new that they find out. They haven't called since they came over yesterday morning to get the names of her closest friends, and anything I could recall about her whereabouts in the days prior to her being missing."

"Did you talk to Melissa today?" Kathleen asked.

"About four times a day. She has been over twice yesterday, and calls every few hours in between to ease and comfort me. She posted Missing Person papers at all the supermarkets and bulletin boards around town and the University. Susan is out there somewhere, I know she is!" He whimpered.

They got their luggage and exited the airport. Driving down the road they crossed a bridge as Jason looked over and said, "I wish there was some way we could get answers to questions that don't seem to have answers for us."

"There is always some way. We just have to be willing to look a little deeper at times," Stephen replied. Kathleen patted Jasons' shoulder from the back seat and asked, "What clues or ideas have been made so far? Does anyone have any suspicions or assumptions?"

"There is really nothing to go on; no clues, no evidence, nothing at all. Like I told you on the telephone the other day, we decided to go camping for her birthday last Saturday. During the afternoon I took a nap in the tent and the kids went to the pool in the campground. Susan said she was going to take a walk down by the duck pond while I had a nap. The kids came in to wake me up and we went out to look for her and couldn't find her. After an hour of talking with people and searching the grounds, we called the police. A search team spent two days combing the area at the campground and came up with nothing. Melissa and her friends have done a lot but still there hasn't been any calls or clues. It almost seems hopeless from the efforts we've made, stupid as it sounds; but I just want something to happen that would help us, some clue to surface…" Jason trailed off, choking back his tears.

The car pulled into the driveway, as they ruefully frowned and exited, appearing sentimentally jaded from the predicament. Entering the house, Jason showed them to their room and said he would meet them in the kitchen when they were ready for a coffee.

"I am a mother, I have children at home waiting for me. Can't you understand that?" Susan begged for her freedom.

"You are wasting your breath, lady," A voice answered through the wretched face of a man with unfortunate stained and crooked teeth, "Here is your meal. We will be back to get you in a few hours."

"What do you people want? Is it money you need? I can arrange to get you some!" Susan pleaded.

"Money? We can get that anywhere. No, it's not money. It is something only you can give us," He sarcastically laughed as he closed and locked her door.

Susan took the tray and sat on her cot. Annoyed and frightened, she began to eat the potatoes and vegetables that they routinely delivered. Her body felt sore in the abdomen and back but she figured it was from the uncomfortable cot she slept on over the past three nights. She didn't have any idea what time of day it was because there was no window in her barren room.

Lying on the bed, she worried about their intentions while waiting to hear back from the smug disciple of the clan. She wished there were some way to send a note or contact her family to let them know that she was alive. Finally she heard someone walking up the hallway and stopping at the door. It became unlocked and opened as she looked up to see a twisted nostalgic face peer inside. The brute tilted his head towards her as an order for her to come outside the room. Susan lifted herself and exited the door for the first time since she arrived. He grabbed her arm and walked down the foul basement hallway, which resembled an abandoned school building.

"Where am I?" she asked her assailant.

"You are back in school, back, back forever," He gasped repugnantly.

"It seemed so much brighter when I was a child. What the hell happened?" Susan said, trying to free her arm from his tight grasp.

"It's the way things have become. I'm only the receptionist. Now, walk faster. Logos hasn't much time to wait!"

"Who? Logos?" she questioned as she stepped up her pace.

At the end of the hall, she walked up some stairs and down another hallway, where he steered her into a vacant room. The uncouth membrane of a menace forced her into a small chair at a child's desk and stood next to her. "Sit here and wait. He will come," The captor leered.

Dressed in attire fit for a mongrel, in walked a tall, slim man with a long, hawk-like nose. His dark, mousy hair was cropped short and slicked to one side. Though his frame looked wiry and frail, one could tell that he walked with confidence and an air of superiority. He smiled a gap-toothed smile as he entered the room. Glancing at Sarah, he licked his thin lips and placed his attaché case on a nearby desk. Standing to his full height, he ran his hand through his hair and said, "I am Logos, and together we are heralding the Anathema Age of Elimination. I welcome you to join us in the coming race of civilization. You may wish other plans, such as to be with your family, but that is not possible. Think of yourself as one of the pioneers of Anathema. We welcome you."

"I don't want to be a pioneer of any Anathema or elimination! I want to go now!" Sarah wailed.

At that instant, Susan heard a thrashing noise through the hallway. Logos hissed and reached into his attaché case, while his foul-mouthed assistant withdrew a pistol from under his jacket. Suddenly, three black-garbed figures kicked the door in and burst into the room. Without hesitation they began shooting at the Logos and his assistant. Logos dove for cover as his assistant jerked spasmodically, taking three shots in the chest. One of the men slid over to Sarah and motioned for her to follow him while the other two kept Logos pinned behind a desk.

As the pair sprinted down the hallway, the hooded man said, "Come with us quickly, there are more of them and they will chase us before long!" Shortly, they reached a fire exit, where a black car awaited their entrance. The hooded man ushered Sarah into the back of the car, then hopped in beside her and slammed the door shut. Abruptly, they drove away from the school and into the country to a recluse haven removed from neighbors and regular traffic.

Sarah was shaking violently as she was overtaken by the emotional hurricane that she had been forced to endure. The hooded man removed his balaclava, revealing a clean-cut man in his late-twenties. "You have to tell us everything you know," he comforted as he offered her a thermos full of warm tea, "They will be after you for the rest of your life. We are a protection agency, sent by a secret organization of informants in the government that have investigated them for a long time."

"What do you have to know? Why did they take me in the first place?" Susan asked, sipping nervously at her tea.

"The only way for us to sort out the enigma is if you tell us everything you possibly can. Why do you think they took you? What have you done in your life in the past year?"

"Raised a couple of children, got remarried, nothing overly dramatic, why?" Susan asked.

"We already know they have contacted your family and took them. The world is at the crisis stage right now. We are a special branch of the government, sent here to recapture those that are being hunted and held hostage by such elite organizations, wishing to conquer the freedom of civilization. You have to trust us in order that we can protect you and keep you from them. Do you understand?"

"What about my family, friends and life?" Susan interjected.

"It is not safe, Susan! There is a plague going on and people have been infected by it." The agent told her about the serious threat and commerce of mankind that was at stake and explained that they would have to do certain tasks as a team to keep the vile forces away for her safety and to help others in the same predicament. Susan was perplexed yet began to believe in the critical importance of her required assistance in the agency to prevent contamination from becoming rampant and spreading into it. They briefed her on the intricate strategies that the Order of Anathema was inducing into society and the importance of her awareness of them.

"You will see it everywhere! In the media, television, people talking and conversing secretly... the contamination is being widespread and very harmful! You have to be extremely cautious, Susan! It is like a vacuum. They have placed intense control mechanisms into every walk of life. If you ignore it, you will not become contaminated, but if you indulge in listening and becoming involved with it, then you will grow to detest it even more and end up running back to the agency, seeking protection."

"What am I to do in the meantime?"

"My name is Agent Carruthers and this is Agent Smythe. If you have any problems, let us know. We will brief you daily and instruct you on methods to become unsusceptible to the infections that are being generated."

"Alright. I hope there is something positive I can do to help," Susan admitted, feeling concerned and obliged.

"There will be several things for you to do. We will give you a partner to work with. She is knowledgeable about the plight we are dealing with here. This is a very serious matter," The agent continued with briefing her on what to do and signs to become aware of in the dangerous society.

Kathleen looked sharply at Jason as he made a suggestion. "We can post her photograph on television, on the news, and get people involved. Someone has to see her somewhere. Someone out there will detect something, realize something wrong somewhere and contact us, I am sure of it."

"That's a great idea! That will add to the flyers that Melissa already distributed." Kathleen replied.

The doorbell rang and Jason jumped up to answer it. Standing outside, a young woman with sandy blonde hair and freckles greeted him with a worried yet determined gaze. "Melissa, glad you came over," Jason smiled, "Susan's sister is here with her husband. They just arrived." Melissa walked in and was introduced by Jason to the guests.

Melissa removed several sheets of paper from her tote bag and spread them out on Jason's coffee table. "Look, I've scanned her photo in color and made copies of it as a Missing Person and added information on contacting us," she offered, holding up the flyer, "I used both your number and mine, if that's alright, Jason."

"That is great of you. They are much better than the ones we already sent out!" Jason said, giving her a hug.

"Kat and I can help post them around the city tomorrow. I want to be involved in any way I can," Stephen acknowledged.

"That's super, Steve, and I appreciate it. You know, strange things like this happen all the time... but inside, I really feel that Susan is still alive and well. I wish there was something I can do to confirm it. The children are not taking this very well at all. It's very traumatic for them and gets more difficult to explain everyday," Jason mentioned, looking down into his coffee.

"We will check in with the authorities tomorrow and get this case moving faster, don't worry," Melissa said as she softly touched his shoulder.

Susan worked diligently with Jill in the garden. She was her cohort and also under protective custody with the agency. Together, they pulled up vegetables in preparation to make the agents their evening meal. It had been a few days of rigorous work, but she had acclimatized to the routine and schedule they set up for her in exchange for her safety and commitment to the secret organization.

"Why don't we do the shopping as well?" Susan inquired, wiping her brow.

"Are you kidding?" Jill asked incredulously. "If we are seen in public, we may not be capable of handling what would happen. There is mass destruction going on everywhere, girl. We have to be very careful and keep a low profile or we can get caught and contaminated like most of society. You know that. I've explained it to you yesterday," Jill looked up to her with weary eyes.

"Why do you sometimes go to agent Smythe's room at night, Jill?" Susan asked, plucking up lettuce from the garden.

"They haven't explained it to you yet? We are going to help by procreation as well. It's our job to prepare a new civilization. He says there are others in different parts of the world doing the same job and that one day we will all be united, but for now it has to be a covert operation," Jill confirmed as she stood up with her bucket.

"I don't know if I am ready for that. I do want to help but this is all so new to me," Susan admonished, shaking her head slightly.

"You'd better get ready soon, darling. Every minute counts and we have to do what is best for the organization!" Jill exclaimed while gesturing her to head back to the house, nestled quietly at the end of the field.

From the upstairs window Smythe looked over to Carruthers with a diligent smile.

"When are you going to begin with her? She looks like a real sweetie, brother," Smythe beamed.

"A little more programming first. I want to make sure I have her indulge in it whole-heartedly. You know what we did with the last one, so I don't want to slip up again. It's happened all too often. You must admit though, little brother, I am getting good at this." Carruthers smiled complacently.

"The old is destroyed to make room for the new. That's our motto and we do it well," Smythe said, grinning from ear to ear.

Melissa came running into Jason's house, apparently excited with some news. "What's all the huffing about?" Jason asked.

"Turn on the television! The news is on and they are going to make an announcement!" Melissa gasped, trying to catch her breath.

"Hey guys, come on down, you have to see something!" Jason yelled to the guests upstairs as he ran for the remote control.

"Susan Jardine, who has been missing now for eight days, was last seen at the Tranquil Peaks Campground on Saturday, July 21st. If anybody has seen this woman, or has any information about her possible whereabouts, they should contact the nearest detachment of the RCMP. Susan has shoulder length blonde hair, light blue eyes and is of medium build and stands five feet seven inches tall…" The News Anchor said clearly.

"That is a good recent image of her," Kathleen sadly voiced.

"Well, with that and the four hundred flyers we posted all day, something may happen," Stephen affirmed in a positive tone.

"I hope so. I'm glad that her mother took the kids today. It is nerve-wracking enough trying to get everything done without seeing their dispirited faces all day and trying to comfort them," Jason sighed.

"It's getting late. We should catch some rest and begin again tomorrow," Kathleen suggested.

"You have done well all week Susan! You are a promising woman for the agency. Tonight, I shall allow you to come to me. Tonight is your night to prove your loyalty and love to the coming race." Carruthers leered into her eyes with his hands over her shoulders.

"I will honor the agency." Susan affirmed as he escorted her into her room and turned to close the door.

"I will welcome you. Come to my room in a little while and I shall be ready to initiate you." He vowed while closing her door silently with a hidden smile.

The heat of midsummer sweltered through the rooms with everyone asleep, turning and twisting in their dreams, traumatized by their plight of uncertainty, and stirred with fear and concern for their loved one. Jason shook abruptly at the sound of the telephone. Quickly his hand reached over to his night table and grabbed it answering, "Yes, hello?"

His face lit up with astonishment. "Are you sure? Where?" He continued, and then paused. "When will we know? Can I meet you there?" Jason asked, listened, then hung up and ran out of his room. "Everyone, wake up!" he yelled while lurching towards the guest room door.

"What's up, Jason?" Kathleen asked in a bleak, half-asleep voice as she and Stephen stepped out of their room.

"You are never going to believe this. I just got off the phone with a Sergeant Liebscher from the city police. They received a call from a mailman that said he saw Susan. He said he saw her while delivering mail outside the city, not far from Langley and she was working outside of a house!" Jason stammered with enthusiasm.

"Working outside of a house? What in heaven's name for? Why on earth would she be doing such a thing? Doesn't she know there is enough housework here to do?" Kathleen jumped in with a pompous rant.

"That's incredible, Jason. Did they give you an address or any more information?" Stephen asked.

"No, they wouldn't. It is an investigation and they just said they are heading over there now and will contact me as soon as possible. I can't sleep anymore. But you guys go back to bed and I will bring you more news when they call back," Jason said.

"Yeah, as if I can sleep. Coffee time!" Kathleen growled, as she was the first one to wiggle her way downstairs rather enthusiastically.

Susan was asleep in her room as two police cars quietly pulled into the driveway. Eyes peered through the window, noticing their arrival, and became alerted with the sight of four officers stepping out of their vehicles. They slowly and methodically approached the walkway, working in pairs to secure the front of the building. The lead man knocked bluntly upon the door. Without hesitation it was opened to the yawning face of Jill.

"Good evening, what may I do for you?" Jill asked, in a stupefied daze.

"Ma'am, we are searching the neighborhood for a missing lady," The officer said as he held up a photograph of Susan.

"Oh my, that looks like my cousin. Her name is Lisa," Jill noted while straining a view of the photo.

"We have confirmation that this lady was seen here very recently. We would like to come in and look around. We have a search warrant," The officer said as the one behind him held out the paper.

"Well, my cousin was visiting," Jill yawned again as the officers barged past her and began to search. "Couldn't you come back tomorrow? It's quite late and was a busy day for me."

"Do you live with anyone, Miss?" Asked another officer, who was holding a flashlight.

"My boyfriend is here, but that is all," She admitted laconically.

"Miss, why is there four bedrooms with four beds presently unmade in them?" An officer asked from upstairs.

"I... I haven't had a chance to do the laundry since my cousin left," Jill stuttered at a loss of words.

Exiting from the washroom was Agent Smythe. "Good evening, what seems to be the problem?" he said while brushing back his hair.

"We are looking for a missing person. Have you seen this lady anywhere?" A voice came from behind him as the photo was held near his face.

"It sort of looks like Jill's cousin, but I can tell it's not," Smythe replied with a flick of his brush.

"May we have her cousin's name and address, please? It's imperative we find this woman as soon as possible," A hasty request came.

"Ah, sure. She lives in Calgary. Actually, she just moved there not so long ago. Just a minute while I get her new address," Smythe said as he walked towards the den to retrieve some information.

An officer on the stairs heard a noise from above. His head turned upwards, followed by his body. Quickly, he pivoted his body and ran up to see what it was.

"Tim, I believe I heard someone sneeze up here," He said as his face disappeared at the top of the steps. Another officer ran up after him and they softly walked through the rooms once again.

"Susan, Susan Jardine! Are you here somewhere? This is the police, if you are here let us know, your family is waiting for you. Susan?" One of the officers said sternly with composure.

"There, behind the wall!" His partner yelled as the sound of a muffled sneeze came through the wall.

"Move the dresser!" he added as his hands wrapped around a corner of it. From behind the piece of furniture they saw a drape on the wall. His hand brushed it aside and within the wall cavity they saw Susan nestled in terror. "Don't take me, I don't want to die!" She cried.

"You are not going to die, Susan. Everybody is looking for you. It's time to go home," The officer assured.

"I will get contaminated, no, please leave me! I want to help the organization. It's my duty!" she beckoned.

"They sure did a number on her, Lenny!" Officer Tim Mahoney said to his partner as he gently held Susan and ushered her downstairs.

"Where is that other fellow at?" Lenny asked the officers downstairs.

"He is in the den, getting an address," Tim replied as he stepped out of the dining room and headed towards the den. When Tim entered the den, he slid his sidearm from its holster and gave the room a quick scan. He noted that the window was open and that the accomplice had vanished.

"You guys search the grounds! He can't be far!" Lenny yelled as he cuffed Jill and made a call for reinforcements and an investigation team to come and assist.

"I wish I had heard something by now but I can wait, as long as it's good news," Jason said to Stephen as he sipped his coffee.

"It sounded promising. At least it was a lead, so let's keep our fingers crossed," Stephen remarked.

"They will call us one way or the other, even if it wasn't her but I feel good about it," Kathleen added. Jason stirred as the telephone rang. "Yes. What? Really?!" he said as the guests looked on with concern. "Can we come down to see her? Tomorrow? Why?" He shouted suspiciously.

"What's happening, Jason?" Kathleen questioned, her voice suddenly becoming panicked.

"Okay, thank you very much," Jason ended as he slammed the receiver down. "They got her!" he yelled with a jump in the air, catching Kathleen and Stephen in an embrace on the way down.

"What did they say?" Kathleen asked.

"She was somehow programmed by a couple of cult people and has to be deprogrammed by some specialists. They said it might take a few days but we can see her tomorrow. She is afraid for her life. They won't allow any visitors tonight but told me to come to the station tomorrow. She is in good health and unharmed," Jason yelped with tears of relief.

"Oh, my god! That's a miracle!" Kathleen added to his excitement.

"I have to make some telephone calls now. I want to let Melissa, our parents and friends know," Jason said with anxious enthusiasm.

The following day at noon, Jason appeared at the police station with Kathleen and Stephen. They were directed to the detective's office and were counseled about the situation.

"You may see her, but won't be able to talk with her for a few more hours," the detective cautioned. "You may come with me and have your friends follow us, Jason. Susan is at a detention center under special care of psychologists." The detective concluded as they got up and prepared to leave.

"What kind of people did this?" Jason asked as they drove through the city streets of Vancouver.

"I hate to use the term loosely, but it is something of a small cult organization. There were two main operators and they are somewhere out there. We have good descriptions of both of them and have dispatched patrols to search for them. Susan wasn't the only one we rescued last night," the detective said, looking over to him, "There was another girl. She had been missing for six months."

"What did these people expect to gain from kidnapping? Why would they do this?" Jason asked.

"To be honest, my friend, I am not so sure. Their reasoning is not like ours. Maybe it was a game to them; maybe they thrilled in the misuse of power over other people. It's hard to determine the reality of such minds that have motives as twisted as their actions," The detective voiced as he pulled into a parking lot with Jason's car behind them.

Kathleen and Stephen anxiously got out of Jason's car and walked alongside Jason and the detective, into the building. Together they entered an office and spoke with Dr. Copeland.

"How is she doing, Doc?" Jason immediately asked.

"Not too bad, considering all the mental programming she has undergone. They apparently used hypnosis on her repeatedly and it may take a few more days here before we release her," Dr. Copeland noted, adjusting his glasses.

"Has she been harmed in any way?" Kathleen inquired.

"Not to our immediate knowledge. She has a few bruises along her ribcage area and upper back. I suspect they did some shrewd physical programming to her body along with her mind. She fears being contaminated by society. She was somehow put into a trance to believe that she was being rescued by this alleged little cult, called the 'Agency'. It sounds like something from the 1970's with the cults that sprung up around then. De-programming is a serious awakening back to reality and it is going to involve some efforts on your part as well." Copeland declared.

"We will do whatever it takes. Can we see her now?" Jason asked.

"Come, it would be good for her to begin recognizing a familiar face," The doctor nodded.

They walked down the hallway and through a set of doors. Opening her door was a bit of a shock to Jason. The room looked like a pleasant hotel suite. Susan was sitting on the bed, looking out the window at the splendid flower garden. Jason walked over to her and looked into her eyes.

"Sweetheart, it's your husband, me, Jason," He said while holding out his hands for her to touch.

"They're going to get me! I don't want them to find me!" Susan echoed through the room.

"Honey, everything is going to be alright. Bad people kidnapped you and told you things that were not true. They are going to jail. You do not have to worry about anything. The kids miss you so much. We want you to come home, Susan. Home where it is safe and beautiful for you."

"I have to do the garden today, the garden!" Susan lamented.

"No, Susan, no. There is no garden to do. You are safe now, safe! You have a family. There are no problems. The bad people are gone, they will never return," Jason said, adding, "Look, Kathleen is here, your sister. We are fine, we are okay and nobody can hurt you."

"Susan, we are welcoming you back home. Mom was so worried about you, and the kids, they are waiting for you. You have to listen to these people here, Susan. They are helping you to come home where it is safe for you," Kathleen said, sitting beside her sister and giving her a soft hug.

"I don't want to be contaminated. There is danger!" Susan shouted, pushing away from Kathleen's embrace.

"That is not true," Stephen said from the side of the room, "It was just a story put in your mind, just a false story, Susan. There is no contamination to worry about. Soon you will know what is true. The people that told you that stuff are contaminated with lies."

Two days later Susan was released and allowed to return home. Her recovery was remarkable except during the following night when she awoke several times with nightmares of food poisoning and getting ill from being bumped by large crowds of people. Jason comforted her and explained to her that the dreams were from negative thoughts that were put into her head to traumatize her. He made her some tea during the coming nights when she awoke and reinforced welcoming her home.

In a new hideout, the evil agents schemed to have their victims returned or demolished. Their work was their pride and through the guise of a cult, they held their powers to be all-important.

"I know where she lives and we have to get her back. I haven't located Jill yet but we can begin with Susan," Carruthers argued with his demented brother and partner in criminality.

"Spells work wonders. Let's dig into her soul," Smythe chuckled, rubbing his hands together.

"Let us gather our energies together, little brother. One way or another, she is going to feel it," Carruthers held his head high in esteem with amoral images.

During the afternoon, Kathleen decided to walk through Stanley Park with her sister. It was a gorgeous day of sunshine and radiance, a complete expression of spectacular serenity. Jason and Stephen walked with them, admiring the colors of the trees and greenery of summer.

"It is such a beautiful day, Susan," Kathleen smiled jovially, "We have to appreciate that."

"It is nice. Where are we going?" Susan asked dubiously.

"Just a walk to cherish the scenery and to feel the freedom in the air." Her sister patted her shoulder as an uneasy silence fell amongst the pleasant stride. Susan slowed her pace to a halt, looking as though she were in pain.

"Is something wrong?" Stephen asked Susan, noticing she was holding her stomach.

"I feel sick. Something is inside of me!" Susan let out, falling to the grass with increasing pain.

"What is it Susan? What do you feel? Do you want a doctor?" Jason anxiously voiced.

"I want help, they are coming!" Susan cried with agony as she pressed deeply into her stomach.

"Quick! Get the car, Jason!" Kathleen yelled.

"I will get it. Take care of her!" Stephen obliged as Jason threw him the keys.

"It's going to be alright," Kathleen comforted her as Jason hauled out his cellular phone and called Dr. Copeland, who instructed him to bring Susan to him immediately. Shortly thereafter, the group arrived at Dr. Copeland's clinic.

"I doubt there is anything physically wrong with her," Copeland said, after examining Susan in his office. "In a few minutes a friend of mine should be here. I discussed this case with him briefly and he is of the opinion that they are waging some form of psychic attacks on her. He wants to spend a few minutes talking with her and perhaps he will recommend something to us."

"Psychic attacks? Is that possible?" Jason argued.

"What we say is not possible, sooner or later may be proved wrong. What some people are susceptible to may prove to be more than a matter of opinion. Whatever it is, we have to resolve it," Copeland explained.

"Doctor, Alex is here to see you," A nurse mentioned through the doorway.

"He is here," Copeland smiled, "I'll be back momentarily."

A few minutes later, Copeland returned and introduced his friend. "Folks, this is Alex and his wife Monika. Alex is a professor at the University and behind the scene he studies and practices techniques of magick. Monika is a psychic and on occasion has assisted the police department in solving crimes."

"I would like to spend about half an hour with Susan if I may," Alex requested pleasantly.

"Sure, anything you can do would be of help to us," Jason said, escorting his friends from the room.

A nurse entered the lounge forty minutes later and requested their return to Copeland's office. Alex looked at them in slight dismay.

"What did you find out?" Jason asked as he looked askance at Alex.

"The mind is like a large bowel," Alex explained, "In it a great mixture of imagination, belief and theories becomes stirred up, clouding the vision into seeing what is reality and what it wants to see. In a nutshell, from what I can determine, they have made a psychic contact with her and are sending an energy for her to sympathetically 'pick-up' or receive."

"What does that mean? What do we have to do?" Kathleen asked.

"There are crevices in her protective aura, her etheric sheath that require mending," Monika remarked, "Whoever is responsible, they have not yet finished with Susan. They are still sending harmful rays into her psyche and maintain contact with her. What I am presuming is that, before long, they will wage some great conflict in order for her to be returned or immersed in a painfully ill disease. Why I say this, is because it is nothing new. It happens more often than we realize. In this case, the invaders are very determined in what they want to accomplish. We have to set up a border, a protective field so that their energies will not be capable of penetrating through to her."

"You figured all that out in just a few minutes?" Jason asked with a perplexed look.

"Time is an illusion, as are so many other things around us. We have to spend some time with her, and I suggest it be at your home, where she can gain the respect and safety that she requires," Alex exclaimed.

"Sure, she has been away long enough. Whatever you think is best. I am open to anything," Jason said as he looked at everyone in turn.

A haunting atmosphere shrouded the backyard of the sinister brothers. Together they were delving into the lore of their complex spells, weaving their energy together and preparing to send it off like a cannonball of fiery power, focused towards Susan in the confines of her home.

"Together we weave this spell and curse, almighty darkness will reimburse!" Smythe and Carruthers echoed through the timbers, strengthening their vocal cords for the operation that was just ahead.

Alex sat motionless in the living room. The house was completely quiet with everyone seated in the kitchen except for Monika and Susan. They were in Susan's bedroom, where Monika was working an energy field around her aura. Alex was projecting from his body into the astral plane and through the concentrated effort of his will, fathomed to build an extensive etheric ectoplasm surrounding the house, providing a border against outside disturbances. Kathleen reached across the table and held Jason's hand, which prompted Kathleen and Stephen to reach around and create a circle with everyone joining hands. They knew whatever they had to say was to be said in silence, as thoughts and feelings, to strengthen their bond with positive affirmation, as Alex previously outlined to them.

The brothers echoed their chants into the fire that was lit in the center of their circle, with candles lit around the circumference. They chanted voraciously in unison, focusing their undivided attention on surging the fireball of destruction to Susan. In the midst of the woods, a bear wandered aimlessly as though summoned from the forces at play. The heightened energy field could be seen by the naked eye. Incredibly, the malicious duo empowered nature's wrath and projected a violent transference towards Susan.

The kitchen table began to shake slowly as though an earthquake was crumbling through the underground, then the whole house shook violently, causing dishes to tumble from the china cabinet. Everyone knew they had to stand their ground and forcefully protect the barriers. Alex had explained the ordeal to them beforehand and brought them in the know. All eyes were closed and poised on the effort. Monika held Susan tightly, her subtle and peaceful efforts enclosing the victim from harm's doom. The front window smashed open as though a rock was hurled through it, scattering shards of glass into the living room. Before long, an eerie stillness ensued. In the kitchen, a whirling sigh could be felt as everyone's eyes opened simultaneously. They knew it was over. There was a palpable scent of relief flowing in the air. Alex felt the projectile and in a mysterious way was aware it had reflected off his astral and double ether barrier of protection.

Like a ball hitting a cement wall, the fiery power projected itself back to the black magicians and smashed like a powerful grenade into the pit of the fire. Flames slew up from the abrupt explosion and caught the brothers' apparel on fire, landing them several feet outside their magic circle of cobblestones and candlelight. With intense distress and agony, the brothers rolled on the ground, attempting to put out their blazing clothing and smoldering skin.

Reverberating from the forest was the harsh howling of a wolf. Clamoring to stand up, Carruthers called to his brother, "Help, I am bleeding, help me!" There was no response. Smythe was unconscious and lying twenty feet from his depraved associate. Carruthers turned his face upward with an added attempt to stand, but facing him was the unforgiving grizzly.

"No, no, go away!" were his final words as the beast ripped across Carruthers' arm with his paw and hurled it out of the man's shoulder effortlessly. A crying pang echoed through the forest as the grizzly stomped upon his bludgeoned body, preparing for an evening feast.

Peace had returned to the distraught family and activities appeared to resume as normal on the following morning. Susan was once again herself as she relished in the stories they told her. She did not recall the incidents that she had previously undergone. The sounds of the doorbell caused a stir in the room as Jason jumped up to answer. A familiar and friendly face entered; it was Detective Leibscher.

"The strangest thing happened this morning…" the detective began. Alex looked on with amusement, holding his wife's gentle hand. "Two felons were found dead early this morning. They were in the backyard of a home they recently rented just outside Chilliwack. It appeared obvious that they were performing some kind of evil ritual and, half burnt, they were gorged to death by a grizzly bear. Their remains were identified and proved them to be the abductors of Susan and Jill."

"That's superb!" Jason smiled.

The detective smiled and continued, "You'll read about it in the paper today, but further to this, the guy named Carruthers stole his identity from a man he murdered last year. He dumped the body in the Strait of Georgia and not long thereafter a fisherman retrieved it in his nets. We couldn't identify the body until some time later. How we actually did identify the victim was from his Rolex watch," the detective paused for breath, "And traced the serial number through the Rolex Company to find the owner's name."

"That is bizarre! Why would he have wanted to steal an identity?" Jason asked.

"Carruthers has been wanted on many felonies under his old name, so perhaps the only way he could escape his damaged life was to steal another name. Anyway, case solved. How is Susan making out?"

"I am fine, detective," Susan smiled as she entered the room, "Thank you for all you've done."

"That's a relief to hear. You have nothing to fear now," The detective reassured her.

"Care for a coffee?" Kathleen asked him.

"Another time, perhaps. There is a homicide downtown I have to check out. Hoodlums! Let's get this planet cleaned up instead of fouled up!" He said stirringly as he returned to the front door.

"Stop by anytime. We would love to see you again," Susan requested.

"I'll do that. Thank you," He added while passing Susan a gift.

"What's this?" Susan asked.

"Mace, pepper spray, a woman's loyal friend in times of need," He grinned, patting her shoulder and departing.

Alex shook his head and grinned as the door closed.

"Looks like we can go home and rest now," Monika mentioned to her lover.

"Rest? Yeah, right!" Alex smirked with a roll of his eyelids.

"Your help was mysterious but most gracious," Kathleen said as she got up to shake his hand.

"Fix that window. It calls for rain tomorrow," Alex grimaced, then burst into a wide grin.

Susan walked over to the sincere couple and then flew into them with a group hug. "I actually feel like my old self again," She admitted.

"Old Self, New Self, False Self or True Self, whatever self we may devise," Alex concluded, "the mind has many rooms and when we spend so much time in one, we tend to neglect the others. Fear, failure, self-esteem, whatever we do and feel at any one moment becomes a reflection from the room we hide within."

"Some reflections are better than others," Susan gestured as she looked into Alex's bright blue eyes.

"It looks as though the brothers grim got their reflection last night. Their tower of destructive Babel became their demise." Alex glowed, then added, "The best reflection comes when we are most honest with ourselves and work hard to shine a glitter of achieved intelligence."

"That sounds rightfully truthful." Susan said as she smiled from the reflection of sincerity coming off his face while the door closed. Turning around, she saw her husband and sister projecting a welcoming light and positive glow of certainty at her revival. ★

CHILDREN OF THE STARS

"The Star, as the Aquarius water-bearer, is the guiding light of the star that revitalizes and nourishes the barren and dry. The Star brings beauty to life…she creates a new age, a new sense of self-esteem based upon a new set of ideals."

New Age Tarot- James Wanless

Venezuela boasts having one of the most beautiful waterfalls the world could ever claim. Untouched by social intervention, in the heart of a mountainside, a gigantic waterfall purls down a steep rugged slope. Very few tourists have ever chanced to see it, since the hike to view it is extensively long and treacherous. Its breathtaking beauty is inescapable. Nature lovers have marveled at the vast rushing force of the water, plummeting thousands of feet to the ravine below and into an estuary of supreme misty serenity. Some have flown over it in small aircraft and others have viewed it from its upper vantage, but never has anyone remarked about seeing it from the lower level. There were two people, however, with lots of time on their hands and more than a passing interest in braving the time and energy for such an adventure.

Michael and Johanne often traveled to remote and forbidden places, photographing rare scenic spectacles and inhabitants, which society paid to marvel at. The twin Cessna plane landed roughly onto the tepid tarmac and slowed to a small building which the locals has as their airport. The side door pushed open as Michael got out and stretched his arms in to the air. Johanne was right behind him, passing large backpacks out from the compartment.

"C'est beau, Michael," she remarked at the warm welcoming climate.

"It was perfect timing to come here now. The rain season just finished and the photography should be splendid," The thirty-three year old Canadian photographer asserted.

"Let's get settled and meet our guide!" She enthusiastically suggested.

The pilot assisted in unloading the plane containing boxes of can and dried foods and other supplies that they picked up in Caracas, the capital, where they spent three days before arriving at their destination. The supplies were put on a dolly from the airport shack and pulled into the building as they followed along inside to meet their associate.

Pedro met them at the door as they entered. "Welcome to Canaima on the Río Carrao, come please in," he said in confidence, "I am Pedro, who talked on telephone with you, Mister McFee. Good to see you arrive!"

"Thank you, Pedro. Please call me Michael. This is my colleague, Johanne. We are very happy to be here, and excited about the trekking expedition," He added.

"That will be good. I have place for you at Inn. All is ready for us to begin in the morning. Mario, bring cart and baggage!" Pedro commanded, looking at his assistant.

To their habitual surprise, the Inn was a rather rugged home, extending into another home that allowed its enlarged size to be considered as two connecting dwellings. Nonetheless it was satisfactory and more than the comfort of the outskirts they were used to surviving.

"Venezuela is a very beautiful country." Michael said to Pedro as they entered the Inn.

"Yes," Pedro agreed, "It brings many people to see the Andes in the west and the steamy Amazonian jungles in the south and many other sites also."

"The hauntingly beautiful Gran Sabana plateau, with its flat-topped mountains, in the east, is truly remarkable. We took photos there last week. The 3000km of white-sand beaches fringed with coconut palms lining the Caribbean coast seems to be a major tourist attraction also," Michael steamed with enthusiasm.

"It also has South America's largest lake, Lake Maracaibo, and third-longest river, the Orinoco," Pedro returned, trying to show he knew as much or more than the tourist did.

"Yes, I read something of that," intervened Johanne, "It is a very adventurous trip to see those places from what I have heard. What kinds of wildlife have you encountered on your journeys, Pedro?"

"I have seen many exotic plants and animals, including the jaguar, a wild one he is! Also the ocelot, tapir, armadillo, anteater, and of course we have the longest snake in the world, the anaconda," He grinned with mock trepidation in his eyes.

"Are there any dangerous areas to avoid?" Michael inquired.

"Just in places along Colombian border in Zulia, Tachira, Apure and Amazonas states but in these places the dangers are with human animals. But also Indian tribes live in remote places in Amazon and is best to go there with familiar guide," The eager scout warned.

"I apologize for not speaking Spanish. Is that the main language here?" Johanne asked.

"Yes it is, but also more than thirty Amerindian languages still spoken by the Arawak, Cariban and Chibcha peoples. When you are ready for food, we can go eat together, all good?" Pedro augmented.

"That sounds inviting. Certainly, and we shall be ready for that in an hour," Michael responded.

They unpacked at the Inn and settled in their room then met Pedro for dinner. The dining area was an enlarged kitchen that allowed the customer to view the cooking.

"Oh, this could be our last good meal for a while, let's make it special." Michael remarked as he took a seat.

"That sounds good to me, are there any good vegetarian dishes, Pedro?" Johanne asked.

"Yes, they have most vegetarian here, not too many animals, it is expensive," Pedro grimaced.

"When will we leave for the hike to Angel Falls?" Asked Michael.

"We are ready now, so in morning we can drive to foothills after breakfast, and begin hiking to bottom of Salto Angel. Is okay with you?" Pedro exclaimed to the voyageurs.

"Sounds superb. We can prepare the packing this evening," Johanne added.

The following morning had a beautiful haze in the east with the sun glimmering through it, covering the landscape with a rosy glow. Johanne stood out on the balcony enjoying the revitalizing fresh air as Michael finished packing his backpack. Pedro was waiting for them with a mountain jeep. The pair loaded their belongings and set out for their adventure.

The drive began quite pleasant but got rougher as they ascended into the hill area of the upcoming mountains.

"Those trees are spectacular, Michael!" Johanne avowed as she looked out the window of the jeep.

"They are extremely lush and towering. I bet most are near a thousand years old," Michael remarked.

"Some are older, and we are happy they are not cut down like so many places are doing today," Pedro commented.

"How far before we begin the adventurous hike?" Michael asked Pedro.

"Not so long, maybe one hour driving. It is my first time to go hike bottom of Angel Falls. It will maybe be two days to arrive by foot for us. Mario and Pedro will take good care of you," Pedro smiled.

"We enjoy your company and it was expected to take at least twelve hours to hike into the Falls area, so dividing it into two days sounds great. I am sure we will enjoy the scenery along the way," Johanne said while looking around at everyone.

The old jeep roared with odd crackling noises as it rumbled up the dusty road and further into the mountain. Pedro and Mario sat in the front as though it was their passion and livelihood to lead the mission. Michael and Johanne clamored in the back seat as the rickety vehicle romped further along. Backpacks stuck out of the rear and upon the roof filled with food and required supplies. Time passed quickly as they enjoyed the new scenery and before long they came to the end of the narrow rugged road. Everyone rigged their large cumbersome packs and began the journey. The photographers had their cameras leashed around their necks, prepared to capture any surprising spectacles.

"So, you never took the lower route to see the Falls from below?" Michael asked Pedro.

"No sir, most people see it from above. It drops over thirty-two hundred feet from the mesa of Auyán Tepuy into the rainforest. Mesa is from Spanish and it means 'table' because the area from where the falls comes from is flat."

"I believe it was discovered in 1935 by James Angel, an American aviator," Johanne noted.

"Yes, that is correct and is in area called Guiana Highlands," Pedro replied.

Mario began walking ahead, cutting some thick bush with his machete to create a route into the dense forest area for ease of hiking. The air was fervent with hot moisture pouring from the extending trees as the morning climbed towards noon with the hot sun. Johanne wiped her brow as she pushed the large leaves aside making her way in front of Michael to keep up with the guides. They stopped for short breaks along the rugged landscape. Evening was approaching and the guides turned to say they would be setting up camp for the night. They pitched the two small tents and began a fire to heat up some soup that they opened from a can and poured into a cooking pot.

"Not too bad with this bread to soak into," Michael chuckled.

"It is good," Mario responded with a smile.

"He talks very seldom, Pedro," Johanne said as she looked at the athletic comrade.

"Yes, Mario is a quiet one but always a good worker," Pedro replied.

They all ate in silence for a while, each taking in the day's adventure and wrapping themselves in their memories like nestling into a blanket. During the meal, Johanne broke the silence. "Michael, this is our seventeenth journey together, you know," she remarked candidly.

"We have enjoyed many places and times together. Adventure is everywhere to be had," He said. Johanne smiled as though she lapsed into the past with many recollections.

"How do you feel Johanne?" Michael asked.

"Oh, I was thinking of the time when you came to my grandmother's house and climbed over the back fence to see me. You were so excited about getting the project in Guyana and gave me a huge hug and flagged the tickets in my face. Then you kissed me and when I looked over your shoulder I could see my grandmother in the upstairs window. She had such a smile, it will stay with me forever," Johanne said with warm emotion.

"You never told me she was watching us! She seemed like a wonderful woman but there was something more about her that I could never figure out. It was like she had some magical powers or knew something of great and important secrecy," Michael remarked.

"She did have powers, Michael. She was very much involved with astrology and could figure things out by calculations of all sorts. She used to tell me so much about my sign of Aquarius, that it had made me realize a lot about myself and how to contend with difficult times in life and with my personality," Johanne said.

The guides talked in Spanish to one another as the evening drew to a close and quietly everyone entered the tents for a night's rest.

"Good morning, good morning!" A voice shouted as Michael and Johanne came out of their tent.

"Hello Mario, have you been awake very long?" Johanne asked.

"We were awake for one hour. We have breakfast ready. Do you like olives? I have some," He smiled.

"Oh certainly, I would like some with breakfast," Michael smiled.

"For dessert we have some fresh coconut also," Pedro remarked with a laugh.

The adventurers ate quickly, eager to continue their trek. Shortly, they were back on the trail.

The hike went well with the rejuvenated and energized bodies eager to reach the destination by late afternoon. Pedro seemed to have a great sense of direction for being in new territory although Michael wasn't sure of where they were at all. But by late afternoon they could see the hills that led to the bottom of the distant waterfalls. They followed the river towards it as the falls roar increased through the air as did it's image as they got closer.

"It looks absolutely magnificent, Michael!" Johanne exclaimed as she took some distant photographs.

"It is a real majestic wonder. One of the most beautiful sights we've ever shared," He replied as he busily snapped photos as well.

As they embarked closer, the sound of harsh rushing water got louder as the falls hit the rocks and river below. It was like multiple smacking sounds of water balloons hitting the pavement from a high-rise building. They halted for a rest at a distance and enjoyed the tranquility before approaching the monstrous and potent vista. The blue sky appeared to have sparkles glittering through it like diamonds reflecting in the atmosphere. It gave them an astonishing feeling to be wrapped in the heart of nature.

They continued the hike towards the bottom of Angel Falls and were excited about taking so many dazzling photographs of nature's wonders. When they reached the bottom, again they were rather fatigued and rested on a crevasse above the riverbed. They wore ear protectors to prevent injury from the disquieting onrush of showering water above their heads.

"These photographs are going to be superb!" Johanne shouted in glee.

"I would like to get up there, on the next ledge, and perhaps go in behind the falls for some outward views," Michael requested in a loud voice.

The guides smiled as they rested lying down and watched him climb the embankment. Johanne looked on and then began to slowly follow him. She halted for a moment as she heard a sound come from above her. She glanced up and saw Michael standing at the top, apparently awestricken from the view. He was stuttering some gibberish she could not understand even after lifting her ear protectors. When she arrived beside him she fell to her knees with a captivated expression.

"Who is she?" Johanne whispered, as their heads were transfixed to the sight of a woman perched on a rock inside a cave, behind the falls.

"Speak English?" Michael said to her in wonderment.

"Come here, come here Pedro, there is a lady up here!" Johanne shouted while waving him upwards. The lady stared into the rushing water as though nobody was there. She did not seem to notice her new visitors at all.

Pedro and Mario climbed up to see what was the matter. They looked at one another after their eyes became captivated by her appearance. She had long brown hair and sparkling blue eyes and wore a tarnished tan robe. Pedro asked her a question in Spanish to which she replied, "Yo soy Yelga y vengo de una tribu de muy lejos de este lugar."

"She says her name is Yelga and she comes many days walk from here. She has been here for a long time," Pedro translated as he looked upon Yelga with a questioning eye.

"Yo vivi por quarenta y nueve anos," Yelga continued.

"She is forty-nine years old, she believes."

"Oh my god, there is a snake crawling from the back of her hair!" Johanne yelped.

Yelga looked to Pedro and spoke again.

"She calls it her fire snake. It is her friend and lives with her always," Pedro answered.

"She looks like a medusa woman," Johanne exclaimed while a bit nerved at the sight.

"How in heavens did a palm tree grow there?" Michael queried as he pointed to the side of a cavern.

"She say it is a marker and points to a star. It helps her to reach the Outer Ones, whatever that means," Pedro exclaimed.

They listened attentively to her as she uttered the word "Babalon" from her straining voice.

Mario grabbed Pedro and said something in his ear.

"Is everything alright?" Michael asked.

"Mario is scared and thinks it is wrong to be here. He said we are disturbing a process or something," Pedro answered.

In utter astonishment, everyone's attention was drawn to little children that had wings like angels and were flying through the waterfalls. There presence was so unreal, yet they exuded a serene radiance.

"Who are those angels?" Johanne questioned in disbelief.

The lady spoke as though she knew the question.

"Estos son mis hijos de Luna. Ellos viven entre los vivos y hacen milagros por la gente enferma y lastimada. Ellos son angeles maravillosos que sacrificaron sus vidas por las vidas de otros."

"She calls them her moon children. They go with the living and make miracles for sick and injured people in life. They are great angels that use their life for life of other people," Pedro replied in translation.

"Are they spirits from the inner worlds?" Michael asked.

Pedro talked with Yelga for a few minutes then replied, "She says spirits cannot have form. Many people think that ghosts and shells, phantoms and elementals that you usually can't see are some kind of spirits but they are mistaken." He looked back and forth, from Yelga to Michael, then continued, "Spirits are of a Universal Consciousness tied directly with the Divine, but Soul is different. The Soul is part of lower nature tied with mind and emotions and works on the levels that such ghost entities are on, so Spirits are the state and not the condition of the center of consciousness. I hope I said that correct, she is very complex," Pedro added.

"That is utterly amazing! Once in a lifetime everyone sees something totally out of the ordinary. This must be our time," Johanne remarked in astonishment.

The little angels flew in and out of the waterfalls as though they could pass through any medium without hindrance. There were four in appearance yet when one flew into the falls it seemed to disappear as though it went somewhere else on earth, but returned only a few seconds later.

"That looks like an Egyptian Ankh around her neck. Where would she have gotten that?" Michael queried as he pointed.

Yelga touched it and said, "La linea horizontal en esta cruz es el horizonte del Sur, y el circulo es la puerta hacia los paraisos para los grandes."

"The line on this cross is the southern horizon and the circle is the gateway into the heavens to the Great Ones," Pedro said in wonderment.

"Who does she believe the Great Ones are?" Asked Johanne.

Pedro asked Yelga to which she replied, "Ellos vienen del cielo y hacen mucho en el mundo desconocido para mucha gente."

"The Great Ones come from the sky and do much in the world unknown to most people," Pedro said.

"She must refer to either other angels or aliens, do you think?" Johanne said with a puzzled look.

"Perhaps aliens as she indicated they are physical when they appear," Pedro remarked.

Yelga again spoke out, "Los angeles vienen y van todo el tiempo. Ellos siempre saben a donde van y se deslizan a travez del tiempo y el espacio en un instante para prevenir que tragedias ocurran a la gente a quien son llamados para ayudar."

"The angels, she says, come and go all the time. They know always where to go. They can slide through time and space at an instant to stop tragedy from occurring to people that they are called to help," Pedro sat on the rock next to Yelga to listen attentively at the remarkable woman.

"She says there are only three ways to be in life, with the Sun, with the Moon or with the Fire."

"What does she mean by that?" Michael asked.

"She said it is the same as to be awake or to be asleep or to be in a deep dream and these ways are mixed with one another so that a person that is awake may have some fire but be primarily asleep. It sounds very strange," Pedro added.

"May we take some photos of her?" Johanne asked.

"She says you may do what you wish." Pedro replied.

They took some photos of her from different angles and elevation points.

"Do you think that a photograph of the angelic children will turn out, Michael?" Johanne asked.

"You mean the Moon Children? Well, I am hoping," He responded as his camera clicked constantly.

"Yelga says that only you can see Moon Children and you will not see them from your machine or camera as you refer to it."

"Maybe it is not a good idea for us to photograph them anyway, Michael," Johanne lamented.

"She seems like some kind of great master, having knowledge of things we have no experience with," Michael responded.

Pedro continued after listening to the elder lady, "Yelga says we are all masters in life and the way to wisdom is to let the light shine in, like through a window when you are on the inside. The way to do it is to seek your star in the heavens and once you find it the light will brighten your inner house."

"Why do you think she tells us so much?" Michael queried.

"She says that she only tells us what comes to her at the time. The mind has many channels and within each channel we learn to a certain level until we are ready for the next. Also that we found her was a sign for her to speak with us."

"How did she come to meet with the angels?" Johanne asked.

"They are workers for each of their particular star systems, she says. They are doing a job assigned to them through the nature of their elements. Each angel is specific for the needs it supplies to earth peoples. There is a great order and they are obeying the order. She left her village a few years ago after the first angel talked to her and she has come here to communicate with the others as she was directed. It is strange, she says, but every place has a particular energy and that is why they met her and why they are in this precise place," Pedro exclaimed.

"Patience must be an extreme virtue, Michael. There is something ageless about all of this," Johanne said with a glow in her eyes.

Pedro smiled and added, "This lady is very special. She has devoted her life to this mission and from it she is growing with great awareness and spiritual quality."

"She is very unique and blessed," Michael replied.

"She says we must come close to her right now," Pedro responded as they walked in and stood next to her. At that moment several rocks thundered from above the Falls, down past them, smashing into the ledge and falling further down towards the river.

"Did she just save our life?" Johanne wheezed in sudden alarm.

"I believe she is in constant communication with forces around her and knows much about what is happening in the world even though she never leaves her spot. She has become gifted through her devotion and attained qualities. I have never known anyone like her but can appreciate her holy sanctification," Michael whispered out of the blue. The others looked at him as though he was touched and affected by the situation.

Pedro chimed in, "Yelga says we are here for purpose and we should take it with us through life. Any time we are in a difficult situation we must only remember that the stars are not just in the sky but inside of us just as talking with the angels are from inside of us. The outside world is limited by our inside visions and when we open our inner eye we can see unlimited connection and have ability or help to change the outside. We are all stars of light and have contact with the unlimited to change anything when we hold up the sacred cup with an opened eye. I think she means by being able to feel good energy we can make a better life," Pedro exhaustively concluded.

"That is so beautiful. She is like a queen of the heavens, a true visionary. I wish I could give her something for being here for us today," Johanne cried.

"I believe she would only want you to give yourself the time to see life's great beauty as she has seen and to live each moment in perfect harmony as though it was the last. Life has many messengers and she has been the one for us this time around," Pedro said in praise.

They all looked at one another and felt that they were given something very special. It was something that did not have a name and could not be named. Somehow they realized it was time for them to leave. As they climbed down from the rocks, Johanne took a glance back at the waterfalls and the angels were gone. Her attention was drawn over to Yelga but all she saw was a ray of light as her head lowered behind the rock ledge, descending with her friends.

They walked on, meeting up with Mario, and did not speak a word. Their silence was filled with joy and their horizon ever expanded through an experience they would never believe, if they heard it from someone else. Inside, they knew they were in touch with the influences of the children of the stars and the angels of destiny. There was a subtle association between the two and being in tune with their harmonious nature gave them the clue to call upon them in times of desperation and need.

The hike back was surprisingly pleasant. Everyone was most cheerful as though they had accomplished something magnificent. They had, in fact, by coming into contact with something beyond normal means, made an attainment surpassing typical experience. Later that day they set camp for the evening and prepared to cook a meal. Michael was digging around in a backpack when he heard a noise coming from the bushes. His head popped up and turned to Johanne, "Did you hear that?"

"Hear what?" She clamored.

At that instant a giant jaguar propped its head from the bush and stared at the four adventures.

"Don't anyone move right away!" Pedro spoke softly as his head raised stiffly.

Michael stared intensely into its eyes and sent a ray of confidence to the beast. With exuberant assurance he lifted himself up and stretched his arms to the sky.

"Let the stars reign, oh mighty one," He blurted in a dazed state of concentration.

The jaguar let out a ravaging roar and swirled its head as it walked towards them, then suddenly turned to go off into another direction.

"What was that all about Michael?" Johanne said as she shook in apparent nervous depletion.

"It's about life, about the stars, about survival." He replied as he sat and began to cook their meal. ★

Her Third Eye

"I reign over ye, saith the God of Justice, in power exalted
above the Firmament of the Wrath, in whose hands the Sun
is as a sword, and the Moon as a through thrusting Fire: who
measureth your Garments in the midst of my Vestures, and
trussed you together as the palms of my hands."
Aleister Crowley- The Vision and the Voice

Nancy stood proudly upon the stage as she looked over her classmates and continued her oral essay in communications class.

"The underlying causes of human behavior are generated from what has been internally stored and reacted upon by the decision making process. People have patterns throughout their day that can be summated as aspects, which make their personality. As I look upon each one of you," Nancy glanced through the class to draw their attention upon her and continued, "I surmise that everyone has particular habits, new and old. These habits may be formed either voluntarily or involuntarily. If, for example, it is a twitching motion that is done with a hand, fingers or feet, it is the release of nervous energy, energy that is not functionally channeled for another purpose."

Throughout her presentation, Nancy looked periodically to her teacher, Ms. Witters. Her expression was a tight scowl, and her eyes appeared to be glazed over, staring off into space. Nancy sighed inwardly. 'Why do I even bother?' she thought to herself.

"In conclusion," Nancy half-heartedly declared, "habits are creatures that we breed, and develop to get through each day and make us relate and react to one thing or another. They can be changed, altered, or released from our physiological complexes if we become aware of them and begin to exchange them with voluntary, conscious alternatives. Habits are a thing we live with and custom our routine with. Thank you."

Rubbing her head, Nancy returned to her seat.

"All right Nancy, your presentation needs some tuning," Ms Witters shouted as she rose from her theatre seat. "Clive, it's your turn."

As Nancy took her seat, her best friend Lisa leaned over and whispered, "Hey Nancy, that was well researched and I liked your ideas in there. You are a funky good orator girl!"

"Oh, well I'm glad you liked it," replied Nancy, fidgeting in her seat to become comfortable. "I wish this headache would go away. It came about half way through my presentation up there and got worse the rest of the way through."

"Are you eating well?"

"Yes and exercising, but they still come almost everyday, and pretty much at school here."

"Did you see the way Ms Witters was looking at you while you read your report? I don't think she was really interested in what you were saying." Lisa frowned.

"I know, and it is not the first time. I think she is part of the reason for most of my headaches." Nancy massaged her temples for emphasis.

The final speaker left the stage. Ms Witters stood up and remarked, "I am pleased with everyone's efforts. Tomorrow morning you will receive your marks and critiques, then we will discuss the final term assignment. Everyone is to read chapter 18 tonight and answer all the questions on the sheet."

The students began exiting the theatre while Ms Witters approached Nancy. Grimacing, she muttered, "I would like to see you in my office to discuss a few things, Nancy."

"Yes, Ms Witters." Nancy calmly replied. Ms. Witters turned sharply and stalked up the aisle.

A few minutes later Nancy was knocking on the teacher's door.

"Come in and sit down," Ms. Witters snapped. Nancy slowly opened the door and entered the office. Taking a seat, she regarded Ms. Witters, who was staring down and reading some papers through her reading glasses. "I will be with you in a minute," she added, face buried in her work.

Nancy sat uneasily, wondering what was wrong. Her headache began to gradually increase as she pressed on the back of her head, attempting to relieve the inner pressures. She took in some deep breaths and rubbed her temples, soothing some of the agony.

Nancy glanced at the clock. The teacher seemed to be ignoring her presence for an extended time.

She turned to Ms. Witters. "Ma'am, I have to be at work in 25 minutes." Quietly, she added, "Sorry to rush you."

Clearing her throat, Ms Witters looked up at her and oozed, "Oh, yes, excuse me. This morning you were five minutes late. I wanted you to feel what it is like to have to wait for someone. We all have schedules to follow, you know. Keep this in mind in the future."

"Yes, Ma'am," Nancy looked uncomfortable. "Will that be all for today?"

"Not exactly. This is an educational institution and your daydreaming in class is not appreciated. You'd better buckle up, young lady, and begin to listen up a little closer so that you don't continue to question everything at the last minute. Do you understand where I am coming from?" Ms Witter's tone was sharp as she stared deeply into Nancy's eyes.

Nancy felt shaken inside. Something about the teacher was penetrating her emotions. It was like the teacher was talking unfairly down to her on one level and emotionally draining her on another.

Nancy blinked a few times to break Ms. Witter's piercing gaze. "Why isn't anyone else treated this way, Ms Witters?" she asked sorrowfully.

Ms. Witter's eyes went wild. "Look here, Nancy. I am the teacher and the one responsible for everyone's education. If I feel that someone needs additional instruction or should prepare work more professionally, it is my decision." Small flecks of spittle flew from her mouth as she ranted, "Do not question me anymore. You are the student. Your job is to do your work the best you can by listening to what I have to tell you. You are here to learn and to experience an education. Do I have to explain this to you again?"

Nancy cringed under the brutal verbal assault. "I understand Ms Witters. I will pay closer attention and try to be on time from now on." Nancy felt lost for words and internally shattered. Something told her the teacher was wrong, that she had rights to vocalize her point of view. Her self-confidence weakened, however, as she felt the older lady absorbing energy from her.

Feeling completely subdued, Nancy asked, "May I rush off to my job now, Ma'am?"

"Yes, go, and we will see you in the morning," Ms. Witters waved her off and looked back down to her papers. Nancy got up reluctantly, bowed for the permission then left the office. While walking down the hallway she tried to regain her stamina. She felt dizzy and drained, and slowed down to get a drink from the water fountain. The teacher was wicked and unjust. Why Nancy felt that she had to apologize and respect the hag was a mystery to even her.

On her way from the schoolyard, she grabbed her bike and made a frantic run to her work. Bicycling across town always made Nancy feel more energetic. She soon arrived at the convenience store where she worked five evenings a week to pay off her student loan and meager bachelor apartment. Despite her best effort she arrived ten minutes late. She had a hollow feeling in her stomach and felt hungry but didn't have time to eat.

As she sprinted through the door, a voice whispered, "Hey! Mr. Phillips was asking about you a few minutes ago. He wanted to know if I had seen you come in.'"

Nancy shrugged and threw her hands into the air. She avowed, with a tone of anguish, "The story of my life lately, John, is that I am late. Just plain late." She rushed past John to get her apron from the employee room.

Trying to regain herself, Nancy put on a smile while serving customers short order foods behind the counter. During the evening there were busy and slow moments. She looked up at the clock. It was coming on nine and already quite dark outside. Her eyes widened when through the door walked Ms Witters, opening her purse to pay for something. The teacher did not notice Nancy working behind the food counter, or at least she pretended not to notice. Nancy kept quiet; she didn't want to draw attention to herself, especially from her teacher. Ms Witters walked around the store looking at things upon the shelves, while Nancy was cleaning some milkshake containers. Nancy felt uneasy with the heinous presence in the store. It was as though the corrupt teacher was sending negative vibes to her and ignoring her at the same time. Nancy kept busy and tried sternly to ignore it, but the bad aura kept chewing away at her resolve. It was as if the teacher looked at everything in the store except at Nancy. 'You crazy woman!' Nancy thought as she shook her head attempting to rid herself of the feelings that were building up inside. Ms Witters left the store without buying anything other than the gas that she got from outside. Nancy went to the ladies' room and felt like vomiting but nothing would come up from her stomach.

It was finally eleven o'clock. Nancy finished cleaning the counters and hurried home to complete her homework. She finally went to sleep at two in the morning. It was anything but a pleasant rest, however. During the night she twisted and turned in bed with recurring dreams of being chased around an old house. Morning came and brought clouded skies with feverish sensations. Nancy had a quick breakfast of toasted waffles and bicycled to the college for nine. Her first class was macro-economics, which went by quickly for a change. At eleven was English class with Ms Witters. She entered the class and noted there wasn't a spare desk available. Nancy sighed, and reluctantly went to the front of the class to ask Ms. Witters if she could get another desk to be seated. Ms. Witters looked into her eyes and responded, "Wait in the back of the class and I will see about one."

Nancy felt ill. She walked to the back of the class and stood there for a few minutes. Her blood began to boil as time passed. She felt left out from the world, excluded from existence for no apparent reason.

"Has everyone handed in their assignments and ready for last night's homework?" The teacher voiced loudly.

Nancy thought she would end up standing for the whole class. She couldn't stand it anymore and rushed out the door to the counselor's office.

Marching into the office, she fumed, "Mr. Wagner, I have a problem with a teacher."

Mr. Wagner looked down his nose at her. "You may come in. In the future, please be seated outside the door and wait for me to invite you into the office." Packing some papers into a file, he asked, "Now, what is your name?"

Nancy took a deep breath. "My name is Nancy O'Keefe and the teacher Ms. Witters has been making me do extra work, staying late most days and puts me down for no apparent justification. Just now, there was a desk missing from the class and she was going to make me stand there the entire class, I'm sure of it." She started to cry.

"Why does she keep you late?" Mr. Wagner asked.

At that instant Ms Witters walked into the office and stood next to Nancy. Icily, she intoned, "She is often late for class, Robert, and if she doesn't complete her assignments as requested, like the rest of the class does, remarks on her semester report are not going to be of any relief to her passing this course."

Nancy cut her off. "Excuse me, this isn't an elementary school. I should be entitled to a desk to sit at when I come to class. You were going to leave me standing all through class, weren't you Ms Witters?"

"No, Nancy," Ms. Witters countered, "You were late as usual, and the class had already begun. I had sent a student for a desk already."

"The class didn't even begin, I…"

Mr. Wagner interjected, "Excuse me ladies. This feud has no purpose. If there is a problem I suggest that you both settle it right now and be prepared to continue on with the education that this institution is acclaimed for. Communicate about what you have to do to move forward without vindication."

Ms. Witters sneered. "Miss O'Keefe should plan her schedule better so that she does not arrive late for any classes. She should also present her reports completed and not hand them in as incomplete. All this having been done, I am sure Miss O'Keefe will not find any problems in my class."

"I see no further problem here. Are you all right with that Nancy?" Mr. Wagner asked

"I'll do my best. We'll see how it goes, Mr. Wagner," Nancy resigned.

During the remainder of the class Ms Witters taught as usual, but did not pay any attention to Nancy. The bad feelings seemed to subside, but somehow there was still a tangible friction in the room. She could feel that the teacher was still her 'cruel self' beyond the mask she wore so well. The vibrations from her were demeaning and focused on penetrating Nancy's soul. It was not imagined, but fact. The darkness that she felt towards the teacher was a daily nightmare, as if the old woman was an incubus sucking life force from the young girl. She longed to get out of the class, which may have worked as a subconscious result of being late for it most days. Again she left the class feeling drained and rubbing her head to ease the strain of a migraine. After school, Nancy decided to walk around the lake at the City Park. She did not have to work tonight and simply wanted to shake things off. She locked her bike to a gate and began to wander. While walking on the trail around the lake, she thought about all of this nonsense. Why she was even worried about anything and why it was beyond her scope to forget about it, went through her mind. She thought it strange that when she looked at other students and casual friends, it was as though she could see their thought patterns—the levels of their mind. She could see an emotional haze around fellow students, somewhat like an aura of feelings that encompassed them. She could tell their mood, but was too enwrapped in her own problems to analyze other people's feelings.

A little footpath led up a hill that overlooked the lake. Nancy followed it and sat alongside a tree at the top, looking out at the reflections on the water. The multiple ripples in the water glimmered with spectacles of sunlight, shaking the atmosphere in its depth. Her eyes wearied at the sight of the sky being gobbled into the water, constantly consumed like there was no end. Her head drooped as she became exhausted and felt herself falling into the water, being drawn in by some force that had grasped her.

Her physical body collapsed from the sitting position and rolled to the ground in exhaustion. Her subconscious struggle brought her to the threshold of the waning moon that lit the sky above her and shimmered in parallel with the sun upon the lake. She felt hauled through a narrow passageway that was guarded by two beasts that had the head of a wolf. Her eyes were glued closed. She could not see before her the way that was dark and dismal. The moonbeams reached to her instinctive awareness but still she could see nothing clearly. Her hands reached out attempting to feel her way through the passage to avoid the unknown, the uncertainty of potential disaster.

Nancy had no idea that this was not a physical experience. To her, she was really trapped in a mysteriously dark place. Suddenly, the head of a jackal rushed towards her and crashed into her forehead. It knocked her backwards as her arms flung to the sides and touched two towers that she fell in between. She scratched her fingernails into their stone sides and lugged herself onwards through the passage. Breathing the moist air through her lungs, it penetrated all parts of her body as she oozed a fluid from deep in her abdomen, which exited her mouth.

Through the gateway of the towers she entered into an open area when suddenly many things seemed to simultaneously occur. A hand touched the back of her head from behind. The most peaceful, tranquil feeling she had ever been aware of came into her body.

She heard the voice whisper, in complete peace and prose, "Follow me, child of the moon or your time will be soon."

Another hand came around her other side and placed a sacred Egyptian beetle on her chest. It clenched with its pincers into her body and sent a light from the Sun towards her brow. As it entered her auric body the light intensified upon her forehead, between her eyes. Darkness became light as her conscious awareness intensified. At that instant she knew her eyes were closed, yet she could see everything, everywhere, all at once. She had a visionary capability to see whatever she directed her mind towards. Her third eye opened, ringed with an orange hue of brilliance.

Nancy could direct each breath she inhaled to go anywhere in her body although it was not her physical body. She could perform functions with conscious intent. It was beautiful bliss and she felt great ease as all her pain vanished. She was beyond normal circumstances and in a place she could transform outcomes. Light emitted from her brow and dispensed all illusion cast into the shadows of death and despair. She did not look back to see the face of the beautiful stranger. The face was immaterial; it was its' spectacular presence that made the difference.

She looked into the horizon and could see illusions cast by emotionally distraught people everywhere. Her body flew forward with the winds sweeping across the gulf of an infinite horizon towards the distant plane.

Souls in pain lurked throughout the plane. Her hands reached out and pulled their anxieties away. She shed light in place of their sorrows, giving them solutions to their distress. Her presence brought certain joy to many hearts. Her ability became incalculably supernormal as the light continued to emanate from her forehead. Her profound conscious state went through a transition, a period of death where she met with forces uncertain and dark in every respect. She held through it all and arose in great splendour with the ability to see through obstacles and become aware of many things that people are not commonly conscious of yet live with in the recesses of their emotions.

She could see the obstacles that other people created. Conscious realization empowered her to rid the darkened restraints and barriers that stood in their way. The light emanating from her third eye opened the door mystically for the other souls and healed their woes. This experience seemed to have been what she vaguely recalls from early childhood as a nightmare. To be faced with blindness and no control over circumstances. That was it! She recalled a bad dream where she once awoke as a child and was blocked inside a long box. It was a tunnel that had no end. She was stuck inside and could not get out. There was no light, no way to move, similar as a state of death awaiting life. Someone opened the box and picked her up, and her fears temporarily vanquished. Then she was chased through different rooms. She sensed that some of these people were experiencing the same thing. That they were put in terrible circumstances and needed light to dispense their darkness and a soul to show them they were going to make it through.

Nancy looked down at her body of light and saw her emotional ailments. It was not unlike a ripped dress that was cut with holes in different parts. She knew her teacher was to blame for the damages in her emotional body. Her hands softly caressed the pained areas and brought healing into them. Light radiated down from her head into all areas and began to mend the lacerations throughout her figure. As she breathed in the tranquil air, energy came with it and perpetuated the healing with the light rays. Her body sank into the ocean as though she left the land of light and entered into a subconscious depth. While she sank down she caught a last glimpse of the sun and moon above which directed her with positive sensations.

Nancy's eyes began to open and she could see the lake in front of her as she regained consciousness. She slowly got up and grabbed her backpack while looking over the calm lake. It looked beautiful and she felt healed and together. She walked over to her bicycle and unlocked it from the gate, and rode home feeling better than she had in a long time.

As she entered her apartment the telephone rang. It was Lisa.

"Hey, you! Did you answer the questions for chapter 18 yet?"

"Haven't even read it yet Lisa. Let's get together on Sunday... I think I am going to visit Mom this weekend."

"Something wrong?" Lisa's tone softened.

"I don't know yet," Nancy sighed, "But I'll tell you all about it when I get back, okay?"

The following day she rode across the city to visit her mother. Something concerned her and she had to find out a particular truth. Her mother was sitting at the kitchen table and drinking a beer when she walked in. They began a casual conversation but Nancy wanted to know about something from her childhood and straight out asked her mother.

Her mother inhaled deeply. "Alright... I was going to tell you eventually... but it isn't easy, you know." She drained the last of her beer from the can and gently placed it on the table.

"Tell me what happened after I was born, Ma. I really have to know."

"Well, your father and I fought about anything and everything. We wanted you to be happy, we really did, but he couldn't keep a job." Nancy's mother got another beer from the fridge and cracked it open. "He left me when you were nine months old and moved out west."

"I never did see a picture of him. Why didn't you have any?" Nancy asked.

"I tore them up. I was disgusted with him because he didn't care anymore. He never contacted me ever again after he left. Three months later I couldn't handle it and didn't have a dime for anything. I had to work and there was no one to take care of you, baby. I wanted the best for you so I talked with an adoption agency who had a lady on a waiting list and told me you would be in good hands." Nancy's mother broke into tears and lowered her head to the table.

Nancy bent over and hugged her mother. "I can understand mom. Really, I can." Rubbing her mother's back, she quietly added, "Please tell me what happened after that. Please."

Sniffing, Nancy's mother raised her head and tried to smile. "The lady's name was Margaret Walters. She could not have children and wanted a little girl. One of her neighbors complained about constant noise one night and called the police. The police arrived and you were crying your eyes out. A social worker came with the police the next day and found you were bruised and mistreated. I am so sorry baby..." She began to cry again.

"Oh mom!" Nancy cried with her, "I am so glad I have you in my life. I know you went through many hard times and it never seems to end, but you were there for me and I will always be here for you." Mother and daughter embraced, comforting one another.

Nancy sat and talked with her mother for hours and went through some photo albums. The next night she talked with Lisa on the telephone about the assignment and of what she learned from her mother.

"What does a person do if they want to dig into their early years and has nobody to tell them about it?" Nancy asked her friend.

"Well, they could see a therapist or a clinical hypnotist. I happen to know a clinical hypnotist in town. She's a friend of the family. Her name is Stephanie Alwood. Hey, and get this, she also does past life regression therapy. Pretty cool huh? Would you like her number?"

Nancy laughed excitedly. "Definitely, and thank you buddy!"

Over the next few days, Nancy pretended to be her normal frail self in class. Yet, behind the facade, she observed the teachers' actions and eye contacts. Ms Witters was, as usual, negative with an abundance of venom.

That Wednesday evening, Nancy found the source of her nightmares through the help of Stephanie. Her adopted mother had tormented her and took her anguish out on Nancy whenever she cried. She would sometimes place Nancy in a cardboard box and close the lid. The child cried even more and felt trapped and unloved. Other times she would be slapped and burnt with a hot spoon. Mrs. Walters was cruel beyond belief. It was Nancy's next concern to find Mrs. Walters. She went to the city directory and found she had married a man who had mysteriously disappeared a few years later. The name of the man was Radley Witters.

Nancy's head fell in grief. She could not believe it. She was once adopted by her cruel teacher and put through torment. How did she end up meeting with the wretched lady again in her life, and how long has the teacher stalked her and sent venomous vibes towards her? For several years, Nancy had terrible headaches and never knew why. During these times she also felt drained but did not recall ever seeing the teacher before in her life. She was now very concerned about Ms Witters having spied and infringed on her personal life throughout the past.

That night she shared her story with Lisa and together they decided to investigate further. They rode their bicycles to Ms Witter's house on Spencer Street. A chilling wind blew as they set their bicycles along a fence and walked carefully towards the front yard of the teacher. Nancy peered over the fence and saw that the teacher's car was not there. Nodding to herself, Nancy said, "I want to go into the house, Lisa."

"Are you sick, girl?" Lisa raised an eyebrow. "What do you plan on finding in there that's worth breaking in for?"

"Probably more than we both can imagine at this point. Are you coming or are you chilling?"

"I'm with you, or at least my curiosity is. Watch out for booby traps, though," her friend chuckled.

Nancy began to climb the fence. She had a leg over the top when she suddenly jolted at the sound of two viscous dogs running towards her. She quickly pulled back and jumped down before they could sink their teeth into her.

"The wicked lady has two Dobermans. Go figure!" Nancy shuddered. "How are we going to get in the house now?"

"Umm, let me think. How about a police warrant?" Lisa said sarcastically.

"Oh yeah, we've got lots of evidence for one of those," Nancy replied in turn.

Lisa chuckled. Peeking back over the fence, she commented, "Did you notice that all the curtains are closed in the windows?"

"Yeah, they are," Nancy frowned. "It will be hell and high water if I am going to let this freaking lady keep making my life miserable. I want to know something about her and the only way is to get into her personal hiding place."

Lisa snapped her fingers. "I got an idea. It might be as silly as I am but I got one." Enthusiastic, she went on, "My brother collects chivalry items and has a complete suit of armor. What if we bring a bunch of meat and bones for the dogs and then you wear the metal costume to walk past them while they are snacking away?"

"Is it bite proof?" Nancy jested.

"Let's go find out!" Lisa giggled excitedly.

The following night they returned with the suit, some meaty treats and a set of walkie-talkies.

As Nancy struggled to put on the armor suit, she grunted, "Ok Lisa, if you see her coming down the road, you call me right away, alright?"

"Don't worry, Nancy, I treasure your friendship. I don't want that big meanie locking you up or anything... "Lisa paused, then added,"... Sorry."

Nancy shrugged, showing that the comment didn't bother her. Tying the last of the armour on, Nancy tested out the joints by walking around. "I'm lucky this stuff is light-weight, all things considered," she smiled a half-smile, "But it looks really stupid." She slowly approached the fence.

"Oh, be quiet you." Lisa mocked being stern. "Now climb up while I prepare to feed the vicious jackals."

Nancy snapped up her walkie-talkie once she got to the top of the fence. "I sure hope they only like dead meat... here they come!"

The wild dogs rushed over from the backyard when they heard the noise and began to bark frantically.

"Hey puppies! Here have a nice treats and take your damn time!" Lisa whispered over to them while tossing in two large hunks of cow flesh. The dogs broke away from Nancy and ran straight at the meat. As they ravaged the meat Nancy swooped down and began wobbling quickly towards the window of the front room. She tried to wedge it open but it did not budge. She tried another one on the side of the house. It didn't open either. Quickly she clamored around to the kitchen window and it luckily slid open. She hauled with all her might up into the cavity and hurled her body into the kitchen.

The dogs had quickly finished the hunks of meat and Lisa threw more to keep them occupied. She decided to save some for when Nancy had to return.

Inside the house, Nancy took off the top of her armor and began walking into the dining room. There was nothing out of the ordinary that she could see. She jolted as a voice murmured, "Come in, come in. Where are you?"

She put the walkie-talkie to her mouth and responded, "I am in and everything looks pretty normal. I am going to walk upstairs, or crawl, whichever works. Is it calm and quiet outside?"

"No monsters in sight yet. Maybe Frankenstein has a date tonight with a werewolf." Lisa hissed.

"Okay, keep me posted. I am walking upstairs sideways, it seems to work in these stiff armored pants. I'd take the lower half off but it takes so long to fit it on again. Over and out."

At the top of the stairs she wobbled into a bedroom. Beside the bed, on a night table there was an old photo album. Nancy opened it and saw some baby photos. Holding the baby in several photos was Ms Witters. Further through the album were newspaper clippings. One of them read: 'Mother loses Child over Mysterious Illness'.

Nancy read the article quickly and found that Ms Witters once had a child that got sick and died. It was not established how the baby got ill but Nancy was suspicious. Further on in the album there were photos of another baby. It was Nancy, as a baby in the photos. She cringed down as she touched the photos. She noticed cuts and bruises on the arms and face of the baby as though she had been brutalized several times. She quickly passed through the rest of the photos, then got up and looked through some clothing drawers and in the closet. Everything seemed fine so she went into the next room.

It was a spare bedroom with a baby crib inside. In the baby crib were a stuffed dolphin and a large orange crab. A small red pillow was partially covered with a baby blanket. It seemed to bulge up slightly so Nancy lifted the cover. She lost her breath when her eyes came upon a sweater underneath that she had lost in school a few weeks earlier. She lifted the sweater and her jaw dropped as a hand painted waxed figure fell onto the mattress. It looked exactly like her. It was an identical painted image with minuté details and had locks of her hair impregnated upon the head. She knew it was her hair when suddenly she had a flashback of trimming her bangs in the girls' washroom at school. Ms Witters was doing some kind of mischievous voodoo out of a sickness or revenge for losing her first child and then for losing Nancy.

"Why? Why would she be like this?" Nancy asked herself.

Nancy grabbed the voodoo doll and her sweater and walked out of the room. Quickly looking around, she opened a nearby hallway closet and found a box on the floor. She yanked off the cover and saw several items that she had lost throughout her life. There were notebooks from when she was in elementary school, a ring from when she was twelve years old, and other things along with photos of her walking down the street and in the shopping malls. This wicked lady had never lost touch with her, ever.

Outside, Lisa crouched beside the fence, scanning the road. It was pitch dark, as there were no streetlights on this road. Slowly the moon crawled up from behind the house and provided some light off the roof. Lisa stopped scanning to look at the moonlight, which she found to be very beautiful. Transfixed, she almost didn't see the set of headlights fast approaching her hiding place. She groped for her walkie-talkie, dropped it, then picked it up and frantically whispered, "Come in Nancy! I mean get out! She is coming towards the gate at the driveway now! Hurry up and find a back way out! Do you hear me?"

"I hear you," Nancy replied, a resigned tone in her voice. "It's too late. I won't get out. Not with this outfit."

"Look, you have time. Are you still upstairs?" Lisa squealed.

"On my way down now. Wish you were here." Nancy scurried her feet one small step at a time sideways down the flight of stairs.

"She's getting out of her truck. Her dogs just ran over to her. Get over to the back window now!" Lisa cried out.

"I am, I am." Nancy bellowed back.

Ms Witters had put her key in the door and began to turn the doorknob. Nancy was walking through the dining room and towards the kitchen when the front door opened.

Nancy paused, and straightened. She steeled herself. "I am not running any more, Lisa. I am confronting her with everything. Wait right there, I will keep the walkie-talkie on so you catch the whole thing."

"Oh God! What do I do if she cuts you up or something?" Lisa yelled.

Nancy grimaced. "It's a chance I have to take. I am done with fear and not going to take this stupidity any longer. Get ready for it…"

Ms Witters walked into the kitchen and was awestruck. She stared for several seconds, then regained her composure. Clicking on the light, Ms Witters sneered, "Well, if it isn't my knight in shining armor. What brings you to my house without invitation young woman?"

Nancy held up her sweater and the doll from behind her back. "I suppose a part of my life has brought me here. Why would it happen to be in your hands after all these years of child abuse?" Nancy yelled sternly.

"What on earth are you talking about?" the teacher yelled back with equal fury.

"I am talking about my original adoption, Margaret Walters." Nancy stepped forward, confronting Ms Witters with the offending objects. "Because you lost a child, you took me in and punished me for something that happened to you in your early lifetime. Well, it caught up to you and fortunately I was set free. You couldn't handle that so you persisted after me, to stalk me. Now I am a grown person and have to fight my own battles, undo the wrongs that made me unknowingly suffer through your torment over all these years. You have been after me for years and the proof upstairs shows it."

"Oh and see this walkie-talkie?" Nancy held it up for Ms. Witters to see. "I have friends, Ms Witters, and they are not far away." She said as she depressed the transmit switch.

A loud voice suddenly came over the walkie-talkie stating, "Not just one friend, but many! Don't do anything foolish! Your place is surrounded and everything has been recorded. You might have a chance if you confess now!" Lisa wiped her brow, swallowed and smiled at her 'police' voice.

Ms Witters dropped her bag of groceries on the floor and then sat on the floor beside them. "What am I supposed to do? Everybody abandoned me! Everyone hurt me and they just left! I was beat up and then punished more. I never hurt anybody. I just wanted them to listen. She died from a disease she was born with. She was my only baby. Nobody would help. They were all too busy. They are always too busy!" she cried as her nails dug into the wooden floor, scratching for some substance.

Nancy looked down upon her pathetic yet sorrowful demeanor. "Why were you after me all those years Margaret? I was only a baby. If you would have treated me for what I was, I might still be with you. If you have any love in your heart you should know it is the most powerful tool for healing the wrongs you have committed." Nancy dropped the wax doll on the floor, and it shattered.

Ms. Witters watched the doll fall, then glanced up at Nancy. "It was too late. It was too late Nancy! I had no one in my life! Nobody! I lived with pain from my own childhood and it hurt me, it always hurts me… do you know what it is like?" the teacher cried.

Nancy released the 'send' button and dropped the walkie-talkie on the floor. She then walked over to the teacher and held out her hand.

"I know what you are saying. I have been there myself. I fought it and it went away! It wouldn't go away for the longest time until I looked at it directly and accepted it. Then I came to know who I am and loved the person I found. I knew I was not alone, that there are many people out there with the same problems. I have seen some of them Margaret. We are no exceptions you know. You have to face your concerns and problems and confront them honestly. It is the only way to survive." Nancy let go of the teachers' hand and picked up the metal chest suit. "I want to see you in your office tomorrow after class Ms Witters. We have some history to recount." She slid the metal breastplate over her head, then retrieved her walkie-talkie.

"Any meat left out there?" she inquired to Lisa over the radio.

"All ready on this end. Come on out with your hands in the air!" Lisa yelled back.

Nancy walked to the front door, leaving the teacher groveling on the floor in sorrow and anguish. She opened the door, walked out on the step and down towards the gate. The dogs were scavenging the meat near the edge of the fence as though they were not fed in days. The moon sprinkled lustrous light across the ominous black gate as her hands reached up to unlock it. At that instant her body jolted from the echoing sound of gunfire coming from the house. Nancy shrieked in torment as she looked up into the sky then closed her eyes and envisioned an Egyptian image of Anubis, a god of death, gliding past her and into the house. Lisa gazed over the fence with her eyes glistening in fright. A dark cloud moved across the moon as the Dobermans howled into the faint night air while chewing on animal flesh.

With closed eyes, Nancy slowly opened the gate and went on the other side. Through her forehead she could see the path before her and was relieved. The wrath had ended and the teacher made her fatal decision through cowardice to accept her mistakes from being controlled by elements she had long allowed to guide her course. The light of the moon was shining the way ahead as Nancy let out a sigh while opening her eyes and feeling her friend's hand caressing the back of her head.

Nancy brokenly whispered into her friend's ear, "There is always danger in losing sight of our potential in life when we remain in the darkness. I was lost in another's emotions and in my own for so many years. It was hard to realize that I had to break through."

"There are waters to tread and darkness to overcome. Every journey appears uphill until you reach the top." Lisa said in comfort.

Nancy smiled. "I faced my fears and found my blind spots. One thing I found out with this ordeal is that if there is a great enough desire, there will be a guide to lead you and a voice to assist you." Nancy and Lisa embraced one another, then got on their bikes and rode home. Nancy had quite a story for her mother, and Lisa needed to get the armor back to her brother before he found it missing. ★

ANGELS ABROAD

"... that mankind is completely astray and that there is nothing - literally nothing - in our science, art, philosophy, religion, in our political and social systems which is not tainted through and through with false notions about man, with egoism and self-deception."

Is There "Life" On Earth? - J.G. Bennett

"Tell me something about your childhood. Something that is really bizarre that you have never told anyone else before," Linda said while looking majestically into David's eyes, watching him lay on the couch in complete relaxation.

"I was thirteen years old at the time it all began," He started, as his head turned and looked up at her. Then he rested back into the large pillow and recalled a piece of history. "Amidst that heap of articles in an old wooden box which my grandfather left in the attic there was one written document which caught my eye. I pulled it closer to me and felt the leather binding through the dust covering its surface. Then I sat in the corner under the circular window as the sun shined down on my arms, and I opened the ancient text. I had never seen anything in this box before and this old book looked like something that dealt with sorcery or some kind magic which are foreign concepts to me. I really had no idea what to think. Just let me tell you how powerful of a subconscious stimulant it was. Linda, I think it was a magical or mystical journey for my mind. In any case, I have tried to analyze it for years and that is why I never mentioned it to anyone before. Now you ask me and I shall tell you. Before finishing its slim nineteen pages my mind began to play tricks on me. I recall the strange apparition I had on page eleven when a circular globe of light came out of the book and went up to the window and through it, into the sky. It was like a ball of fire, a miniature sun radiating an energy field and coming into life, right out of an old book. Before that happened though, on page six the letters seemed to move around the page making it very difficult to read through it. I swear the letters were dancing as I tried to read it. I rubbed my eyes a few times and everything went out of focus then finally I got through that page. Really, I was just bored in the beginning, looking for something to do and went to the attic in search of anything to occupy my time."

"So David, would you say that you were bored and finding this mystical book put you into some kind of trance?" She asked while squinting and listening attentively.

"I don't know. I mean I don't think I was in a trance, just experiencing something from my normal state of mind and I was shook up by it. The book had powers... it had to have powers because there was no way things such as that can just happen. While trying to read through the final page, an apparition of a very large person came into the attic and startled me to death. It was a ghostly appearance, at least twice the size of a normal man. I have never seen a ghost before in my life and this bizarre looking entity was actually there. At first I was really freaked out by it. It moved around me in a controlled yet abrupt manner, like it was in a hurry to get somewhere or find something. I cringed in the corner holding the book to my chest but the entity never seemed to notice me at all as it scathed through the attic. Everything happened so quickly, I didn't even notice if it had eyes. There was a peculiar radiance emanating from its body, like a glowing light was inside of it," He stopped for some air and moved his arms around above his chest, looking at them strangely.

Linda noticed he was affected by recalling the incident. "Did you feel frightened by its presence, David?" She asked while sipping some water to clear her throat.

"I was shook up inside, and at first I was living with inconsequential fears. But I never really felt threatened by it. The large figure transported itself outside through the glass patio doors and onto the attic balcony. I sat there staring out and suddenly it vanished off the balcony. Then I was drawn back into the article. The thought of abolishing the subject entered my mind as I began to analyze why I was seeing such strange appearances, which over ran my logic and comprehension. Then I read at the middle of the last page something about transforming your mind into any energy field and going places and doing things at certain times and under certain circumstances. I tried to fathom the potential of that concept and that is when it all began," He sighed and rolled over, grasping his hands together and feeling a bit anxious.

"What did you do next David? Do your remember what you were thinking?" She asked while watching his uneasiness grow.

"How could written words have so much affect upon somebody's life? How could I allow it to infringe on my most personal feelings? It was responsible for what happened in my life since then. I am trapped in it like a person inside their skin. I didn't feel ready for this, but yet it happened anyway. I went to bed shortly after reading it. It was getting late anyway and I was tired. As soon as I fell asleep it was like real life but I told myself it was only a dream. A woman came in and took me out of the room. She wore a large floating gown. Everything seemed to be in a haze, like a warm fog surrounded us. I couldn't say no or yes to anything at that moment. I simply felt compelled to go with her."

"Were you concerned about anything at all?" Linda asked.

"No. I was beyond normal concerns, such as the feeling of fears or pain. There was no such thing as worry at that moment in that world. Somehow, the image of a large eye suddenly appeared. It drew my entire being into it. I was absorbed by its magnetic pull. It was an unwavering sensation as I recall but then a vacuum feeling came upon me. I was not concerned about it. It was like something that was meant to be or to happen anyway. I believe this was the beginning of some transportation process, which brought me to a totally new awareness for the remainder of the night. My emotions about the ordeal are complicated but the incident is unforgettable. It was like I was transformed into a higher awareness of myself. My body filled with some kind of new energy. I never tried to explain any of this to anyone before. My consciousness was projected closer into the eye as it seemed to move further and further backwards like a hypnotic disc spinning slowly and drawing me into it stronger and deeper. I didn't feel any physical reactions. I mean my body was likely intact and completely at ease, yet my conscious awareness was expanding into some undeniable depths as it was separated from my body. I was about to experience a realization about the importance of life. It was similar to approaching the brink or edge of my mind and realizing everything that is associated to my life simultaneously."

Again he paused to look back into her eyes. Small beads of sweat began to form on her brow, and she started to shiver as he connected with her. Unnerved, he turned back and continued, "My whole life before and behind me was capable of being changed at that instant when I passed through the eye. It was like I was given a choice to make some advancement in life for myself and perhaps for anyone I was ready to concentrate upon. I was projected forward into a large open space where vibrations could be felt very easily. It was the beginning of some extreme awareness of all things good and bad, light and dark, total opposites within relativity. It was moving my soul into another dimension beyond time. It was like a space journey at first because I thought suddenly about the moon, which flared by me, as if I passed it. A void opened before me. I stood on some other plane but could still use my senses. I was in a field of sunflowers and the Sun was brilliantly shining from the side. I know the first thing that came into my mind then. It was the meaning or concept of total purpose. I wanted it to be some divine purpose or sacred mission for me being there. Energy seemed to flow though my body again, like a refueling sensation or being charged up and I got a little excited from that sensation."

Linda interjected, "What kind of excitement did it give you exactly, David?"

David furrowed his brow, as though he were annoyed at the interruption. "It was an excitement of beauty or realization," he said tentatively, "I am still unsure as to what it was all about. With every ounce of my will I flowed in the direction I was drawn towards. Then something summoned my attention. It would be incorrect to call it a voice, but rather something picked up by the inner senses, which we all possess but are not fully aware of. I know this now, but couldn't fathom it then. It was almost like a voice within deep silence that gave me information and direction. My arms arched upwards but they were not my physical arms. Suddenly two vague images appeared on both sides of me and took my hands as I was transported over some great sea or ocean. The sky was yellow and gold and in the distance I seen a tincture of orange. It is something I will always remember, because of the great beauty I felt while being there. During the movement, which seemed timeless in some way, I recall looking at both of them. They were some kind of angels that came to help me or guide me. The experience was being digested in my body and I could feel it in my heart. I cannot properly translate what these messages were but in some way it appeared that mankind's destiny was at stake and something had to be done. There was a great confidence about the outcome and it seemed to have some definite relation to the little book I read back in the attic. The two angels are responsible for bringing me to this realization and they seemed to have such a great awareness of what to do for humanity. They were beyond anything I have ever sensed with any person in my life. They were connected somehow with the book, I am sure of it."

"Why would you connect them with the book?" Linda asked, tilting her head.

"At first I marveled at the book and even thought it might be evil. Then inside I realized that evil was really my ignorance of not knowing things in life. The book didn't suggest doing anything to cause harm or such. It was just a power tool and these angels seemed to be associated with what the book focussed on. It also emphasized the opening of light centers inside you to make things happen. It was as if inside of a person there are many doors and valves. By opening a door and then a valve, you can make things happen chemically within you and in other ways. It can even cause healing and other significant changes to occur, even changes with DNA. The whole experience made me desire to dramatically develop my life while I can. It made me very determined to find my destiny and set some special example by doing that. The whole episode was so enlightening and vivid as I look back upon it."

"What was the title of the old book?"

"It was 'The Flaming Serpent'. It had a picture on the first page of a serpent entwined around a long rod or wand and seven little suns lit up through the wand as the serpent reached the top. I remember there being seven suns because I counted them and my little sister was also seven at the time."

"Do you know where the book is now, David?" She asked softly.

"The unfortunate thing is that the following weekend my family moved to another town. The book somehow got misplaced and was never seen again. That is what I experienced that night when I met with angels abroad. What do you think about that, Linda?"

"What did you do that most impressed you for the years after that, David?" she countered, keeping the attention on him.

"When I was sixteen I met you and wanted to share this experience with you but could never bring myself to really explain it. Now that I know how important destiny is I want you to know about it also. Don't let me forget to tell you about something, promise me that."

"Alright, I promise I will remind you," She replied, arching an eyebrow and gesturing pleasure to further entice the conversation.

"I know that I was sidetracked a lot and did many foolish things in my life. I should have known better, really. There was so much I really wanted to do but never focused upon those things enough. I haven't done anything that truly impressed me yet, but now that I am twenty-two I will work towards something important," He vowed with confidence.

"You are twenty-three David. Not twenty-two," She slipped in a reply with sudden sadness.

"What do you mean Linda? I am only twenty-two."

"David, six months ago you had an accident with your motor-cycle. I didn't want to share this with you tonight but I have to, in hope of bringing us closer together. I cried every night and talked with you in my dreams. I want you to touch your face again, my love," She beckoned.

He lifted his hand and it went through his face and into the pillow.

"What is this, what is happening, Linda?" He said with grand disbelief.

"Sweetheart, you are in another world. I am contacting you again like I did last week. This week is much better. Last week you would come and go and not realize it. We had to work on it and I think we perfected it somehow," She began to cry.

"What are you saying? What… are you… trying to say, Linda?" He continued, his voice becoming more frantic and broken.

"Baby, you are not here anymore. Your physical body did not make it through the accident. I am so sorry but I had to find a way to be with you again, even if just to talk with you. I had to know what happened with your loving soul and if we could meet again somehow because I miss you so much. We shared such love and such important moments together. Inside I knew it was not over but didn't know how to contact you in the after-life. You know my friend Charlie at the store, well he explained briefly how I could contact you and so for a few months I worked on it and finally was able to sense you come back home. I read books on how to do it and now I know it works. Last week you were finally visible and could talk to me in broken words. There was a lot of things I had to prepare but at least we can meet again my love," She continued as waves of emotion filled her.

David's mouth opened wide with shock as his body slowly evaporated into the air.

"Come back, David! We are not finished tonight. Come back, come back!" She echoed in the chilling air.

His body reappeared slowly, and by his pained expression, it appeared to require much effort on David's part.

"What must I remind you to tell me, David? You have to tell me something," She said while directing her arms out towards him.

"Do not get on the bus tomorrow. Go to work a different way," His voice said faintly as he again began to vanish back into the other world.

"I love you, I do," She whispered in tears as she got up and ready for bed.

In the morning Linda remembered what he told her and decided to take a taxi to work, just for the sake of it. That night while reading a book and glancing at the television she noticed that a city bus had exploded downtown, apparently from a bomb that was placed on it. In great grief she put the book down and hugged onto the pillow on the couch that David rested upon the previous night. She realized it to be the bus that she would have taken to work.

"What a cruel world! He saved my life today," She thought while reflecting the incident as though it pinged off one emotion to another.

"If he cannot come to me, I will go to him," She decided as she went to bed holding his watch that she kept in her jewelry box as a commemoration.

Before falling asleep Linda repeated to herself, "I will come to see you tonight, David. Take me to see David, take me to him…" She repeated over and over, bidding to the invisible helpers.

As she drifted deeper to sleep she relaxed yet continually willed the projection of her mind to leave out of her body. She imagined her body getting up outside of itself and leaving the room, beckoning to the higher forces to bring her to him. She felt a separation as her consciousness disconnected from her body and drifted into the air. She felt fully aware of herself floating above her body and could see a great light through an archway that she was drawn towards. As her body glided to it she met with another presence. Her hands lifted up towards its face and she became aware that it was David.

"We are together on your side, my love," She spoke in a subtle voice.

"Come with me, you must meet them," He said with a delighted expression.

Together they whirled through a vibrant tunnel and entered a spacious garden on the other side.

"Where are we, David?" Linda asked, bewildered.

"I know where we are but I cannot explain. I am not David anymore. I am a residual of my Self. David was the name given to me for a certain time and now I am going to become someone anew," He answered with a voice of great certainty.

Linda looked ahead and could see two glowing, radiant people that floated towards her. "Are they the angels you met before?" She quickly questioned.

"They are the ones. They want to show you something, Linda. Something you should see," He replied as their lustrous natures coincided in harmony.

They came close to her and she could reach out to touch them but before she did they reached over to touch her head. She saw the most golden radiant globule of energy circulate around her body which began to emit a spectrum of particles, flourishing her with stimulating electrical vibrations.

"It is so beautiful. I am filling with sunlight," She gleamed with energetic ecstasy.

"The light is in you and its rays consume you," Her lover spoke as he looked on with great interest from a distance. "Take this with you and remember it is always there; you must just reach inside and you can feel it and use it to any ends. All answers come when you have this light permeating inside you Linda," He said as his vague body scintillatingly rushed closer to her.

Together they danced in the light, in another world within this one, engulfed in the Sun of immemorial splendor. The angel's presence was intensely invigorating. She could feel them as though she was part of their core. It was as real as reality could be. It was just like she was next to somebody that had a supreme emotional influence upon her. Everything seemed to be at oneness inside of her.

The lovers were ushered through a long corridor, which seemed to have windows elongated down each side. Was it the halls of Boabdil or was it the mezzanine of time? They fathomed through, amidst recognizance as they held back and glanced into innumerable shades to openings of the past. In one window they saw a man writing in a book, perhaps it was Plato or Aristotle, they did not know. In another window they saw a spaceship leaving the Earth and yet in another they saw pyramids and pictorials of history, one after another like a show of historical time. It was immemorial. The angels were there, but not seen; they had influence over the visions, but it was not obvious. They had remarkable abilities, but it was not known.

Linda witnessed events that took place through time and was astonished at what she saw, as though she was living there for each episode. She was living it as an experience within time; transported by an inner time-space capsule to a huge orange colored brilliance called Mercury. Life is truly miraculous and becomes profoundly intriguing when such awareness sprouts. The partners were led to the outskirts of Mercurial Intelligence. They entered the sphere of Hod as a conscious awareness and were dazzled by the perplexity of information that was stored within it. All written texts, all data from all time was encompassed within the sphere in an area that was beyond the conception of space. Every thought, theory, mathematical formula and conception was somehow transcribed in the inconceivable sphere. She had an interest to look around, to see through another set of eyes, and look through the angelic beings to find answers. Linda strained to look at them and they vanished into the light as she became infused with glistening sensations. She reverently uttered. "Everything in life means something. Everything is connected to these inner worlds and exists from them."

Her lover looked into the distance and said, "Heru-ra-ha! Lord of Light and Lion of Strength. Helios, Apollo, Ra, Surya, gods of the Sun, of life and everlasting light, abounding throughout the limitless world, enter through us so that we may fulfill our great destiny and promise to existence."

At that instant energy streamed up her spine to her head. It was like a shooting fire through her that lit and invigorated her chakras into activity. Her eyes opened widely, but not her physical eyes. It was a new vision that enabled her to see multitudinous patterns across the plane that she shared with her partner.

"My body is disintegrating, it is returning to the roots!" David bellowed with a subtle cry.

"Don't leave me now. I love you David, I need you!" Linda beckoned.

"Love yourself, love the world, we are all a part of it; all together, all together…" He returned as his astral body swept across hers along the path that they tread with mystery at every turn.

"I will always carry you as a part of me. Thank you for bringing me here, for being a part of my life." She whispered as his image evaporated into the ethers.

Her astral body and consciousness was called back inside her physical body upon her bed. She left the path and returned to the sphere of Malkuth, where a Great Guide delivered her to familiar territory. She re-entered her body and rested in perfect peace yet conscious of everything in her life and what she was to do. She felt like an oracle of transcendent revelation capable of visualizing anything she focused on in the future, past or present. Her soul mate continued his destiny and she was prepared to realize and continue hers. Words were not necessary, as everything was as it should be, without distortion or question.

What happened that night was something she would hold deep within and recognize for the rest of her days as a special capability to vanish all perils and problems. Life sometimes shatters hopes and dreams, sometimes it brings loss and suffering, but it always continues with ups and downs, ruin and fortune, melancholy and joy. Yet, there is that special connection it holds like a giant hand attached to an arm then a body then to a system of greater complexity. Still the elements are all there; they are all fitting and encompassing to make the system function scientifically and in majestic order. What once carried laughter, love and experience is never lost; it never becomes gone forever but lives on in the vastness of the unseen, only recognized when recalled by one who is in touch with it.

As she relaxed contently in her bed, Linda recalled something peculiarly enlightening about the angels. They radiated a supreme brilliance about simplicity; about being in touch with their core, their nucleus, and free to do their duty without the whims of constraint. 'That is what we all strive for', she thought, 'to be free and unhampered by anything so we can fly; fly high into the inner worlds and touch the beauty that is within all, to bring it back and smile upon its arrival.' ★

THE RISING OF AQUARIUS

"...the Astral Light is the great book of divinations; the faculty of reading therein is either natural or acquired, and there are hence two classes of seers, the instinctive and the initiated. This is why children, uneducated people, shepherds, even idiots, have more aptitude for natural divination than scholars and thinkers."

Transcendental Magic- Eliphas Levi

"What is it all about, what is life playing out there? Where are we going?" the Disciple asked the Master.

"We are not here, but everywhere. We are not one but a portion of the many. We are going on the journey, it is time to leave," The master responded as the cloaked figures walked between the pillars and up the winding staircase. They exited a door onto the rooftop and sat on two prepared seats, facing the west.

"Listen attentively to the silence echoing from beyond through the sounds in the winds." The master whispered as they closed their eyes.

It was the disciple's fifth year at the temple and daily preparations were made for this occasion. They sat quietly and breathed in a regular, deep, slow rhythm. Feeling in complete accord with the master, the disciple projected his consciousness out of his body and was lead throughout the land to witness events occurring simultaneously beginning in their country of Tibet and then to other countries around the planet.

In some places tragedy and sorrow were seen to occur while in other places excitement and happiness were vividly displayed. Events of every imaginable kind were taking place somewhere. From country to country they traveled and were inserted in every situation that the master chose from which the student could learn. A broad bandwidth of pain to ecstasy was experienced as their consciousness swept through one episode after another. Depression, hunger, delirium, hate, joy, love, jealousy, and loneliness were encountered in the majority of occurrences. Each country appeared to have a particular vibration to its mass consciousness stemming from the culture and social communal of its inhabitants.

The disciple continued to sit perfectly still, without displaying any sign of emotion or life. Even the most disturbing of incidents did not provoke an emotion. Together, their consciousness shared the same incidents that were occurring in every place that was visited. They saw murder, brutality, disease, birth, pleasure, and the growth of life in all places. Creation and destruction seemed to cancel one another out with the incidents, the thoughts and the emotions that most people experienced. Where there was greed, around the corner there would be charitable offerings to those in need. Where there was sorrow in one person, there would be joy in another to help uplift the friend or partner. Where there was a chemical dumping taking place by one company in the land and water, there would be the seeding of trees and beautiful plants by several others...

The morning mist forged through the trees as children left their meager homes and walked up the winding dirt road on their way to the schoolhouse. Pai and Hui walked to school together every day, as they lived next door to one another. Hui had a habit of skipping school, and today was no exception. "You better come to school. You are going to be in trouble again if you do not come!" Pai would scold, but Hui would have none of it. "I have to go some place important. I will be at school later, do not worry about it!" He yelled and proceeded to run through the trees, down his familiar pathway. A few minutes later he came to the large hill upon which sat the sacred Buddhist temple. There, he stood behind some trees and awaited to see the monks come outside.

Hui was seven years old and was born in northern Thailand. Once a week he would bring some fruit to a master at the temple. Today he brought three apples. His eyes squinted through the leaves and suddenly the monks came out and walked through the courtyard, heading to various points around the monastery. A great smile grew upon his face as he saw Master Sing walk solemnly to his usual position. He stood in silence until the morning ritual was completed. Hui did not understand what they were performing but knew that, whatever it was, it was for the good of the world. Different chants echoed from all sides of the monastery into the distant horizon. When they were finished and walked in unison back to the courtyard, Hui slowly approached and waited until they went inside. Master Sing slowed down and greeted the young boy at the entrance pillars.

"Master Sing," Hui greeted, bowing reverently, "My family worries of a flood they say will come soon. They do not want to lose crops again."

Master Sing smiled. "It will not happen this season, Hui. There will be no flood this time."

"There are many children at school who make bad comments about less fortunate ones. Why is there no peace in all the places around the world?" Hui asked.

"The world has all things good and bad but peace alone can only be within a man who is upon the path."

"Why is it that others must mock the less fortunate, Master Sing?"

"If the less fortunate hear the words enough they will believe it. There are pure fools and common fools; purity is found in balance without diversion, when the path is walked in a straight line," The master intoned. "My choice is to be pure. There are too many common fools." Withdrawing his gift of apples from his knapsack, Hui added, "I must go to school now Master Sing. Here are three apples. Someday I will be in the temple and learn more of such great truths."

Master Sing bowed, accepting the gift. "The only truths to learn are those that cannot be shattered and they exist deep inside of your body; for your body is the true temple. That is where you will find reality, awareness and enlightenment."

"Thank you, Master Sing. I wish all the powers in the sky to be with you," Hui answered as he turned to run down the hill.

Just outside Paris, Jacques was walking through a field of grapes with his girlfriend, Vicki. A resplendent rainbow shot across the sky, marking the end of a long rain.

"The rainbow, Jacques, look, it is so beautiful," Vicki said as she clenched on to his arm.

"It looks like it goes across the country, and the colors are plentiful," He replied.

"What does it mean, do you think it means something?" She asked.

"It means there will be peace and harmony. Its' colors mean life will be fulfilled for those who see through it, into the future." He answered.

"How can we see into the future?" she asked.

"We become the future." He smiled.

Deep within the Kalahari, an African tribe danced around a fire, wearing paint upon their face. They were building up energy to create the firestorm. As they danced faster they threw their burdens into the fire and watched the flames engulf all of their problems and grief. They continued dancing while moving their heads to the stars and back towards earth. They were worshiping the powers taught by their ancient ancestors, who became friends with the sky that delivered them a future.

On the third floor of a high-rise apartment building, Shawnee sat motionless. Her spirit guide brought her in touch with psychic visions and the progression of mankind through the ages. Her teenage daughter, Meaghan, sat next to her, as she often did when her mother went into trance, and listened once again to some remarkable information that she had no idea how her mother knew.

"There were twelve of eighty-eight constellations used throughout the world to mark the cyclical events of time. From the perspective of Earth, the motion of the sun and planets encompass an eighteen-degree wide band that stretches around the celestial sphere, considered as the zodiac. Nearly six thousand years ago the Babylonians developed the common zodiac representations as constellations having thirty degrees to their width and twelve in number, giving three hundred and sixty degrees as the circle of the celestial starry heaven. The Aztecs and Mayans incorporated it, and later the Egyptians, Chinese, Christian, Hindu and Moslem cultures used it as a clock in the heavens to organize life with time. Every period of two thousand years there would be a precession in the spring equinox and our planet would fall back into the next zodiacal sign."

Meaghan looked on with enthusiasm and began making notes from her mother's words, as she continued.

"In the Age of Taurus during the time of 4450 BC, the ancient Egyptians and Hindus gave worship to the bull or cow as a sacred symbol of their spirituality. Two thousand years after that period, in the Age of Aries, the ram was heralded as the sacred animal. When the precession entered the Age of Pisces during 200 BC, the Christians used the fish and its symbolic message to represent important facets of their cultural beliefs. At the vernal equinox, in the year 2000, the precession of the equinox occurred into the Age of Aquarius. It will last for 2126 years before the next precession occurs. It is represented by the figure of a person, illustrating that he or she will rise up to be equal amongst all others with human rights, becoming aware of the essence of star quality and likeness of God that is within."

Shawnee took a deep breath as her head circled and continued uttering messages from beyond.

"Technology advances with the dawning of the new age and humankind will begin the technology to live in places other than planet Earth. In the coming thousand years, people will venture to nearby stars and collect universal information from inter-galactic communications. The militant-technological advancement over the past hundred years developed branches of knowledge that is available to all people. Products are made smaller, cheaper, and generated to everyone so that they can utilize their creative efforts to stimulate economic growth for their country and society. Harmony between countries rises with the ease of communication and connection rapidly developing. Global powers are uniting together and weakening the smaller powers that wage conflict and war. All great changes arrive with disadvantages, sacrifices and responsibilities. The inhabitants of planet Earth have to prepare, educate, and develop their personal needs to journey into a future of turbulent times with change."

Meaghan sat breathless, in awe of her mother's words. 'Other planets? World peace? It sounds like Star Trek,' She pondered, 'Could that really happen?'

"Scientists and prophets make the future look grim in a variety of ways. The Mayans note a new era beginning in 2012, around the time that scientists are concerned about severe drought situations, atmosphere damage and civilization burdens. A comet heading into the direction of Earth during 2028 brings fear. Ice caps continue to melt faster, the axis of the earth shifts slowly, the poles may move soon. Sudden drastic changes in humankind begin to take effect. Through the coming century, the North Celestial Pole will pass through Ursa Minor, the little bear, by approaching the star that guides travelers as the jewel in the night sky, named Polaris. Ursa Minor, with its Polar Age on Earth and the constellation of Aquarius, will have combined effect on the state of evolution."

Meaghan shivered uncomfortably. 'I hope that doesn't happen.' She thought to herself.

"It is the age of man and the age of the Goddess, it is time to rise and become one with spirit. All life is precious and equally valuable for the continuance of human civilization. Judgement takes affect with the awakening to the realization of unification into future mobility. Individual consciousness expands to become one with worldly consciousness, to reach the spiritual planes through development of astral conscious initiation. Intuition is a recognized sixth sense in daily usage. Some people progress slower, clinging on to old routines, fears and habits and live in limitations and sorrow. Some rapidly consume the viable vibrations delivering them into the liberation of radiant light, progression. They become the crowned and conquering amongst all. They excel through the ordeals and enter the other side prepared for the stand. Judgement requires adjustment to balance the ills and foes that have not been distilled to advance into a unified consciousness."

Shawnee's eyes opened and looked at a painting of planets and stars on the wall. Meaghan held out her hand as her mother touched it. Together they smiled but displayed sadness in their eyes for those who have not prepared. Together they shared the secret of the dawning future but did not discuss it.

In Santa Monica, California, Veronica walked out of a grocery store with her child in her arms. A driver in a van was coming down the street and was distracted by his son sitting next to him. The van turned into the grocery store parking area and came towards the lady and her child. The man and son were arguing in the van and he did not see the lady proceeding across the street as he came within a few feet of her. An older man grabbed the lady's arm and pulled her back as the van suddenly swerved around her.

"Oh my, oh no," She gasped as she saw her life flash quickly before her.

"You are fine. It was not your time to go," The man said in a sincere voice as he touched her arm.

"Thank you, thank you. You saved us from a possible tragedy," She sobbed, stammering in shock.

"Everybody has so many chances and choices. Take the next opportunity to use it and you will gain another chance."

Wiping the tears, she asked, "But how will I know what the opportunity is?"

"If you follow your heart, and listen carefully, it will come to you," He whispered and continued his journey.

"The time has come, you must go now," A voice said through an archway. Lawrence got up from his knees and walked out the door of a small villa upon a hill in Mexico. He rushed up to a mosque and made the sign of the equal armed cross upon his chest as he entered. Within it he stood at the altar vibrating sacred names into the air.

"By the powers and momentum of the mighty names of God in the Sun behind the Sun, Adonai, EL Hai, Shaddai, Elohim Tzevaoth, Adonai Tzevaoth, Adonai, Elohim, EL, Yah, Eheh Asher Eheh, send the Light throughout the World. All Cosmic Beings, ascended Masters of the Light and Divine Names of God, Divine Spirit of the Great White Brotherhood, Archangels and Lords of the Universe watch over this change about to occur. I call upon the seven great solar logos to come and aid in the transformation: Osiris and Isis, Krishna and Sophia, Helios and Vesta, Apollo and Diana, Hercules and Amazon, Dawn and Luz, Aureole and Aurea. Governors of the worlds and planets, of the twelve solar hierarchies that serve the temples around our solar system, great Legions of Light and Hosts of Angels abide through the coming ordeals. Forces of the Elements, Watchers in the Silence and angels of the fourteen etheric cities of our planet, guide the Intelligence of ALL through the turbulence that becomes. Masters of Healing, Be there. Love, Harmony, Music, Hope, Purity, Balance, Victory, bring humankind into spiritual realization, to use their means towards their spiritual progress to know all Beings, Sacred and Divine, Holy and True."

Lawrence looked through the stained glass window above the altar as a brilliant light came through and enveloped his body. Around the mosque he could see Beings from beyond enter and leave as though he was heard and they acknowledged.

In Auckland, New Zealand, two Freemasons sat at a table in the lodge, indulging in a game of chess.

"What do you suppose the most destructive thing on earth could be, Arthur?" Phillip asked as he moved his knight to the center of the board.

"The inferiority complex that creates its own destruction?" The opponent wagered as he moved his own knight out on the board, while broadening his glance across the table.

"So what can that complex do that is so destructive?" Arthur asked.

"False interpretation and belief are the ingredients that create havoc. The sense of lost freedom and the creation of duality, they all play a part in the hierarchy." The other shook his head in affirmation.

"Are you proposing that the mind is the most destructive of tools as well as the most creative?"

"Indeed, mate. Look at the concept of fear and Judgement Day. In the past people were uncertain about the future, as they are today, but their religious beliefs created visions of a final day. Emmanuel Swedenbourg claimed to have visions of the final days of earth, as did so many other people. Eternal judgement is always upon us. It is one of those things we live with for being in a world of indulgences and manipulation."

"Eternal can only mean something if we are alive, for it is then that we have a concept of time, otherwise eternity would not exist as we know it." Arthur noted, taking one of Philip's pawns.

"Sure enough. Churches have used a variety of tools to keep people in line and in fear. Judgement Day is one of those tools. History has shown that churches can be wrong and destructive in both doctrine and life. If enough people go through life believing in world destruction in the future, it can do nothing positive in the end. All thoughts create something in this world, agreed?" Philip offered, pondering his next move.

"Agreed, each thought has a vibration and to create a destructive one about the concept of Judgement Day is nothing outside of evil itself. So would you say, then, that the church is preaching evil?"

Philip slid his bishop, claiming Arthur's knight. "Not everyone believes in Judgement day. Eternal punishment rests within the history of one word. That word is the Greek word aionios, which translates as eternal or everlasting. That word is the adjective of the Greek word Aeon, which means age. Aionios is used seventy times through the New Testament. Eternity is something we are living now, it is the combination of all possible states of mind and recognition."

Frowning, Arthur advanced another of his pawns. "Are you suggesting that there is no end, that as we die we transform and continue on and that death is an illusion, something people create sorrow from?"

"That is partial, but let me say this. Judgement is the making of karma, of debts you must overcome in order to spiritually advance, and it exists each minute during life and after life into the next life. If we alter the word 'Judgement' to the word 'Aeon' we can realize that there is nothing to fear in the future, nothing to fear in the present, and nothing to fear but fear itself. Living in each eternal moment is the spiritual quintessence of transformation."

"So we should awake each day and feel the beauty, the love and aspire to each moment in life. We should fill the world with positive thoughts and feelings and love one another with burning hearts under the infinite and majestic cosmic conception. We should work diligently in the here and now with our compass and square, filling each minute with the rapture of creative expression." Arthur smiled as he moved his rook to capture Phillip's pawn.

"We are capable of seeing several moves ahead in life, and so can avoid moves that will hamper our progression. Relinquishing some things in order to gain others is a philosophy of principles and tactics, my dear friend," Phillip grinned, as he accepted the loss of his pawn.

"So there will be no Judgement Day in the future, for the world?" Arthur questioned.

"Everyone has different beliefs. Some beliefs are rather ridiculous from a spiritual point of view. There is only one thing I can guarantee and that is now for reality. What else should matter and why would people want to spend a lifetime stagnating in fears and beliefs. It sounds rather religious and quite unspiritual." Philip sent the power of his rook forward.

"A system to keep people in check, perhaps?" Arthur questioned.

"Perhaps checkmate, making it the end of their game, their existence and to lose in the end when all along they were played a hat trick to believe that they would be saved."

"Who then becomes the victorious?" Arthur asked, sliding his rook to capture Philip's rook.

"Those who know the answers and have no belief. Those who have aspired and attained and do not simply pretend they are holy by telling others that they are. Those who opened their minds and hearts and have become master adepts, my friend, are the only victorious ones." Philip couldn't help but smile as he moved his queen to seize Arthur's rook.

Arthur's eyes went wide. "The rest are apparent pawns, not realizing their potential nor attaining it in the higher planes. I see where you are leading to, Phillip," Arthur sighed inwardly as he moved his last pawn forward.

"Do you really?" Phillip smiled as his right eyebrow raised. Hopping his knight forward, he added, "Check and mate my friend."

"You are a witty player amongst other things. I shall see you Tuesday evening, congratulations on the victory," Arthur concluded as he shook the victorious opponent's hand.

In Thailand, the small boy Hui looked up as though he knew someone was watching him. He raised his hands to the sky wanting to embrace the universe and sent out a radiant smile for the consciousness to witness. In France, Vicki was making love with her boyfriend, Jacques. They looked around the room and felt the presence of bliss and serenity and then into one another's eyes and became engulfed in the splendorous beauty of rising love. In the Kalahari a witchdoctor miraculously healed an ailing man of malaria. In America, numerous spiritual organizations were engaged in teaching positive holistic channeling while others programmed their followers to hate outsiders, believe in the end of civilization and gain material wealth before it is 'too late'. Incidents of child neglect, abuse and emotional punishment were also rampant. The master wanted the disciple to see every variety of manipulations that occurred concurrently throughout the world. Selfish and selfless, everything mattered and was part of the spiritual evolution of where the planet was heading. There was a drastic contrast between one circumstance and the next. It was to illustrate that the world was full of colors, full of emotions and occurrences that provoked one after another.

The disciple was impartial to what took place, as it was an experiment of non-involvement. He was to maintain the Taoist view of harmony and not consider one thing against another. Every incident however seemed to have an active and passive side. One to send and another to receive and react in a continuous momentum of manipulation and provocation. It was a circle of events involving the yin and yang characteristics in every person to create their desires, whether for the good or not of another person or their self. The disciple was aware that not all events involved the same level of reality. It was as if reality was layered from gross to subtle and incidents occurred in these layers according to the quality of love and devotion that the players incited and focused within.

There were large circles of people who worked in harmony and developed qualities into their personalities. It was as if they were holding hands and became stronger through the efforts and companionship they refined. There were also numerous circles of disenchantment and discord. People that brought one another down, thrived on their false sense of superiority, and provoked suffering for the excitement of feeling powerful and instilling fears. The disciple could see those people stuck in a particular layer working with limitations of their own making as they were disconnected from understanding and wisdom to channel spiritual aspirations.

The master led the disciple into the higher planes where he became aware of the hierarchy of angelic beings and genii of the adeptus level. A transformation of ego-self into divine love brought the disciple into complete and indivisible union with enlightened awareness. The impersonal connection illuminated the divine vibration with the Eternal Being into a vibration compatible with the soul consciousness of the disciple. The master became the link for the vibration to manifest into a state of perfect harmony. The ego's collective consciousness with its addiction to "Doing" was left behind as the Soul became the medium for the disciple to experience "Being", a Buddhic Awareness through the language of symbols, light, and a voice within the silence. The disciple became initiated into another level. It became a duty to come into contact with someone in extreme distress and to instruct the person with a method of clarity.

A suitable candidate was contacted. It was the lady in Santa Monica, named Veronica. Her husband, who was under a nauseating intoxication influence, was constantly abusing her emotionally. They shared a beautiful child together yet that child was also trapped between two souls that were lost in separate directions. She had deep-rooted anger inside and had been bottling it up for several years. She did not want to leave him yet she felt trapped, abused and not appreciated. She wished for her husband to communicate with her to distill the problems and release the angers that have developed. If only there was a way to reach out to her husband, to lift him out of the stupor that he trapped himself into. When her husband slapped her face out of emotional turmoil, Veronica left and went outside to sit in solitude.

She recalled the man who saved her life and told her that she had choices and chances to live with. She looked up into the sky and said to herself: "What is this world coming to? How can there be any peace when everything creates stress, people live in the shadows, and burdens come day after day between two people that once shared the beauty of love?"

The disciple connected with the vibrations of her cry for help. As she visualized the anger in her emotions, she felt something reacting inside of her stomach. The anger was lifted towards her chest, as though it followed a stream into an ocean. She felt a change occur as it spiraled into a higher state of vibrations. Anger took on a transformation. It became love, and infused her with sudden joy. At first she was perplexed, and then she surrendered. She was instructed to rise into another awareness, another level to connect with and allow the pouring through of light into her heart center. Veronica was given a truth, an ability to change any given situation for the better simply by lifting it to a higher level and allowing for it's transformation process to occur. She knew love emanated through the heart and now she was given the strength through realization that she could lift any emotion or thought into that center.

A subtle voice told her that she had to speak a truth, to speak it continuously, twenty-four hours a day to exercise the muscles of the emotional, mental and spiritual layers of her inner self. If she did this, held her truth unconditionally, she would exercise her will power to transform all situations that she was confronted with and to create positive results for her path ahead. She was determined to align her love with her husband's once again, to bring him into the unchanging reality that love offers. She was not about to allow illusions and self-pity to ruin their future. She looked up and then down towards her heart and whispered, "Thank you." Veronica stood up proudly and walked back into the house to radiate the entire place with immense love and begin communication on an uplifted level, to control the situation. There was nothing that would dissuade her actions of ambition. Not alcohol, not the lowly state of confused verbosity that her husband ranted, nothing could sever the bond of love she had with herself, her heart and her determination. Communication is a two-way street and she was about to pave it.

The master looked on with interest. It was time for the disciple to be challenged. There was a country about to begin a disastrous conflict with a neighboring country. The opposing sides confronted one another persistently over situations that could be laughed upon, as nothing is worth the taking of innocent lives. The determination was to bring realization of soul qualities into the leaders during their moment of communication about to take place.

The qualities that the disciple had to bring into awareness simultaneously were creativity, peace, spontaneity, love, and enthusiasm. The method was to bridge the negative to positive polarities that each leader held. Every person contains a soul, a medium for qualities to filter through and it became the task of the disciple to heighten the awareness of these qualities that the leaders were narrow sighted in. Their outlook encompassed control, power, protection, criticizing, and defending in a drama played on the material level. The lives of several innocent people were at stake so the method required assured success. The only way to control others, or the world, is to control self. The only way to control self is through love and love leads to light and light contains no negative effects. From a psychological perspective, analysis and deep insight were required tools in order for understanding to be delivered through the souls of the leaders. The psychic energy, which they entertained from one another, was simply a way to dupe responsibility. Their responsibilities were coldly focused on their lower senses, their ego-personalities that were molded as a pattern through judgement and suffering.

Through a trick that the master once taught the disciple, it was possible to induce change, to excite them into a higher vibration, such that their awareness was not enclosed in the physical plane but to have an inspiration occur, through their detachment, into their spiritual mental level. Another core issue was to relinquish control, which is a function of the ego. What appears impossible to some, especially when dealing with unbending mentalities as leaders generally display, becomes a task of concentrated effort for the holy person. When detached from the ego, there is no such thing as to try or to attempt. Everything is in the state of being and simply occurs. Failure is not a consideration.

It was accomplished. Endurance is success. The gap was bridged as the leaders shook hands. It only took a moment in the apparent time scale of physical realization, but the opposing polarities were merged through the inspiration of recognizing divine detachment. They began discussions in an impersonal way to achieve peace, becoming aware of the big picture and the consideration of the lives of innocent people. Who could predict the future of a race if one life was saved, it was not for them to judge, but to accept. The disciple was pleased and amazed at the sacredness of existence.

The disciple realized many things that night. Life consists of numerous levels and states of consciousness, with an apparent meshing for continuity. No two people are the same, yet there are increasing and intense problems in every country, every place around the planet. The ultimate way to avoid increasing problems, to prepare mankind for the future, to usher global consciousness into a positive direction of success to uplift all of humanity into spiritual awareness was through a pure heart. The result would be a greater love of and connection with nature, abandonment of conflicts that hampers the freedom of each person to accomplish their will and destiny and the negation of confusion and manmade disasters.

There are multitudes of Beings on every level, helping and assisting one another, sharing experience and answers. Some may be ascended masters, some may be as physically close as neighbors. The disciple had a mission to complete the training before ascending to the next level. It was a mission to bring awareness of life, love, light, liberty and the law of finding and performing the inherent destiny or True Will into the hearts of all.

The Age of Aquarius has arrived and the Aeon of Horus, the crowned and conquering One, is upon civilization. It is the time and place to become one, to seek unity with the Higher Self, to become spiritually aware of all things and situations. The time to act is now, to connect directly with the inner spirit, perform the True Will, and move forward as a team of humanitarian love around the corner of space we are about to witness and experience. ★

COSMIC SILENCE

"Dancing (Bright Lady) then began to be,
When the first seeds whereof the world did spring,
The Fire, Air, Earth, and Water did agree,
By Love's persuasion, Nature's mighty King,
To leave their first disordered combating;
And in dance such measure to observe,
As all the world their motion should preserve."
Strong, Splendour at Court, 140 (Sir John Davies)

Summer arrived with terrestrial beauty and a special calling was in the air for two individuals longing to escape the chaos of metropolitan Detroit. Mathew and Sarah had waited six months for this day to arrive. Their friends in California invited them for the summer to flee to Hawaii by taking a retreat on their yacht. It was almost like a second honeymoon for the weary city dwellers. Mathew and Sarah had been married for five years and neither had managed to escape the tiresome responsibilities that constantly burdened them.

Making their way through the airport was part relief and part stress as people around them neglected to have any concern about being ignorant and pushy. Getting on the aircraft was one step closer to a sense of freedom. Tracy and Richard were waiting for them at the other end when they arrived at the San Francisco airport. They received a warm embrace from their long time friends who had moved to California three years previous after winning a lottery.

"We've missed having you both as neighbors so much," Sarah said to Tracy, wiping a small tear from her cheek.

"How is our old house and the new people in it?" Richard asked.

"They are rather quiet next door but seem quite pleased with living there. Has it been three years already? I mean, wow! You folks look like you are getting younger instead of older!" Sarah declared with a hint of envy in her tone.

Richard smiled at the compliment. "Less stress, doing what we most desire to do, eating well and exercising daily are all keys to that, Sarah. Mathew, how has everything been with you?"

"Let's just say it's great to be here. Work is fine, but you know what routine is like sometimes. Have to loosen the strings and not take things too serious at times," Mathew replied with a sigh.

"Of course," Richard nodded compassionately, "Sometimes it is necessary to loosen the restrictions imposed by work and time and instead of being possessed by it, to shake it off and look at life with a refreshing perspective."

"That sounds harmonious," Sarah cut in, "Are you still studying Taoism?"

"To study or to be, that is the question," Richard laughed as they went to the car and proceeded to their home. "Oh, by the way... once we get home, would you folks care to join us in some margaritas?"

"That sounds quite inviting. Frozen margaritas I hope," Mathew urged with a smile.

"That's the way I make them," Tracy replied while turning around in the front seat of the car.

They entered an elegant, clean and modern house upon a hill with a lovely view of downtown. Mathew and Sarah tried hard not to stare, but their faces betrayed their thoughts. "It's not much," Richard said sarcastically, "But we make do." Tracy took Sarah by the hand and chirped excitedly about this purchase and that item as she took her for a tour of the house. Richard and Mathew shrugged to one another as they followed mutely behind.

"And here is our guest room," Tracy said cheerfully to Mathew and Sarah, "You can unpack some things here, but not too much, Saturday is just two days away and then we're leaving for Maui!"

"Hey, this looks pretty comfortable," Mathew said with a wide grin, "Maybe we could just stay here and house-sit for you for a few months?"

They settled in and enjoyed a few drinks with their compliant hosts, catching up on old times and toasting in the new.

"Here's to a wonderful reunion of neighbors that shared many great times!" Richard toasted.

"Chin chin my friends!" Mathew said and added, "This wine savors my palate perfectly."

"Did you know they have a pill on the market that does the same thing as wine except it is void of alcohol?" Richard asked as the ladies squinted at him.

"Mmm, really, what kind of pill?" Sarah asked sipping the Chardonnay.

"It's called a grape." Richard grinned.

"Ha, ha! Grape joke!" Mathew laughed not expecting the answer to be a jest, as the ladies rolled their eyes.

Though years had passed, it seemed as though the two couples still lived side by side. They watched the sun set over the downtown area, then chatted and drank until the wee hours of the morning.

The following day they went shopping for all the necessities they would need for the trip. It was a beautiful day in San Francisco and enjoyable for the reminiscent neighbors to be together once again. Richard then brought them to the yacht and organized everything in preparation for the following morning's voyage.

That evening they went to sleep around nine to be ready for an early departure. In the middle of the night Sarah was twisting and turning in the bed. Mathew awoke and assumed that she was having a bothersome dream. He began to gently shake her out of it. "Darling, is everything alright? Are you feeling fine?" He asked.

"Huh? Oh, oh Mathew, I was having this awful nightmare," She said in a groggy voice and began to stretch as she awoke.

"Will you be ok to go back to sleep?" He asked.

"I don't know. What a terrible dream I had. I was driving in a minivan and came to the end of a road, near a tunnel and had to stop for some reason. Suddenly there was some man standing on a ledge with a gun and began to shoot at me right through the windshield. I jumped down quickly to hide behind the engine compartment and wanted to crawl towards the back door to escape. That is when you woke me up," She said with a look of concern.

He began to rub her back and hug her gently. "Everything is alright now. We are out of Detroit so you can forget about those kinds of dreams," He added in hopes of making her realize she was in a safe place.

"Oh babe, I never have nightmares. Maybe cause we are sleeping in a strange place my mind is playing bad tricks on me," She relinquished.

"That's quite likely. Let's try to get some rest again honey," He said while cuddling back into the pillow.

The following morning the two couples were excitedly setting off from the city in a beautiful yacht named Endeavor.

"Au revoir, California! See you in the autumn," Richard said as he waved, upon leaving the marina.

"This is so exciting. We've never been on a long boat cruise before," Sarah said as she embraced her husband on the deck, looking at the city floating past them as they disembarked.

"It's going to be a fantastic voyage. Richard and I haven't gone to Hawaii yet either, so this will be the longest trip we've ever taken on our boat," Tracy said as she looked at her friends.

"New journeys, meeting with old friends, a new view upon life, that is what my horoscope said last week, Tracy," Sarah replied.

"Old friends? Did it say how old we are?" Tracy laughed as she poured some sun lotion on her arms.

"Yeah, there is something about that term 'old'. To me, the pyramids are old, but people can never get old, they just slow down a speck and do less strenuous sports," Richard remarked with a chuckle.

"This is quite a great feeling, Richard. Usually we see cities get larger and larger but as we move away from them, they appear smaller and smaller," Mathew said, out of the blue.

"Yes, it's called the limitation of the eyeball," Richard laughed jokingly.

The yacht distanced itself from land and soon America became an abstract horizon. Evening came upon them as Sarah and Mathew looked upon Richard and Tracy dancing joyously under the stars on the bow of the boat.

"They look like they have something exciting going on there, Mathew," Sarah exclaimed.

"Looks like an East-Indian dance. Quite joyful, for sure. Wish I knew those motions," Mathew said with slight angst.

"Did you learn that in Tai Chi class, Richard?" Sarah asked, sipping a margarita.

"We were in India for two months last year. Couldn't resist," Richard yelled towards the stars.

"Mathew, buy some lottery tickets, for God's sake," Sarah giggled.

As the evening entertainment came to an end they decided to take shifts at the wheel to ensure that the yacht kept the proper heading.

Daylight broke a bright red horizon that lit the inside of the cabin and woke up Sarah. She noticed that Mathew was not beside her. She got up and stretched and wore her housecoat out to the kitchenette. He was standing at the stove making omelets for everybody.

"I didn't hear any roosters this morning. What brings you out of bed so early, my sweetie?" Sarah asked.

"You don't recall the kisses and me telling you that breakfast is going to be a feast?" Mathew replied.

"Mmm, it sure looks and smells like it will be. I don't think I will ever trade you in," She winked as her arms came around his waist.

"Hmph! I was thinking the same thing about you," He said while enjoying her rapturous caress.

"Where is our captain and his first lady?" Sarah asked.

"She is at the wheel and he is doing some kind of yoga thing in his cabin," He replied.

"Yoga thing? Not like the one we did last night I bet," She said as she pinched him.

Richard walked into the kitchenette with a warm smile. "Hey there you folks, that breakfast smells deliciously superb," He began.

"Ah, I hope this food is fit for a yoga man," Mathew smiled back.

"If it isn't my body will conform it to be," Richard chuckled.

"What kind of yoga have you been practicing, Richard?" Mathew asked with great curiosity.

"It is an eastern form of kundalini yoga. Raising of energy through your body, basically," He replied.

"I've heard of that. It is power connected through the chakras to bring them into greater activation, correct?" Mathew asked.

"You've heard about the chakras, Mathew?" Richard queried.

"Not a lot, but in some books I've read they were mentioned. It is a pretty large field of study."

"Yes, most definitely," Richard confirmed, taking a seat at the breakfast table, "The kundalini is also called a fire snake for its great awakening powers and resides at the base of the spine, coiled fifty and a half times. When the person is properly developed through years of work, it can be gradually lifted through the centers to activate them. Each coil is a dimension that corresponds to a particular Intelligence whether it is gross or subtle. Overall, kundalini is considered to be the Goddess, which is asleep at the basal chakra and as activation occurs, dangers could result as particular siddis or magical powers are developed."

Tracy walked in as Mathew was prepared to serve portions of his omelet. "Just in time. Anybody get seasick last night?" she asked.

"Not at all, the ride was really pleasant, especially for being so far out from land," Sarah admitted.

"Mmm, yum, great work on this breakfast Mathew!" Richard commented.

"Thank you. So the chakras are not operative in an average person?" Mathew replied.

"Not very much," Richard sputtered through a mouthful of omelet, "There is a lot involved in a chakra. They have outer rings and inner rings and many petals attached throughout. These are like petals of a lotus and gateways to activate them. A chakra may require up to seventy-three particular participants to be involved, if the Suvasini is included to make it fully operative."

"No wonder it requires a lot of training to be prepared for the kundalini force to activate them," Sarah curiously added.

"Yes, especially without causing damage, internally and for so many other reasons. Basically a mystic raises the kundalini whereas a magician that works with that energy raises it and brings it back down, materializing the effects she, the kundalini goddess, causes. One seeks liberation from phenomenal existence whereas the other seeks control over it and thereby attains magical powers but in either case supreme knowledge becomes an experience," Richard said.

"Does special breathing play an important part in this kind of meditation practice?" Mathew asked.

"Indeed, as yoga practice advances, the individual experiences levels of awareness through pranayama or breath control. It stimulates the sushumna, which is the subtle central stream along the etheric spinal column and as the energies rise through the nerve centers to the highest chakra the yogi becomes aware of the supreme knowledge. There is vitality in the air and when you practice controlling that vitality through your left and right breathing passages you stimulate the vital nerve centers throughout, developing states of harmony then a mystical congress of consciousness and power ensues," Richard remarked.

"That is truly interesting. I am sure there is much more to it but it makes a person realize that enlightenment is really only achieved through real arduous dedication although there are many not so enlightened people out there that would try to make a person think otherwise," Mathew added.

"Oh definitely there are, Mathew. To dedicate a daily routine of mastering a system for several years is really what it comes down to. Nothing is achieved over a weekend and even less through someone that is deceptive. Think of a person lying in a pig stein, around a bunch of mud and dirt and filth. If we let that represent the illusions that trap a person and then they decide to fight it all off and get up and focus towards the shower room, they are starting the process of awakening. Cleansing every part of their internal and external world and not being sidetracked by entertaining temptations, allowing progression to take it's slow course, then you will have a very basic idea of what it entails."

"Some people may think this is too much for them, that it involves a lot of work and perhaps confusing in a number of ways," Sarah interjected.

"Sure enough," Richard beamed, "They may not be ready but sooner or later they will have to go through a process in order to evolve, to keep up with the consciousness that is expanding into the future. Thinking in those terms, would you prefer to be in grade two for twenty years while others are in grade four, eight and twelve? It's a difficult choice and one that most people refuse to acknowledge but essentially to be above deception and all the emotions that trigger increasing problems throughout life a person has to do some internal work. They have to balance one thing with another and they have to complete what they begin in one form or another and they then eventually subconsciously stop to invite problems into their life."

"That makes a lot of sense. Do you think that the reason you won a large lottery a few years ago has anything to do with the spiritual direction you have chosen? I know it sounds silly but I was just curious to ask," Sarah queried as she finished eating.

"No question is too silly," Richard said, mocking a serious face, "They are there for a reason but to tell you the truth I do not know the answer. There are millions of people on spiritual paths of every imaginable variety and they do not acquire wealth from that. Anything that you achieve in material form can be lost as easily but in the spiritual sense, anything worked for remains precious and intensifies. Winning money for us was perhaps a kind of reward to go further, perhaps a button was pressed that I was not aware of in order for it to occur. We actually find our life busier now than when we worked regular jobs." Richard paused to sip his orange juice, then continued, "Sometimes people sacrifice some physical things to achieve greater things, and in our case we made a lot of sacrifices to learn what we share today. Tracy and I are on a journey as partners and we communicate about things in many ways and on many levels. It keeps a bright light in front of us along the way and we can feel one another even though we are not within visual range. Most people have this ability and feel the thoughts and emotions of their partner not only when they are around one another but at a distance as well."

"This is an interesting concept. It is like saying that thoughts have the ability to travel and that people are attracted to them," Sarah nodded to herself.

"They do carry or travel in a particular vibration and in some subtle way when you and your partner are tuned to one another's thoughts and emotions, they are easier to pick up and read. That is to say, easier for the consciousness to register and translate them, like a radio picking up a frequency," Richard agreed.

"Alright, Richard, I am thinking of a number between one and ten. Tell me what it is," Mathew challenged with a smile.

"It is ten, the wheel of life goes round and around," Richard replied with a laugh.

"That was just a lucky guess, want to try it again?" Mathew returned.

"Let's enjoy the sun out on the deck." Tracy interjected.

"Ah, that sounds more like a vacation," Sarah said as everyone left the table to go up and breath in the Pacific Ocean air.

The view was majestically serene. Nothing could be seen around for endless miles, bringing a sense of total peace to their hearts. The sky was blue except for in the distant west, where clouds appeared but ever so out of range.

"All legs on deck, dance-athon begins in five minutes!" Yelled the captain.

"Aye, aye! We have to keep in shape, even on vacation," Sarah yelled back with a salute.

Tracy turned up some music as they danced and poured mineral water over their faces and playfully tossed some upon one another.

"Hey Richard," Sarah shouted, "In the eyes of an enlightened person, do people with regular routine problems appear like burdened fanatics, trapped in a little world of their own creation?"

"That is a tough call, without offending the general mass of civilization, since I would say that 'enlightened people' is a very relative term. In an extreme case I would say that those who are above bringing such considered problems and burdens into their life realize that those who do are simply unaware most of the time. Also, everyone is in what I think of as shifting states, since they know what is right and wrong and sometimes they simply yield to decisions that later prove unfavorable, in the end. Have you ever watched a nature show where lions attack a buffalo? Well, the buffalo gives in once the female lion holds onto the snout long enough, although inside there is a capability of fighting it off, it simply decides to lay down and accepts to be eaten. Perhaps there are latent instincts in people that make them want to give in from stress or from a particular situation that they are confronted with. It's a tough call and depends on so many things. I am not at the stage where I think you and Mathew are burdened fanatics however," Richard laughed as he sprayed water on both of them.

"That's great then, I guess we won't be thrown overboard and will end up at Hawaii after all." Mathew jumped with joy.

"I don't think that will be a problem. You are part of the crew for this long journey. We need you as much as you need us," Tracy smiled.

"Hey did you ever hear about little Johnny?" Mathew inquired as he looked at everyone's faces, "For his birthday, Little Johnny asked for a 10-speed bicycle. His father said, 'Son, we'd love to give you one, but the mortgage on our house is $80,000, and there is no way we can afford it this year.' Well, the next day his father saw Little Johnny heading out the door with a suitcase. So, his father asked, 'Son where are you going?' Little Johnny replied, 'I was walking past your room last night and I heard you tell Mom you were pulling out. I heard her tell you to wait, because she was coming too. And I'll be damned if I'm sticking around here by myself with an $80,000 mortgage and no means of transportation!'" Everyone laughed and got joking on a roll, adding to the humorous mood.

Every day they entertained with different games for amusement and enjoyed the great relaxation of vitality rejuvenation being on the vast ocean. Before they knew it the following week was upon them and soon they would be on one of America's most renowned of vacation islands.

"I could do this forever and never get tired of it," Mathew smiled with enjoyment as he tanned his body under the sun.

"Definitely, this is quite a life," Sarah remarked, "We sure appreciate you great ex-neighbours inviting us along on such a wonderful journey. Even though we had to take work off for the whole summer, it was worth it."

"We are very grateful to have you with us, it's been so long since we've been together. This makes up for lost time," Tracy said as she offered them some afternoon drinks.

Another day had past and nightfall brought a tired crew to sleep without a sound. The moon glistened over the ocean as the yacht continued skipping over little waves, keeping its course, with Sarah taking first shift. She adored the beauty of such spaciousness upon the ocean and in the sky with stars twinkling like they have done so many millions of years and guiding civilization into the future. At one in the morning she went to awaken Richard for his shift. "How was your shift?" Richard asked, rolling out of bed.

"It was really beautiful out there under the stars," Sarah replied.

"Oh, wonderful! Sleep well," He bid to Sarah as he got ready and went above.

The following day was another routine of good food, good company and creative entertainment. As nightfall came once again, the stars were no longer visible. Clouds roamed across the atmosphere bringing winds and larger waves, rocking the boat as it glided over them.

"The weather warning states a storm coming overnight. It will not be a big concern. This boat has gone through a lot worse. If you have any concerns, just call me on the intercom," Richard said as Mathew took the wheel.

"Not a problem, friend. It is part of the course in life to handle some bumps," Mathew attested. He listened to music on CDs while keeping watch on the front of the boat. Spotlights made several feet in front of the yacht amply visible through the surrounding darkness to ensure that it did not ram into anything afloat upon the ocean. By the end of his shift, the water was rather choppy and the winds were gusting heavily. He went to awaken Tracy for her shift.

"It's a bit rough out there as you can probably feel, Tracy," He mentioned as she came out of her room.

"Yes, I woke up a few times, so it could be a rugged night ahead. Just buckle yourself into the blankets and try to sleep well," Tracy smiled.

The voyage got rougher on the ocean as the shifting boat kept Tracy alert for the next two hours. Waves swirled up along the sides, upon the deck, but she was enclosed in the control compartment, out of the wind and tormenting waves. It was an exhausting time, certainly a change from other nights but she held through and kept the boat from veering off course. At four in the morning she called Richard on the intercom, not wanting to leave her station. A few minutes later he arrived for his shift.

"This storm isn't dissipating Tracy. It is actually getting worse," Richard noted as he arrived in the control cabin.

"I know, babe. We are taking an awful pounding here tonight. I am going to curl up with a blanket right over here on the sofa beside you tonight. I want to stay up here, okay, Richard?" She said while expressing concern for their safety.

"That is fine sweetheart. We will ride this storm through," He replied while looking at the radar screen, which was suggestive of gale force winds ahead. Richard kept the boat as steady as possible riding over the waves and wondering in the back of his mind if it wouldn't be better to steer off into another direction. It was not an easy decision, however, as Richard could not predict the result of turning to any other direction with the storm completely surrounding the boat. The waves seemed to gather strength as they pushed the vessel around in the rushing ocean as if it was an old toy, waiting to be disposed. Below deck, Mathew and Sarah awoke from the clashing sound of dishes outside their door.

"This wasn't in the itinerary," Sarah said to her husband as they quickly got dressed and went to the control cabin.

"I've never imagined it to be so rough this time of year," He answered as they clenched the walls, rumbling back and forth while making their way towards the skipper.

"I hope it wasn't my steering that woke you folks up so early," Richard grinned as he held tightly onto the wheel.

"This is quite a wild storm; is it what they call a white squall? Should we radio in to let them know we are out here?" Mathew asked.

"I just did that. I let them know our position and the conditions and they said the storm is not going to let up for several hours. There is a coast guard ship about one hundred miles away. If we don't contact port every half hour they will send it in our direction unless we request it beforehand," Richard said.

"That is a relief. I think we will stay up here until things settle down," Mathew said.

"Tracy doesn't look to be very deeply asleep there," Sarah remarked.

"I am not getting much sleep tonight," Tracy whispered in a semi-conscious state, "Trying to, but it isn't so easy to sleep on a roller coaster."

"I don't like the look of the water ahead. It is so dark and the waves are relentless," Mathew commented to Richard.

"I know, but there isn't much we can do right now except try to ride them through. These tropical storms pick up when you least expect them to. I was going to turn towards another direction, but it wouldn't do much good, the storm is the same thirty miles out in every direction. The ocean is free to do as it pleases. Unfortunately it doesn't consider us as being of any great importance." Richard said sarcastically as the yacht hurled upon another twenty-foot wave.

The sun was about to rise from the east, as the deep indigo clouds appeared to hold a tinge of light within them. The little yacht continued to whirl over magnificent crests of gushing ocean in its attempt of staying afloat. Drastic winds spiraled around the boat pulling away everything that wasn't fastened directly to it. With only a day and a half to arrive at the Hawaiian Islands, it wasn't a pleasant welcome. The boat smashed up against an even larger wave and tumbled over the other side without warning. Everyone was thrown towards the inner walls and onto the floor.

"I think it's time to call for a rescue," Richard grimaced with a cut down his face and admitted, "If there is anything of value to you downstairs you'd better run to grab it now."

Everyone ran to grab any valuables that would fit in their pockets and proceeded to put on life jackets. The floor below deck had a foot of water in it. It was coming in faster than the pump would exert it back out.

"Mayday, mayday, this is US vessel Endeavor, vessel number 943825-4, we require urgent assistance," Richard yelled on the radio.

"Here, keep these life preservers close to your body," Tracy said as they ran from the kitchen to the upper deck. Water was everywhere in the boat and throughout the upper decks.

"Can we detach the little motor boat and use it as a float?" Mathew yelled.

"We'll have to prepare for that. Let's hold out as long as we can," Tracy yelled back, breaking through the noise of the surrounding torrential winds and clashing waves.

They entered the control cabin and looked at Richard, still hurling the boat over the pitiless ocean as though it was nature's plot of life or death. Sarah stared at the front window as a gigantic wave crashed through and over everyones head. She was forced backwards towards the engine compartment door and recollected her nightmare before she left San Francisco. Water gushed in the cabin and began filling it slowly up to their knees. With her clothes drenched, Tracy looked into Richard's eyes with concern and said, "I love you. We are going to make it through this, babe."

"Yes, I know we will, just have to keep everyone's head above water," He replied as he spewed water from his mouth and cranked the wheel hard right to float above another blasting wave.

"What can I do to help?" Mathew asked Richard.

"Tie yourself onto a rope and go unhook the speed boat from the rear. Try to get it ready in case we have to plunge off this thing," Richard yelled.

Sarah and Mathew ran to the back to prepare the small boat for an emergency dismount. Winds and waves threw him from side to side effortlessly as Sarah held the end of the rope from around his waist, tied through a metal loop near the door. The speedboat was ready for a sudden escape, although in the gashing waters it would likely be devoured before long into the depths of the ocean and would not be of lasting comfort.

"This is outrageous! It is only suppose to happen in the movies!" Sarah cried as she leeched onto her husband.

"Sweetheart, we will make it. It is not our time to go yet. Keep your head as high as you can possibly imagine. Rescue is on their way," Mathew asserted as he held her tightly beside his body while pulling their way back towards the control cabin.

"It's ready, Richard. Let's hope we won't have to use it for a while," Mathew yelled to the commander who was maintaining their lives above water.

"I say we have about twenty minutes before this boat decides to go under. Everyone keep together at all times. If the speedboat doesn't last, remember to keep together and we will join in a small circle and fight to stay above water. Keep your strength and don't ever loose it. Breath slowly and don't panic." He yelled as he grabbed on to the emergency satchel. Tracy was behind him holding him steady and giving him a final strong embrace.

The boat carried them forward another half-hour but was ready to sink at any moment. They were barely above water and decided to run towards the small speedboat before they would loose it as well. Everyone jumped in and pushed it away from the arduous 'Endeavor' that kept them alive for as long as it could. The waves were lessening to fifteen feet high but still too much for the little craft to withstand. It was tossed and hurled around in the storm as they took their last look of the sinking yacht, disappearing below the savage sea.

"This dinghy is going to flip any minute. What are we going to do out in that ocean?" Sarah yelled with fear flowing through her veins.

"Do not panic and keep very positive, my love. We will make it, we just have to fight it and go through it." Mathew said while looking deep into her eyes at her longing soul.

"Let's tie the life preservers together so we can keep together if we are thrown into the ocean," Richard yelled as he pulled out some rope and quickly gained their assistance.
A large wave pulled the little craft up on its crest as everyone held on to the sides tightly. As it came down, it darted into the water and its back toppled over, throwing everyone into the ocean. They all held onto the tied life preservers as they were hurled around helplessly with the ravaging currents.

"Let's get together, swim together!" Richard yelled to the others as they attempted to swim towards one another, reaching for the life preservers. The rain pelted on their foreheads as they were thrown carelessly around in the torrent.

"Hold on, let's keep our arms locked around these preservers and never let go. Breathe slowly and keep everything together," Richard directed.

"Mathew, I don't want to die. I don't want us to go like this," Sarah cried.

"Keep your strength, sweetheart. We are not going to die. I love you and am not going to let you go, don't worry, we are going to make it!" Mathew yelled to her as he reached over to kiss her cheek.

"Sarah, we can make it. People go through the toughest imaginable times every day around the world. Sometimes they think all hope is lost, but go beyond that, go beyond your hope and there will be life! Reach out and hold onto your life! Escape beyond your limitations!" Tracy yelled with positive affirmation as water pelted across her face.

"We are going to make it! Help will come. Help will come." Sarah yelled back with an estranged smile through her deepest despair.

"Mathew, that little Johnny joke wasn't that bad after all. Now that I have some free time, I can laugh at it," Richard remarked across the circlet of life preservers with a continuous slight laughter.

"I can't think of any other jokes right now, but I am sure they will come," Mathew said as he pointed his hand towards the sky of dark avenging clouds.

They huddled together as the waves picked them up and threw them over the other side, back into the gully of ravaging, swirling tides.

"Is everybody alright?" Mathew yelled.

"It's getting hard to hold on. The forces keep pulling me away," Sarah yelled to him as a wave belted her across the face.

Mathew gasped for a bit of air and hauled his body closer to hers and wrapped his arm around the inside of hers. "Stay with me honey. Keep our arms locked. We are going to make it one way or the other. Hold on and relax whenever you can. Never let go, baby," He said while reaching to quickly kiss her forehead.

Their bodies were dragged like inanimate objects over the rushing tides and then suddenly whisked down repeatedly into the depths of desperation. They felt like they were thrown into hell over and over and then hauled out for the momentary awareness that life still existed. Richard appeared to maintain the greatest control by displaying reinforced positive gestures with his fancied facial expressions. Somehow the others gathered strength from his presence and continued to hold on despite the forces tearing at their bodies. Average strength would have dissipated long ago and have made them surrender. They would have preferred to let go and be taken to the ocean floor rather than be torn and twisted with the ongoing everlasting revenge, but a group force held them together.

"How will anyone ever find us? How will they ever see us?" Sarah cried in anguish.

"You are not alone Sarah. We are all together and together we will survive," Tracy replied with comfort in her voice.

For two hours they rode the waves as the storm began to slowly subside. They were all drained of energy and longed to lay on anything that was solid. All of the potential energy was vacuumed out of them as they held on and spoke to one another every ten minutes to keep awake and partially alert. Richard looked around to see if the Coast Guard ship was in sight but there was nothing to be seen anywhere but water and dubious skies. All hope seemed to be lost except that small spark within them that told them they were still alive and had vague memories of incidents throughout their life.

Mathew put his arm around Sarah and spoke softly into her ear. "Never give up, sweetheart. There is nothing that can take us apart, nothing in the world."

She looked over to him slowly and whispered back, "I can't feel my legs. I can't feel anything down below the water."

"Sarah, it is from being tired. Soon we will be on a ship and resting. You have to hold on and picture the ship coming for us. We will see it soon, Sarah," Tracy whispered back to her, in extreme fatigue.

"Why is life so cruel? What did we do to make this happen?" Sarah said in a broken voice filled with sorrow.

"It is not a fault of life. We didn't see the storm coming soon enough. It is something, something that just happens," Richard intervened as he struggled to keep his arm locked around Tracy's.

"Is that the ship, is that them coming?" Sarah murmured.

Everyone twisted their heads and looked into the distance. A large dark object was coming towards them as it appeared over the waves and then disappeared under them. As it came closer Richard squinted his eyes with great effort to discern the object.

"It is, it is a whale," He laughed appallingly at the hallucination as he looked around to his dying friends.

"Everybody, that is a sign of something. It means something," He whispered trying to get their attention focused once again.

Mathew looked towards the whale but it was gone. It plunged into the depths and turned towards another direction.

For the next few hours everyone contributed to keeping one another alive in any miniscule way they could summon from their emotional core. It was like the final effort of survival, as they were depleted of any life force that they previously held. Life has a very precious meaning, one that can only be felt when on the brink of losing it. When the body is completely drained of its supreme essence that keeps the consciousness intact, a voice comes into it and speaks to the soul. It is a voice from the silence of the unknown. A voice that can break the barrier that a person has crossed through the most severe of ordeals. It is not unlike a faint whisper that guides the person onwards after death or to give them direction in a course they must pursue. Some may refer to the voice as an inner guide that arrives at the absolute moment of transition between life and death. In a very personal way, the voice feels the soul of the person and awakens them to a specific realization. It cuts through the web of being ensnared with limitations and liberates the soul into a realization of a four-fold reality, a reality beyond the threshold.

Everyone's eyes were closed. They were drifting aimlessly upon the ocean and were about to let go at any moment and drop into the water to be swallowed into the other side of life, with the forces of the tide. The sun broke through the clouds and shined on Richard's forehead. His eyes slowly opened to feel the radiant energy enter into him as the rays penetrated through his eyelids. The waves became large ripples and he could see an image in the horizon, as though land in the far distance existed. Sluggishly he turned his head to the left and could see an image in the background. It was a vessel of some kind. He breathed as deep as he could into his lungs to activate himself into awakening. His arm was still wrapped around his wife and tied on to the life preserver rope. His wrists were cut and badly bruised from the arduous forces of the rope. Unleashing an arm, he reached into his satchel and pulled out a flare. He stuck it into his mouth and pulled off the end and managed to strike it after several attempts. It shot up into the air and flamed into a bright red glow.

"Everybody wake up. Everybody, Tracy, Mathew, Sarah, wake up!" Richard wheezed. No one moved a muscle. They were rigidly attached to one another around the floating devices, wearing pale faces. Richard slowly hauled out another flare. It felt like it weighed a hundred pounds. He commanded action through his body as though it wasn't his any longer, for some energy to awaken and strike another flare. By some magnificent feat, he managed to shoot another one into the sky. His eyes looked at it as the redness from its fiery beacon made the call. A few minutes later, the distant boat appeared to turn towards their direction. "Help us, help us," His bleary voice echoed throughout the open ocean. He looked into his pack but there were no more flares. He hauled out a red flag on a one-foot pole and held it in his hand as his eyes pulled shut.

Twenty minutes later a large shadow came over his head. His eyes reopened slowly and looked up. The boat had arrived. A splash of water washed over everyone as a diver jumped into the ocean, beside the victims. The diver hauled Sarah's body close to the boat as two men hoisted her up. The diver then grabbed on to Tracy and pushed her body towards the hoist. Mathew was then pushed alongside the boat, followed by Richard, and lifted to the platform. Everyone was brought into the cabin and put upon beds to rest. Richard slowly lifted his mouth into a smile and whispered to an old man looking upon him:

"I saw you, knew you would come. How are my friends?" he asked.

"They look very exhausted, young fellow. I think they will be fine after a while of rest," The captain replied.

Richard's smile grew in relief. The boat headed to shore as the storm victims slept for several hours. Sarah awoke as the sun began to set. A young lady brought her some hot co-co and sat at the edge of the bed to talk with her.

"How are you feeling now?" A feminine voice echoed through her ears.

She began to lift herself up from the bed, all covered with heavy blankets. "I feel alive again. Where is Mathew? Where is everybody else?" She asked with sudden concern.

"They are all fine. Everyone is still resting. We should be at the island in a few more hours."

"How did you find us? Who sent you?" Sarah asked in a semi-conscious state.

"We were out fishing for a few days on my uncle's boat. We left Hawaii this morning as the storm lifted. One of you folks lit up a flare and I saw it and told my uncle. After that another one was seen and we went in its direction and found everyone huddled together. We were really happy to find everybody alive. My name is Melanie, by the way. Anyway, we will talk later, you should rest more," Melanie said as she lifted the covers to Sarah's chest.

"I want to see the others. I want to see Mathew," Sarah replied as she lifted herself slowly from the bed.

"I'd better help you. Take it really slow," Melanie suggested.

Sarah attempted to stand on her feet but found it impossible. The weight of her body made her collapse to the floor.

"You just need to regain your energy. You have to take it really slow for a while," Melanie asserted with confidence.

"Help me, I want to lay down beside Mathew, please," Sarah requested.

"All right, let's move very carefully then," Melanie said as she lifted Sarah from the bed and walked her slowly to the next compartment.

"Mathew, Mathew, we are going to be fine," Sarah said as she looked at his emotionless face.

His eyes opened as she crawled in to cuddle beside him.

"Yes, we made it, we all made it. Richard helped us to survive, I know he did," Mathew whispered shakily.

"They both helped us. They are beautiful people and they are our friends," Sarah laughed with an intense happiness flowing through her body. Their arms reached around one another as they fell into a comforting sleep, embraced with a gratitude and appreciation for life and survival.

Melanie walked into the next bedroom and saw Richard sitting beside Tracy. "You are quick to revive yourself," She said with a pleasant smile.

"There is something very special in life that revives all of us. May I ask what the name of this boat is?" He requested whilst returning the smile.

"Certainly. It is my uncle's boat and it is called 'Essence'." Melanie replied.

"That is the special something in life that keeps us together, as one and as a part of all humanity within that one. I thank you so much for being there, for bringing 'Essence' to save our life," He said to Melanie while gently rubbing his wife's forehead. Tracy's eyes opened as she reached up to touch his arm.

"Richard, we are alive again," Tracy gratefully whispered in astonishment.

"Yes, we made it through, everybody made it through." He said with such satisfied happiness.

The boat traveled through the darkness, towards Hawaii, and would be docked within a few hours. Richard and Tracy visited their recovering friends on the boat then walked out on the deck. They stood on the bow, looking up at the stars through the dark sky.

"It is so beautiful to see life, to see the things I almost lost forever," Tracy said to her lover as she stood by his side.

"The universe is bright with life and force and strength, but between each star there is a gap, a space, cold and unforgiving. It is up to us to fill that space that lives within us, with an essence, to connect, to appreciate, to feel our place amongst the stars so that we can treasure it and live it as a destiny," Richard whispered in her ear.

"That essence brings it all together, connects everything and allows the stars to shine and helps us in distress… to break through the barriers that prevent us from being free to live in the eternal moment," She smiled as her eyes were captivated into the heavenly twinkles above.

"What is it that brings us into contact with the essence?" Richard asked as his senses became invigorated. Tracy looked deeper into the stars. She suddenly realized that anything could be configured through connecting them together in any particular and desired way. It was like the sky was a great message board. As she breathed in the warm ocean breeze she saw a word in the stars, which was the answer to her husband's question.

"Love brings us to the essence that bonds everything in life within the universe." She whispered back with a deeply affectionate smile. ★